SOLUTIONS MANUAL FOR PHYSICAL CHEMISTRY

SOLUTIONS MANUAL FOR PHYSICAL CHEMISTRY

FOURTH EDITION

P. W. ATKINS

W. H. FREEMAN AND COMPANY
NEW YORK

ISBN 0-7167-2109-0

Printed in the United States of America

2 3 4 5 6 7 8 9 0 VB 9 9 8 7 6 5 4 3 2 1

This edition has been authorized by the Oxford University Press for sale in the USA and Canada only and not for export therefrom.

Preface to the fourth edition

I have reworked all the solutions in this edition from scratch and in the light of comments received on the earlier editions. I have also adopted, within the constraints of space to which a *Solutions manual* is subject, a slightly more generous style, with more words, more details, a more open layout, and more guidance.

The solutions have been examined in detail by Michael Fuson, of Denison University, Granville, Ohio and by Charles Trapp, of the University of Louisville, Louisville, Kentucky. I am greatly indebted to them both for their good advice, which I have tried to follow, and their detailed comments. If errors remain, they are probably at locations where I ignored what they advised.

Oxford,
April 1990

P.W.A.

Contents

PART 1: EQUILIBRIUM

1. The properties of gases

Exercises

1.1 $p_f = \dfrac{V_i}{V_f} \times p_i$ [3]

$V_i = 1.0\ \text{L} = 10\overline{00}\ \text{cm}^3$, $V_f = 100\ \text{cm}^3$, $p_i = 1.00\ \text{atm}$

$$p_f = \frac{10\overline{00}\ \text{cm}^3}{100\ \text{cm}^3} \times 1.00\ \text{atm} = 10 \times 1.00\ \text{atm} = \underline{10\ \text{atm}}$$

1.2 (a) Find what pressure a perfect gas exerts from $pV = nRT$. Since the molar mass of Xe is $131\ \text{g mol}^{-1}$, the sample has $n = 1.00\ \text{mol Xe}$. Therefore, with $p = nRT/V$,

$$p = \frac{1.00\ \text{mol} \times 0.0821\ \text{L atm K}^{-1}\ \text{mol}^{-1} \times 298.15\ \text{K}}{1.0\ \text{L}} = \underline{24\ \text{atm}}$$

That is, the sample has $p = 24\ \text{atm}$, not 20 atm.

(b) The van der Waals equation is [11]:

$$p = \frac{nRT}{V - nb} - \frac{an^2}{V^2}$$

For xenon, Table 1.4 gives $a = 4.194\ \text{L}^2\ \text{atm mol}^{-1}$ and

$b = 5.105 \times 10^{-2}\ \text{L mol}^{-1}$. Since $n = 1.00\ \text{mol}$ and $V = 1.0\ \text{L}$,

$$\frac{nRT}{V - nb} = \frac{1.00\ \text{mol} \times 0.0821\ \text{L atm K}^{-1}\ \text{mol}^{-1} \times 298.15\ \text{K}}{(1.0 - 0.051)\text{L}} = 25.\overline{8}\ \text{atm}$$

$$\frac{an^2}{V^2} = \frac{4.194\ \text{L}^2\ \text{atm mol}^{-1} \times (1.00\ \text{mol})^2}{(1.0\ \text{L})^2} = 4.1\overline{94}\ \text{atm}$$

Therefore,

$$p = 25.\overline{8}\ \text{atm} - 4.1\overline{94}\ \text{atm} = \underline{22\ \text{atm}}$$

1.3 $p_i = \frac{V_f}{V_i} \times p_f$ [3]

$V_f = 4.65\ \text{L},\ V_i = 4.65\ \text{L} + 2.20\ \text{L} = 6.85\ \text{L}$

$p_f = 3.78 \times 10^3\ \text{Torr}$

Therefore

(a) $p_i = \frac{4.65\ \text{L}}{6.85\ \text{L}} \times 3.78 \times 10^3\ \text{Torr} = \underline{2.57 \times 10^3\ \text{Torr}}$

(b) Since 1 atm = 760 Torr exactly,

$p_i = 2.57 \times 10^3\ \text{Torr} \times \frac{1\ \text{atm}}{760\ \text{Torr}} = \underline{3.38\ \text{atm}}$

1.4 $T_f = \frac{V_f}{V_i} \times T_i$ [5]

$V_i = 1.0\ \text{L},\ V_f = 100\ \text{cm}^3,\ T_i = 298\ \text{K}$

$T_f = \frac{100\ \text{cm}^3}{1\overline{0}00\ \text{cm}^3} \times 298\ \text{K} = \underline{30\ \text{K}}$

1.5 $p_f = \frac{T_f}{T_i} \times p_i$ [5]

Internal pressure = quoted pressure + atmospheric pressure

$p_i = 24\ \text{lb in}^{-2} + 14.7\ \text{lb in}^{-2} = 38.\overline{7}\ \text{lb in}^{-2}$

$T_i = 268\ \text{K}\ (-5\ °\text{C}),\ T_f = 308\ \text{K}\ (35\ °\text{C})$

$p_f = \frac{308\ \text{K}}{268\ \text{K}} \times 38.\overline{7}\ \text{lb in}^{-2} = 44.\overline{5}\ \text{lb in}^{-2}$

Therefore

$p(\text{internal}) = 44.\overline{5}\ \text{lb in}^{-2} - 14.7\ \text{lb in}^{-2} = \underline{30\ \text{lb in}^{-2}}$

Complications include the change in volume of the tyre, the change in rigidity of the material from which it is made, and loss of pressure by leaks and diffusion.

1.6 $T_f = \frac{V_f}{V_i} \times T_i$ [5]

$V_f = 1.14\ V_i$ (a 14 per cent increase), $T_i = 340\ \text{K}$

Therefore,

$$T_f = \frac{1.14\,V_i}{V_i} \times 340\text{ K} = 1.14 \times 340\text{ K} = \underline{388\text{ K}}$$

1.7 $V_f = \frac{p_i}{p_f} \times V_i$ [3]

$V_i = 2.0\text{ m}^3$, $p_i = 755\text{ Torr}$, $p_f =$ (a) 100 Torr, (b) 10 Torr

Therefore:

(a) $V_f = \frac{755\text{ Torr}}{100\text{ Torr}} \times 2.0\text{ m}^3 = \underline{15\text{ m}^3}$

(b) $V_f = \frac{755\text{ Torr}}{10\text{ Torr}} \times 2.0\text{ m}^3 = \underline{1.5 \times 10^2\text{ m}^3}$

1.8 $p = \frac{nRT}{V}$ [1]

$$n = \frac{0.255\text{ g}}{20.18\text{ g mol}^{-1}} = 1.26 \times 10^{-2}\text{ mol},\ T = 122\text{ K},\ V = 3.00\text{ L}$$

Therefore,

$$p = \frac{1.26 \times 10^{-2}\text{ mol} \times 0.0821\text{ L atm K}^{-1}\text{ mol}^{-1} \times 122\text{ K}}{3.00\text{ L}} = \underline{4.22 \times 10^{-2}\text{ atm}}$$

1.9 (a) $V = \frac{n_J RT}{p_J}$ [7]

$$n(\text{Ne}) = \frac{0.225\text{ g}}{20.18\text{ g mol}^{-1}} = 1.11\bar{5} \times 10^{-2}\text{ mol},\ p(\text{Ne}) = 66.5\text{ Torr},\ T = 300\text{ K}$$

Therefore, since there is only one volume,

$$V = \frac{1.11\bar{5} \times 10^{-2}\text{ mol} \times 62.36\text{ L Torr K}^{-1}\text{ mol}^{-1} \times 300\text{ K}}{66.5\text{ Torr}} = \underline{3.14\text{ L}}$$

(b) $p = \frac{nRT}{V}$ [1], $n = n(\text{CH}_4) + n(\text{Ar}) + n(\text{Ne})$

$$n(\text{CH}_4) = \frac{0.320\text{ g}}{16.04\text{ g mol}^{-1}} = 1.99\bar{5} \times 10^{-2}\text{ mol}$$

$$n(\mathrm{Ar}) = \frac{0.175\ \mathrm{g}}{39.95\ \mathrm{g\ mol^{-1}}} = 4.38\bar{0} \times 10^{-2}\ \mathrm{mol}$$

$$n_T = (1.99\bar{5} + 4.38\bar{0} + 1.11\bar{5}) \times 10^{-2}\ \mathrm{mol} = 7.49\bar{0} \times 10^{-2}\ \mathrm{mol}$$

Therefore

$$p = \frac{7.49\bar{0} \times 10^{-2}\ \mathrm{mol} \times 62.36\ \mathrm{L\ Torr\ K^{-1}\ mol^{-1}} \times 300\ \mathrm{K}}{3.13\bar{7}\ \mathrm{L}} = \underline{447\ \mathrm{Torr}}$$

1.10 $n = \dfrac{pV}{RT}$ [1], $n = \dfrac{m}{M}$ and $\rho = \dfrac{m}{V}$

Therefore, $M = \dfrac{mRT}{pV} = \rho\dfrac{RT}{p}$

$\rho = 1.23\ \mathrm{g\ L^{-1}}$, $T = 330\ \mathrm{K}$, $p = 150\ \mathrm{Torr}$

Hence

$$M = \frac{1.23\ \mathrm{g\ L^{-1}} \times 62.36\ \mathrm{L\ Torr\ K^{-1}\ mol^{-1}} \times 330\ \mathrm{K}}{150\ \mathrm{Torr}} = \underline{169\ \mathrm{g\ mol^{-1}}}$$

1.11 $M = \rho\dfrac{RT}{p}$ [Exercise 1.10]

$\rho = \dfrac{33.5\ \mathrm{mg}}{250\ \mathrm{mL}} = 0.134\bar{0}\ \mathrm{g\ L^{-1}}$, $p = 152\ \mathrm{Torr}$, $T = 298\ \mathrm{K}$

$$M = \frac{0.1340\ \mathrm{g\ L^{-1}} \times 62.36\ \mathrm{L\ Torr\ K^{-1}\ mol^{-1}} \times 298\ \mathrm{K}}{152\ \mathrm{Torr}} = \underline{16.4\ \mathrm{g\ mol^{-1}}}$$

1.12 (a) $p = \dfrac{nRT}{V}$ [1]

$n = 1.0\ \mathrm{mol}$, $T = 273.15\ \mathrm{K}$ (i) or $100\ \mathrm{K}$ (ii)

$V = 22.414\ \mathrm{L}$ (i) or $100\ \mathrm{cm^3}$ (ii)

(i) $$p = \frac{1.0\ \mathrm{mol} \times 8.206 \times 10^{-2}\ \mathrm{L\ atm\ K^{-1}\ mol^{-1}} \times 273.15\ \mathrm{K}}{22.414\ \mathrm{L}} = \underline{1.0\ \mathrm{atm}}$$

(ii) $$p = \frac{1.0\ \mathrm{mol} \times 8.206 \times 10^{-2}\ \mathrm{L\ atm\ K^{-1}\ mol^{-1}} \times 1000\ \mathrm{K}}{0.100\ \mathrm{L}} = \underline{8.2 \times 10^{2}\ \mathrm{atm}}$$

(b) $p=\dfrac{nRT}{V-nb}-\dfrac{an^2}{V^2}$ [11]

From Table 1.4, $a=5.489\ \mathrm{L^2\ atm\ mol^{-2}}$ and $b=6.380\times10^{-2}\ \mathrm{L\ mol^{-1}}$.

Therefore,

(i) $\dfrac{nRT}{V-nb}=\dfrac{1.0\ \mathrm{mol}\times8.206\times10^{-2}\ \mathrm{L\ atm\ K^{-1}\ mol^{-1}}\times273.15\ \mathrm{K}}{(22.414-1.0\times6.380\times10^{-2})\ \mathrm{L}}=1.0\overline{03}\ \mathrm{atm}$

$\dfrac{an^2}{V^2}=\dfrac{5.489\ \mathrm{L^2\ atm\ mol^{-2}}\times(1.0\ \mathrm{mol})^2}{(22.414\ \mathrm{L})^2}=1.0\overline{9}\times10^{-2}\ \mathrm{atm}$

and $p=1.00\overline{3}\ \mathrm{atm}-1.0\overline{9}\times10^{-2}\ \mathrm{atm}=0.992\ \mathrm{atm}=\underline{1.0\ \mathrm{atm}}$

(ii) $\dfrac{nRT}{V-nb}=\dfrac{1.0\ \mathrm{mol}\times8.206\times10^{-2}\ \mathrm{L\ atm\ K^{-1}\ mol^{-1}}\times1000\ \mathrm{K}}{(0.100-0.06380)\mathrm{L}}=2.2\overline{7}\times10^3\ \mathrm{atm}$

$\dfrac{an^2}{V^2}=\dfrac{5.489\ \mathrm{L^2\ atm\ mol^{-1}}\times(1.0\ \mathrm{mol})^2}{(0.100\ \mathrm{L})^2}=5.4\overline{9}\times10^2\ \mathrm{atm}$

and $p=2.2\overline{7}\times10^3\ \mathrm{atm}-5.49\times10^2\ \mathrm{atm}=\underline{1.7\times10^3\ \mathrm{atm}}$

1.13 $V_c=3b$[12a] $=3\times0.0226\ \mathrm{L\ mol^{-1}}=\underline{6.78\times10^{-2}\ \mathrm{L\ mol^{-1}}}$

$p_c=\dfrac{a}{27b^2}$ [12b] $=\dfrac{0.751\ \mathrm{L^2\ atm\ mol^{-1}}}{27\times(0.0226\ \mathrm{L\ mol^{-1}})^2}=\underline{54.5\ \mathrm{atm}}$

$T_c=\dfrac{8a}{27Rb}$ [12c] $=\dfrac{8\times0.751\ \mathrm{L^2\ atm\ mol^{-1}}}{27\times8.206\times10^{-2}\ \mathrm{L\ atm\ K^{-1}\ mol^{-1}}\times0.0226\ \mathrm{L\ mol^{-1}}}$

$=\underline{120\ \mathrm{K}}$

1.14 $Z=\dfrac{pV_m}{RT}$ [9]; for a perfect gas $V_m^0=RT/p$. Since the molar volume is 12 per cent smaller than that of a perfect gas,

$V_m=0.88\,V_m^0=0.88\,\dfrac{RT}{p}$

Therefore,

(a) $Z=\dfrac{p}{RT}\times0.88\,\dfrac{RT}{p}=\underline{0.88}$

(b) $V_m=\dfrac{ZRT}{p}=\dfrac{0.88\times8.206\times10^{-2}\ \mathrm{L\ atm\ K^{-1}\ mol^{-1}}\times300\ \mathrm{K}}{20\ \mathrm{atm}}=\underline{1.1\ \mathrm{L}}$

Since $V_m < V_m^0$, attractive forces dominate

1.15 $Z = \frac{pV_m}{RT}$ [9], implying that $V_m = \frac{ZRT}{p}$

Since $Z = 0.86$, $T = 300$ K, $p = 20$ atm,

$$V_m = \frac{0.86 \times 8.206 \times 10^{-2}\ \text{L atm K}^{-1}\ \text{mol}^{-1} \times 300\ \text{K}}{20\ \text{atm}} = 1.0\overline{59}\ \text{L mol}^{-1}$$

(a) $V = nV_m = 8.2 \times 10^{-3}\ \text{mol} \times 1.0\overline{59}\ \text{L mol}^{-1}$

$= \underline{8.7\ \text{mL}}$

(b) $B = V_m\left(\frac{pV_m}{RT} - 1\right)$ [10b] $= V_m(Z - 1)$

$= 1.0\overline{59}\ \text{L mol}^{-1} \times (0.86 - 1) = \underline{-0.15\ \text{L mol}^{-1}}$

1.16 $n = n(H_2) + n(N_2) = 2.0\ \text{mol} + 1.0\ \text{mol} = 3.0\ \text{mol}$

(a) $x(H_2) = \frac{2.0\ \text{mol}}{3.0\ \text{mol}} = \underline{0.67}$

$x(N_2) = \frac{1.0\ \text{mol}}{3.0\ \text{mol}} = \underline{0.33}$

(b) $p_J = n_J \frac{RT}{V}$ [7]

$$\frac{RT}{V} = \frac{8.206 \times 10^{-2}\ \text{L atm K}^{-1}\ \text{mol}^{-1} \times 273.15\ \text{K}}{22.4\ \text{L}} = 1.00\ \text{atm mol}^{-1}$$

$p(H_2) = 2.0\ \text{mol} \times 1.00\ \text{atm mol}^{-1} = \underline{2.0\ \text{atm}}$

$p(N_2) = 1.0\ \text{mol} \times 1.00\ \text{atm mol}^{-1} = \underline{1.0\ \text{atm}}$

(c) $p = p(H_2) + p(N_2)$ [7]

$= 2.0\ \text{atm} + 1.0\ \text{atm} = \underline{3.0\ \text{atm}}$

1.17 $b = \frac{1}{3}V_c$ [12a, $V_c = 98.7\ \text{cm}^3\ \text{mol}^{-1}$]

$= \frac{1}{3} \times 98.7\ \text{cm}^3\ \text{mol}^{-1} = \underline{32.9\ \text{cm}^3\ \text{mol}^{-1}}$

$a = 27b^2p_c = 3V_c^2p_c$ [12b, $p_c = 45.6$ atm]

$= 3 \times (98.7 \times 10^{-3}\ \text{L mol}^{-1})^2 \times 45.6\ \text{atm} = \underline{1.33\ \text{L}^2\ \text{atm mol}^{-2}}$

As b is approximately the volume occupied per mole of particles

$$v_{\rm mol} \approx \frac{b}{N_{\rm A}} = \frac{32.9\times10^{-6}\ {\rm m^3\ mol^{-1}}}{6.022\times10^{23}\ {\rm mol^{-1}}} = 5.46\times10^{-29}\ {\rm m^3}$$

Then, with $v_{\rm mol} = \frac{4}{3}\pi r^3$,

$$r \approx \left(\frac{3}{4\pi}\times5.46\times10^{-29}\ {\rm m^3}\right)^{1/3} = \underline{0.24\ {\rm nm}}$$

1.18 (a) $T_{\rm B} = \dfrac{a}{bR}$ [14]

From Table 1.4, $a = 6.493\ {\rm L^2\ atm\ mol^{-2}}$, $b = 5.622\times10^{-2}\ {\rm L\ mol^{-1}}$. Therefore,

$$T_{\rm B} = \frac{6.493\ {\rm L^2\ atm\ mol^{-2}}}{5.622\times10^{-2}\ {\rm L\ mol^{-1}}\times8.206\times10^{-2}\ {\rm L\ atm\ K^{-1}\ mol^{-1}}} = \underline{1.4\times10^3\ {\rm K}}$$

(b) As in Example 1.17, $v_{\rm mol} \approx \dfrac{b}{N_{\rm A}} = \dfrac{5.622\times10^{-5}\ {\rm m^3\ mol^{-1}}}{6.022\times10^{23}\ {\rm mol^{-1}}} = 9.3\times10^{-29}\ {\rm m^3}$

$$r \approx \left(\frac{3}{4\pi}\times9.3\times10^{-29}\ {\rm m^3}\right)^{1/3} = \underline{0.28\ {\rm nm}}$$

1.19 At 25 °C and 10 atm, the reduced temperature and pressure [Section 1.5] of hydrogen are

$$T_{\rm r} = \frac{298\ {\rm K}}{33.23\ {\rm K}} = 8.96\overline{8} \quad [T_{\rm c} = 33.23\ {\rm K},\ \text{Table 1.3}]$$

$$p_{\rm r} = \frac{1.0\ {\rm atm}}{12.8\ {\rm atm}} = 0.078\overline{1} \quad [p_{\rm c} = 12.8\ {\rm atm},\ \text{Table 1.3}]$$

Hence, the gases named will be in corresponding states at $T = 8.96\overline{8}\times T_{\rm c}$ and at $p = 0.078\overline{1}\times p_{\rm r}$.

(a) For ammonia, $T_{\rm c} = 405.5$ K and $p_{\rm c} = 111.3$ atm [Table 1.3], so

$T = 8.96\overline{8}\times405.5\ {\rm K} = \underline{3.64\times10^3\ {\rm K}}$

$p = 0.078\overline{1}\times111.3\ {\rm atm} = \underline{8.7\ {\rm atm}}$

(b) For xenon, $T_{\rm c} = 289.75$ K and $p_{\rm c} = 58.0$ atm, so

$T = 8.96\overline{8}\times289.75\ {\rm K} = \underline{2.60\times10^3\ {\rm K}}$

$p = 0.078\bar{1} \times 58.0\ \text{atm} = \underline{4.5\ \text{atm}}$

(c) For helium, $T_c = 5.21$ K and $p_c = 2.26$ atm, so

$T = 8.96\bar{8} \times 5.21\ \text{K} = \underline{46.7\ \text{K}}$

$p = 0.078\bar{1} \times 2.26\ \text{atm} = \underline{0.18\ \text{atm}}$

Problems

1.1 $V_f = \dfrac{p_i}{p_f} \times V_i$ [3] and $p = \rho g h$ [Example 1.2]

Total pressure: $p_i = 1.0$ atm

$$p_f = 1.0\ \text{atm} + \rho g h$$

$\rho g h = 1.025 \times 10^3\ \text{kg m}^{-3} \times 9.81\ \text{m s}^{-2} \times 50\ \text{m} = 5.0\bar{3} \times 10^5\ \text{Pa}$

Hence, $p_f = 1.0\bar{1} \times 10^5\ \text{Pa} + 5.0\bar{3} \times 10^5\ \text{Pa} = 6.0\bar{4} \times 10^5\ \text{Pa}$

$$V_f = \frac{1.0\bar{1} \times 10^5\ \text{Pa}}{6.0\bar{4} \times 10^5\ \text{Pa}} \times 3\ \text{m}^3 = \underline{0.5\ \text{m}^3}$$

1.2 External pressure is p_i and pressure at foot of column is $p_f + \rho g h$. At equilibrium the two pressures are the same, so

$$\begin{aligned} p_f - p_i &= \rho g h \\ &= 1.0 \times 10^3\ \text{kg m}^{-3} \times 9.81\ \text{m s}^{-2} \times 0.15\ \text{m} \\ &= \underline{1.5 \times 10^3\ \text{Pa}}\ (= 1.5 \times 10^{-2}\ \text{atm}) \end{aligned}$$

1.3 $pV = nRT$ [1] implies that, with n constant,

$$\frac{p_f V_f}{T_f} = \frac{p_i V_i}{T_i}$$

or

$$p_f = \frac{V_i}{V_f} \times \frac{T_f}{T_i} \times p_i = \left(\frac{r_i}{r_f}\right)^3 \times \frac{T_f}{T_i} \times p_i \quad [\text{since } V = \tfrac{4}{3}\pi r^3]$$

$$= \left(\frac{1.0\ \text{m}}{3.0\ \text{m}}\right)^3 \times \frac{253\ \text{K}}{293\ \text{K}} \times 1.0\ \text{atm} = \underline{3.2 \times 10^{-2}\ \text{atm}}$$

1.4 $n = \dfrac{pV}{RT}$ and $n = \dfrac{m}{M}$, hence $\rho = \dfrac{m}{V} = \dfrac{Mp}{RT}$

That is, $p=\rho\frac{RT}{M}$, or $\frac{p}{\rho}=\frac{RT}{M}$

For a real gas

$$p=\frac{nRT}{V}(1+B'p+\cdots)=\rho\frac{RT}{M}(1+B'p+\cdots)$$

which rearranges to

$$\frac{p}{\rho}=\frac{RT}{M}+\frac{RTB'}{M}p+\cdots$$

Therefore, plot p/ρ against p and expect a straight line with intercept RT/M at $p=0$. Draw up the following table:

p/Torr	91.74	188.93	277.3	452.8	639.3	760.0
$\rho/(\mathrm{kg\ m^{-3}})$	0.225	0.456	0.664	1.062	1.468	1.734
$(p/\rho)/(10^5\ \mathrm{m^2\ s^{-3}})$	0.544	0.552	0.557	0.568	0.581	0.584

The points are plotted in Fig. 1.1, and the limiting behaviour is confirmed

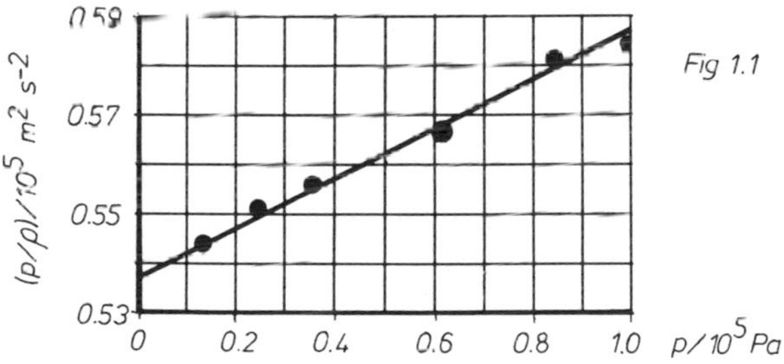

Fig 1.1

The intercept at $p=0$ is at

$$\frac{p}{\rho}\Big/(10^5\ \mathrm{m^2\ s^{-2}})=0.540,\ \text{or}\ p/\rho=0.540\times10^5\ \mathrm{m^2\ s^{-2}}$$

Therefore,

$$M=\frac{RT}{0.540\times10^5\ \mathrm{m^2\ s^{-2}}}$$

$$=\frac{8.314\ \mathrm{J\ K^{-1}\ mol^{-1}} \times 298.15\ \mathrm{K}}{0.540 \times 10^5\ \mathrm{m^2\ s^{-2}}}$$

$$=4.59 \times 10^{-2}\ \mathrm{kg\ mol^{-1}} = \underline{45.9\ \mathrm{g\ mol^{-1}}}$$

1.5 $n=\frac{pV}{RT}[1],\ V=\frac{4\pi}{3}r^3=\frac{4\pi}{3}\times(3.0\mathrm{m})^3=11\bar{3}\ \mathrm{m^3}$

$p=1.0\ \mathrm{atm},\ T=298\ \mathrm{K}$

(a) $n=\frac{1.0\ \mathrm{atm} \times 11\bar{3} \times 10^3\ \mathrm{L}}{8.206 \times 10^{-2}\ \mathrm{L\ atm\ K^{-1}\ mol^{-1}} \times 298\ \mathrm{K}}=\underline{4.6\bar{2} \times 10^3\ \mathrm{mol}}$

(b) $m(\mathrm{H_2})=nM(\mathrm{H_2})=4.6\bar{2}\times 10^3\ \mathrm{mol} \times 2.02\ \mathrm{g\ mol^{-1}}=9.3\bar{3}\times 10^3\ \mathrm{g}$

Mass of displaced air $=11\bar{3}\ \mathrm{m^3}\times 1.22\ \mathrm{kg\ m^{-3}}=1.3\bar{8}\times 10^2\ \mathrm{kg}$

Therefore, the payload is $138\ \mathrm{kg}-9.3\bar{3}\ \mathrm{kg}=\underline{12\bar{9}\ \mathrm{kg}}$

(c) For helium, $m=nM(\mathrm{He})=4.6\bar{2}\times 10^3\ \mathrm{mol}\times 4.00\ \mathrm{g\ mol^{-1}}=18\ \mathrm{kg}$

The payload is now $13\bar{8}\ \mathrm{kg}-18\ \mathrm{kg}=\underline{120\ \mathrm{kg}}$

1.6 The mass of displaced gas is ρV, where V is the volume of the bulb and ρ is the density of the gas. The balance condition for the two gases is

$$m(\mathrm{bulb})=\rho V(\mathrm{bulb}),\ m(\mathrm{bulb})=\rho' V(\mathrm{bulb})$$

which implies that $\rho=\rho'$. however, because [Problem 1.4]

$$\rho=\frac{pM}{RT}$$

the balance condition is

$$pM=p'M'$$

which implies that

$$M'=\frac{p}{p'}\times M$$

This relation is valid in the limit of zero pressure (for a gas behaving perfectly).

In experiment 1, $p=423.22$ Torr, $p'=327.10$ Torr; hence

$$M'=\frac{423.22\ \mathrm{Torr}}{327.10\ \mathrm{Torr}}\times 70.014\ \mathrm{g\ mol^{-1}}=90.59\ \mathrm{g\ mol^{-1}}$$

In experiment 2, $p = 427.22$ Torr, $p' = 293.22$ Torr; hence

$$M' = \frac{427.22\ \text{Torr}}{293.22\ \text{Torr}} \times 70.014\ \text{g mol}^{-1} = 102.0\ \text{g mol}^{-1}$$

In a proper series of experiments one should reduce the pressure (e.g. by adjusting the balanced weight). Experiment 2 is closer to zero pressure than experiment 1, it may be safe to conclude that $M \approx 102\ \text{g mol}^{-1}$. The molecule CH_2FCF_3 has $M \approx 102\ \text{g mol}^{-1}$.

1.7 At constant volume, $p = \frac{T}{T_3} \times p_3$ where T_3 and p_3 are the temperature and pressure of the triple point. Therefore,

(a) $$p_{274.16\,\text{K}} - p_{273.16\,\text{K}} = \left(\frac{274.16\ \text{K}}{273.16\ \text{K}} - 1\right) p_3$$

$$= \frac{1}{273.16} \times p_3 = \frac{1}{273.16} \times 50.2\ \text{Torr} = 0.184\ \text{Torr}$$

(b) For 100 °C (373 K)

$$p = \frac{373\ \text{K}}{273.16\ \text{K}} \times 50.2\ \text{Torr} = 68.6\ \text{Torr}$$

(c) $$p_{374\,\text{K}} - p_{373\,\text{K}} = \left(\frac{374\ \text{K}}{373\ \text{K}} - 1\right) p_{373\,\text{K}} = \frac{68.6\ \text{Torr}}{373} = 0.184\ \text{Torr}$$

1.8 Draw up the following table, which is based on the reaction

$N_2 + 3H_2 \rightarrow 2NH_3$

	N_2	H_2	NH_3	Total
Initial amounts	n	n'	0	$n + n'$
Final amounts	$n - \frac{1}{3}n'$	0	$\frac{2}{3}n'$	$n + \frac{1}{3}n'$
Specifically	0.33 mol	0	1.33 mol	1.66 mol
Mole fractions	0.20	0	0.80	1.00

$$p = \frac{nRT}{V} = 1.66\ \text{mol} \times \frac{8.206 \times 10^{-2}\ \text{L atm K}^{-1}\ \text{mol}^{-1} \times 273.15\ \text{K}}{22.4\ \text{L}}$$

$= \underline{1.66\text{ atm}}$

$p(H_2) = x(H_2)p = \underline{0}$

$p(N_2) = x(N_2)p = 0.20 \times 1.66\text{ atm} = \underline{0.33\text{ atm}}$

$p(NH_3) = x(NH_3)p = 0.80 \times 1.66\text{ atm} = \underline{1.33\text{ atm}}$

1.9 (a) $V_m = \dfrac{RT}{p} = \dfrac{8.206\times10^{-2}\text{ L atm K}^{-1}\text{ mol}^{-1}\times 350\text{ K}}{2.30\text{ atm}}$

$= \underline{12.5\text{ L mol}^{-1}}$

(b) From $p = \dfrac{RT}{V_m - b} - \dfrac{a}{V_m^2}$ [11b], we obtain $V_m = \dfrac{RT}{p + \dfrac{a}{V_m^2}} + b$ [rearrange 11b]

Then, with a and b from Table 1.4,

$$V_m \approx \frac{8.206\times10^{-2}\text{ L atm K}^{-1}\text{ mol}^{-1}\times 350\text{ K}}{2.30\text{ atm} + \dfrac{6.493\text{ L}^2\text{ atm mol}^{-2}}{(12.5\text{ L mol}^{-1})^2}} + 5.622\times10^{-2}\text{ L mol}^{-1}$$

$$\approx \frac{28.7\bar{2}\text{ L mol}^{-1}}{2.34} + 5.622\times10^{-2}\text{ L mol}^{-1}$$

$\approx \underline{12.3\text{ L mol}^{-1}}$

Substitution of 12.3 L mol^{-1} into the denominator of the first expression results in $V_m = 12.3\text{ L mol}^{-1}$, so the cycle of approximation may be terminated.

1.10 $T_c = \dfrac{2}{3}\left(\dfrac{2a}{3bR}\right)^{1/2} = \dfrac{2}{3}\times\dfrac{12p_c b}{R}$ [Table 1.5]

$= \dfrac{8}{3}\times\dfrac{p_c V_c}{R}$

$= \dfrac{8}{3}\times\dfrac{40\text{ atm}\times 160\times10^{-3}\text{ L mol}^{-1}}{8.206\times10^{-2}\text{ L atm K}^{-1}\text{ mol}^{-1}} = \underline{21\bar{0}\text{ K}}$

$$v_{mol} = \frac{b}{N_A} = \frac{1}{3}\frac{V_c}{N_A} = \frac{160\times10^{-6}\text{ m}^3\text{ mol}^{-1}}{3\times 6.022\times10^{23}\text{ mol}^{-1}} = 8.86\times10^{-29}\text{ m}^3$$

$$v_{mol} = \frac{4\pi}{3}r^3$$

Hence, with V_c and T_c from Table 1.3,

$$r=\left(\frac{3}{4\pi}\times 8.86\times 10^{-29}\ \text{m}^3\right)^{1/3}=\underline{0.28\ \text{nm}}$$

1.11 $V_c=2b,\ T_c=\dfrac{a}{4bR}$ [Table 1.5]

Hence

$$b=\tfrac{1}{2}V_c=\tfrac{1}{2}\times 118.8\ \text{cm}^3\ \text{mol}^{-1}=\underline{59.4\ \text{cm}^3\ \text{mol}^{-1}}$$

$$a=4bRT_c=2RT_cV_c$$

$$=2\times 8.206\times 10^{-2}\ \text{L atm K}^{-1}\ \text{mol}^{-1}\times 289.75\ \text{K}\times 118.8\times 10^{-3}\ \text{L mol}^{-1}$$

$$=\underline{5.649\ \text{L}^2\ \text{atm mol}^{-2}}$$

Hence

$$p=\frac{RT}{V_m-b}\,e^{-a/RTV_m}$$

$$=\frac{nRT}{V-nb}\,e^{-na/RTV}$$

$$=\frac{1.0\ \text{mol}\times 8.206\times 10^{-2}\ \text{L atm K}^{-1}\ \text{mol}^{-1}\times 298\ \text{K}}{1.0\ \text{L}-1.0\ \text{mol}\times 59.4\times 10^{-3}\ \text{L mol}^{-1}}$$

$$\times\exp\left(-\frac{1.0\ \text{mol}\times 5.649\ \text{L}^2\ \text{atm mol}^{-2}}{8.206\times 10^{-2}\times 298\times 1.0\ \text{L}^2\ \text{atm mol}^{-1}}\right)$$

$$=26.\bar{0}\ \text{atm}\times e^{-0.23\bar{1}}$$

$$=\underline{21\ \text{atm}}$$

1.12 $p=\dfrac{RT}{V_m-b}-\dfrac{a}{V_m^2}$ [11b]

$$=\frac{RT}{V_m\left(1-\dfrac{b}{V_m}\right)}-\frac{a}{V_m^2}$$

$$=\frac{RT}{V_m}\left(1+\frac{b}{V_m}+\frac{b^2}{V_m^2}+\cdots\right)-\frac{a}{V_m^2}$$

$$=\frac{RT}{V_m}\left(1+\left[b-\frac{a}{RT}\right]\frac{1}{V_m}+\frac{b^2}{V_m^2}+\cdots\right)$$

Compare this expansion with

$$p=\frac{RT}{V_m}\left(1+\frac{B}{V_m}+\frac{C}{V_m^2}+\cdots\right)\ [10b]$$

and hence find

$\underline{B=b-\frac{a}{RT}}$ and $\underline{C=b^2}$

Since $C=1200\ \text{cm}^6\ \text{mol}^{-2}$, $b=C^{1/2}=\underline{34.6\ \text{cm}^3\ \text{mol}^{-1}}$

$$a=RT(b-B)$$
$$=8.206\times10^{-2}\times273\ \text{L atm mol}^{-1}\times(34.6+21.7)\ \text{cm}^3\ \text{mol}^{-1}$$
$$=22.4\overline{0}\ \text{L atm mol}^{-1}\times56.3\times10^{-3}\ \text{L mol}^{-1}=\underline{1.26\ \text{L}^2\ \text{atm mol}^{-2}}$$

1.13 $p=\frac{RT}{V_m-b}\,e^{-a/RTV_m}$ [Table 1.5] $=\frac{RT}{V_m\left(1-\frac{b}{V_m}\right)}\,e^{-a/RTV_m}$

Now use the expansions $\frac{1}{1-x}=1+x+x^2+\cdots$ and $e^{-x}=1-x+\frac{1}{2}x^2+\cdots$

and obtain

$$p=\frac{RT}{V_m}\left\{1+\frac{b}{V_m}+\frac{b^2}{V_m^2}+\cdots\right\}\left\{1-\frac{a}{RTV_m}+\frac{1}{2}\left(\frac{a}{RTV_m}\right)^2+\cdots\right\}$$
$$=\frac{RT}{V_m}\left\{1+\left(b-\frac{a}{RT}\right)\frac{1}{V_m}+\left(b^2-\frac{ab}{RT}+\frac{a^2}{2R^2T^2}\right)\frac{1}{V_m^2}+\cdots\right\}$$

Comparing with the virial expansion [10b] gives

$\underline{B=b-\frac{a}{RT}}$ and $\underline{C=b^2-\frac{ab}{RT}+\frac{a^2}{2R^2T^2}}$

To find a and b we form

$C-\frac{1}{2}B^2=\frac{1}{2}b^2$, implying that $b=(2C-B^2)^{1/2}$

and then use $a=RT(b-B)$.

From the data:

$$b = (2\times 1200\ \text{cm}^6\ \text{mol}^{-2} - 471\ \text{cm}^6\ \text{mol}^{-2})^{1/2} = \underline{43.9\ \text{cm}^3\ \text{mol}^{-1}}$$

$$a = 22.4\bar{0}\ \text{L atm mol}^{-1} \times (43.9 + 21.7)\times 10^{-3}\ \text{L mol}^{-1}$$

$$= \underline{1.47\ \text{L}^2\ \text{atm mol}^{-2}}$$

1.14 For critical behaviour, show that there is a point of inflexion with zero slope, and identify the critical constants.

$$p = \frac{RT}{V_\text{m}} - \frac{B}{V_\text{m}^2} + \frac{C}{V_\text{m}^3}$$

$$\left.\begin{aligned} \frac{dp}{dV_\text{m}} &= -\frac{RT}{V_\text{m}^2} + \frac{2B}{V_\text{m}^3} - \frac{3C}{V_\text{m}^4} = 0 \\ \frac{d^2p}{dV_\text{m}^2} &= \frac{2RT}{V_\text{m}^3} - \frac{6B}{V_\text{m}^4} + \frac{12C}{V_\text{m}^5} = 0 \end{aligned}\right\}\ \text{at the critical point}$$

That is,

$$\left.\begin{aligned} -RT_\text{c}V_\text{c}^2 + 2BV_\text{c} - 3C &= 0 \\ RT_\text{c}V_\text{c}^2 - 3BV_\text{c} + 6C &= 0 \end{aligned}\right\}$$

which solve to

$$V_\text{c} = \underline{\frac{3C}{B}},\ T_\text{c} = \underline{\frac{B^2}{3RC}}$$

Now use the equation of state to find p_c:

$$p_\text{c} = \frac{RT_\text{c}}{V_\text{c}} - \frac{B}{V_\text{c}^2} + \frac{C}{V_\text{c}^3}$$

$$= \frac{RB^2}{3RC} \times \frac{B}{3C} - B\left(\frac{B}{3C}\right)^2 + C\left(\frac{B}{3C}\right)^3 = \underline{\frac{B^3}{27C^2}}$$

It follows that

$$Z_\text{c} = \frac{p_\text{c}V_\text{c}}{RT_\text{c}} = \left(\frac{B^3}{27C^2}\right)\left(\frac{3C}{B}\right)\cdot\frac{1}{R}\cdot\left(\frac{3RC}{B^2}\right) = \underline{\frac{1}{3}}$$

1.15 $$\frac{pV_\text{m}}{RT} = 1 + B'p + C'p^2 + \cdots\ [10\text{a}]$$

$$\frac{pV_\text{m}}{RT} = 1 + \frac{B}{V_\text{m}} + \frac{C}{V_\text{m}^2} + \cdots\ [10\text{b}]$$

whence

$$B'p+C'p^2\cdots=\frac{B}{V_m}+\frac{C}{V_m^2}+\cdots$$

Now multiply through by V_m, replace pV_m by $RT\{1+(B/V_m)+\cdots\}$, and equate coefficients of powers of $1/V_m$:

$$B'RT+\frac{BB'RT+C'R^2T^2}{V_m}+\cdots=B+\frac{C}{V_m}+\cdots$$

Hence, $B'RT=B$, implying that $\underline{B'=\frac{B}{RT}}$

Also, $BB'RT+C'R^2T^2=C$, or $B^2+C'R^2T^2=C$, implying that $\underline{C'=\frac{C-B^2}{R^2T^2}}$

1.16 $\frac{p}{\rho}=\frac{RT}{M}+\frac{B'RT}{M}p+\cdots$ [Problem 1.4].

Therefore, the limiting slope of a plot of p/ρ against p is $B'RT/M$. From Fig. 1.1, the slope is

$$\frac{B'RT}{M}=\frac{(0.584-0.544)\times10^5\ \mathrm{m^2\,s^{-2}}}{(1.013-0.122)\times10^5\ \mathrm{Pa}}=4.5\times10^{-2}\ \mathrm{kg^{-1}\,m^3}$$

Therefore, since the intercept lies at $RT/M=0.540\times10^5\ \mathrm{m^2\,s^{-2}}$ [Problem 1.4]

$$B'=\frac{4.5\times10^{-2}\ \mathrm{kg^{-1}\,m^3}}{0.540\times10^5\ \mathrm{m^2\,s^{-2}}}=8.3\times10^{-7}\ \mathrm{Pa^{-1}}\ [1\ \mathrm{Pa}=1\ \mathrm{kg\,m^{-1}\,s^{-2}}]$$

Hence, $B'=8.3\times10^{-7}\ \mathrm{Pa^{-1}}\times1.0133\times10^5\ \mathrm{Pa\,atm^{-1}}=\underline{8.4\times10^{-2}\ \mathrm{atm^{-1}}}$

Since $B=RTB'$ [Problem 1.15]

$$B=8.206\times10^{-2}\ \mathrm{L\,atm\,K^{-1}\,mol^{-1}}\times298\ \mathrm{K}\times8.4\times10^{-2}\ \mathrm{atm^{-1}}$$

$$=\underline{2.1\ \mathrm{L\,mol^{-1}}}$$

1.17 Hydrostatic pressure is given by $p=\rho gh$ [example 1.2]; therefore

$\mathrm{d}p=-\rho g\,\mathrm{d}h$ [p decreases as h increases]

Since $\rho=\frac{pM}{RT}$ [Problem 1.4]

$$\mathrm{d}p = -\frac{pMg\,\mathrm{d}h}{RT}, \text{ implying that } \frac{\mathrm{d}p}{p} = -\frac{Mg\,\mathrm{d}h}{RT}$$

This relation integrates to

$$p = p_0\,\mathrm{e}^{-Mgh/RT}$$

For air, $M \approx 29\ \mathrm{g\ mol^{-1}}$ and at 298 K

$$\frac{Mg}{RT} \approx \frac{29\times10^{-3}\ \mathrm{kg\ mol^{-1}}\times 9.81\ \mathrm{m\ s^{-2}}}{2.48\times10^{3}\ \mathrm{J\ mol^{-1}}} = 1.1\bar{5}\times10^{-4}\ \mathrm{m^{-1}}\quad [1\ \mathrm{J} = 1\ \mathrm{kg\ m^2\ s^{-2}}]$$

(a) $h = 15\ \mathrm{cm}$

$$p = p_0 \times \mathrm{e}^{-0.15\ \mathrm{m}\times 1.1\bar{5}\times10^{-4}\ \mathrm{m^{-1}}} = \underline{0.99\overline{998}p_0}$$

(b) $h = 1350\ \mathrm{ft}$, which is equivalent to 412 m [1 inch = 2.54 cm]

$$p = p_0\,\mathrm{e}^{-412\ \mathrm{m}\times 1.1\bar{5}\times10^{-4}\ \mathrm{m^{-1}}} = \underline{0.95p_0}$$

2. The first law: the concepts

Exercises

2.1 $w = -mgh$ [3]

(a) $w = -1.0\ \text{kg} \times 9.81\ \text{m s}^{-2} \times 10\ \text{m} = \underline{-98\ \text{J}}$

(b) $w = -1.0\ \text{kg} \times 1.60\ \text{m s}^{-2} \times 10\ \text{m} = \underline{-16\ \text{J}}$

2.2 $w = -mgh$ [3]

$= -65\ \text{kg} \times 9.81\ \text{m s}^{-2} \times 4.0\ \text{m} = \underline{-2.6\ \text{kJ}}$

2.3 $w = -p_{\text{ex}}\Delta V$ [5]

$p_{\text{ex}} = 1.0\ \text{atm} \times 1.013 \times 10^5\ \text{Pa atm}^{-1} = 1.0\overline{1} \times 10^5\ \text{Pa}$

$\Delta V = 100\ \text{cm}^2 \times 10\ \text{cm} = 1.0 \times 10^3\ \text{cm}^3 = 1.0 \times 10^{-3}\ \text{m}^3$

$w = -1.0\overline{1} \times 10^5\ \text{Pa} \times 1.0 \times 10^{-3}\ \text{m}^3 = \underline{-1.0 \times 10^2\ \text{J}}$

as $1\ \text{Pa m}^3 = 1\ \text{J}$.

2.4 (a) $w = -p_{\text{ex}}\Delta V$ [5]

$p_{\text{ex}} = 200\ \text{Torr} \times 133.3\ \text{Pa Torr}^{-1} = 2.66\overline{6} \times 10^4\ \text{Pa}$

$\Delta V = 3.3\ \text{L} = 3.3 \times 10^{-3}\ \text{m}^3$

Therefore, $w = -2.66\overline{6} \times 10^4\ \text{Pa} \times 3.3 \times 10^{-3}\ \text{m}^3 = \underline{-88\ \text{J}}$

(b) $w = -nRT \ln \dfrac{V_{\text{f}}}{V_{\text{i}}}$ [7]

$$n = \frac{4.50\ \text{g}}{16.04\text{g mol}^{-1}} = 0.280\overline{5}\ \text{mol}$$

$RT = 2.577\ \text{kJ mol}^{-1}$, $V_{\text{i}} = 12.7\ \text{L}$, $V_{\text{f}} = 16.0\ \text{L}$

$$w = -0.280\overline{5}\ \text{mol} \times 2.577\ \text{kJ mol}^{-1} \times \ln \frac{16.0\ \text{L}}{12.7\ \text{L}} = \underline{-167\ \text{J}}$$

2.5 $w = -nRT \ln \dfrac{V_{\text{f}}}{V_{\text{i}}}$ [7]

$V_f = \frac{1}{3}V_i$

$nRT = 52.0 \times 10^{-3}\ \text{mol} \times 8.314\ \text{J K}^{-1}\ \text{mol}^{-1} \times 260\ \text{K}$

$= 1.12\overline{4} \times 10^2\ \text{J}$

$w = -1.12\overline{4} \times 10^2\ \text{J} \times \ln \frac{1}{3} = \underline{+124\ \text{J}}$

2.6 $w = -p_{ex}\Delta V$ [5]

$p_{ex} = 95\ \text{bar} = 95 \times 10^5\ \text{Pa}$

$\Delta V = -0.450\ \text{L} \times 0.67 = -0.30\overline{2}\ \text{L} = -0.30\overline{2} \times 10^{-3}\ \text{m}^3$

Therefore,

$w = +95 \times 10^5\ \text{Pa} \times 0.30\overline{2} \times 10^{-3}\ \text{m}^3 = \underline{+2.9\ \text{kJ}}$

2.7 $w = -p_{ex}\Delta V$ [5]

$\text{Mg}(s) + 2\text{HCl}(aq) \rightarrow \text{H}_2(g) + \text{MgCl}_2(aq),\ M(\text{Mg}) = 24.31\ \text{g mol}^{-1}$

$V_i = 0,\ V_f = \dfrac{nRT}{p_f},\ p_f = p_{ex}$

$w = -p_{ex}(V_f - V_i) = -p_{ex} \times \dfrac{nRT}{p_{ex}} = -nRT$

$n = \dfrac{15\ \text{g}}{24.31\ \text{g mol}^{-1}} = 0.61\overline{7}\ \text{mol},\ RT = 2.479\ \text{kJ mol}^{-1}$

Hence, $w = -0.61\overline{7}\ \text{mol} \times 2.479\ \text{kJ mol}^{-1} = \underline{-1.5\ \text{kJ}}$

2.8 $\Delta H^{\ominus}_{fus} = 2.60\ \text{kJ mol}^{-1}$ [Table 2.2].

$n = \dfrac{750 \times 10^3\ \text{g}}{22.99\ \text{g mol}^{-1}}$

$q = n\Delta H^{\ominus}_{fus} = \dfrac{750 \times 10^3\ \text{g}}{22.99\ \text{g mol}^{-1}} \times 2.60\ \text{kJ mol}^{-1} = \underline{8.5 \times 10^4\ \text{kJ}}$

2.9 $C = \dfrac{q}{\Delta T}$ [Section 2.5] $= \dfrac{229\ \text{J}}{2.55\ \text{K}} = 89.8\ \text{J K}^{-1}$

The molar heat capacity (at constant pressure) is therefore

$C_p = \dfrac{89.8\ \text{J K}^{-1}}{3.0\ \text{mol}} = \underline{30\ \text{J K}^{-1}\ \text{mol}^{-1}}$

For a pefect gas,

$C_p - C_V = R$ [16, molar quantities]

Hence

$$C_V = C_p - R = (30 - 8.3)\ \text{J K}^{-1}\ \text{mol}^{-1} = \underline{22\ \text{J K}^{-1}\ \text{mol}^{-1}}$$

2.10 $q = C\Delta T,\ C = nC_p,\ V = 75\ \text{m}^3$

$$n = \frac{pV}{RT} = \frac{1.0\ \text{atm} \times 75 \times 10^3\ \text{L}}{8.206 \times 10^{-2}\ \text{L atm K}^{-1}\ \text{mol}^{-1} \times 298\ \text{K}} = 3.0\overline{7} \times 10^3\ \text{mol}$$

$$q \approx 3.0\overline{7} \times 10^3\ \text{mol} \times 21\ \text{J K}^{-1}\ \text{mol}^{-1} \times 10\ \text{K} = \underline{6.4 \times 10^2\ \text{kJ}}$$

Since $q = P \times t$, where P is the power of the heater and t is the time for which it operates,

$$t = \frac{q}{P} = \frac{6.4 \times 10^5\ \text{J}}{1.0 \times 10^3\ \text{J s}^{-1}} = \underline{6.4 \times 10^2\ \text{s}}\ \text{(about 11 min)}$$

In practice, the walls and furniture of a room are also heated.

2.11 $q = \underline{-1.2\ \text{kJ}}$ [energy leaves the sample]

$\Delta H = \underline{-1.2\ \text{kJ}}$ [$\Delta H = q$ at constant pressure]

$$C = \frac{q}{\Delta T} = \frac{1.2\ \text{kJ}}{15\ \text{K}} = \underline{80\ \text{J K}^{-1}}$$

2.12 $q = C\Delta T = nC_p\Delta T$

$$= 3.0\ \text{mol} \times 29.4\ \text{J K}^{-1}\ \text{mol}^{-1} \times 25\ \text{K} = +2.2\ \text{kJ}$$

$$\Delta H = q\ [10\text{a}] = \underline{+2.2\ \text{kJ}}$$

$$\begin{aligned}\Delta U &= \Delta H - \Delta(pV)\ [9] = \Delta H - \Delta(nRT)\\ &= \Delta H - nR\Delta T\\ &= 2.2\ \text{kJ} - 3.0\ \text{mol} \times 8.314\ \text{J K}^{-1}\ \text{mol}^{-1} \times 25\ \text{K}\\ &= 2.2\ \text{kJ} - 0.62\ \text{kJ} = +\underline{1.6\ \text{kJ}}\end{aligned}$$

2.13 $q = 0.50\ \text{mol} \times 26.0\ \text{kJ mol}^{-1} = \underline{+13\ \text{kJ}}$

$$w = -p_{\text{ex}}\Delta V\ [5] \approx -p_{\text{ex}}V(g)\ [V(g) \gg V(l)]$$

$$\approx p_{\text{ex}} \times \frac{nRT}{p_{\text{ex}}} = -nRT$$

Therefore, $w \approx -0.50\ \text{mol} \times 8.314\ \text{J K}^{-1}\ \text{mol}^{-1} \times 250\ \text{K} = \underline{-1.0\ \text{kJ}}$

$\Delta H = q\ [10\text{a}] = \underline{+13\ \text{kJ}}$

$\Delta U = q + w = +13\ \text{kJ} - 1.0\ \text{kJ} = \underline{+12\ \text{kJ}}$

2.14 $C_6H_5C_2H_5(l) + \frac{21}{2}O_2(g) \rightarrow 8CO_2(g) + 5H_2O(l)$

$\Delta H_c^\ominus = 8\Delta H_f^\ominus(CO_2, g) \rightarrow 5\Delta H_f^\ominus(H_2O, l) - \Delta H_f^\ominus(\text{eb}, l)$ [eb = ethylbenzene]

$= 8(-393.51) + 5(-285.83) - (-12.5)\ \text{kJ mol}^{-1}$

$= \underline{-4564.7\ \text{kJ mol}^{-1}}$

2.15 $C_6H_{12}(l) + 9O_2(g) \rightarrow 6CO_2(g) + 6H_2O(l) \quad \Delta H_c^\ominus = -4003\ \text{kJ mol}^{-1}$

$C_6H_{14}(l) + \frac{19}{2}O_2(g) \rightarrow 6CO_2(g) + 7H_2O(l) \quad \Delta H_c^\ominus = -4163\ \text{kJ mol}^{-1}$

The difference of these two reactions is

$C_6H_{12}(l) + H_2O(l) \rightarrow C_6H_{14}(l) + \frac{1}{2}O_2(g) \quad \Delta H^\ominus = +160\ \text{kJ mol}^{-1}$

To replace the H_2O by H_2 we subtract

$H_2O(l) \rightarrow H_2(g) + \frac{1}{2}O_2(g) \quad \Delta H^\ominus = -\Delta H^\ominus(H_2O, l) = +285.83\ \text{kJ mol}^{-1}$

Giving

$C_6H_{12}(l) + H_2(g) \rightarrow C_6H_{14}(l) \quad \underline{\Delta H^\ominus = -126\ \text{kJ mol}^{-1}}$

2.16 $3C(s) + 3H_2(g) + O_2(g) \rightarrow CH_3COOCH_3(l) \quad \Delta H_f^\ominus = -442\ \text{kJ mol}^{-1}$

$\Delta U = \Delta H - \Delta n_g RT$ [11], $\quad \Delta n_g = -4\ \text{mol}$

$\Delta n_g RT = -4\ \text{mol} \times 2.479\ \text{kJ mol}^{-1} = -9.916\ \text{kJ}$

Therefore

$\Delta U_f^\ominus = -442\ \text{kJ mol}^{-1} + 9.9\ \text{kJ mol}^{-1} = \underline{-432\ \text{kJ mol}^{-1}}$

2.17 $C_{10}H_8(s) + 12O_2(g) \rightarrow 10CO_2(g) + 4H_2O(l) \quad \Delta H_c^\ominus = -5157\ \text{kJ mol}^{-1}$

The reverse reaction is

$10CO_2(g) + 4H_2O(l) \rightarrow C_{10}H_8(s) + 12O_2(g) \quad \Delta H^\ominus = +5157\ \text{kJ mol}^{-1}$

The CO_2 and H_2O can be replaced by adding the following two reactions [and using $\Delta H_f^\ominus(CO_2)$ and $\Delta H_f^\ominus(H_2O)$, Table 2.10]:

$10C(s) + 10O_2(g) \rightarrow 10CO_2(g) \quad \Delta H^\ominus = -3935\ \text{kJ mol}^{-1}$

$4H_2(g) + 2O_2(g) \rightarrow 4H_2O(l) \quad \Delta H^\ominus = -1143\ \text{kJ mol}^{-1}$

Thus overall:

$10C(s) + 4H_2(g) \rightarrow C_{10}H_8(s)$

$\Delta H^\ominus = +5157 - 3935 - 1143\ \text{kJ mol}^{-1} = \underline{+79\ \text{kJ mol}^{-1}}$

2.18 $C=\dfrac{q}{\Delta T}$ and $q=IVt$ [section 2.5]

Hence

$$C=\frac{3.20\ \text{A}\times 12.0\ \text{V}\times 27.0\ \text{s}}{1.617\ \text{K}}=\underline{641\ \text{J K}^{-1}}$$

because 1 A V s = 1 J.

2.19 $q=n\Delta H_c^{\ominus}$, $\Delta H_c^{\ominus}=-5157\ \text{kJ mol}^{-1}$ [Table 2.9]
Therefore,

$$|q|=\frac{120\times 10^{-3}\ \text{g}}{128.18\ \text{g mol}^{-1}}\times 5157\ \text{J mol}^{-1}=4.83\ \text{kJ}$$

$$C=\frac{q}{\Delta T}=\frac{4.83\ \text{kJ}}{3.05\ \text{K}}=\underline{1.58\ \text{kJ K}^{-1}}$$

When phenol is used, since $\Delta H_c^{\ominus}=-3054\ \text{kJ mol}^{-1}$ [Table 2.9],

$$|q|=\frac{100\times 10^{-3}\ \text{g}}{94.12\ \text{g mol}^{-1}}\times 3054\ \text{kJ mol}^{-1}=3.24\overline{5}\ \text{kJ}$$

Therefore,

$$\Delta T=\frac{q}{C}=\frac{3.24\overline{5}\ \text{kJ}}{1.58\ \text{kJ K}^{-1}}=\underline{2.05\ \text{K}}$$

2.20 $q=C\Delta T$, $|\Delta H_c|=\dfrac{q}{n}=\dfrac{C\Delta T}{n}=\dfrac{MC\Delta T}{m}$ [m: mass of sample]

Therefore, since $M=180.16\ \text{g mol}^{-1}$,

$$|\Delta H_c|=\frac{180.16\ \text{g mol}^{-1}\times 641\ \text{J K}^{-1}\times 7.793\ \text{K}}{0.3212\ \text{g}}=280\overline{2}\ \text{kJ mol}^{-1}$$

Therefore, since the combustion is exothermic, $\Delta H_c=\underline{-2.80\ \text{MJ mol}^{-1}}$
The combustion reaction is

$$C_6H_{12}O_6(s)+6O_2(g)\rightarrow 6CO_2(g)+6H_2O(l)\qquad \Delta n_g=0$$

Hence $\Delta U_c=\Delta H_c$; therefore $\Delta U_c=\underline{-2.80\ \text{MJ mol}^{-1}}$
For the enthalpy of formation we combine

$6CO_2(g)+6H_2O(l)\rightarrow C_6H_{12}O_6(s)+6O_2(g)$	$\Delta H=+2.8\ \text{MJ mol}^{-1}$
$6C(s)+6O_2(g)\rightarrow 6CO_2(g)$	$\Delta H=-2.36\ \text{MJ mol}^{-1}$
$6H_2(g)+3O_2(g)\rightarrow 6H_2O(l)$	$\Delta H=-1.72\ \text{MJ mol}^{-1}$

The sum of the three is

$$6C(s)+6H_2(g)+3O_2(g)\rightarrow C_6H_{12}O_6(s)$$

$$\Delta H_f = 2.80 - 2.36 - 1.72\ \text{MJ mol}^{-1} = \underline{-1.28\ \text{MJ mol}^{-1}}$$

2.21 $AgCl(s)\rightarrow Ag^+(aq)+Cl^-(aq)$

$$\Delta H^\ominus = \Delta H_f^\ominus(Ag^+, aq) + \Delta H_f^\ominus(Cl^-, aq) - \Delta H_f^\ominus(AgCl, s)$$

$$= 105.58 + (-167.16) - (-127.07)\ \text{kJ mol}^{-1}$$

$$= \underline{+65.49\ \text{kJ mol}^{-1}}$$

2.22 $NH_3SO_2 \rightarrow NH_3 + SO_2 \qquad \Delta H^\ominus = +40\ \text{kJ mol}^{-1}$

$NH_3 + SO_2 \rightarrow NH_3SO_2 \qquad \Delta H^\ominus = -40\ \text{kJ mol}^{-1}$

$$\Delta H_f^\ominus(NH_3SO_2, s) = \Delta H_f^\ominus(NH_3, g) + \Delta H_f^\ominus(SO_2, g) - 40\ \text{kJ mol}^{-1}$$

$$= -46.11 - 296.83 - 40\ \text{kJ mol}^{-1} = \underline{-383\ \text{kJ mol}^{-1}}$$

2.23 $C(gr) + O_2(g) \rightarrow CO_2(g) \qquad \Delta H^\ominus = -393.51\ \text{kJ mol}^{-1}$

$C(d) + O_2(g) \rightarrow CO_2(g) \qquad \Delta H^\ominus = -395.41\ \text{kJ mol}^{-1}$

The difference is

$$C(gr) \rightarrow C(d) \qquad \Delta H_{trs}^\ominus = -393.51 - (-395.41)\ \text{kJ mol}^{-1} = \underline{-1.90\ \text{kJ mol}^{-1}}$$

2.24 $q = n\Delta H_c^\ominus$

$$= \frac{1.5\ \text{g}}{342.3\ \text{g mol}^{-1}} \times (-5645\ \text{kJ mol}^{-1}) = \underline{-25\ \text{kJ}}$$

Effective work available $\approx 25\ \text{kJ} \times 0.25 = 6.2\bar{5}\ \text{kJ}$

Since $w = mgh$, with $m \approx 65$ kg

$$h \approx \frac{6.2\bar{5} \times 10^3\ \text{J}}{65\ \text{kg} \times 9.81\ \text{m s}^{-2}} = \underline{9.8\ \text{m}}$$

2.25 $C_3H_8(l) + 5O_2(g) \xrightarrow{\Delta H_{vap}^\ominus} C_3H_8(g) + 5O_2(g) \xrightarrow{\Delta H_c^\ominus(g)} 3CO_2(g) + 4H_2O(l)$

(a) $\Delta H_c^\ominus(l) = \Delta H_{vap}^\ominus + \Delta H_c^\ominus(g)$

$$= 15\ \text{kJ mol}^{-1} - 2220\ \text{kJ mol}^{-1} = \underline{-2205\ \text{kJ mol}^{-1}}$$

(b) $\Delta n_g = -2$ [$5O_2$ replaced by $3CO_2$]

Therefore $\Delta U_c^{\ominus}(l) = \Delta H_c^{\ominus}(l) - (-2)RT$

$$= -2205 \text{ kJ mol}^{-1} + 2 \times 2.479 \text{ kJ mol}^{-1}$$

$$= \underline{-2200 \text{ kJ mol}^{-1}}$$

2.26 $\Delta H^{\ominus} > 0$ indicates an endothermic reaction and $\Delta H^{\ominus} < 0$ an exothermic reaction. Therefore, (a) is exothermic, (b) and (c) are endothermic.

2.27 $0 = \sum_J \nu_J S_J$; hence

(a) $0 = CO_2 + 2H_2O - CH_4 - 2O_2$

$\nu(CO_2) = +1,\ \nu(H_2O) = +2,\ \nu(CH_4) = -1,\ \nu(O_2) = -2$

(b) $0 = C_2H_2 - 2C - H_2$

$\nu(C_2H_2) = +1,\ \nu(C) = -2,\ \nu(H_2) = -1$

(c) $0 = Na^+(aq) + Cl^-(aq) - NaCl(s)$

$\nu(Na^+) = +1,\ \nu(Cl^-) = +1,\ \nu(NaCl) = -1$

2.28 (a) $\Delta H^{\ominus} = \Delta H_f^{\ominus}(N_2O_4, g) - 2\Delta H_f^{\ominus}(NO_2, g)$

$$= 9.16 - 2 \times 33.18 \text{ kJ mol}^{-1} = \underline{-57.20 \text{ kJ mol}^{-1}}$$

(b) $\Delta H^{\ominus} = \Delta H_f^{\ominus}(NH_4Cl, s) - \Delta H_f^{\ominus}(NH_3, g) - \Delta H_f^{\ominus}(HCl, g)$

$$= -314.43 - (-46.11) - (92.31) \text{ kJ mol}^{-1} = \underline{-176.01 \text{ kJ mol}^{-1}}$$

(c) $\Delta H^{\ominus} = \Delta H_f^{\ominus}(\text{propane}, g) - \Delta H_f^{\ominus}(\text{cyclopropane}, g)$

$$= 20.42 - 53.30 \text{ kJ mol}^{-1} = \underline{-32.88 \text{ kJ mol}^{-1}}$$

(d) The net ionic reaction is obtained from

$H^+(aq) + Cl^-(aq) + Na^+(aq) + OH^-(aq) \rightarrow Na^+(aq) + Cl^-(aq) + H_2O(l)$

and is

$H^+(aq) + OH^-(aq) \rightarrow H_2O(l)$

$\Delta H^{\ominus} = \Delta H_f^{\ominus}(H_2O, l) - \Delta H_f^{\ominus}(H^+, aq) - \Delta H_f^{\ominus}(OH^-, aq)$

$$= -285.83 - 0 - (-229.99) \text{ kJ mol}^{-1} = \underline{-55.84 \text{ kJ mol}^{-1}}$$

2.29 The sum of the three reactions is

	$\Delta H^{\ominus}/(\text{kJ mol}^{-1})$
$2NO(g) + O_2(g) \rightarrow 2NO_2(g)$	-114.1
$\frac{1}{2}O_2(g) + 2NO_2(g) \rightarrow N_2O_5(g)$	$\frac{1}{2}(-110.2)$
$N_2(g) + O_2(g) \rightarrow 2NO(g)$	180.5
$N_2(g) + \frac{5}{2}O_2(g) \rightarrow N_2O_5(g)$	$+11.3$

Hence, $\Delta H_f^{\ominus}(N_2O_5, g) = \underline{+11.3\ \text{kJ mol}^{-1}}$

2.30 (a)

	$\Delta H^{\ominus}/(\text{kJ mol}^{-1})$
$K(s) + \frac{1}{2}Cl_2(g) \rightarrow KCl(s)$	-436.75
$KCl(s) + \frac{3}{2}O_2(g) \rightarrow KClO_3(s)$	$\frac{1}{2}(89.4)$
$K(s) + \frac{1}{2}Cl_2(g) + \frac{3}{2}O_2(g) \rightarrow KClO_3(s)$	-392.1

Hence, $\Delta H_f^{\ominus}(KClO_3, s) = \underline{-392.1\ \text{kJ mol}^{-1}}$

(b)

$Na(s) + \frac{1}{2}O_2(q) + \frac{1}{2}H_2(g) \rightarrow NaOH(s)$	-425.61
$NaOH(s) + CO_2(g) \rightarrow NaHCO_3(s)$	-127.5
$C(s) + O_2(g) \rightarrow CO_2(g)$	-393.51
$Na(s) + C(s) + \frac{1}{2}H_2(g) + \frac{3}{2}O_2(g) \rightarrow NaHCO_3(s)$	-946.6

Hence, $\Delta H_f^{\ominus}(NaHCO_3, s) = \underline{-946.6\ \text{kJ mol}^{-1}}$

(c)

$\frac{1}{2}N_2(g) + \frac{1}{2}O_2(g) \rightarrow NO(g)$	$+90.25$
$NO(g) + \frac{1}{2}Cl_2(g) \rightarrow NOCl(g)$	$-\frac{1}{2}(75.5)$
$\frac{1}{2}N_2(g) + \frac{1}{2}O(g) + \frac{1}{2}Cl_2(g) \rightarrow NOCl(g)$	$+52.5$

Hence, $\Delta H_f^{\ominus}(NOCl, g) = \underline{52.5\ \text{kJ mol}^{-1}}$

2.31 $\Delta H^{\ominus}(T_2) = \Delta H^{\ominus}(T_1) + \Delta C_p \Delta T$ [Example 2.12]

$\Delta C_p = C_p(N_2O_4, g) - 2C_p(NO_2, g)$

$= 77.28 - 2 \times 37.20\ \text{J K}^{-1}\ \text{mol}^{-1} = +2.88\ \text{J K}^{-1}\ \text{mol}^{-1}$

$\Delta H^{\ominus}(373\ \text{K}) = \Delta H^{\ominus}(298\ \text{K}) + \Delta C_p \Delta T$

$= -57.20\ \text{kJ mol}^{-1} + 2.88\ \text{J K}^{-1} \times 75\ \text{K}$

$= -57.20 + 0.22\ \text{kJ mol}^{-1} = \underline{-56.98\ \text{kJ mol}^{-1}}$

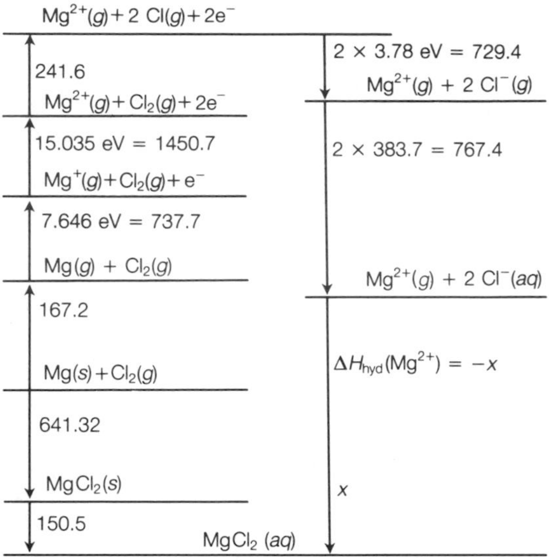

2.32
Distance up on left = distance down on right.
Therefore,

$$150.5 + 641.32 + 167.2 + 737.7 + 1450.7 + 241.6 = x + 767.4 + 729.4$$

Solving to $x = 1822.2$, implying that $\Delta H^{\ominus}_{\text{hyd}}(\text{Mg}^{2+}) = \underline{-1822.2 \text{ kJ mol}^{-1}}$

Problems

2.1 (a) $w = -p_{\text{ex}}\Delta V$ [5]

$V_{\text{i}} = 100 \text{ cm}^3 = 1.00 \times 10^{-4} \text{ m}^3$, $p = 1.0 \text{ atm} = 1.0\overline{13} \times 10^5 \text{ Pa}$

$$V_{\text{f}} = \frac{nRT}{p} = \frac{5.0 \text{ g}}{44.01 \text{ g mol}^{-1}} \times \frac{8.206 \times 10^{-2} \text{ L atm K}^{-1} \text{ mol}^{-1} \times 293 \text{ K}}{1.0 \text{ atm}}$$

$$= 2.7\overline{3} \text{ L} = 2.7\overline{3} \times 10^{-3} \text{ m}^3$$

Therefore, $w = -1.0\overline{13} \times 10^5 \text{ Pa} \times (2.7\overline{3} \times 10^{-3} - 1.00 \times 10^{-4}) \text{ m}^3$

$$= -26\overline{7} \text{ Pa m}^3 = \underline{-0.27 \text{ kJ}}$$

(b) $w = -nRT \ln \dfrac{V_{\text{f}}}{V_{\text{i}}}$ [7]

$$= \frac{-5.0 \text{ g}}{44.01 \text{ g mol}^{-1}} \times 8.314 \text{ J K}^{-1} \text{ mol}^{-1} \times 293 \text{ K} \times \ln \frac{2.7\overline{3} \times 10^{-3} \text{ m}^3}{1.00 \times 10^{-4} \text{ m}^3}$$

$$= -27\overline{7} \text{ J} \times \ln 27.\overline{3} = \underline{-0.92 \text{ kJ}}$$

2.2 $w = -p_{ex}\Delta V$ [5]

$$V_f = \frac{nRT}{p_{ex}} \gg V_i; \text{ so } \Delta V \approx V_f$$

Hence $w \approx -p_{ex} \times \dfrac{nRT}{p_{ex}} = -nRT$

$$\approx -1.0\,\text{mol} \times 8.314\,\text{J K}^{-1}\,\text{mol}^{-1} \times 1073\,\text{K}$$

$$\approx \underline{-8.9\,\text{kJ}}$$

Even if there is no physical piston, the gas drives back the atmosphere, so the work is also $\underline{-8.9\,\text{kJ}}$

2.3 Since the volume is fixed, $\underline{w=0}$.

Since $\Delta U = q$ at constant volume, $\underline{\Delta U = +2.35\,\text{kJ}}$

$\Delta H = \Delta U + \Delta(pV) = \Delta U + V\Delta p$ as $\Delta V = 0$. From the van der Waals equation [Table 1.5],

$$p = \frac{RT}{V_m - b} - \frac{a}{V_m^2}$$

$$\Delta p = \frac{R\Delta T}{V_m - b} \quad [\Delta V_m = 0 \text{ at constant volume}]$$

Therefore,

$$\Delta H = \Delta U + \frac{RV\Delta T}{V_m - b}$$

From the data,

$$V_m = \frac{15.0\,\text{L}}{2.0\,\text{mol}} = 7.5\,\text{L mol}^{-1}$$

$$V_m - b = 7.5 - 4.3 \times 10^{-2}\,\text{L mol}^{-1} = 7.4\bar{6}\,\text{L mol}^{-1}$$

$$\frac{RV\Delta T}{V_m - b} = \frac{8.314\,\text{J K}^{-1}\,\text{mol}^{-1} \times 15.0\,\text{L} \times 41\,\text{K}}{7.4\bar{6}\,\text{L mol}^{-1}} = 0.68\,\text{kJ}$$

Therefore,

$$\Delta H = 2.35\,\text{kJ} + 0.68\,\text{kJ} = \underline{+3.03\,\text{kJ}}$$

2.4 $w = -\displaystyle\int_i^f p\,dV = -n\int_i^f \frac{RT}{V_m}\left(1 + \frac{B}{V_m}\right) dV_m$

$$= -nRT\ln\frac{V_f}{V_i} + nBRT\left(\frac{1}{V_{mf}} - \frac{1}{V_{mi}}\right)$$

From the data,

$nRT = 70\times10^{-3}\,\text{mol}\times8.314\,\text{J K}^{-1}\,\text{mol}^{-1}\times373\,\text{K} = 21\bar{7}\,\text{J}$

$$V_{mi} = \frac{5.25\,\text{cm}^3}{70\,\text{mmol}} = 75.\bar{0}\,\text{cm}^3\,\text{mol}^{-1},\ V_{mf} = \frac{6.29\,\text{cm}^3}{70\,\text{mmol}} = 89.\bar{9}\,\text{cm}^3\,\text{mol}^{-1}$$

and so

$$B\left(\frac{1}{V_{mf}} - \frac{1}{V_{mi}}\right) = -28.7\,\text{cm}^3\,\text{mol}^{-1}\times\left(\frac{1}{75.0\,\text{cm}^3\,\text{mol}^{-1}} - \frac{1}{89.\bar{9}\,\text{cm}^3\,\text{mol}^{-1}}\right)$$

$$= -6.3\bar{4}\times10^{-2}$$

Therefore,

$$w = -21\bar{7}\,\text{J}\ln\frac{6.29}{5.25} - 21\bar{7}\,\text{J}\times6.3\bar{4}\times10^{-2}$$

$$= -39.\bar{2}\,\text{J} - 13.8\,\text{J} = \underline{-53\,\text{J}}$$

Since $\Delta U = q + w$ and $\Delta U = +83.5\,\text{J}$,

$$q = \Delta U - w = 83.5 + 53\,\text{J} = \underline{+136\,\text{J}}$$

$$\Delta H = \Delta U + \Delta(pV) \text{ with } pV = nRT\left(1 + \frac{B}{V_m}\right)$$

$$\Delta(pV) = nRTB\Delta\left(\frac{1}{V_m}\right) = nRTB\left(\frac{1}{V_{mf}} - \frac{1}{V_{mi}}\right) \text{ as } \Delta T = 0$$

$$= 21\bar{7}\,\text{J}\times(-6.3\bar{4}\times10^{-2}) = -13.\bar{8}\,\text{J}$$

Therefore,

$$\Delta H = 83.5\,\text{J} - 13.\bar{8}\,\text{J} = \underline{69.\bar{7}\,\text{J}}$$

2.5 $\Delta H = q$ [constant pressure] $= \underline{+22.2\,\text{kJ}}$

$$\Delta H_{vap} = \frac{q}{n} = \frac{18.02\,\text{g mol}^{-1}}{10\,\text{g}}\times22.2\,\text{kJ} = \underline{+40\,\text{kJ mol}^{-1}}$$

$$\Delta U = \Delta H - \Delta n_g RT,\ \Delta n_g = \frac{10\,\text{g}}{18.02\,\text{g mol}^{-1}} = 0.55\bar{5}\,\text{mol}$$

Hence $\Delta U = 22.2\text{ kJ} - 0.55\bar{5}\text{ mol} \times 8.314\text{ J K}^{-1}\text{ mol}^{-1} \times 373\text{ K}$

$= 22.2\text{ kJ} - 1.7\bar{2}\text{ kJ} = \underline{+20.5\text{ kJ}}$

$w = q - \Delta U$ [as $\Delta U = q + w$] $= 22.2\text{ kJ} - 20.5\text{ kJ} = \underline{1.7\text{ kJ}}$

2.6 $q = ItV = 0.232\text{ A} \times 12.0\text{ V} \times 650\text{ s} = 1.81\text{ kJ}$

$\Delta H = q + 1.81\text{ kJ}$

$$\Delta H_{\text{vap}} = \frac{\Delta H}{n} = \frac{102\text{ g mol}^{-1}}{1.871\text{ g}} \times 1.81\text{ kJ} = \underline{98.7\text{ kJ mol}^{-1}}$$

$\Delta V_{\text{vap}} = \Delta H_{\text{vap}} - RT\ [\Delta n_g = +1]$

$= 98.7\text{ kJ mol}^{-1} - 8.314\text{ J K}^{-1}\text{ mol}^{-1} \times 351\text{ K} = \underline{95.8\text{ kJ mol}^{-1}}$

2.7 $q = n\Delta H_{\text{vap}}$, so $n = \dfrac{q}{\Delta H_{\text{vap}}}$ with $\Delta H_{\text{vap}} = 8.18\text{ kJ mol}^{-1}$ [Table 2.2]

The volume occupied by the gas at a pressure p is $V = nRT/p$; therefore

$$V = \frac{qRT}{p\Delta H_{\text{vap}}}$$

$$= \frac{32.5\text{ kJ} \times 8.314\text{ J K}^{-1}\text{ mol}^{-1} \times 112\text{ K}}{1.013 \times 10^5\text{ Pa} \times 8.18\text{ kJ mol}^{-1}}$$

$= 3.65 \times 10^{-2}\text{ m}^3 = \underline{36.5\text{ L}}$

2.8 $2C(s) + 3H_2(g) \rightarrow C_2H_6(g)$

$$\Delta H_f^{\ominus}(T_2) = \Delta H_f^{\ominus}(T_1) + \int_1^2 \Delta C_p\,dT\ [17]$$

$\Delta C_p = C_p(C_2H_6) - 2C_p(C) - 3C_p(H_2)$

$$C_p(C_2H_6)/(\text{J K}^{-1}\text{ mol}^{-1}) = 14.73 + \frac{0.1272}{\text{K}}T$$

$$C_p(C, s)/(\text{J K}^{-1}\text{ mol}^{-1}) = 16.86 + \frac{4.77 \times 10^{-3}}{\text{K}}T - \frac{8.54 \times 10^5\text{ K}^2}{T^2}$$

$$C_p(H_2, g)/(\text{J K}^{-1}\text{ mol}^{-1}) = 27.28 + \frac{3.26 \times 10^{-3}}{\text{K}}T + \frac{0.50 \times 10^5\text{ K}^2}{T^2}$$

$$\Delta C_p/(\mathrm{J\,K^{-1}\,mol^{-1}}) = -100.83 + \frac{0.1079T}{\mathrm{K}} + \frac{1.56\times 10^6\,\mathrm{K}^2}{T^2}$$

$$\int_1^2 \frac{\Delta C_p\,\mathrm{d}T}{\mathrm{J\,K^{-1}\,mol^{-1}}} = -100.83(T_2 - T_1) + \tfrac{1}{2}\times 0.1079\,\mathrm{K}^{-1}(T_2^2 - T_1^2)$$

$$-1.56\times 10^6\,\mathrm{K}^2\left(\frac{1}{T_2} - \frac{1}{T_1}\right)$$

$$= -100.83\times 52\,\mathrm{K} + \tfrac{1}{2}\times 0.1079\times(350^2 - 298^2)\,\mathrm{K}$$

$$-1.56\times 10^6\times\left(\frac{1}{350} - \frac{1}{298}\right)\mathrm{K}$$

$$= -2.65\times 10^3\,\mathrm{K}$$

Therefore $\int_1^2 \Delta C_p\,\mathrm{d}T = -2.65\,\mathrm{kJ\,mol^{-1}}$

Hence $\Delta H_f^\ominus(350\,\mathrm{K}) = \Delta H_f^\ominus(298\,\mathrm{K}) - 2.65\,\mathrm{kJ\,mol^{-1}}$

$$= -84.68\,\mathrm{kJ\,mol^{-1}} - 2.65\,\mathrm{kJ\,mol^{-1}}$$

$$= \underline{-87.33\,\mathrm{kJ\,mol^{-1}}}$$

2.9 (a) $q = \Delta H_c^\ominus$ at constant pressure. Therefore, the heat outputs per mole are:

	Butane	pentane	octane
$\lvert\Delta H_c/(\mathrm{kJ\,mol^{-1}})\rvert$	2878	3537	5471

(b) The heat outputs per gram are $\lvert\Delta H_c\rvert/M$, and are:

$M/(\mathrm{g\,mol^{-1}})$	58.13	72.15	114.23
$(\Delta H_c/M)/(\mathrm{kJ\,g^{-1}})$	49.51	49.02	47.89

2.10 $\Delta H_{trs} - \Delta U_{trs} = \Delta(pV_m) = p\Delta V_m$

$V_m = \dfrac{M}{\rho}$ where ρ is the density; therefore:

$$\Delta H_{trs} - \Delta U_{trs} = pM\Delta\frac{1}{\rho} = pM\left(\frac{1}{\rho(\mathrm{d})} - \frac{1}{\rho(\mathrm{gr})}\right)$$

$$= 500\times 10^3\times 10^5\,\mathrm{Pa}\times 12.01\,\mathrm{g\,mol^{-1}}$$

$$\times\left(\frac{1}{3.52\text{ g cm}^{-3}}-\frac{1}{2.27\text{ g cm}^{-3}}\right)$$

$$=-9.39\times10^{10}\text{ Pa cm}^3\text{ mol}^{-1}$$

$$=-9.39\times10^{4}\text{ Pa m}^3\text{ mol}^{-1}=-9.39\times10^{4}\text{ J mol}^{-1}$$

$$=\underline{-93.9\text{ kJ mol}^{-1}}$$

2.11 $C_5H_{10}O_5(s)+5O_2(s)\rightarrow 5CO_2(g)+5H_2O(l),\ \Delta n_g=0$

For benzoic acid

$$\Delta U=\frac{0.825\text{ g}}{122.12\text{ g mol}^{-1}}\times(-3251\text{ kJ mol}^{-1})=-21.9\bar{6}\text{ kJ}$$

Since $\Delta T=1.940\ K$,

$$C=\frac{|q|}{\Delta T}=\frac{21.9\bar{6}\text{ kJ}}{1.940\text{ K}}=11.3\bar{2}\text{ kJ K}^{-1}$$

For D-ribose,

$$\Delta U=-C\Delta T=-11.3\bar{2}\text{ kJ K}^{-1}\times0.910\text{ K}$$

Therefore,

$$\Delta U_r=\frac{\Delta U}{n}=-11.3\bar{2}\text{ kJ K}^{-1}\times0.910\text{ K}\times\frac{150.13\text{ g mol}^{-1}}{0.727\text{ g}}$$

$$=\underline{-212\bar{7}\text{ kJ mol}^{-1}}$$

$$\Delta H_r=\Delta U_r[\Delta n_g=0]=\underline{-2130\text{ kJ mol}^{-1}}$$

The standard enthalpy of formation is obtained from the sum

	$\Delta H/(\text{kJ mol}^{-1})$
$5CO_2(g)+5H_2O(l)\rightarrow C_5H_{10}O_5(s)+5O_2(g)$	2130
$5C(s)+5O_2(g)\rightarrow 5CO_2(g)$	$5\times(-393.51)$
$5H_2(g)+\frac{5}{2}O_2(g)\rightarrow 5H_2O(l)$	$5\times(-285.83)$
$5C(s)+5H_2(g)+\frac{5}{2}O_2(g)\rightarrow C_5H_{10}O_5(s)$	-1267

Hence, $\Delta H_f^\ominus=\underline{-1267\text{ kJ mol}^{-1}}$

2.12 $Cr(C_6H_6)_2(s)\rightarrow Cr(s)+2C_6H_6(g),\qquad \Delta n_g=+2\text{ mol}$

$$\Delta H_r=\Delta U_r+2RT$$

$$= 8.0\ \text{kJ mol}^{-1} + 2 \times 8.314\ \text{J K}^{-1}\ \text{mol}^{-1} \times 583\ \text{K} = \underline{+17.7\ \text{kJ mol}^{-1}}$$

$$\Delta H_f^\ominus\ (583\ \text{K}) = 2\Delta H_f^\ominus(C_6H_6,\ g,\ 583\ \text{K}) - 17.7\ \text{kJ mol}^{-1}$$

The enthalpy of formation of benzene gas at 583 K is related to its value at 298 K by

$$\begin{aligned}\Delta H_f^\ominus(\text{benzene, 583 K}) = \Delta H_f^\ominus&(\text{benzene, 298 K}) + (T_b - 298\ \text{K})C_p(l)\\ &+ (583\ K - T_b)C_p(g) + \Delta H_{\text{vap}}^\ominus\\ &- 6(583\ \text{K} - 298\ \text{K})C_p(\text{graphite})\\ &- 3(583\ \text{K} - 298\ \text{K})C_p(H_2,\ g)\end{aligned}$$

where T_b is the boiling temperature of benzene (353 K). We shall assume that the heat capacities of graphite and hydrogen are approximately constant in the range of interest, and use their values from Table 2.10:

$$\begin{aligned}\Delta H_f^\ominus(583\ \text{K}) = 49.0\ \text{kJ mol}^{-1} &+ (353 - 298)\text{K} \times 140\ \text{J K}^{-1}\ \text{mol}^{-1}\\ &+ (583 - 353)\text{K} \times 28\ \text{J K}^{-1}\ \text{mol}^{-1} + 30.8\ \text{kJ mol}^{-1}\\ &- 6(583 - 298)\text{K} \times 8.53\ \text{J K}^{-1}\ \text{mol}^{-1}\\ &- 3(583 - 298)\text{K} \times 28.82\ \text{J K}^{-1}\ \text{mol}^{-1}\\ = 49.0 + 7.70 &+ 6.44 + 30.8 + 14.59 + 24.64\ \text{kJ mol}^{-1}\\ = \underline{+54.7}&\underline{\ \text{kJ mol}^{-1}}\end{aligned}$$

Therefore, for the metallocene,

$$\Delta H_f^\ominus(583\ \text{K}) = 2 \times 54.7 - 17.7\ \text{kJ mol}^{-1} = \underline{+91.7\ \text{kJ mol}^{-1}}$$

2.13 $C_{12}H_{22}O_{11} + H_2O \rightarrow 4CH_3CH(OH)COOH$

$$\begin{aligned}\Delta H^\ominus &= 4\Delta H_f^\ominus(\text{lactic acid}) - \Delta H_f^\ominus(\text{sucrose}) - \Delta H_f^\ominus(H_2O,\ l)\\ &= 4 \times (-694.0) - (-2222) - (-285.8)\ \text{kJ mol}^{-1}\\ &= -268\ \text{kJ mol}^{-1}\end{aligned}$$

$C_{12}H_{22}O_{11} + 12O_2 \rightarrow 12CO_2 + 11H_2 \qquad \Delta H_c^\ominus = -5645\ \text{kJ mol}^{-1}$

Therefore, $\Delta H_c^\ominus$ is more exothermic by 5376 kJ mol^{-1} than the hydrolysis reaction.

2.14 (a) KF, $C = 4.168\ \text{kJ mol}^{-1}$

m/(mol KF/kg CH_3COOH)	0.184	0.590	0.821	1.208
ΔT/K	1.592	4.501	5.909	8.115
$q = -C\Delta T$/kJ	−6.635	−18.76	−24.63	−33.82
ΔH/(kJ mol^{-1})	−34.2	−31.8	−30.0	−28.0

Plot ΔH against m (Fig. 2.1a) and find the best straight line, or else do a least-squares best fit (Appendix):

$\Delta H/(\text{kJ mol}^{-1}) = -35.4 + 6.2m/(\text{mol KF/kg CH}_3\text{COOH})$

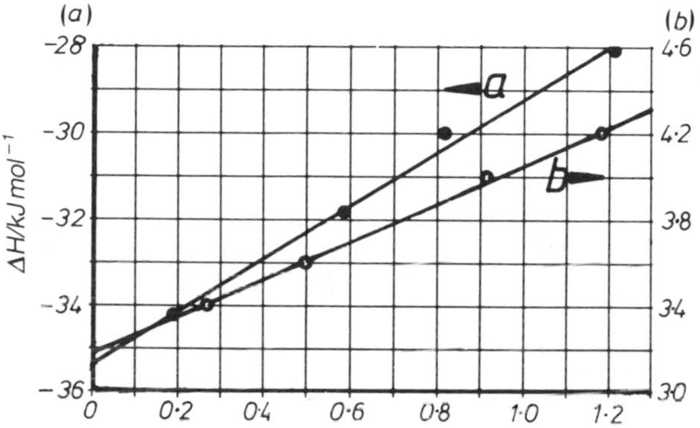

Fig 2.1

Therefore, the limiting value (at $m \to 0$) is $\underline{\Delta H = -35.4 \text{ kJ mol}^{-1}}$

(b) $\text{KF} \cdot \text{CH}_3\text{COOH}$, $C = 4.203 \text{ kJ K}^{-1}$

$m/(\text{mol KF/kg CH}_3\text{COOH})$	0.280	0.504	0.910	1.190
$\Delta T/\text{K}$	−0.227	−0.432	−0.866	−1.189
$q = -C\Delta T/\text{kJ}$	+0.954	1.816	3.64	5.00
$\Delta H/(\text{kJ mol}^{-1})$	+3.4	+3.6	+4.0	+4.2

Plot ΔH against m (Fig. 2.1b) or make a least-squares best fit:

$\Delta H/(\text{kJ mol}^{-1}) = 3.15 + 0.9m/(\text{mol kF/kg CH}_3\text{COOH})$

Therefore, the limiting value (at $m \to 0$) is $\underline{\Delta H = +3.15 \text{ kJ mol}^{-1}}$

See the original reference for further details.

2.15 Draw up the following thermodynamic cycle:

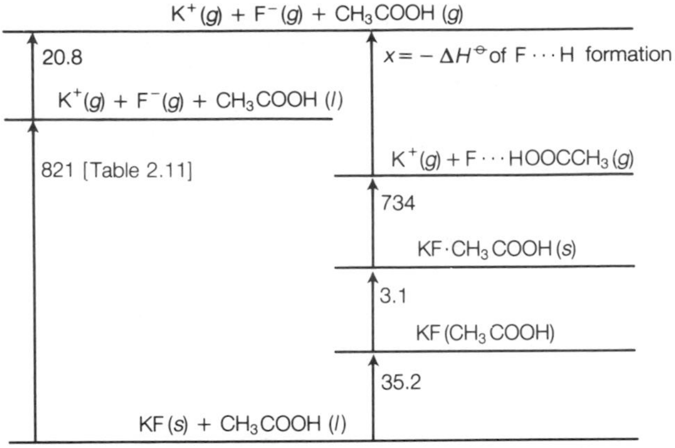

Since distance up on left = distance up on right,

$$821 + 20.8 = x + 734 + 3.1 + 35.2, \text{ so } x = 69.5$$

Therefore, $\underline{\Delta H^{\ominus} = -70 \text{ kJ mol}^{-1}}$

2.16 $w = -\int_1^2 F\,\mathrm{d}z$ [Section 2.3], $F(z) = F \sin \pi z/a$

$$w = -F \int_1^2 \sin \frac{\pi z}{a}\,\mathrm{d}z = \frac{Fa}{\pi}\left(\cos \frac{\pi z_2}{a} - \cos \frac{\pi z_1}{a}\right)$$

(a) $z_2 = a$, $z_1 = 0$

$$w = \frac{Fa}{\pi}(\cos \pi - \cos 0) = \underline{-2Fa/\pi}$$

(b) The force opposes extension only up to $z = a$, and no work needs to be done from $z = a$ to $z = za$; hence the work is $-2Fa/\pi$. If, however, the external force is balanced against the internal (so that the overall extension is reversible), then the system does work in the region from a to $2a$, and overall $\underline{w = 0}$.

2.17 $w = -\int_1^2 p\,\mathrm{d}V$ [6]

$$p = nRT\left(\frac{1}{V} + \frac{nB}{V^2} + \frac{n^2C}{V^3} + \cdots\right) \qquad [V = nV_{\mathrm{m}}]$$

Therefore,

$$W = -nRT\int_1^2\left(\frac{1}{V}+\frac{nB}{V^2}+\frac{n^2C}{V^3}+\cdots\right)dV$$

$$= -nRT\ln\frac{V_2}{V_1}+n^2RTB\left(\frac{1}{V_2}-\frac{1}{V_1}\right)+\tfrac{1}{2}n^3RTC\left(\frac{1}{V_2^2}-\frac{1}{V_1^2}\right)$$

For argon, $n = 1.0$ mol, and

$nRT = 1.0\ \mathrm{mol}\times 8.314\ \mathrm{J\,K^{-1}\,mol^{-1}}\times 273\ \mathrm{K} = 2.2\overline{7}\ \mathrm{kJ}$

From Table 1.2, $B = -21.7\ \mathrm{cm^3\,mol^{-1}}$, $C = 1200\ \mathrm{cm^6\,mol^{-2}}$, so

$n^2BRT = 1.0\ \mathrm{mol}\times(-21.7\ \mathrm{cm^3\,mol^{-1}})\times 2.2\overline{7}\ \mathrm{kJ} = -49.\overline{3}\ \mathrm{kJ\,cm^3}$

$\tfrac{1}{2}n^3CRT = \tfrac{1}{2}(1.0\ \mathrm{mol})^2\times(1200\ \mathrm{cm^6\,mol^{-2}})\times 2.2\overline{7}\ \mathrm{kJ} = +13\overline{62}\ \mathrm{kJ\,cm^6}$

Therefore,

(a) $w = -2.2\overline{7}\ \mathrm{kJ}\ln 2 - 49.3\ \mathrm{kJ}\left(\frac{1}{1000}-\frac{1}{500}\right)+13\overline{62}\ \mathrm{kJ}\left(\frac{1}{1000^2}-\frac{1}{500^2}\right)$

$= -1.5\overline{7}+0.049-4.1\times10^{-3}\ \mathrm{kJ}$

$= -1.\overline{52}\ \mathrm{kJ} = \underline{-1.5\ \mathrm{kJ}}$

(b) For a perfect gas, only the first term contributes, so $w - = 1.5\overline{7}\ \mathrm{kJ} = \underline{-1.6\ \mathrm{kJ}}$

2.18 $w = -\int_1^2 p\,dV$ with $p = \frac{nRT}{V-nb}-\frac{n^2a}{V^2}$ [Table 1.5]

Therefore,

$$w = -nRT\int_1^2\frac{dV}{V-nb}+n^2a\int_1^2\frac{dV}{V^2}$$

$$\underline{= -nRT\ln\left(\frac{V_2-nb}{V_1-nb}\right)-n^2a\left(\frac{1}{V_2}-\frac{1}{V_1}\right)}$$

Suppose $nb \ll V$, then $\ln(V-nb) = \ln V + \ln\left(1-\frac{nb}{V}\right) \approx \ln V - \frac{nb}{V}$.

Then

$$w \approx -nRT \ln \frac{V_2}{V_1} + n^2bRT\left(\frac{1}{V_2} - \frac{1}{V_1}\right) - n^2a\left(\frac{1}{V_2} - \frac{1}{V_1}\right)$$

$$\approx -nRT \ln \frac{V_2}{V_1} - n^2(a - bRT)\left(\frac{1}{V_2} - \frac{1}{V_1}\right)$$

$$\approx -w^\circ - n^2(a - bRT)\left(\frac{1}{V_2} - \frac{1}{V_1}\right)$$

where w° is the perfect gas value. In a reversible compression, $V_2 < V_1$, and so $w < w^\circ$ if $bRT < a$ but $w > w^\circ$ if $bRT > a$. If attractions dominate repulsions ($bRT < a$), we should expect less work to be done on compression and $w < w^\circ$, as found.

2.19 $w = -nRT \ln\left(\frac{V_2 - nb}{V_1 - nb}\right) - n^2a\left(\frac{1}{V_2} - \frac{1}{V_1}\right)$ [Problem 2.18]

$$= -nR\frac{T}{T_c}T_c \ln\left(\frac{V_2/V_c - nb/V_c}{V_1/V_c - nb/V_c}\right) - \frac{n^2a}{V_c}\left(\frac{V_c}{V_2} - \frac{V_c}{V_1}\right)$$

$T_r = \frac{T}{T_c}$, $\quad V_r = \frac{V}{V_c}$, $\quad T_c = \frac{8a}{27Rb}$, $\quad V_c = 3nb$ [Table 1.5]

$$w = -\frac{8na}{27b}T_r \ln\left(\frac{V_{r,2} - \frac{1}{3}}{V_{r,1} - \frac{1}{3}}\right) - \frac{na}{3b}\left(\frac{1}{V_{r,2}} - \frac{1}{V_{r,1}}\right)$$

Define $w_r = \frac{3bw}{a}$, then

$$\underline{w_r = -\tfrac{8}{9}nT_r \ln\left(\frac{V_{r,2} - 1}{V_{r,1} - 1}\right) - n\left(\frac{1}{V_{r,2}} - \frac{1}{V_{r,1}}\right)}$$

Along the critical isotherm, $T_r = 1$ and $V_{r,1} = 1$, $V_{r,2} = x$. Hence:

$$\underline{w_r/n = -\tfrac{8}{9}\ln\left(\frac{3x - 1}{2}\right) - \frac{1}{x} + 1}$$

2.20 (a) $\left(\frac{\partial p}{\partial T}\right)_V = \left(\frac{\partial}{\partial T}\left(\frac{nRT}{V}\right)\right)_V = \frac{nR}{V} = \frac{p}{T}$

$$\left(\frac{\partial p}{\partial V}\right)_T = \left(\frac{\partial}{\partial V}\left(\frac{nRT}{V}\right)\right)_T = -\frac{nRT}{V^2} = -\frac{p}{V}$$

$$\frac{\partial^2 p}{\partial V \partial T} = \left(\frac{\partial}{\partial V}\left(\frac{\partial p}{\partial T}\right)_V\right)_T = \left(\frac{\partial}{\partial V}\frac{nR}{V}\right)_T = -\frac{nR}{V^2}$$

Equal

$$\frac{\partial^2 p}{\partial T \partial V} = \left(\frac{\partial}{\partial T}\left(\frac{\partial p}{\partial V}\right)_T\right)_V = \left(\frac{\partial}{\partial T}\left(\frac{-nRT}{V^2}\right)\right)_V = -\frac{nR}{V^2}$$

(b) $p = \frac{nRT}{V-nb}\mathrm{e}^{-na/RTV}$ [Table 1.5, $V = nV_\mathrm{m}$]

$$\left(\frac{\partial p}{\partial T}\right)_V = \frac{nR}{V-nb}\mathrm{e}^{-na/RTV} + \left(\frac{na}{RT^2V}\right)\left(\frac{nRT}{V-nb}\right)\mathrm{e}^{-na/RTV}$$

$$= \left(\frac{nR}{V-nb}\right)\left(1+\frac{na}{RTV}\right)\mathrm{e}^{-na/RTV} = \underline{\left(1+\frac{na}{RTV}\right)\frac{p}{T}}$$

$$\left(\frac{\partial p}{\partial V}\right)_T = \frac{-nRT}{(V-nb)^2}\mathrm{e}^{-na/RTV} + \left(\frac{na}{RTV^2}\right)\left(\frac{nRT}{V-nb}\right)\mathrm{e}^{-na/RTV}$$

$$= \left(\frac{nRT}{V-nb}\right)\left(\frac{na}{RTV^2} - \frac{1}{V-nb}\right)\mathrm{e}^{-na/RTV}$$

$$= \underline{\left(\frac{na}{RTV} - \frac{V}{V-nb}\right)\frac{p}{V}}$$

$$\frac{\partial^2 p}{\partial V \partial T} = \left(\frac{\partial}{\partial V}\left(\frac{\partial p}{\partial T}\right)_V\right)_T = \left(\frac{\partial}{\partial V}\left(1+\frac{na}{RTV}\right)\frac{p}{T}\right)_T$$

$$= \left(\frac{\partial}{\partial V}\frac{p}{T}\right)_T + \left(\frac{\partial}{\partial V}\left(\frac{na}{RTV}\cdot\frac{p}{T}\right)\right)_T$$

$$\frac{\partial^2 p}{\partial V \partial T} = \left(\frac{\partial}{\partial T}\left(\frac{\partial p}{\partial V}\right)_T\right)_V = \left(\frac{\partial}{\partial T}\left(\frac{nap}{RTV^2} - \frac{p}{V-nb}\right)\right)_V$$

$$= \frac{na}{RTV^2}\left(\frac{\partial p}{\partial T}\right)_V - \frac{nap}{RT^2V^2} - \frac{1}{V-nb}\left(\frac{\partial p}{\partial T}\right)_V$$

$$= \frac{n^2a^2p}{R^2T^3V^3} - \frac{p}{T(V-nb)} - \frac{nap}{RT^2V(V-nb)}$$

Hence, $\dfrac{\partial^2 p}{\partial V \partial T} = \dfrac{\partial^2 p}{\partial T \partial V}$

2.21 $\Delta H(T_2) = \Delta H(T_1) + \int_1^2 \Delta C_p \, dT$ [17]

$$C_p = a + bT + \frac{c}{T^2}$$

$$\Delta C_p = \Delta a + \Delta bT + \frac{\Delta c}{T^2} \text{ where } \Delta a = \sum_J \nu_J a_J, \text{ etc.}$$

Hence,

$$\Delta H(T_2) = \Delta H(T_1) + \int_1^2 \left(\Delta a + \Delta bT + \frac{\Delta c}{T^2}\right) dT$$

$$= \underline{\Delta H(T_1) + \Delta a(T_2 - T_1) + \tfrac{1}{2}\Delta b(T_2^2 - T_1^2) - \Delta c\left(\frac{1}{T_2} - \frac{1}{T_1}\right)}$$

For the reaction

$H_2(g) + \frac{1}{2}O_2(g) \rightarrow H_2O(l)$ $\quad \Delta H_f^\ominus(T) = -285.83\ \text{kJ mol}^{-1}$

we need [Table 2.16]

	$H_2O(l)$	$H_2(g)$	$O_2(g)$
$a/(\text{J K}^{-1}\text{ mol}^{-1})$	75.29	27.28	29.96
$b/(\text{J K}^{-2}\text{ mol}^{-1})$	0	3.26×10^{-3}	4.18×10^{-3}
$c/(\text{J K mol}^{-1})$	0	0.50×10^5	-1.67×10^5

$\Delta a = 75.29 - 27.28 - \frac{1}{2} \times 29.96\ \text{J K}^{-1}\text{ mol}^{-1} = 33.03\ \text{J K}^{-1}\text{ mol}^{-1}$

$\Delta b = 0 - 3.26 \times 10^{-3} - \frac{1}{2} \times 4.18 \times 10^{-3}\ \text{J K}^{-2}\text{ mol}^{-1} = -5.35 \times 10^{-3}\ \text{J K}^{-2}\text{ mol}^{-1}$

$$\Delta c = 0 - 0.50 \times 10^5 + \tfrac{1}{2} \times 1.67 \times 10^5 \text{ J K mol}^{-1} = 0.34 \times 10^5 \text{ J K mol}^{-1}$$

$$\begin{aligned}
\Delta H_f^{\ominus}(373.15 \text{ K} &= 285.83 \text{ kJ mol}^{-1} + 33.03 \text{ J K}^{-1} \text{ mol}^{-1} \times 75.00 \text{ K} \\
&\quad - \tfrac{1}{2} \times 5.35 \times 10^{-3} \text{ J K}^{-2} \text{ mol}^{-1} \times \{(373.15 \text{ K})^2 - (298.15 \text{ K})^2\} \\
&\quad - 0.34 \times 10^5 \text{ J K mol}^{-1} \times \left(\frac{1}{373.15 \text{ K}} - \frac{1}{298.15 \text{ K}}\right) \\
&= (-285.83 + 2.36) \text{ kJ mol}^{-1} \\
&= \underline{-283.47 \text{ kJ mol}^{-1}}
\end{aligned}$$

If instead we use [Table 2.10]

$C_p(H_2O) = 75.29 \text{ J K}^{-1} \text{ mol}^{-1}$, $C_p(H_2) = 28.82 \text{ J K}^{-1} \text{ mol}^{-1}$, and $C_p(O_2) = 29.36 \text{ J K}^{-1} \text{ mol}^{-1}$ (the values at 298.15 K),

$$\begin{aligned}
\Delta H_f^{\ominus}(373 \text{ K}) &\approx \Delta H_f^{\ominus}(298 \text{ K}) + 31.79 \text{ J K}^{-1} \text{ mol}^{-1} \times (373.15 \text{ K} - 298 \text{ K}) \\
&\approx (-285.83 + 2.38) \text{ kJ mol}^{-1} \\
&\approx \underline{-283.45 \text{ kJ mol}^{-1}}
\end{aligned}$$

which is the same to the stated number of significant figures.

3. The first law: the machinery

Exercises

3.1 Show that $\dfrac{\partial^2 f}{\partial x\,\partial y}=\dfrac{\partial^2 f}{\partial y\,\partial x}$ [Box 3.1]

(a) $$\frac{\partial^2 f}{\partial y\,\partial x}=\frac{\partial}{\partial y}(2xy)=2x$$

$$\frac{\partial^2 f}{\partial x\,\partial y}=\frac{\partial}{\partial x}(x^2+6y)=2x$$

(b) $$\frac{\partial^2 f}{\partial y\,\partial x}=\frac{\partial}{\partial y}(\cos xy-xy\sin xy)=-x\sin xy-x\sin xy-x^2y\cos xy$$

$$=-2x\sin xy-x^2y\cos xy$$

$$\frac{\partial^2 f}{\partial x\,\partial y}=\frac{\partial}{\partial x}(-x^2\sin xy)=-2x\sin xy-x^2y\cos xy$$

(c) $$\frac{\partial^2 f}{\partial s\,\partial t}=\frac{\partial}{\partial s}(2t+\mathrm{e}^s)=\mathrm{e}^s$$

$$\frac{\partial^2 f}{\partial t\,\partial s}=\frac{\partial}{\partial t}(t\,\mathrm{e}^s+2s)=\mathrm{e}^s$$

3.2 $$\left(\frac{\partial C_V}{\partial V}\right)_T=\left(\frac{\partial}{\partial V}\left(\frac{\partial U}{\partial T}\right)_V\right)_T=\left(\frac{\partial}{\partial T}\left(\frac{\partial U}{\partial V}\right)_T\right)_V=0$$

because $(\partial U/\partial V)_T=0$ for a perfect gas [Section 3.1]

3.3 $H=U+pV$

$$\left(\frac{\partial H}{\partial U}\right)_p=1+p\left(\frac{\partial V}{\partial U}\right)_p$$

$$\left(\frac{\partial H}{\partial U}\right)_p=\left(\frac{\partial H}{\partial V}\right)_p\Big/\left(\frac{\partial U}{\partial V}\right)_p \text{ [Box 3.1]}=\left(\frac{\partial V}{\partial U}\right)_p\left(\frac{\partial}{\partial V}(U+pV)\right)_p$$

$$=\left(\frac{\partial V}{\partial U}\right)_p\left\{\left(\frac{\partial U}{\partial V}\right)_p+p\right\}$$

$$=1+p\left(\frac{\partial V}{\partial U}\right)_p$$

3.4 $dV = \left(\frac{\partial V}{\partial p}\right)_T dp + \left(\frac{\partial V}{\partial T}\right)_p dT$

We use $\alpha = \frac{1}{V}\left(\frac{\partial V}{\partial T}\right)_p$ [4] and $\kappa = -\frac{1}{V}\left(\frac{\partial V}{\partial p}\right)_T$ [7] and obtain

$$d\ln V = \frac{1}{V}dV = \frac{1}{V}\left(\frac{\partial V}{\partial p}\right)_T dp + \frac{1}{V}\left(\frac{\partial V}{\partial T}\right)_p dT$$

$$= \underline{-\kappa\, dp + \alpha\, dT}$$

3.5 $\left(\frac{\partial U}{\partial V}\right)_T = \left(\frac{\partial}{\partial V}\left(\frac{3}{2}nRT\right)\right)_T = \underline{0}$

$H = U + pV = U + nRT$ $[pV = nRT]$

$$\left(\frac{\partial H}{\partial V}\right)_T = \left(\frac{\partial U}{\partial V}\right)_T + \left(\frac{\partial nRT}{\partial V}\right)_T = 0 + 0 = \underline{0}$$

3.6 $\alpha = \frac{1}{V}\left(\frac{\partial V}{\partial T}\right)_p$ [4]

$$V = V'\{0.75 + 3.9\times 10^{-4}\, T/\mathrm{K} + 1.48\times 10^{-6}\,(T/\mathrm{K})^2\}$$

$$\frac{1}{V_{320}} = \frac{0.974}{V_{300}}$$

$$\left(\frac{\partial V}{\partial T}\right)_p = V_{300}(3.9\times 10^{-4}/\mathrm{K} + 2.96\times 10^{-6}\, T/\mathrm{K}^2)$$

$$\left(\frac{\partial V}{\partial T}\right)_{p,320} = V_{300}(3.9\times 10^{-4}/\mathrm{K} + 2.96\times 10^{-6}\times 320/\mathrm{K}) = 1.3\times 10^{-3}\,\mathrm{K}^{-1}\,V_{300}$$

$$\alpha_{320} = \frac{1}{V_{320}}\left(\frac{\partial V}{\partial T}\right)_{p,320} = \frac{0.97}{V_{300}}\times 1.3\times 10^{-3}\,\mathrm{K}^{-1}\,V_{300}$$

$$= 0.97\times 1.3\times 10^{-3}\,\mathrm{K}^{-1} = \underline{1.3\times 10^{-3}\,\mathrm{K}^{-1}}$$

3.7 $\kappa = -\frac{1}{V}\left(\frac{\partial V}{\partial p}\right)_T$

$$\frac{dV}{V} = -\kappa\, dp \quad [\text{at constant } T]$$

$$\frac{d\rho}{\rho} = \frac{V}{m}d\left(\frac{m}{V}\right) = -\frac{V\,dV}{V^2} = -\frac{dV}{V} = \kappa\, dp$$

Therefore $\dfrac{\delta\rho}{\rho} \approx \kappa\delta p$

For $\delta\rho/\rho = 0.08\times10^{-2} = 8\times10^{-4}$

$$\delta p \approx \frac{8\times10^{-4}}{\kappa} = \frac{8\times10^{-4}}{7.35\times10^{-7}\ \text{atm}^{-1}} = \underline{1.\bar{1}\times10^{3}\ \text{atm}}$$

3.8 $\left(\dfrac{\partial H}{\partial p}\right)_T = -\mu C_p$ [10]

$$= -0.25\ \text{K atm}^{-1}\times 29\ \text{J K}^{-1}\ \text{mol}^{-1} = \underline{-7.2\ \text{J atm}^{-1}\ \text{mol}^{-1}}$$

$$q = -\left(\frac{\partial H}{\partial p}\right)_T \delta p = 7.2\ \text{J atm}^{-1}\ \text{mol}^{-1}\times 15\ \text{mol}\times 75\ \text{atm} = \underline{8.1\ \text{kJ}}$$

3.9 $q = \underline{0}$ [adiabatic process]

$$w = -p_{\text{ex}}\,\Delta V = -600\ \text{Torr}\times\frac{1.013\times10^{5}\ \text{Pa}}{760\ \text{Torr}}\times 40\times10^{-3}\ \text{m}^{3} = \underline{-3.2\ \text{kJ}}$$

$$\Delta T = -\frac{p_{\text{ex}}\,\Delta V}{C_V}\ [15] = \frac{-3.2\times10^{3}\ \text{J}}{4.0\ \text{mol}\times 21.1\ \text{J K}^{-1}\ \text{mol}^{-1}} = \underline{-38\ \text{K}}$$

$\Delta U = q + w = 0\text{–}3.2\ \text{kJ} = \underline{-3.2\ \text{kJ}}$

$\Delta H = \Delta U + \Delta(pV) = \Delta U + nR\,\Delta T$

$= -3.2\ \text{kJ} + 4.0\ \text{mol}\times 8.314\ \text{J K}^{-1}\ \text{mol}^{-1}\times -38\ \text{K}$

$= \underline{-1.9\ \text{kJ}}$

3.10 $q = \underline{0}$ [adiabatic process]

$\Delta U = C_V\,\Delta T = 3.0\ \text{mol}\times 27.5\ \text{J K}^{-1}\ \text{mol}^{-1}\times 50\ \text{K} = \underline{+4.1\ \text{kJ}}$

$w = \Delta U - q = 4.1\ \text{kJ} - 0 = \underline{+4.1\ \text{kJ}}$

$\Delta H = \Delta U + nRT\,\Delta T$

$= 4.1\ \text{kJ} + 3.0\ \text{mol}\times 8.314\ \text{J K}^{-1}\ \text{mol}^{-1}\times 50\ \text{K} = \underline{+5.4\ \text{kJ}}$

$$V_{\text{i}} = \frac{nRT_{\text{i}}}{p_{\text{i}}} = \frac{3.0\ \text{mol}\times 8.206\times10^{-2}\ \text{L atm K}^{-1}\ \text{mol}^{-1}\times 200\ \text{K}}{2.0\ \text{atm}} = 24.6\ \text{L}$$

$$V_{\text{f}} = V_{\text{i}}\left(\frac{T_{\text{i}}}{T_{\text{f}}}\right)^{c}\ [17\text{a}],\quad c = \frac{C_V}{R} = \frac{27.5\ \text{J K}^{-1}\ \text{mol}^{-1}}{8.314\ \text{J K}^{-1}\ \text{mol}^{-1}} = 3.31$$

$$V_f = 24.6\ \text{L} \times \left(\frac{200\ \text{K}}{250\ \text{K}}\right)^{3.31} = \underline{11.8\ \text{L}}$$

$$p_f = \frac{nRT_f}{V_f} = \frac{3.0\ \text{mol} \times 8.206 \times 10^{-2}\ \text{L atm K}^{-1}\ \text{mol}^{-1} \times 250\ \text{K}}{11.8\ \text{L}}$$

$$= \underline{5.2\ \text{atm}}$$

3.11 $$V_i = \frac{nRT_i}{p_i} = \frac{1.0\ \text{mol} \times 8.206 \times 10^{-2}\ \text{L atm K}^{-1}\ \text{mol}^{-1} \times 310\ \text{K}}{3.25\ \text{atm}} = 7.8\bar{3}\ \text{L}$$

$$\gamma = \frac{C_p}{C_V} = \frac{C_V + R}{C_V} = \frac{(20.8 + 8.31)\ \text{J K}^{-1}\ \text{mol}^{-1}}{20.8\ \text{J K}^{-1}\ \text{mol}^{-1}} = 1.40$$

$1/\gamma = 0.714$

$$V_f = V_i\left(\frac{p_i}{p_f}\right)^{1/\gamma}\ [21] = 7.8\bar{3}\ \text{L} \times \left(\frac{3.25\ \text{atm}}{2.50\ \text{atm}}\right)^{0.714} = \underline{9.4\bar{4}\ \text{L}}$$

$$T_f = \frac{p_f V_f}{nR} = \frac{2.50\ \text{atm} \times 9.4\bar{4}\ \text{L}}{1.0\ \text{mol} \times 8.206 \times 10^{-2}\ \text{L atm K}^{-1}\ \text{mol}^{-1}} = \underline{28\bar{8}\ \text{K}}$$

$$w = C_V(T_f - T_i)\ [15] = 20.8\ \text{J K}^{-1}\ \text{mol}^{-1} \times 1.0\ \text{mol} \times (288\ \text{K} - 310\ \text{K})$$

$$= \underline{-0.46\ \text{kJ}}$$

3.12 $$\Delta V \approx \left(\frac{\partial V}{\partial T}\right)_p \Delta T = \alpha V\, \Delta T\ [4]$$

(a) Mercury, $\alpha = 1.82 \times 10^{-4}\ \text{K}^{-1}$,

$$\Delta V \approx 1.82 \times 10^{-4}\ \text{K}^{-1} \times 1.0\ \text{cm}^3 \times 5\ \text{K}$$

$$\approx 9.\bar{1} \times 10^{-4}\ \text{cm}^3 = \underline{0.9\ \text{mm}^3}$$

(b) Diamond, $\alpha = 0.03 \times 10^{-4}\ \text{K}^{-1}$

$$\Delta T \approx 0.03 \times 10^{-4}\ \text{K}^{-1} \times 1.0\ \text{cm}^3 \times 5\ \text{K} = \underline{0.02\ \text{mm}^3}$$

3.13 $$\mu = \left(\frac{\partial T}{\partial p}\right)_H, \text{ so } \Delta p \approx \frac{\Delta T}{\mu}$$

For $\Delta T = -5.0\ \text{K}$,

$$\Delta p \approx \frac{-5.0\ \text{K}}{1.2\ \text{K atm}^{-1}} = \underline{-4.2\ \text{atm}}$$

3.14 $\mu = \left(\frac{\partial T}{\partial p}\right)_H = \lim_{\delta p \to 0} \left(\frac{\delta T}{\delta p}\right)_H$

Draw up the following table:

p/atm	32	24	18	11	8	5
δp/atm	−31	−23	−17	−10	−7	−4
δT/K	−22	−18	−15	−10	−7.4	−4.6
$(\delta T/\delta p)/(\text{K atm}^{-1})$	0.71	0.78	0.88	1.00	$1.0\overline{6}$	$1.\overline{15}$

Plot $\delta T/\delta p$ against δp (Fig. 3.1) and extrapolate to $\delta p = 0$. Hence we find that $\mu = \underline{1.3 \text{ K atm}^{-1}}$

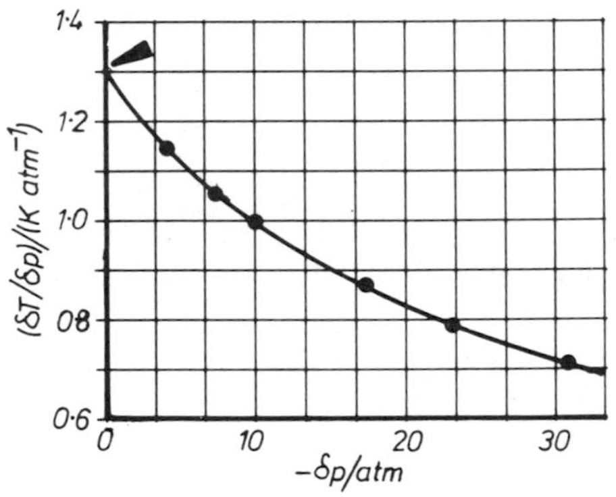

Fig 3·1

3.15 $w = C_V T_i \left\{ \left(\frac{V_i}{V_f}\right)^{1/c} - 1 \right\}$ [18]

$$c = \frac{C_V}{R} = \frac{37.11 - 8.31}{8.31} \quad [C_p - C_V = R,\ C_p \text{ from Table 2.10}]$$

$$= 3.47$$

$$V_i = \frac{nRT_i}{p_i} = \frac{2.0\ \text{mol} \times 8.206 \times 10^{-2}\ \text{L atm K}^{-1}\ \text{mol}^{-1} \times 298\ \text{K}}{10\ \text{atm}}$$

$$= 4.8\overline{9}\ \text{L} = 4.8\overline{9} \times 10^3\ \text{cm}^3$$

$$V_f = V_i + 20\ \text{cm} \times 10\ \text{cm}^2 = 4.8\overline{9} \times 10^3\ \text{cm}^3 + 200\ \text{cm}^3 = 5.0\overline{9} \times 10^3\ \text{cm}^3$$

$$w = 2.0\ \text{mol} \times 298\ \text{K} \times 28.80\ \text{J K}^{-1}\ \text{mol}^{-1}$$

$$\times \left\{ \left(\frac{4.8\bar{9}}{5.0\bar{9}}\right)^{1/3.47} - 1 \right\} = \underline{-200\ \text{J}}$$

$q = 0$ [adiabatic process]

$\Delta U = q + w = \underline{-200\ \text{J}}$

$$T_f = \left(\frac{V_i}{V_f}\right)^{1/c} T_i\ [17b]$$

$$= \left(\frac{4.8\bar{9}}{5.0\bar{9}}\right)^{1/3.47} \times 298\ \text{K} = \underline{295\ \text{K}}$$

$\Delta H = \Delta U + \Delta(pV) = \Delta U + nRT\,\Delta T,\ \Delta T = -3\ \text{K}$

$$= -20\bar{0}\ \text{J} + 2.0\ \text{mol} \times 8.314\ \text{J K}^{-1}\ \text{mol}^{-1} \times (-3\ \text{K})$$

$$= \underline{-250\ \text{J}}$$

3.16 (a) $T_f = \left(\frac{V_i}{V_f}\right)^{1/c} \times T_i$ [17b] and $\frac{V_i}{V_f} = \left(\frac{p_f}{p_i}\right)^{1/\gamma}$ [19]

Hence $T_f = \left(\frac{p_f}{p_i}\right)^{1/c\gamma} \times T_i,\ c\gamma = \frac{C_V}{R} \times \frac{C_p}{C_V} = \frac{C_p}{R}$

$C_p = 20.79\ \text{J K}^{-1}\ \text{mol}^{-1}$ [Table 2.10], so $c\gamma = 2.501$

$$T_f = \left(\frac{1.00\ \text{atm}}{2.00\ \text{atm}}\right)^{1/2.501} \times 298\ \text{K} = \underline{226\ \text{K}}$$

(b) $\Delta T = -p_{ex}\frac{\Delta V}{C_V}$ [16]

$$T_f - T_i = -\frac{p_{ex}}{C_V}(V_f - V_i) = -\frac{p_{ex}}{C_V}nR\left(\frac{T_f}{p_f} - \frac{T_i}{p_i}\right)$$

That is, since $p_{ex} = p_f$,

$$\left(1 + \frac{nR}{C_V}\right)T_f = T_i + \frac{nRT_i p_{ex}}{C_V p_i} \quad \text{or} \quad T_f = \frac{1 + nRp_{ex}/C_V p_i}{1 + nR/C_V} \times T_i$$

We use $n = \frac{63.09\ \text{g}}{131.3\ \text{g mol}^{-1}} = 0.495\ \text{mol}$

and $C_V = C_p - R = (20.79 - 8.314)\ \mathrm{J\,K^{-1}\,mol^{-1}} = 12.48\ \mathrm{J\,K^{-1}\,mol^{-1}}$

and obtain

$$\frac{nRp_{\mathrm{ex}}}{C_V p_{\mathrm{i}}} = \frac{0.49\bar{5}\ \mathrm{mol} \times 8.314\ \mathrm{J\,K^{-1}\,mol^{-1}} \times 1.00\ \mathrm{atm}}{0.59\bar{5}\ \mathrm{mol} \times 12.48\ \mathrm{J\,K^{-1}\,mol^{-1}} \times 2.00\ \mathrm{atm}} = 0.333$$

$$\frac{nR}{C_V} = \frac{8.314\ \mathrm{J\,K^{-1}\,mol^{-1}}}{12.48\ \mathrm{J\,K^{-1}\,mol^{-1}}} = 0.666$$

Therefore, $T_{\mathrm{f}} = \dfrac{1 + 0.333}{1 + 0.666} \times 298\ \mathrm{K} = \underline{238\ \mathrm{K}}$

Problems

3.1 $\kappa = 2.3 \times 10^{-6}\ \mathrm{atm} = \dfrac{2.3 \times 10^{-6}}{\mathrm{atm}}$

$$= \frac{2.3 \times 10^{-6}}{1.013 \times 10^{5}\ \mathrm{Pa}} = \underline{2.3 \times 10^{-11}\ \mathrm{Pa^{-1}}}$$

$$\Delta V \approx \left(\frac{\partial V}{\partial p}\right)_T \Delta p = -\kappa V\,\Delta p,\quad \Delta p = \rho g h$$

$\Delta p = 1.03 \times 10^{3}\ \mathrm{kg\,m^{-3}} \times 9.81\ \mathrm{m\,s^{-2}} \times 1000\ \mathrm{m} = 1.01\bar{0} \times 10^{7}\ \mathrm{Pa}$

Consequently, since $V = 1000\ \mathrm{cm^3} = 1.0 \times 10^{-3}\ \mathrm{m^3}$,

$$\Delta V \approx -2.3 \times 10^{-11}\ \mathrm{Pa^{-1}} \times 1.0 \times 10^{-3}\ \mathrm{m^3} \times 1.01\bar{0} \times 10^{7}\ \mathrm{Pa}$$

$$= -2.3 \times 10^{-7}\ \mathrm{m^3},\ \text{or}\ \underline{-0.23\ \mathrm{cm^3}}$$

For the change of volume with temperature, we use

$$\alpha = \frac{1}{V}\left(\frac{\partial V}{\partial T}\right)_p$$

$$\Delta V \approx \left(\frac{\partial V}{\partial T}\right)_p \Delta T = \alpha V\,\Delta T$$

$$\approx 8.61 \times 10^{-5}\ \mathrm{K^{-1}} \times 1.0 \times 10^{-3}\ \mathrm{m^3} \times (-30\ \mathrm{K})$$

$$\approx -2.6 \times 10^{-6}\ \mathrm{m^3},\ \text{or}\ \underline{-2.6\ \mathrm{cm^3}}$$

Overall, $\Delta V \approx \underline{-2.8\ \mathrm{cm^3}}$

3.2 $C_p - C_V = \dfrac{\alpha^2 TV}{\kappa}$ [13]

For molar quantities interpret V as V_m and use

$V_m = \dfrac{M}{\rho}$ where ρ is the density and M the molar mass.

Then

$$C_p - C_V = \frac{\alpha^2 TM}{\kappa\rho}$$

(a) For copper, $\alpha = 0.501 \times 10^{-4}\ \mathrm{K^{-1}}$ and $\kappa = 7.35 \times 10^{-7}\ \mathrm{atm^{-1}} = 7.26 \times 10^{-12}\ \mathrm{Pa^{-1}}$ [Table 3.1 and Problem 3.1]. Also,

$\rho = 8.960\ \mathrm{g\ cm^{-3}} = 8.960 \times 10^3\ \mathrm{kg\ m^{-3}}$, $M = 63.54\ \mathrm{g\ mol^{-1}}$

Hence,

$$C_p - C_V = \frac{(0.501 \times 10^{-4}\ \mathrm{K^{-1}})^2 \times 298.15\ \mathrm{K} \times 63.54 \times 10^{-3}\ \mathrm{kg\ mol^{-1}}}{7.26 \times 10^{-12}\ \mathrm{Pa^{-1}} \times 8.960 \times 10^3\ \mathrm{kg\ m^{-3}}}$$

$$= \underline{0.731\ \mathrm{J\ K^{-1}\ mol^{-1}}}$$

(b) For ethanol, $\alpha = 1.12 \times 10^{-3}\ \mathrm{K^{-1}}$, $\kappa = 7.68 \times 10^{-5}\ \mathrm{atm^{-1}} = 7.58 \times 10^{-10}\ \mathrm{Pa^{-1}}$,

$\rho = 0.789 \times 10^3\ \mathrm{kg\ m^{-3}}$, $M = 46.06\ \mathrm{g\ mol^{-1}}$. Hence

$$C_p - C_V = \frac{(1.12 \times 10^{-3}\ \mathrm{K^{-1}})^2 \times 298.15\ \mathrm{K} \times 46.06 \times 10^{-3}\ \mathrm{kg\ mol^{-1}}}{7.58 \times 10^{-10}\ \mathrm{Pa^{-1}} \times 7.89 \times 10^2\ \mathrm{kg\ m^{-3}}}$$

$$= \underline{28.8\ \mathrm{J\ K^{-1}\ mol^{-1}}}$$

The difference in energy required as heat is

$$\Delta q = n(C_p - C_V)\,\Delta T = \frac{m}{M}(C_p - C_V)\,\Delta T$$

Therefore, for copper

$$\Delta q = \frac{500\ \mathrm{g}}{63.54\ \mathrm{g\ mol^{-1}}} \times 0.731\ \mathrm{J\ K^{-1}\ mol^{-1}} \times 50\ \mathrm{K} = \underline{0.29\ \mathrm{kJ}}$$

For ethanol,

$$\Delta q = \frac{500\ \mathrm{g}}{46.06\ \mathrm{g\ mol^{-1}}} \times 28.8\ \mathrm{J\ K^{-1}\ mol^{-1}} \times 50\ \mathrm{K} = \underline{16\ \mathrm{kJ}}$$

3.3 $\Delta U_{\rm m} \approx \left(\frac{\partial U_{\rm m}}{\partial T}\right)_p \Delta T$

$$\left(\frac{\partial U}{\partial T}\right)_p = C_V + \alpha V_{\rm m}\left(\frac{\partial U}{\partial V}\right)_T [5] = C_V + \alpha \pi_T V_{\rm m}$$

Since $C_p - C_V = \alpha V_{\rm m}(p + \pi_T)$ [12], we know that

$$\pi_T = \frac{C_p - C_V}{\alpha V} - p$$

and hence that

$$\left(\frac{\partial U_{\rm m}}{\partial T}\right)_p = C_V + \alpha V_{\rm m}\left(\frac{C_p - C_V}{\alpha V} - p\right) = C_p - \alpha p V_{\rm m}$$

$C_p = 75.29\ {\rm J\ K^{-1}\ mol^{-1}}$ [Table 2.10], $\alpha = 2.1\times10^{-4}\ {\rm K^{-1}}$ [Table 3.1] and $V_{\rm m} = 18.07\times10^{-6}\ {\rm m^3\ mol^{-1}}$. Therefore

$$\begin{aligned}\left(\frac{\partial U}{\partial T}\right)_p &= 75.29\ {\rm J\ K^{-1}\ mol^{-1}} - 2.1\times10^{-4}\ {\rm K^{-1}}\times1.013\times10^{5}\ {\rm Pa}\\ &\quad\times 18.07\times10^{-6}\ {\rm m^3\ mol^{-1}}\\ &= 75.29\ {\rm J\ K^{-1}\ mol^{-1}} - 3.8\times10^{-4}\ {\rm J\ K^{-1}\ mol^{-1}}\\ &= 75.29\ {\rm J\ K^{-1}\ mol^{-1}}\end{aligned}$$

Therefore, $\Delta U \approx 75.29\ {\rm J\ K^{-1}\ mol^{-1}} \times 10\ {\rm K} = \underline{0.75\ {\rm kJ\ mol^{-1}}}$

(b) $\Delta H_{\rm m} \approx \left(\frac{\partial H_{\rm m}}{\partial T}\right)_p \Delta T = C_p\,\Delta T = \underline{0.75\ {\rm kJ\ mol^{-1}}}$

The difference is

$$\Delta H_{\rm m} - \Delta U_{\rm m} = \alpha p V_{\rm m}\,\Delta T = 3.8\ {\rm mJ\ mol^{-1}}$$

which is the change in energy as a result of doing expansion work.

3.4 $T_{\rm f} = \left(\frac{p_{\rm f}}{p_{\rm i}}\right)^{1/c\gamma} \times T_{\rm i}$ [Exercise 3.16a]

Hence $c\gamma \ln\frac{T_{\rm f}}{T_{\rm i}} = \ln\frac{p_{\rm f}}{p_{\rm i}}$

Since $c\gamma = \frac{C_V}{R}\times\frac{C_p}{C_V} = \frac{C_p}{R}$,

$$C_p = R\frac{\ln(p_f/p_i)}{\ln(T_f/T_i)}$$

$$= 8.314\ \mathrm{J\,K^{-1}\,mol^{-1}} \times \frac{\ln\left(\frac{613.85}{1522.2}\right)}{\ln\left(\frac{248.44}{298.15}\right)} = \underline{41.40\ \mathrm{J\,K^{-1}\,mol^{-1}}}$$

3.5 Use the formula derived in Problem 3.13:

$$C_p - C_V = \lambda R \quad \frac{1}{\lambda} = 1 - \frac{(3V_r - 1)^2}{4V_r^3 T_r}$$

which gives

$$\gamma = \frac{C_p}{C_V} = \frac{C_V + \lambda R}{C_V} = 1 + \frac{\lambda R}{C_V}$$

In conjunction with $C_V = \frac{3}{2}R$ for a monatomic, perfect gas, this gives

$$\gamma = 1 + \tfrac{2}{3}\lambda$$

For a van der Waals gas $V_r = \frac{V_m}{V_c} = \frac{V_m}{3b}$, $T_r = \frac{T}{T_c} = \frac{27RbT}{8a}$ [Table 1.5] with $a =$ $4.194\ \mathrm{L^2\,atm\,mol^{-2}}$ and $b = 5.105 \times 10^{-2}\ \mathrm{L\,mol^{-1}}$ [Table 1.4]. Hence, at 100 °C and 1.00 atm, where $V_m \approx RT/p = 30.6\ \mathrm{L\,mol^{-1}}$

$$V_r \approx \frac{30.6\ \mathrm{L\,mol^{-1}}}{3 \times 5.105 \times 10^{-2}\ \mathrm{L\,mol^{-1}}} = 200$$

$$T_r \approx \frac{27 \times 8.206 \times 10^{-2}\ \mathrm{L\,atm\,K^{-1}\,mol^{-1}} \times 30.6\ \mathrm{L\,mol^{-1}} \times 373\ \mathrm{K}}{8 \times 4.194\ \mathrm{L^2\,atm\,mol^{-2}}}$$

$$\approx 754$$

Hence

$$\frac{1}{\lambda} = 1 - \frac{(3 \times 200 - 1)^2}{4 \times 200^3 \times 754} = 1 - 1.5 \times 10^{-5} \approx 1$$

$$\gamma \approx 1 + \frac{2}{3} = \underline{1.67}$$

3.6 For $p = p(V, T)$,

$$\mathrm{d}p = \left(\frac{\partial p}{\partial V}\right)_T \mathrm{d}V + \left(\frac{\partial p}{\partial T}\right)_V \mathrm{d}T$$

As $V = V(t)$ and $T = T(t)$, divide by dt and obtain

$$\frac{\mathrm{d}p}{\mathrm{d}t} = \left(\frac{\partial b}{\partial V}\right)_T \frac{\mathrm{d}V}{\mathrm{d}t} + \left(\frac{\partial p}{\partial T}\right)_V \frac{\mathrm{d}T}{\mathrm{d}t}$$

For a perfect gas

$$\left(\frac{\partial p}{\partial V}\right)_T = -\frac{p}{V}, \left(\frac{\partial p}{\partial T}\right)_V = \frac{p}{T} \text{[Problem 2.20]}$$

Therefore,

$$\frac{\mathrm{d}p}{\mathrm{d}t} = -\frac{p}{V}\frac{\mathrm{d}V}{\mathrm{d}t} + \frac{p}{T}\frac{\mathrm{d}T}{\mathrm{d}t}$$

$$\frac{1}{p}\frac{\mathrm{d}p}{\mathrm{d}t} = -\frac{1}{V}\frac{\mathrm{d}V}{\mathrm{d}t} + \frac{1}{T}\frac{\mathrm{d}T}{\mathrm{d}t}$$

Hence

$$\frac{\mathrm{d}\ln p}{\mathrm{d}t} = -\frac{\mathrm{d}\ln V}{\mathrm{d}t} + \frac{\mathrm{d}\ln T}{\mathrm{d}t}$$

For Newtonian (exponential) cooling

$$T = T_\mathrm{i}\,\mathrm{e}^{-t/\tau_T} \text{ so } \frac{\mathrm{d}\ln T}{\mathrm{d}t} = -\frac{1}{\tau_T}$$

For exponential compression

$$V = V_\mathrm{i}\,\mathrm{e}^{-t/\tau_V}, \text{ so } \frac{\mathrm{d}\ln p}{\mathrm{d}t} = \frac{1}{\tau_T}$$

Therefore,

$$\frac{\mathrm{d}\ln p}{\mathrm{d}t} = \frac{1}{\tau_V} - \frac{1}{\tau_T}$$

which integrates to

$$\underline{p = p_\mathrm{i}\,\mathrm{e}^{-t/\tau} \text{ with } \frac{1}{\tau} = \frac{1}{\tau_T} - \frac{1}{\tau_V}}$$

When $\tau_T = \tau_V$, $p = p_\mathrm{i}$ independent of the time.

3.7 $\mathrm{d}p=\left(\frac{\partial p}{\partial V}\right)_T \mathrm{d}V+\left(\frac{\partial p}{\partial T}\right)_V \mathrm{d}T$ with $p=\frac{nRT}{V-nb}-\frac{n^2a}{V^2}$ [Table 1.5]

$$\left(\frac{\partial p}{\partial V}\right)_T=\frac{-nRT}{(V-nb)^2}+\frac{2n^2a}{V^3}=\frac{-p}{V-nb}+\frac{n^2a}{V^3}\left(\frac{V-2nb}{V-nb}\right)$$

$$\left(\frac{\partial p}{\partial T}\right)_V=\frac{nR}{V-nb}=\frac{p}{T}+\frac{n^2a}{TV^2}$$

Therefore,

$$\mathrm{d}p=\frac{-p\,\mathrm{d}V}{V-nb}+\frac{n^2a}{V^3}(V-2nb)\frac{\mathrm{d}V}{V-nb}+\frac{p\,\mathrm{d}T}{T}+\frac{n^2a}{V^2}\frac{\mathrm{d}T}{T}$$

$$=\frac{n^2a(V-2nb)/V^3-p}{V-nb}\mathrm{d}V+\frac{p+n^2a/V^2}{T}\mathrm{d}T$$

3.8 $p=\frac{nRT}{V-nb}-\frac{n^2a}{V^2}$ [Table 1.5]

Hence $T=\frac{p}{nR}(V-nb)+\frac{na}{RV^2}(V-nb)$

$$\left(\frac{\partial T}{\partial p}\right)_V=\frac{V-nb}{nR}=\frac{1}{\left(\frac{\partial p}{\partial T}\right)_V}$$

For Euler's chain relation, we need to show that

$$\left(\frac{\partial T}{\partial p}\right)_V\left(\frac{\partial p}{\partial V}\right)_T\left(\frac{\partial V}{\partial T}\right)_p=-1$$

Hence, in addition to $(\partial T/\partial p)_V$ and $(\partial p/\partial V)_T$ [Problem 3.7] we need

$$\left(\frac{\partial V}{\partial T}\right)_p=\frac{1}{\left(\frac{\partial T}{\partial V}\right)_p}$$

which can be found from

$$\left(\frac{\partial T}{\partial V}\right)_p=\frac{p}{nR}+\frac{na}{RV^2}-\frac{2na}{RV^2}(V-nb)$$

$$=\frac{T}{V-nb}-\frac{2na}{RV^2}(V-nb)$$

Therefore,

$$\left(\frac{\partial T}{\partial p}\right)_V\left(\frac{\partial p}{\partial V}\right)_T\left(\frac{\partial V}{\partial T}\right)_p=\left(\frac{\partial T}{\partial p}\right)_V\left(\frac{\partial p}{\partial V}\right)_T\bigg/\left(\frac{\partial T}{\partial V}\right)_p$$

$$=\frac{\dfrac{V-nb}{R}\left(\dfrac{-nRT}{(V-nb)^2}+\dfrac{2n^2a}{V^3}\right)}{\dfrac{T}{V-nb}-\dfrac{2na}{RV^3}(V-nb)}=\frac{\dfrac{-T}{V-nb}+\dfrac{2na}{RV^3}(V-nb)}{\dfrac{T}{V-nb}-\dfrac{2na}{RV^3}(V-nb)}$$

$$=-1$$

3.9 $\alpha=\dfrac{1}{V}\left(\dfrac{\partial V}{\partial T}\right)_p=\dfrac{1}{V\left(\dfrac{\partial T}{\partial V}\right)_p}$ [Relation 2]

$$=\frac{1}{V}\frac{1}{\dfrac{T}{V-nb}-\dfrac{2na}{RV^3}(V-nb)}\text{ [Problem 3.8]}=\frac{RV^2(V-nb)}{RTV^3-2na(V-nb)^2}$$

$\kappa=-\dfrac{1}{V}\left(\dfrac{\partial V}{\partial p}\right)_T=\dfrac{-1}{V\left(\dfrac{\partial V}{\partial p}\right)_T}$ [Relation 2]

$$=-\frac{1}{V}\frac{1}{\dfrac{-nRT}{(V-nb)^2}+\dfrac{2n^2a}{V^3}}\text{ [Problem 3.7]}=\frac{V^2(V-nb)^2}{nRTV^3-2n^2a(V-nb)^2}$$

Then $\dfrac{\kappa}{\alpha}=\dfrac{V-nb}{nR}$, implying that $\kappa R=\alpha(V_m-b)$

From the chain relation,

$$\frac{\kappa}{\alpha}=-\left(\frac{\partial V}{\partial p}\right)_T\bigg/\left(\frac{\partial V}{\partial T}\right)_p\text{ [definition]}$$

$$=-1\bigg/\left(\frac{\partial p}{\partial V}\right)_T\left(\frac{\partial V}{\partial T}\right)_p\text{ [Relation 2]}$$

$$= \left(\frac{\partial T}{\partial p}\right)_V \text{ [Chain relation]}$$

$$= \frac{V - nb}{nR} \text{ [Problem 3.8]}$$

Hence, $\kappa R = \alpha(V_m - b)$

For the introduction of reduced variables, define

$$\kappa_r = -\frac{1}{V_r}\left(\frac{\partial V_r}{\partial p_r}\right)_T = -\frac{1}{V}\left(\frac{\partial V}{\partial p}\right)_T p_c = \kappa p_c$$

$$\alpha_r = \frac{1}{V_r}\left(\frac{\partial V_r}{\partial T_r}\right)_p = \frac{1}{V}\left(\frac{\partial V}{\partial T}\right)_p T_c = \alpha T_c$$

Therefore, $\kappa R = \alpha(V_m - b)$ becomes

$$\frac{R\kappa_r}{p_c} = \frac{\alpha_r}{T_c}(V_m - b) \text{ or } \kappa_r = \alpha_r(V_r - b/V_c)\frac{p_c V_c}{RT_c}$$

However, from Table 1.5, $\frac{p_c V_c}{RT_c} = \frac{3}{8}$, $\frac{b}{V_c} = \frac{1}{3}$; therefore

$$\underline{8\kappa_r = \alpha_r(3V_r - 1)}$$

3.10 $\mu C_p = T\left(\frac{\partial V}{\partial T}\right)_p - V = \frac{T}{\left(\frac{\partial T}{\partial V}\right)_p} - V$ [Relation 2]

$$\left(\frac{\partial T}{\partial V}\right)_p = \frac{T}{V - nb} - \frac{2na}{RV^3}(V - nb) \text{ [Problem 3.8]}$$

Hence,

$$\mu C_p = \frac{2na(V - nb)^2 - nbRTV^2}{RTV^3 - 2na(V - nb)^2} \times V$$

Then, introducing $\zeta = \frac{RTV^3}{2na(V - nb)^2}$ to simplify the expression,

$$\mu C_p = \left(\frac{1 - nb\zeta/V}{\zeta - 1}\right)V \text{ [The final } V \rightarrow V_m \text{ for molar quantities]}$$

For xenon, $V_m = 24.6\ \text{L mol}^{-1}$, $T = 298\ \text{K}$, $a = 4.194\ \text{L}^2\ \text{atm mol}^{-2}$, $b = 5.105 \times 10^{-2}\ \text{L mol}^{-1}$,

$$\frac{nb}{V} = \frac{b}{V_m} = \frac{5.105 \times 10^{-2}\ \text{L mol}^{-1}}{24.6\ \text{L mol}^{-1}} = 2.08 \times 10^{-3}$$

$$\zeta = \frac{8.206 \times 10^{-2}\ \text{L atm K}^{-1}\ \text{mol}^{-1} \times 298\ \text{K} \times (24.6\ \text{L mol}^{-1})^3}{2 \times 4.194\ \text{L}^2\ \text{atm mol}^{-2} \times (24.6\ \text{L mol}^{-1} - 5.105 \times 10^{-2}\ \text{L mol}^{-1})^2}$$

$$= 72.0$$

Therefore, $\mu C_p = \dfrac{1 - 72.0 \times 2.08 \times 10^{-3}}{71.0} \times 24.6\ \text{L mol}^{-1}$

$$= 0.294\ \text{L mol}^{-1}$$

$C_p = 20.79\ \text{J K}^{-1}\ \text{mol}^{-1}$ [Table 2.10], so

$$\mu = \frac{0.294\ \text{L mol}^{-1}}{20.79\ \text{J K}^{-1}\ \text{mol}^{-1}} = \frac{0.294 \times 10^{-3}\ \text{m}^3\ \text{mol}^{-1}}{20.79\ \text{J K}^{-1}\ \text{mol}^{-1}}$$

$$= 1.41 \times 10^{-5}\ \text{K m}^3\ \text{J}^{-1} = 1.41 \times 10^{-5}\ \text{K Pa}^{-1}$$

$$= 1.41 \times 10^{-5} \times 1.013 \times 10^5\ \text{K atm} = \underline{1.43\ \text{K atm}^{-1}}$$

The value of μ changes sign at $T = T_I$ and when the sign of the numerator $1 - nb\zeta/V$ changes sign ($\zeta - 1$ is positive). Hence

$$\frac{b\zeta}{V_m} = 1 \text{ at } T = T_I$$

or $\dfrac{RT_I bV^3}{2na(V - nb)^2 V_m} = 1$, implying that $T_I = \dfrac{2a(V_m - b)^2}{RbV_m^2}$

that is,

$$T_I = \frac{2a}{Rb}\left(1 - \frac{b}{V_m}\right)^2 = \frac{27}{4} T_c \left(1 - \frac{b}{V_m}\right)^2$$

For xenon,

$$\frac{2a}{Rb} = \frac{2 \times 4.194\ \text{L}^2\ \text{atm mol}^{-2}}{8.206 \times 10^{-2}\ \text{L atm K}^{-1}\ \text{mol}^{-1} \times 5.105 \times 10^{-2}\ \text{L mol}^{-1}} = 2000\ \text{K}$$

and so

$$T_I = 2000\ \text{K} \times \left(1 - \frac{5.105 \times 10^{-2}}{24.6}\right)^2 \approx \underline{2000\ \text{K}}$$

3.11 $\left(\frac{\partial H}{\partial p}\right)_T=\left(\frac{\partial H}{\partial V}\right)_T\left(\frac{\partial V}{\partial p}\right)_T$ [change of variable]

$$=\left(\frac{\partial(U+pV)}{\partial V}\right)_T\left(\frac{\partial V}{\partial p}\right)_T \text{ [definition of } H\text{]}$$

$$=\left(\frac{\partial U}{\partial V}\right)_T\left(\frac{\partial V}{\partial p}\right)_T+\left(\frac{\partial pV}{\partial V}\right)_T\left(\frac{\partial V}{\partial p}\right)_T$$

$$=\left\{T\left(\frac{\partial p}{\partial T}\right)_V-p\right\}\left(\frac{\partial V}{\partial p}\right)_T+\left(\frac{\partial pV}{\partial p}\right)_T \text{ [equation for } (\partial U/\partial V)_T\text{]}$$

$$=T\left(\frac{\partial p}{\partial T}\right)_V\left(\frac{\partial V}{\partial p}\right)_T-p\left(\frac{\partial V}{\partial p}\right)_T+V+p\left(\frac{\partial V}{\partial p}\right)_T$$

$$-T\left(\frac{\partial p}{\partial T}\right)_V\left(\frac{\partial V}{\partial p}\right)_T+V$$

$$=-T\Big/\left(\frac{\partial T}{\partial V}\right)_p+V \text{ [chain relation]}$$

$$=-T\left(\frac{\partial V}{\partial T}\right)_p+V \text{ [Relation 2]}$$

3.12 $\mu=\left(\frac{\partial T}{\partial p}\right)_H$

$$\left(\frac{\partial p}{\partial T}\right)_H\left(\frac{\partial H}{\partial p}\right)_T\left(\frac{\partial T}{\partial H}\right)_p=-1 \text{ [chain relation]}$$

$$\left(\frac{\partial p}{\partial T}\right)_H = 1/\mu \qquad \left(\frac{\partial T}{\partial H}\right)_p = 1/C_p$$

Therefore,

$$\mu C_p=-\left(\frac{\partial H}{\partial p}\right)_T=T\left(\frac{\partial V}{\partial T}\right)_p-V \text{ [Problem 3.11]}=T^2\left(\frac{\partial}{\partial T}\frac{V}{T}\right)_p$$

The equation of state

$$\frac{pV}{nRT}=1+\frac{nB}{V}$$

converts to

$$\left(\frac{p}{nRT}\right)V^2 - V - nB = 0, \text{ so } V = \frac{nRT}{2p}\left\{1 + \left(1 + \frac{4pB}{RT}\right)^{1/2}\right\}$$

Write $\xi = \left(1 + \frac{4pB}{RT}\right)^{1/2}$, then

$$\frac{V}{T} = \frac{nR}{2p}(1+\xi)$$

$$\left(\frac{\partial}{\partial T}\frac{V}{T}\right)_p = \frac{nR}{2p}\left(\frac{\partial \xi}{\partial T}\right)_p = \frac{nR}{2p}\cdot\frac{4p}{R}\cdot\frac{1}{2\xi}\left(\frac{\partial}{\partial T}\frac{B}{T}\right)_p = \frac{n}{\xi}\left(\frac{\partial}{\partial T}\frac{B}{T}\right)_p$$

Hence,

$$\mu C_p = \frac{nT^2}{\xi}\left(\frac{\partial}{\partial T}\frac{B}{T}\right)_p$$

If $4pB/RT \ll 1$, $\xi \approx 1$ and $\mu C_p \approx nT^2\left(\frac{\partial}{\partial T}\frac{B}{T}\right)_p$

and for molar heat capacities,

$$\underline{\mu = \frac{T^2}{C_p}\left(\frac{\partial}{\partial T}\frac{B}{T}\right)_p}$$

For argon at 25 °C, using the virial coefficients from Table 1.2

$$\left(\frac{\partial}{\partial T}\frac{B}{T}\right)_p \approx \frac{\frac{B_{373}}{373\text{ K}} - \frac{B_{273}}{273\text{ K}}}{373\text{ K} - 273\text{ K}} = \frac{\frac{-4.2\text{ cm}^3\text{ mol}^{-1}}{373\text{ K}} - \frac{-21.7\text{ cm}^3\text{ mol}^{-1}}{273\text{ K}}}{100\text{ K}}$$

$$\approx 6.8 \times 10^{-4}\text{ cm}^3\text{ K}^{-2}\text{ mol}^{-1}$$

$C_p = 20.78\text{ J K}^{-1}\text{ mol}^{-1}$ [Table 2.10]. Therefore,

$$\mu \approx \frac{(298\text{ K})^2 \times (6.8 \times 10^{-10}\text{ m}^3\text{ K}^{-2}\text{ mol}^{-1})}{20.78\text{ J K}^{-1}\text{ mol}^{-1}} = 2.9\bar{1} \times 10^{-6}\text{ K Pa}^{-1}$$

$$\approx 2.9\bar{1} \times 10^{-6} \times 1.013 \times 10^5\text{ K atm}^{-1} = \underline{0.29\text{ K atm}^{-1}}$$

We can check that $4pB/RT \ll 1$ by substituting $B \approx -4.4\text{ cm}^3\text{ mol}^{-1}$, which gives $4pB/RT \approx 7 \times 10^{-4} \ll 1$.

3.13 $C_p - C_V = \frac{\alpha^2 TV}{\kappa}$ [13] $= \alpha TV\left(\frac{\partial p}{\partial T}\right)_V$ [the line above 13]

$$\left(\frac{\partial p}{\partial T}\right)_V = \frac{nR}{V-nb} \text{ [Problem 3.8]}$$

$$\alpha V = \left(\frac{\partial V}{\partial T}\right)_p = \frac{1}{\left(\frac{\partial T}{\partial V}\right)_p}$$

$$\left(\frac{\partial T}{\partial V}\right)_p = \frac{T}{V-nb} - \frac{2na}{RV^3}(V-nb) \text{ [Problem 3.8]}$$

$$C_p - C_V = T\left(\frac{\partial p}{\partial T}\right)_V \Big/ \left(\frac{\partial T}{\partial V}\right)_p$$

$$= \frac{nRT/(V-nb)}{T/(V-nb) - (2na/RV^3)(V-nb)} = n\lambda R$$

For molar quantities,

$$C_p - C_V = \lambda R \text{ with } \frac{1}{\lambda} = 1 - \frac{2a(V_m - b)^2}{RTV_m^3}$$

Now introduce the reduced variables and use $T_c = 8a/27Rb$, $V_c = 3b$:

$$\frac{2a(V_m - b)^2}{RTV_m^3} = \frac{(3V_r - 1)^2}{4T_rV_r^3}$$

Hence,

$$\underline{\frac{1}{\lambda} = 1 - \frac{(3V_r - 1)^2}{4T_rV_r^3}}$$

For xenon, $V_m \approx 2.46\ \mathrm{L\,mol^{-1}}$, $V_c = 118.8\ \mathrm{cm^3\,mol^{-1}}$, $T_c = 289.8\ \mathrm{K}$

Hence, $V_r = 20.7$ and $T_r = 1.03$; therefore

$$\frac{1}{\lambda} \approx 1 - \frac{(62.1-1)^2}{4 \times 1.03 \times 20.7^3} = 0.90, \text{ giving } \lambda \approx 1.1$$

and

$$C_p - C_V \approx 1.1R = \underline{9.2\ \mathrm{J\,K^{-1}\,mol^{-1}}}$$

3.14 $\mathrm{d}H = V\,\mathrm{d}p$, so $\Delta H = \int_i^f V\,\mathrm{d}p$

For a reversible, adiabatic change, $pV^{\gamma}=\text{const}(A)$, so $V=A/p^{1/\gamma}$

$$\Delta H=A\int_{\mathrm{i}}^{\mathrm{f}}\frac{\mathrm{d}p}{p^{1/\gamma}}=\left\{\frac{A}{1-\frac{1}{\gamma}}\right\}\left\{\frac{1}{p^{1/\gamma-1}}\right\}\Bigg|_{p_i}^{p_\mathrm{f}}$$

$$=\frac{\gamma A}{\gamma-1}\left(\frac{1}{p_\mathrm{f}^{1/\gamma-1}}-\frac{1}{p_\mathrm{i}^{1/\gamma-1}}\right)=\frac{\gamma A}{\gamma-1}\left(\frac{p_\mathrm{f}}{p_\mathrm{f}^{1/\gamma}}-\frac{p_\mathrm{i}}{p_\mathrm{i}^{1/\gamma}}\right)$$

$$=\left(\frac{\gamma}{\gamma-1}\right)(p_\mathrm{f}V_\mathrm{f}-p_\mathrm{i}V_\mathrm{i})=\frac{nR\gamma}{\gamma-1}(T_\mathrm{f}-T_\mathrm{i})$$

$$\frac{\gamma}{\gamma-1}=\frac{1}{1-\frac{1}{\gamma}}=\frac{1}{1-\frac{C_V}{C_p}}=\frac{C_p}{C_p-C_V}=\frac{C_p}{R}$$

Hence, $\underline{\Delta H=nC_p(T_\mathrm{f}-T_\mathrm{i})}$

3.15 $c_\mathrm{s}=\left(\frac{RT\gamma}{M}\right)^{1/2}$, $p=\rho\frac{RT}{M}$, so $\frac{RT}{M}=\frac{p}{\rho}$

Hence $\underline{c_\mathrm{s}=\left(\frac{\gamma p}{\rho}\right)^{1/2}}$

For argon, $\gamma=\frac{5}{3}$ so

$$c_\mathrm{s}=\left(\frac{8.314\ \mathrm{J\ K^{-1}\ mol^{-1}}\times 298\ \mathrm{K}\times\frac{5}{3}}{39.95\times10^{-3}\ \mathrm{kg\ mol^{-1}}}\right)^{1/2}=\underline{322\ \mathrm{m\ s^{-1}}}$$

4. The second law: the concepts

Exercises

4.1 $\Delta S = \dfrac{q_{\text{rev}}}{T}$ [4b]

(a) $\Delta S = \dfrac{25\times 10^3\ \text{J}}{273.15\ \text{K}} = \underline{92\ \text{J K}^{-1}}$

(b) $\Delta S = \dfrac{25\times 10^3\ \text{J}}{373.15\ \text{K}} = \underline{67\ \text{J K}^{-1}}$

4.2 $\Delta S_{\text{m}} = C_V \ln \dfrac{T_2}{T_1}$ [8b], $C_V = 12.48\ \text{J K}^{-1}\ \text{mol}^{-1}$

$$S_{\text{m}}\ (500\ \text{K}) = 146.22\ \text{J K}^{-1}\ \text{mol}^{-1} + 12.48\ \text{J K}^{-1}\ \text{mol}^{-1} \times \ln \frac{500}{298}$$

$$= 146.22 + 6.46\ \text{J K}^{-1}\ \text{mol}^{-1} = \underline{152.68\ \text{J K}^{-1}\ \text{mol}^{-1}}$$

4.3 For $C_p = a + bT$ [Table 2.16]

$$\text{Heat extracted} = \int_1^2 C_p\, \text{d}T = \int_1^2 (a+bT)\, \text{d}T$$

$$= a(T_2 - T_1) + \tfrac{1}{2}b(T_2^2 - T_1^2)$$

$$= 20.67 \times (300 - 265) + \tfrac{1}{2} \times 12.38 \times 10^{-3}\ (300^2 - 265^2)\ \text{J mol}^{-1}$$

$$= 845.\bar{9}\ \text{J mol}^{-1}$$

Therefore, $q = \dfrac{1.75\times 10^3\ \text{g}}{26.98\ \text{g mol}^{-1}} \times 845.\bar{9}\ \text{J mol}^{-1} = \underline{54.\bar{9}\ \text{kJ}}$

$$\Delta S = \int_1^2 \frac{C_p\, \text{d}T}{T} = \int_1^2 \left(\frac{a}{T} + b\right) \text{d}T = a \ln \frac{T_2}{T_1} + b(T_2 - T_1)$$

$$= 20.67\ \text{J K}^{-1}\ \text{mol}^{-1} \ln \frac{265}{300} - 12.38 \times 10^{-3}\ \text{J K}^{-1}\ \text{mol}^{-1} \times (300 - 265)$$

$$= -3.00\ \text{J K}^{-1}\ \text{mol}^{-1}$$

Therefore, for the stated amount,

$$\Delta S = \frac{1.75\times10^3\ \text{g}}{26.98\ \text{g mol}^{-1}}\times(-3.00\ \text{J K}^{-1}\ \text{mol}^{-1}) = \underline{-195\ \text{J K}^{-1}}$$

4.4 $\Delta S = nR\ln\frac{p_\text{i}}{p_\text{f}}$ [7 and $pV=nRT$]

$$= \frac{25\ \text{g}}{16.04\ \text{g mol}^{-1}}\times 8.314\ \text{J K}^{-1}\ \text{mol}^{-1}\times\ln\frac{18.5\ \text{atm}}{2.5\ \text{atm}} = \underline{+26\ \text{J K}^{-1}}$$

4.5 $\Delta S = nR\ln\frac{V_\text{f}}{V_\text{i}}$ [7]

$$nR = \frac{p_\text{i}V_\text{i}}{T_\text{i}} = \frac{1.00\ \text{atm}\times15.0\ \text{L}}{250\ \text{K}}$$

$$= \frac{1.01\bar{3}\times10^5\ \text{Pa}\times15.0\times10^{-3}\ \text{m}^3}{250\ \text{K}} = 6.08\ \text{J K}^{-1}$$

$$\ln\frac{V_\text{f}}{V_\text{i}} = \frac{\Delta S}{nR} = \frac{-5.0\ \text{J K}^{-1}}{6.08\ \text{J K}^{-1}} = -0.82\bar{3}$$

Hence

$$V_\text{f} = V_\text{i}\,\text{e}^{-0.82\bar{3}} = 15.0\ \text{L}\times0.43\bar{9} = \underline{6.6\ \text{L}}$$

4.6 Find the common final temperature T_f by noting that the heat lost by the hot sample is gained by the cold sample:

$$n_\text{i}C_p(T_\text{f}-T_\text{i1}) = n_2C_p(T_\text{f}-T_\text{i2})$$

Hence, $T_\text{f} = \frac{n_\text{i}T_\text{i1}+n_2T_\text{i2}}{n_1+n_2}$

Since $n_1/n_2 = \frac{1}{2}$,

$$T_\text{f} = \tfrac{1}{3}(353\ \text{K}+2\times283\ \text{K}) = 306\ \text{K}$$

The total change in entropy is therefore

$$\Delta S = \Delta S_1+\Delta S_2 = n_1C_p\ln\frac{T_\text{f}}{T_\text{i1}} + n_2C_p\ln\frac{T_\text{f}}{T_\text{i2}}$$

$$= \frac{50\ \text{g}}{18.02\ \text{g mol}^{-1}}\times75.5\ \text{J K}^{-1}\ \text{mol}^{-1}\times\left(\ln\frac{306}{353}+2\ln\frac{306}{283}\right)$$

$$= \underline{2.8\ \text{J K}^{-1}}$$

4.7 $\Delta S_{vap} = \frac{\Delta H_{vap}}{T_b} = \frac{29.4 \times 10^3\ J\ mol^{-1}}{334.88\ K} = \underline{+87.8\ J\ K^{-1}\ mol^{-1}}$

Since the vaporization occurs reversibly, $\Delta S_{tot} = 0$ so $\Delta S_{surr} = \underline{-87.8\ J\ K^{-1}\ mol^{-1}}$

4.8 (a) $\Delta S^{\ominus} = 2S^{\ominus}(CH_3COOH, l) - 2S^{\ominus}(CH_3CHO, g) - S^{\ominus}(O_2, g)$

$= 2 \times 159.8 - 2 \times 250.3 - 205.14\ J\ K^{-1}\ mol^{-1} = \underline{-386.1\ J\ K^{-1}\ mol^{-1}}$

(b) $\Delta S^{\ominus} = 2S^{\ominus}(AgBr, s) + S^{\ominus}(Cl_2, g) - 2S^{\ominus}(AgCl, s) - S^{\ominus}(Br_2, l)$

$= 2 \times 107.1 + 223.07 - 2 \times 96.2 - 152.23\ J\ K^{-1}\ mol^{-1}$

$= \underline{+92.6\ J\ K^{-1}\ mol^{-1}}$

(c) $\Delta S^{\ominus} = S^{\ominus}(HgCl_2, s) - S^{\ominus}(Hg, l) - S^{\ominus}(Cl_2, g)$

$= 146.0 - 76.02 - 223.07\ J\ K^{-1}\ mol^{-1} = \underline{-153.1\ J\ K^{-1}\ mol^{-1}}$

(d) $\Delta S^{\ominus} = S^{\ominus}(Zn^{2+}, aq) + S^{\ominus}(Cu, s) - S^{\ominus}(Zn, s) - S^{\ominus}(Cu^{2+}, aq)$

$= -112.1 + 33.15 - 41.63 + 99.6\ J\ K^{-1}\ mol^{-1} = \underline{-21.0\ J\ K^{-1}\ mol^{-1}}$

(e) $\Delta S^{\ominus} = 12S^{\ominus}(CO_2, g) + 11S^{\ominus}(H_2O, l) - S^{\ominus}(C_{12}H_{22}O_{11}, s) - 12S^{\ominus}(O_2, g)$

$= 12 \times 213.74 + 11 \times 69.91 - 360.2 - 12 \times 205.14\ J\ K^{-1}\ mol^{-1}$

$= \underline{+512.0\ J\ K^{-1}\ mol^{-1}}$

4.9 $\Delta G^{\ominus} = \Delta H^{\ominus} - T\Delta S^{\ominus}$

(a) $\Delta H^{\ominus} = 2\Delta H_f^{\ominus}(CH_3COOH, l) - 2\Delta H_f^{\ominus}(CH_3CHO, g)$

$= 2 \times (-484.5) - 2 \times (-166.19)\ kJ\ mol^{-1} = -636.6\bar{2}\ kJ\ mol^{-1}$

$\Delta G^{\ominus} = -636.6\bar{2}\ kJ\ mol^{-1} - 298.15\ K \times (-386.1\ J\ K^{-1}\ mol^{-1})$

$= \underline{-521.5\ kJ\ mol^{-1}}$

(b) $\Delta H^{\ominus} = 2\Delta H_f^{\ominus}(AgBr, s) - 2\Delta H_f^{\ominus}(AgCl, s)$

$= 2 \times (-100.37) - 2 \times (-127.07)\ kJ\ mol^{-1} = +53.40\ kJ\ mol^{-1}$

$\Delta G^{\ominus} = +53.40\ kJ\ mol^{-1} - 298.15\ K \times 92.6\ J\ K^{-1}\ mol^{-1}$

$= \underline{+25.8\ kJ\ mol^{-1}}$

(c) $\Delta H^{\ominus} = \Delta H_f^{\ominus}(HgCl_2, s) = -224.3\ kJ\ mol^{-1}$

$\Delta G^{\ominus} = -224.3\ kJ\ mol^{-1} - 298.15\ K \times (-153.1\ J\ K^{-1}\ mol^{-1})$

$= \underline{-178.7\ kJ\ mol^{-1}}$

(d) $\Delta H^{\ominus} = \Delta H_f^{\ominus}(Zn^{2+}, aq) - \Delta H_f^{\ominus}(Cu^{2+}, aq)$

$= +153.89 - 64.77\ kJ\ mol^{-1} = -218.66\ kJ\ mol^{-1}$

$$\Delta G^{\ominus} = -218.66\ \text{kJ mol}^{-1} - 298.15\ \text{K} \times (-21.0\ \text{J K}^{-1}\ \text{mol}^{-1})$$
$$= \underline{-212.40\ \text{kJ mol}^{-1}}$$

(e) $\Delta H^{\ominus} = \Delta H_c^{\ominus} = -5645\ \text{kJ mol}^{-1}$

$$\Delta G^{\ominus} = -5645\ \text{kJ mol}^{-1} - 298.15\ \text{K} \times 512.0\ \text{J K}^{-1}\ \text{mol}^{-1}$$
$$= \underline{-5798\ \text{kJ mol}^{-1}}$$

4.10 (a) $\Delta G^{\ominus} = 2\Delta G_f^{\ominus}(\text{CH}_3\text{COOH}, l) - 2\Delta G_f^{\ominus}(\text{CH}_3\text{CHO}, g)$
$$= 2 \times (-389.9) - 2 \times (-128.86)\ \text{kJ mol}^{-1} = \underline{-522.1\ \text{kJ mol}^{-1}}$$

(b) $\Delta G^{\ominus} = 2\Delta G_f^{\ominus}(\text{AgBr}, s) - 2\Delta G_f^{\ominus}(\text{AgCl}, s)$
$$= 2 \times (-96.90) - 2 \times (-109.79)\ \text{kJ mol}^{-1} = \underline{+25.78\ \text{kJ mol}^{-1}}$$

(c) $\Delta G^{\ominus} = \Delta G_f^{\ominus}(\text{HgCl}_2, s) = \underline{-178.6\ \text{kJ mol}^{-1}}$

(d) $\Delta G^{\ominus} = \Delta G_f^{\ominus}(\text{Zn}^{2+}, aq) - \Delta G_f^{\ominus}(\text{Cu}^{2+})$
$$= -147.06 - 65.49\ \text{kJ mol}^{-1} = \underline{-212.55\ \text{kJ mol}^{-1}}$$

(e) $\Delta G^{\ominus} = 12\Delta G_f^{\ominus}(\text{CO}_2, g) + 11\Delta G_f^{\ominus}(\text{H}_2\text{O}, l) - \Delta G_f^{\ominus}(\text{C}_{12}\text{H}_{22}\text{O}_{11}, s)$
$$= 12 \times (-394.36) + 11 \times (-237.13) - (-1543)\ \text{kJ mol}^{-1}$$
$$= \underline{-5798\ \text{kJ mol}^{-1}}$$

4.11 $6\text{C}(s) + 3\text{H}_2(g) + \tfrac{1}{2}\text{O}_2(g) \rightarrow \text{C}_6\text{H}_5\text{OH}(s)$

$$\Delta S^{\ominus} = S^{\ominus}(\text{C}_6\text{H}_5\text{OH}, s) - 6S^{\ominus}(\text{C}, s) - 3S^{\ominus}(\text{H}_2, q) - \tfrac{1}{2}S^{\ominus}(\text{O}_2, g)$$
$$= 144.0 - 6 \times 5.740 - 3 \times 130.68 - \tfrac{1}{2} \times 205.14 = -385.0\overline{5}\ \text{J K}^{-1}\ \text{mol}^{-1}$$

$\text{C}_6\text{H}_5\text{OH}(s) + 7\text{O}_2(g) \rightarrow 6\text{CO}_2(g) + 3\text{H}_2\text{O}(l)$

$$\Delta H_c^{\ominus} = 6\Delta H_f^{\ominus}(\text{CO}_2, g) + 3\Delta H_f^{\ominus}(\text{H}_2\text{O}, l) - \Delta H_f^{\ominus}(\text{C}_6\text{H}_5\text{OH}, s)$$

Hence,

$$\Delta H_f^{\ominus}(\text{C}_6\text{H}_5\text{OH}, s) = 6\Delta H_f^{\ominus}(\text{CO}_2, g) + 3\Delta H_f^{\ominus}(\text{H}_2\text{O}, l) - \Delta H_c^{\ominus}$$
$$= 6 \times (-393.51) + 3(-285.83) - (-305.4)\ \text{kJ mol}^{-1}$$
$$= -164.\overline{55}\ \text{kJ mol}^{-1}$$

Hence

$$\Delta G_f^{\ominus} = -164.5\overline{5}\ \text{kJ mol}^{-1} - 298.15\ \text{K} \times (-385.0\overline{5}\ \text{J K}^{-1}\ \text{mol}^{-1})$$
$$= \underline{-49.\overline{8}\ \text{kJ mol}^{-1}}$$

4.12 (a) $\Delta S(\text{gas}) = nR \ln \dfrac{V_f}{V_i}$.

$$= \frac{14\text{ g}}{28.02\text{ g mol}^{-1}} \times 8.314\text{ J K}^{-1}\text{ mol}^{-1} \times \ln 2$$

$$= \underline{+2.9\text{ J K}^{-1}}$$

$\Delta S(\text{surroundings}) = \underline{-2.9\text{ J K}^{-1}}$ [overall zero entropy production]

$\Delta S(\text{total}) = \underline{0}$

(b) $\Delta S(\text{gas}) = \underline{+2.9\text{ J K}^{-1}}$ [S a state function]

$\Delta S(\text{surroundings}) = \underline{0}$ [Section 4.4]

$\Delta S(\text{total}) = \underline{+2.9\text{ J K}^{-1}}$

(c) $\Delta S(\text{gas}) = 0$ [$q_{\text{rev}} = 0$]

$\Delta S(\text{surroundings}) = 0$ and ΔS (total) $= 0$

4.13 The samc final state is attained if the change takes place in two stages, one isothermal compression:

$$\Delta S_1 = nR \ln \frac{V_f}{V_i} = nR \ln \tfrac{1}{2} - -nR \ln 2$$

and the sccond, heating at constant volume:

$$\Delta S_2 = nC_V \ln \frac{T_f}{T_i} = nC_V \ln 2$$

the overall entropy change is therefore

$$\Delta S = -nR \ln 2 + nC_V \ln 2$$

$$= \underline{n(C_V - R) \ln 2}$$

4.14 $CH_4(g) + 2O_2(g) \rightarrow CO_2(g) + 2H_2O(l)$, $\Delta G^{\ominus} = -817.90\text{ kJ mol}^{-1}$ [Table 2.9]

Therefore, the maximum non-expansion work is $\underline{817.90\text{ kJ mol}^{-1}}$ [since $|w_e| = |\Delta G|$].

4.15 $\varepsilon = 1 - \dfrac{T_c}{T_h}$ [11]

(a) $\varepsilon = 1 - \dfrac{333\text{ K}}{373\text{ K}} = \underline{0.11}$ (11 per cent efficiency)

(b) $\varepsilon = 1 - \dfrac{353\text{ K}}{573\text{ K}} = \underline{0.38}$ (38 per cent efficiency)

4.16 $\Delta S_{\text{trs}} = \dfrac{\Delta H_{\text{trs}}}{T_{\text{trs}}} = \dfrac{+1.9\text{ kJ mol}^{-1}}{2000\text{ K}} = \underline{+0.95\text{ J K}^{-1}\text{ mol}^{-1}}$

4.17 (a) No work need be done because the cooling is spontaneous.

(b) $\varepsilon = \dfrac{T_{\text{c}}}{T_{\text{h}} - T_{\text{c}}}\,[15] = \dfrac{295\text{ K}}{303\text{ K} - 295\text{ K}} = 36.9$

$$w_{\min} = \frac{nC_p\,\Delta T}{\varepsilon} = \frac{(75\text{ m}^3 \times 1.3 \times 10^3\text{ g m}^{-3})/(29\text{ g mol}^{-1})}{36.9} \times 29\text{ J K}^{-1}\text{ mol}^{-1} \times 8\text{ K}$$

$$= \underline{20\text{ kJ}}$$

4.18 $\dfrac{q_{\text{h}}}{q_{\text{c}}} = \dfrac{T_{\text{h}}}{T_{\text{c}}}$, therefore

$$T_{\text{c}} = \frac{q_{\text{c}}}{q_{\text{h}}} \times T_{\text{h}} = \frac{45\text{ kJ}}{67\text{ kJ}} \times 300\text{ K} = \underline{201\text{ K}}$$

4.19 $w = \dfrac{q}{c} = \left(\dfrac{T_{\text{h}} - T_{\text{c}}}{T_{\text{c}}}\right) \times q\ [13, 15]$

$$= \frac{200\text{ K} - 80\text{ K}}{80\text{ K}} \times 2.10\text{ kJ} = \underline{3.15\text{ kJ}}$$

4.20 $c = \dfrac{T_{\text{c}}}{T_{\text{h}} - T_{\text{c}}}\,[15]$

(a) $c = \dfrac{273\text{ K}}{20\text{ K}} = \underline{14}$

(b) $c = \dfrac{263\text{ K}}{30\text{ K}} = \underline{8.8}$

4.21 $$w=\frac{q}{c}=\left(\frac{T_{\mathrm{h}}-T_{\mathrm{c}}}{T_{\mathrm{c}}}\right)\times\Delta H=\left(\frac{293\ \mathrm{K}-273\ \mathrm{K}}{273\ \mathrm{K}}\right)\times\frac{250\ \mathrm{g}}{18.02\ \mathrm{g\ mol^{-1}}}$$

$$\times 6.01\ \mathrm{kJ\ mol^{-1}}$$

$$=\underline{6.11\ \mathrm{kJ}}$$

This amount of work can be done in

$$t=\frac{6.11\ \mathrm{kJ}}{100\ \mathrm{J\ s^{-1}}}=\underline{61.1\ \mathrm{s}}$$

Problems

4.1 (a) $\Delta S_{\mathrm{trs}}(l\rightarrow s,T)=\Delta S_{\mathrm{trs}}(l\rightarrow s,T_{\mathrm{f}})-\Delta C_p\ln\frac{T}{T_{\mathrm{f}}}$

with $\Delta C_p=C_p(l)-C_p(s)=+37.3\ \mathrm{J\ K^{-1}\ mol^{-1}}$

Therefore,

$$\Delta S_{\mathrm{trs}}(l\rightarrow s,T)=\frac{-\Delta H_{\mathrm{fus}}}{T_{\mathrm{f}}}-\Delta C_p\ln\frac{T}{T_{\mathrm{f}}}$$

$$=\frac{-6.01\times10^{3}\ \mathrm{J\ mol^{-1}}}{273\ \mathrm{K}}-37.3\ \mathrm{J\ K^{-1}\ mol^{-1}}\times\ln\frac{268}{273}$$

$$=\underline{-21.3\ \mathrm{J\ K^{-1}\ mol^{-1}}}$$

$$\Delta S(\text{surroundings})=\frac{\Delta H_{\mathrm{fus}}(T)}{T}=\frac{\Delta H_{\mathrm{fus}}(T_{\mathrm{f}})}{T}+\Delta C_p\frac{(T-T_{\mathrm{f}})}{T}$$

$$=\frac{6.01\ \mathrm{kJ\ mol^{-1}}}{268\ \mathrm{K}}+37.3\ \mathrm{J\ K^{-1}\ mol^{-1}}\times\frac{268-273}{268}$$

$$=\underline{+21.7\ \mathrm{J\ K^{-1}\ mol^{-1}}}$$

$\Delta S(\text{total})=21.7-21.3\ \mathrm{J\ K^{-1}\ mol^{-1}}=+0.4\ \mathrm{J\ K^{-1}\ mol^{-1}}$

Since $\Delta S(\text{total})>0$, the transition $l\rightarrow s$ is spontaneous at $-5\ ^{\circ}\mathrm{C}$.

(b) $\Delta S_{\mathrm{trs}}(l\rightarrow g,T)=\Delta S_{\mathrm{trs}}(l\rightarrow g,T_{\mathrm{b}})+\Delta C_p\ln\frac{T}{T_{\mathrm{b}}}$

$$=\frac{\Delta H_{\text{vap}}}{T_{\text{b}}}+\Delta C_p \ln\frac{T}{T_{\text{b}}},\ \Delta C_p=-41.9\ \text{J K}^{-1}\ \text{mol}^{-1}$$

$$\Delta S_{\text{trs}}(l\rightarrow g,\ T)=\frac{40.7\ \text{kJ mol}^{-1}}{373\ \text{K}}-41.9\ \text{J K}^{-1}\ \text{mol}^{-1}\times\ln\frac{368}{373}$$

$$=\underline{+109.7\ \text{J K}^{-1}\ \text{mol}^{-1}}$$

$$\Delta S(\text{surroundings})=\frac{-\Delta H_{\text{vap}}(T)}{T}$$

$$=\frac{-\Delta H_{\text{vap}}(T_{\text{b}})}{T}-\frac{\Delta C_p(T-T_{\text{b}})}{T}$$

$$=\frac{-40.7\ \text{kJ mol}^{-1}}{378\ \text{K}}-(-41.9\ \text{J K}^{-1}\ \text{mol}^{-1})\times\frac{368-373}{368}$$

$$=\underline{-111.2\ \text{J K}^{-1}\ \text{mol}^{-1}}$$

$$\Delta S(\text{total})=109.7-111.2\ \text{J K}^{-1}\ \text{mol}^{-1}=\underline{-1.5\ \text{J K}^{-1}\ \text{mol}^{-1}}$$

Since $\Delta S(\text{total})<0$, the reverse transition, $g\rightarrow l$, is spontaneous at 95 °C.

4.2 $$\Delta S=\int_1^2 C_p\frac{\text{d}T}{T}=\int_1^2\left(\frac{a+bT}{T}\right)\text{d}T$$

$$=a\ln\frac{T_2}{T_1}+b(T_2-T_1)$$

$$=91.47\ \text{J K}^{-1}\ \text{mol}^{-1}\ln\frac{300\ \text{K}}{273\ \text{K}}+0.075\ \text{J K}^{-1}\ \text{mol}^{-1}\times 27\ \text{K}$$

$$=10.\overline{7}\ \text{J K}^{-1}\ \text{mol}^{-1}$$

Therefore, for 1.00 mol, $\underline{\Delta S=+11\ \text{J K}^{-1}}$

4.3 $$\Delta S=\int_1^2 C_p\frac{\text{d}T}{T}=\int_1^2\left(\frac{a}{T}+b+\frac{c}{T^3}\right)\text{d}T$$

$$=a\ln\frac{T_2}{T_1}+b(T_2-T_1)-\tfrac{1}{2}c\left(\frac{1}{T_2^2}-\frac{1}{T_1^2}\right)$$

At 298 K, $S^\ominus(\text{NH}_3,g)=192.45\ \text{J K}^{-1}\ \text{mol}^{-1}$. Therefore,

(a) $S^{\ominus}(373\ \text{K}) = 192.45\ \text{J K}^{-1}\ \text{mol}^{-1} + 29.75\ \text{J K}^{-1}\ \text{mol}^{-1} \times \ln \dfrac{373}{298}$

$$+ 25.10 \times 10^{-3}\ \text{J K}^{-2}\ \text{mol}^{-1} \times 75.0\ \text{K}$$

$$+ \frac{1}{2} \times 1.55 \times 10^{5}\ \text{J K}^{-1}\ \text{mol}^{-1} \times \left(\frac{1}{373.15^{2}} - \frac{1}{298.15^{2}}\right)$$

$$= \underline{200.7\ \text{J K}^{-1}\ \text{mol}^{-1}}$$

(b) $S^{\ominus}(773\ \text{K}) = 192.45\ \text{J K}^{-1}\ \text{mol}^{-1} + 29.75\ \text{J K}^{-1}\ \text{mol}^{-1} \ln \dfrac{773}{298}$

$$+ 25.10 \times 10^{-3}\ \text{J K}^{-2}\ \text{mol}^{-1} \times 475\ \text{K}$$

$$+ \frac{1}{2} \times 1.55 \times 10^{5}\ \text{J K}^{-1}\ \text{mol}^{-1} \times \left(\frac{1}{773^{2}} - \frac{1}{298^{2}}\right)$$

$$= \underline{232.0\ \text{J K}^{-1}\ \text{mol}^{-1}}$$

4.4 ΔS depends on only the initial and final states, so we can use

$$\Delta S = nC_p \ln \frac{T_f}{T_i}$$

Since $q = nC_p(T_f - T_i)$,

$$T_f = T_i + \frac{q}{nC_p} = T_i + \frac{I^2Rt}{nC_p} \quad [q = ItV = I^2Rt]$$

That is,

$$\Delta S = nC_p \ln\left(1 + \frac{I^2Rt}{nC_pT_i}\right)$$

Since $n = \dfrac{500\ \text{g}}{63.6\ \text{g mol}^{-1}} = 7.86\ \text{mol}$,

$$\Delta S = 7.86\ \text{mol} \times 24.4\ \text{J K}^{-1}\ \text{mol}^{-1}$$

$$\times \ln\left(1 + \frac{(1.00\ \text{A})^2 \times 1000\ \Omega \times 15.0\ \text{s}}{7.86 \times 24.4\ \text{J K}^{-1} \times 293\ \text{K}}\right)$$

$$= 192\ \text{J K}^{-1} \times \ln 1.27 = \underline{+45.4\ \text{J K}^{-1}}$$

For the second experiment,

$dq_{rev}(\text{net}) = 0$; therefore $dS = 0$ and $\Delta S = 0$.

However, for the water

$$\Delta S = \int \frac{dq_{rev}}{T} = \frac{q_{rev}}{T} = \frac{I^2Rt}{T}$$

$$= \frac{(1.00\ \text{A})^2 \times 1000\ \Omega \times 15.0\ \text{s}}{293\ \text{K}} = \underline{+51.2\ \text{J K}^{-1}}$$

$[1\ \text{J} = 1\ \text{A V s} = 1\ \text{A}^2\ \Omega\ \text{s}]$

4.5 $C(s) + \frac{1}{2}O_2(g) + 2H_2(g) \rightarrow CH_3OH(l)$, $\Delta n_g = -2.5\text{mol}$

$$\Delta A^{\ominus} = \Delta G^{\ominus} - \Delta(pV) = \Delta G^{\ominus} - \Delta n(RT) = \Delta G^{\ominus} + 2.5RT$$

$$= -166.27 + 2.5 \times 2.479\ \text{kJ mol}^{-1}$$

$$= \underline{-160.07\ \text{kJ mol}^{-1}}$$

4.6 Calculate the final temperature as in Exercise 4.6:

(a) $$T_f = \frac{n_1T_{i1} + n_2T_{i2}}{n_1 + n_2} = \tfrac{1}{2}(T_{i1} + T_{i2}) = 318\ \text{K}\ [n_1 = n_2]$$

$$\Delta S = n_1C_p \ln \frac{T_f}{T_{i1}} + n_2C_p \ln \frac{T_f}{T_{i2}}$$

$$= n_1C_p \ln \frac{T_f^2}{T_{i1}T_{i2}}\ [n_1 = n_2]$$

$$= \frac{200\ \text{g}}{18.02\ \text{g mol}^{-1}} \times 75.5\ \text{J K}^{-1}\ \text{mol}^{-1} \times \ln \frac{318^2}{273 \times 363} = \underline{+17.0\ \text{J K}^{-1}}$$

(b) Heat required for melting $= n_1\,\Delta H_{fus} = 11.1\ \text{mol} \times 6.01\ \text{kJ mol}^{-1}$

$$= 66.8\ \text{kJ}$$

The decrease in temperature of the hot water as a result of its causing the melting is $\Delta T = \dfrac{q}{nC_p} = \dfrac{66.8\ \text{kJ}}{11.1\ \text{mol} \times 75.5\ \text{J K}^{-1}\ \text{mol}^{-1}} = 79.6\ \text{K}$

At this stage the system consists of 200 g water at 0 °C and 200 g water at 90 °C − 79.6 °C = 10 °C (283 K). The entropy change so far is therefore

$$\Delta S = \frac{n\,\Delta H_{fus}}{T_f} + nC_p \ln \frac{283\ \text{K}}{363\ \text{K}}$$

$$= \frac{11.1\ \text{mol} \times 6.01\ \text{kJ mol}^{-1}}{273\ \text{K}} + 11.1\ \text{mol} \times 75.5\ \text{J K}^{-1}\ \text{mol}^{-1} \ln \frac{283\ \text{K}}{363\ \text{K}}$$

$$= 244\ \text{J K}^{-1} - 208.\bar{6}\ \text{J K}^{-1} = +35.\bar{7}\ \text{J K}^{-1}$$

The final temperature is $T_f = \frac{1}{2}(273\ \text{K} + 283\ \text{K}) = 278\ \text{K}$, and the entropy change in this step is

$$\Delta S = nC_p \ln \frac{T_f^2}{T_{i1}T_{i2}} = 11.1 \times 75.5\ \text{J K}^{-1} \ln \frac{278^2}{273 \times 283} = +0.27\ \text{J K}^{-1}$$

Therefore, overall, $\Delta S = 35.\bar{7}\ \text{J K}^{-1} + 0.27\ \text{J K}^{-1} = \underline{+36\ \text{J K}^{-1}}$

4.7 We need ΔG and ΔA under the stated conditions, and begin by calculating ΔG for the transition $l \rightarrow s$:

$$\Delta G(T) = \Delta H(T) - T\,\Delta S(T)$$

$$= \Delta H(T_f) - \Delta C_p(T - T_f) - T\left\{\Delta S(T_f) - \Delta C_p \ln \frac{T}{T_f}\right\}$$

$$= \Delta H(T_f) - \frac{T}{T_f}\Delta H(T_f) - \Delta C_p\left\{T - T_f - T \ln \frac{T}{T_f}\right\}$$

$$= \left(\frac{T}{T_f} - 1\right)\Delta H_{\text{fus}}(T_f) - \Delta C_p\left\{T - T_f - T \ln \frac{T}{T_f}\right\}$$

$T = 268\ \text{K}$, $T_f = 273\ \text{K}$, $\Delta H_{\text{fus}} = 6.01\ \text{kJ mol}^{-1}$, $\Delta C_p = +37.3\ \text{J K}^{-1}\ \text{mol}^{-1}$:

$$\Delta G(268\ \text{K}) = \left(\frac{268}{273} - 1\right) \times 6.01\ \text{kJ mol}^{-1}$$

$$- 37.3\ \text{J mol}^{-1} \times \left\{268 - 273 - 268 \ln \frac{268}{273}\right\}$$

$$= -0.11\ \text{kJ mol}^{-1}$$

For ΔA we use

$$\Delta A = \Delta G - \Delta(pV) = \Delta G - p\,\Delta V$$

$$= \Delta G - pM\,\Delta(1/\rho)$$

$$= -0.11\ \text{kJ mol}^{-1} - 1.013 \times 10^5\ \text{Pa} \times 18.02 \times 10^{-3}\ \text{kg mol}^{-1}$$

$$\times\left(\frac{1}{917\ \text{kg m}^{-3}}-\frac{1}{999\ \text{kg m}^{-3}}\right)$$

$$=-0.11\ \text{kJ mol}^{-1}$$

Therefore:

(a) Maximum work is $\underline{0.11\ \text{kJ mol}^{-1}}$

(b) Maximum non-expansion work is also $\underline{0.11\ \text{kJ mol}^{-1}}$

4.8 $S_m(T)=S_m(0)+\int_0^T \frac{C_p\,dT}{T}$

From the data, draw up the following table:

T/K	10	15	20	25	30	50
$\frac{C_p}{T}\Big/(\text{J K}^{-2}\ \text{mol}^{-1})$	0.284	0.47	0.540	0.564	0.550	0.428

T/K	70	100	150	200	250	298
$\frac{C_p}{T}\Big/(\text{J K}^{-2}\ \text{mol}^{-1})$	0.333	0.245	0.169	0.129	0.105	0.089

Plot C_p/T against T (Fig. 4.1). This has been done on two scales. The region 0 to 10 K has been constructed using $C_p=aT^3$ fitted to the point at $T=10$ K, at which $C_p=2.8\ \text{J K}^{-1}\ \text{mol}^{-1}$, so $a=2.8\times10^{-3}\ \text{J K}^{-4}\ \text{mol}^{-1}$. The area can be determined (primitively) by counting squares, which gives area A = $38.28\ \text{J K}^{-1}\ \text{mol}^{-1}$, area B (up to 0 °C) = $25.60\ \text{J K}^{-1}\ \text{mol}^{-1}$, area B (up to 25 °C) = $27.80\ \text{J K}^{-1}\ \text{mol}^{-1}$. Hence:

$$S_m(273\ \text{K})=S_m(0)+\underline{63.88\ \text{J K}^{-1}\ \text{mol}^{-1}}$$

$$S_m(298\ \text{K})=S_m(0)+\underline{66.08\ \text{J K}^{-1}\ \text{mol}^{-1}}$$

4.9 $\varepsilon=\frac{T_h-T_c}{T_h}=\frac{1200\ \text{K}}{2273\ \text{K}}=0.53$

$w=mgh,\ w=\varepsilon q,\ q=n\,\Delta H_c$

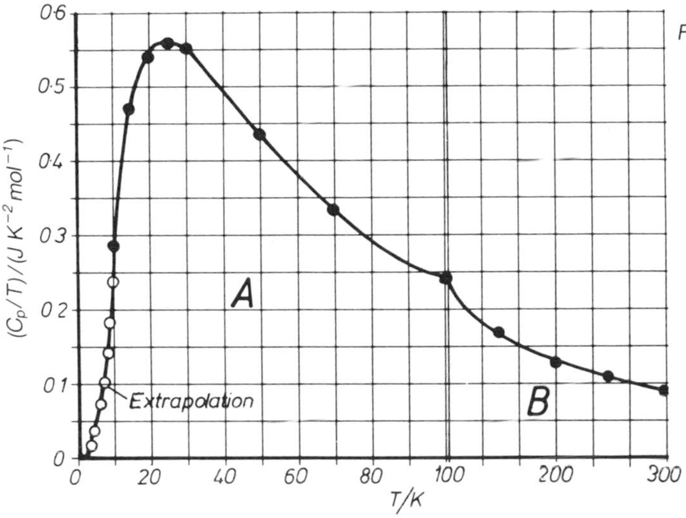

Fig 4.1

$$\text{Hence } h=\frac{\varepsilon q}{mg}=0.53\times\frac{3\times10^3\ \text{g}}{114.2\ \text{g mol}^{-1}}\times\frac{5512\times10^3\ \text{J mol}^{-1}}{1000\ \text{kg}\times9.81\ \text{m s}^{-2}}$$

$$=\underline{7.8\ \text{km}}$$

4.10 $\Delta G^\ominus=\Delta H^\ominus-T\Delta S^\ominus=26.120\ \text{kJ mol}^{-1}$

$\Delta H^\ominus=+55.000\ \text{kJ mol}^{-1}$

$$\text{Hence } \Delta S^\ominus=\frac{(55.000-26.120)\ \text{kJ mol}^{-1}}{298.15\ \text{K}}=\underline{+96.864\ \text{J K}^{-1}\ \text{mol}^{-1}}$$

$$\Delta S^\ominus=4S^\ominus(\text{K}^+,aq)+S^\ominus([\text{Fe(CN)}_6]^{4-},aq)+3S^\ominus(\text{H}_2\text{O},l)$$
$$-S^\ominus(\text{K}_4[\text{Fe(CN)}_6]\cdot3\text{H}_2\text{O},s)$$

Therefore,

$$S^\ominus([\text{Fe(CN)}_6]^{4-},aq)=\Delta S^\ominus-4S^\ominus(\text{K}^+,aq)-3S^\ominus(\text{H}_2\text{O},l)$$
$$+S^\ominus(\text{K}_4[\text{Fe(CN)}_6]\cdot3\text{H}_2\text{O},s)$$
$$=96.864-4\times102.5-3\times69.9+599.7\ \text{J K}^{-1}\ \text{mol}^{-1}$$
$$=\underline{+76.9\ \text{J K}^{-1}\ \text{mol}^{-1}}$$

4.11 Draw up the following table:

T/K	10	20	30	40	50	60
(C_p/T)/ ($J\,K^{-1}\,mol^{-1}$)	0.209	0.722	1.215	1.564	1.741	1.850

T/K	70	80	90	100	110	120
(C_p/T)/ ($J\,K^{-1}\,mol^{-1}$)	1.877	1.868	1.837	1.796	1.753	1.708

T/K	130	140	150	160	170	180
(C_p/T)/ ($J\,K^{-1}\,mol^{-1}$)	1.665	1.624	1.584	1.546	1.508	1.473

T/K	190	200
(C_p/T)/ ($J\,K^{-1}\,mol^{-1}$)	1.437	1.402

Plot C_p/T against T (Fig. 4.2a). Extrapolate to $T=0$ using $C_p=aT^3$ fitted to the point at $T=10$ K, which gives $a=2.09$ mJ K^{-2} mol^{-1}. Determine the area under the graph up to each T and plot S_m against T (Fig. 4.2b).

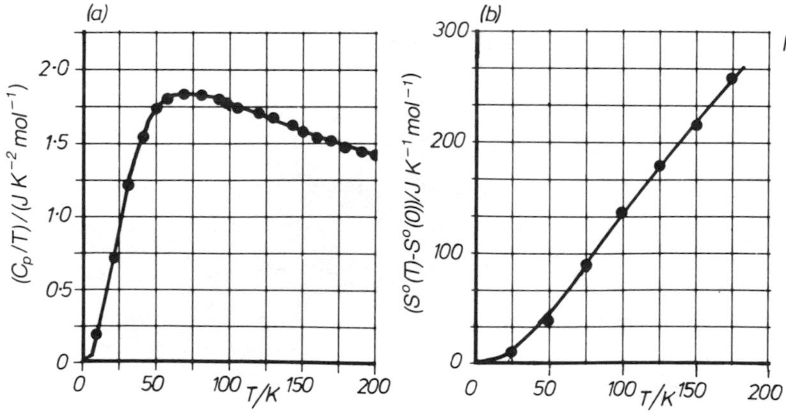

Fig 4.2

T/K	25	50	75	100	125	150	175	200
$\{S_m - S_m(0)\}$/ ($J\,K^{-1}\,mol^{-1}$)	9.25	43.50	88.50	135.00	178.25	219.0	257.3	293.5

4.12 Draw up the following table and proceed as in Problem 4.11:

T/K	14.14	16.33	20.03	31.15	44.08	64.81	100.90	140.86
(C_p/T)/ ($J\,K^{-2}\,mol^{-1}$)	0.671	0.778	0.908	1.045	1.063	1.024	0.942	0.861

T/K	183.59	225.10	262.99	298.06
(C_p/T)/ ($J\,K^{-2}\,mol^{-1}$)	0.787	0.727	0.685	0.659

Plot C_p against T (Fig. 4.3a) and C_p/T against T (Fig. 4.3b), extrapolating to

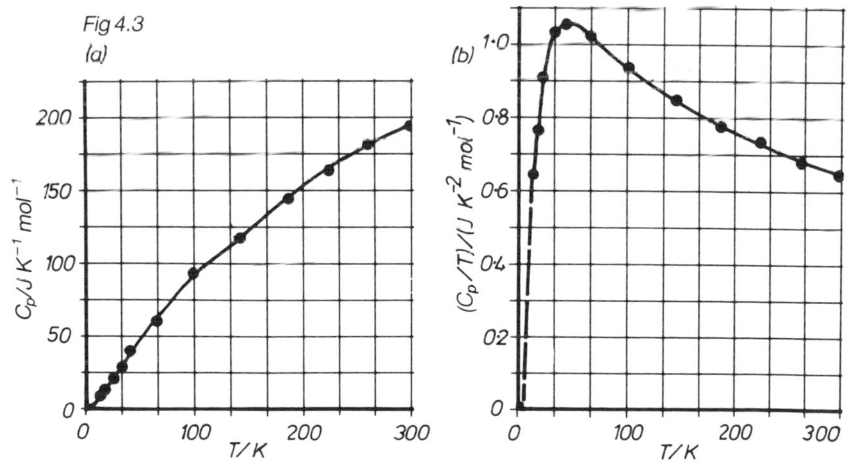

$T=0$ with $C_p = aT^3$ fitted at $T = 14.14$ K, which gives $a = 3.36$ mJ K^{-3} mol^{-1}. It then follows that

$$\int_0^{298\,\mathrm{K}} C_p\,\mathrm{d}T = 34.4\ \mathrm{kJ\,mol^{-1}},\ \text{so}\ H_\mathrm{m}(298\ \mathrm{K}) = H_\mathrm{m}(0) + \underline{34.4\ \mathrm{kJ\,mol^{-1}}}$$

$$\int_0^{298\,\mathrm{K}} \frac{C_p\,\mathrm{d}T}{T} = 243\ \mathrm{J\,K^{-1}\,mol^{-1}},\ \text{so}\ S_\mathrm{m}(298\ \mathrm{K}) = S_\mathrm{m}(0) + \underline{243\ \mathrm{J\,K^{-1}\,mol^{-1}}}$$

4.13 $c = \dfrac{T_\mathrm{c}}{T_\mathrm{h} - T_\mathrm{c}},\ w = \dfrac{q}{c} = \dfrac{nC_p\,\Delta T}{c}$

$T_\mathrm{h} = 1.20\ \mathrm{K},\ (T_\mathrm{c})_\mathrm{mean} = \frac{1}{2}(1.10\ \mathrm{K} + 0.10\ \mathrm{K}) = 0.60\ \mathrm{K}$

$$c = \frac{0.60\ \mathrm{K}}{1.20\ \mathrm{K} - 0.60\ \mathrm{K}} = 1.00$$

$$w = \frac{1.0\ \mathrm{g}}{63.54\ \mathrm{g\,mol^{-1}}} \times \frac{3.9 \times 10^{-5}\ \mathrm{J\,K^{-1}\,mol^{-1}} \times 1.00\ \mathrm{K}}{1.00} = \underline{0.61\ \mu\mathrm{J}}$$

For the more realistic calculation,

$$\begin{aligned} w &= -\int_\mathrm{i}^\mathrm{f} nC_p(T_\mathrm{c}) \times \left(\frac{T_\mathrm{h} - T_\mathrm{c}}{T_\mathrm{c}}\right) \mathrm{d}T_\mathrm{c} \\ &= -n\int_\mathrm{i}^\mathrm{f} (AT_\mathrm{c}^2 + B)(T_\mathrm{h} - T_\mathrm{c})\,\mathrm{d}T_\mathrm{c} \\ &= n\int_\mathrm{i}^\mathrm{f} (AT_\mathrm{c}^3 - AT_\mathrm{h}T_\mathrm{c}^2 + BT_\mathrm{c} - BT_\mathrm{h})\,\mathrm{d}T_\mathrm{c} \\ &= n\{\tfrac{1}{4}A(T_\mathrm{f}^4 - T_\mathrm{i}^4) - \tfrac{1}{3}A(T_\mathrm{f}^3 - T_\mathrm{i}^3)T_\mathrm{h} + \tfrac{1}{2}B(T_\mathrm{f}^2 - T_\mathrm{i}^2) - B(T_\mathrm{f} - T_\mathrm{i})T_\mathrm{h}\} \end{aligned}$$

We evaluate this expression with $n = 0.016\ \mathrm{mol}$, $A = 4.82 \times 10^{-5}\ \mathrm{J\,K^{-4}\,mol^{-1}}$, $B = 6.88 \times 10^{-4}\ \mathrm{J\,K^{-2}\,mol^{-1}}$, $T_\mathrm{h} = 1.20\ \mathrm{K}$, $T_\mathrm{i} = 1.10\ \mathrm{K}$, $T_\mathrm{f} = 0.10\ \mathrm{K}$:

$w = 0.016\ \mathrm{mol.} \times 4.21 \times 10^{-4}\ \mathrm{J\,mol^{-1}} = \underline{6.7\ \mu\mathrm{J}}$

4.14 The four episodes of heat transfer are

(a) $q_\mathrm{h} = nRT_\mathrm{h} \ln \dfrac{V_\mathrm{B}}{V_\mathrm{A}} \qquad \dfrac{q_\mathrm{h}}{T_\mathrm{h}} = nR \ln \dfrac{V_\mathrm{B}}{V_\mathrm{A}}$

(b) 0 [adiabatic]

(c) $q_\mathrm{c} = nRT_\mathrm{c} \ln \dfrac{V_\mathrm{D}}{V_\mathrm{C}} \qquad \dfrac{q_\mathrm{c}}{T_\mathrm{c}} = nR \ln \dfrac{V_\mathrm{D}}{V_\mathrm{C}}$

(d) 0 [adiabatic]

Therefore $\oint \frac{dq}{T} = \frac{q_h}{T_h} + \frac{q_c}{T_c} = nR \ln \frac{V_B V_D}{V_A V_C}$

However,

$$\frac{V_B V_D}{V_A V_C} = \frac{V_B}{V_C}\frac{V_D}{V_A} = \left(\frac{T_c}{T_h}\right)^c \left(\frac{T_h}{T_c}\right)^c \text{ [17 of Section 3.4]} = 1$$

Therefore $\oint \frac{dq}{T} = 0$

If the first stage is replaced by isothermal, irreversible expansion,

$w = -p_{ex}(V_B - V_A)$, implying that $q = p_{ex}(V_B - V_A)$ [as $\Delta U = 0$]

Therefore,

$$\frac{q_h}{T_h} = \frac{p_{ex}}{T_h}(V_B - V_A)$$

However, $p_{ex}(V_B - V_A) < nRT_h \ln \frac{V_B}{V_A}$

because less work is done in the irreversible expansion, so

$$\oint \frac{dq}{T} < nR \ln \frac{V_B}{V_A} + nR \ln \frac{V_D}{V_C} = 0$$

That is, $\oint \frac{dq}{T} < 0$

4.15 The isotherms correspond to T = constant, and the reversibly traversed adiabats correspond to S = constant. Thus we can represent the cycle as in Fig. 4.4.

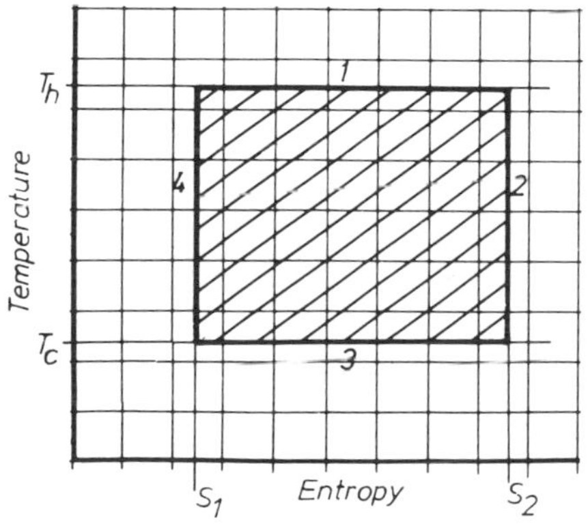

Fig 4.4

The area within the rectangle is

$$\text{Area} = \oint T\,\mathrm{d}S = (T_\mathrm{h} - T_\mathrm{c}) \times (S_2 - S_1) = (T_\mathrm{h} - T_\mathrm{c})\,\Delta S$$

$$= (T_\mathrm{h} - T_\mathrm{c}) nR \ln \frac{V_\mathrm{B}}{V_\mathrm{A}} \text{ [isothermal expansion]}$$

But $w = q\varepsilon = nRT_\mathrm{h} \ln \frac{V_\mathrm{B}}{V_\mathrm{A}} \times \left(\frac{T_\mathrm{h} - T_\mathrm{c}}{T_\mathrm{h}}\right)$

$$= nR(T_\mathrm{h} - T_\mathrm{c}) \ln \frac{V_\mathrm{B}}{V_\mathrm{A}}$$

Therefore, the area is equal to the work done.

4.16 $\Delta S = nC_p \ln \frac{T_\mathrm{f}}{T_\mathrm{h}} + nC_p \ln \frac{T_\mathrm{f}}{T_\mathrm{c}}$ [T_f is the final temperature, $T_\mathrm{f} = \frac{1}{2}(T_\mathrm{h} + T_\mathrm{c})$]

$$= nC_p \ln \frac{T_\mathrm{f}^2}{T_\mathrm{h} T_\mathrm{c}} = nC_p \ln \frac{(T_\mathrm{h} + T_\mathrm{c})^2}{4T_\mathrm{h} T_\mathrm{c}}$$

In the present case, $T_\mathrm{f} = 375\ \mathrm{K}$.

$$\Delta S = \frac{500\ \mathrm{g}}{63.54\ \mathrm{g\ ml^{-1}}} \times 24.4\ \mathrm{J\ K^{-1}\ mol^{-1}} \times \ln \frac{375^2}{500 \times 250}$$

$$= \underline{+22.6\ \mathrm{J\ K^{-1}}}$$

4.17 $g = f + yz$

$\mathrm{d}g = \mathrm{d}f + y\,\mathrm{d}z + z\,\mathrm{d}y$

$= a\,\mathrm{d}x - z\,\mathrm{d}y + y\,\mathrm{d}z + z\,\mathrm{d}y$

$= a\,\mathrm{d}x + y\,\mathrm{d}z$

4.18 $c(T_\mathrm{c}) = \frac{T_\mathrm{c}}{T_\mathrm{h} - T_\mathrm{c}}$, $\mathrm{d}q = -C_p\,\mathrm{d}T$

$$\mathrm{d}w = \frac{\mathrm{d}q}{c(T_\mathrm{c})} = \frac{-C_p\,\mathrm{d}T}{c(T_\mathrm{c})}$$

Therefore,

$$w = -\int_{i}^{f} \frac{C_p\,dT}{c(T_c)} \approx -C_p \int_{i}^{f} \left(\frac{T_h}{T_c} - 1\right) dT_c$$

$$\approx C_p \left\{ T_f - T_i - T_h \ln \frac{T_f}{T_i} \right\}$$

$w = w(\text{cooling}) + w(\text{freezing})$

$$|w(\text{cooling})| = \frac{250\ \text{g}}{18.02\ \text{g mol}^{-1}} \times 75.5\ \text{J K}^{-1}\ \text{mol}^{-1} \times \left\{ -20\ \text{K} - 293\ \text{K} \ln \frac{273}{293} \right\}$$

$$= 0.72\ \text{kJ}$$

$$|w(\text{freezing})| = \frac{n\,\Delta H_{\text{fus}}}{c_0} = \frac{250\ \text{g}}{18.02\ \text{g mol}^{-1}} \times 6.01\ \text{kJ mol}^{-1} \times \frac{20}{273}$$

$$= 6.11\ \text{kJ}$$

Therefore, the total work is

$$w = 0.72\ \text{kJ} + 6.11\ \text{kJ} = \underline{6.83\ \text{kJ}}$$

If the initial temperature were 25 °C, no additional work would be needed because cooling from 25 °C to 20 °C is spontaneous.

5. The second law: the machinery

Exercises

5.1 $\Delta G = nRT \ln \frac{p_f}{p_i}$ [11] $= nRT \ln \frac{V_i}{V_f}$

$$= 3.0 \times 10^{-3}\,\text{mol} \times 8.314\,\text{J K}^{-1}\,\text{mol}^{-1} \times 300\,\text{K} \ln \frac{36}{60}$$

$$= \underline{-3.8\,\text{J}}$$

5.2 $\Delta S = -\left(\frac{\partial \Delta G}{\partial T}\right)_p$ [6] $= -\frac{\partial}{\partial T}\left(-85.40\,\text{J} + 36.5\,\text{J} \times \frac{T}{\text{K}}\right)$

$$= \underline{-36.5\,\text{J K}^{-1}}$$

5.3 $\Delta G = V\Delta p$ [10], $\rho = \frac{m}{V}$

Therefore,

$$\rho = \frac{m\,\Delta p}{\Delta G} = \frac{35\,\text{g} \times 2999 \times 1.013 \times 10^5\,\text{Pa}}{12 \times 10^3\,\text{J}}$$

$$= 8.9 \times 10^5\,\text{g m}^{-3} = \underline{0.89\,\text{g cm}^{-3}}$$

5.4 $\Delta S = nR \ln \frac{V_f}{V_i} = nR \ln \frac{p_i}{p_f}$

Hence,

$$p_f = p_i\,\text{e}^{-\Delta S/nR} = 3.50\,\text{atm} \times \text{e}^{-(-25.0\,\text{J K}^{-1})/(2.00 \times 8.314\,\text{J K}^{-1})}$$

$$= 3.50\,\text{atm} \times \text{e}^{1.50} = \underline{15.7\,\text{atm}}$$

$\Delta G = nRT \ln \frac{p_f}{p_i}$ [11] $= -T\,\Delta S$

$$= -330\,\text{K} \times (-25.0\,\text{J K}^{-1}) = \underline{+8.25\,\text{kJ}}$$

5.5 $\Delta\mu = RT\ln\frac{p_f}{p_i}$ [14]

$$= 8.314\ \mathrm{J\,K^{-1}\,mol^{-1}} \times 313\ \mathrm{K} \times \ln\frac{29.5}{1.8} = \underline{+7.3\ \mathrm{kJ\,mol^{-1}}}$$

5.6 $\mu - \mu^{\circ} = RT\ln\frac{f}{p}$ [15 minus 14]

$$= RT\ln\gamma = 8.314\ \mathrm{J\,K^{-1}\,mol^{-1}} \times 200\ \mathrm{K} \times \ln 0.72$$

$$= \underline{-0.55\ \mathrm{kJ\,mol^{-1}}}$$

5.7 $B' = \frac{B}{RT}$ [Problem 1.15] $= \frac{-81.7\times10^{-6}\ \mathrm{m^3\,mol^{-1}}}{8.314\ \mathrm{J\,K^{-1}\,mol^{-1}}\times 373\ \mathrm{K}}$

$$= \underline{-2.63\times10^{-8}\ \mathrm{Pa^{-1}}}$$

$\gamma = e^{B'p+\cdots}$ [Above Example 5.7]

$$= e^{-2.63\times10^{-8}\ \mathrm{Pa^{-1}}\times 50\times 1.013\times10^{5}\ \mathrm{Pa}}$$

$$= e^{-0.13\bar{3}} = \underline{0.88}$$

5.8 $\Delta G = V\Delta p$ [10]

$$= 1.0\times10^{-3}\ \mathrm{m^3}\times 99\times 1.013\times10^{5}\ \mathrm{Pa}$$

$$= 10\ \mathrm{kPa\,m^3} = \underline{+10\ \mathrm{kJ}}$$

5.9 $\Delta G_m = RT\ln\frac{p_f}{p_i}$ [11] $= 8.314\ \mathrm{J\,K^{-1}\,mol^{-1}}\times 298\ \mathrm{K}\times\ln\frac{100.0}{1.0}$

$$= \underline{+11\ \mathrm{kJ\,mol^{-1}}}$$

Problems

5.1 $\left(\frac{\partial}{\partial T}\frac{\Delta G^{\ominus}}{T}\right)_p = -\frac{\Delta H^{\ominus}}{T^2}$

$$\int_{\mathcal{T}}^{T} d\frac{\Delta G^{\ominus}}{T} = -\int_{\mathcal{T}}^{T}\frac{\Delta H^{\ominus}\,dT}{T^2} \approx -\Delta H^{\ominus}\int_{\mathcal{T}}^{T}\frac{dT}{T^2} = \Delta H^{\ominus}\left(\frac{1}{T}-\frac{1}{\mathcal{T}}\right)$$

Therefore

$$\frac{\Delta G^{\ominus}(T)}{T}-\frac{\Delta G^{\ominus}(\mathcal{T})}{\mathcal{T}}\approx\Delta H^{\ominus}\left(\frac{1}{T}-\frac{1}{\mathcal{T}}\right)$$

and so

$$\Delta G^{\ominus}(T)=\frac{T}{\mathcal{T}}\Delta G^{\ominus}(\mathcal{T})+\left(1-\frac{T}{\mathcal{T}}\right)\Delta H^{\ominus}(\mathcal{T})$$

$$=\tau\,\Delta G^{\ominus}(\mathcal{T})+(1+\tau)\,\Delta H^{\ominus}(\mathcal{T})\qquad \tau=T/\mathcal{T}$$

For the reaction

$$2CO(g)+O_2(g)\rightarrow 2CO_2(g)$$

$$\Delta G^{\ominus}(\mathcal{T})=2\Delta G_f^{\ominus}(CO_2,g)-2\Delta G_f^{\ominus}(CO,g)$$

$$=2\times(-394.36)-2\times(-137.17)\text{ kJ mol}^{-1}=-514.38\text{ kJ mol}^{-1}$$

$$\Delta H^{\ominus}(\mathcal{T})=2\Delta H_f^{\ominus}(CO_2,g)-2\Delta H_f^{\ominus}(CO,g)$$

$$=2\times(-393.51)-2\times(-110.53)\text{ kJ mol}^{-1}=-565.96\text{ kJ mol}^{-1}$$

Therefore, since $\tau=375/298.15=1.25\overline{8}$

$$\Delta G^{\ominus}(375\text{ K})=1.25\overline{8}\times(-514.38)+(1-1.25\overline{8})\times(-565.96\text{ kJ mol}^{-1})$$

$$=\underline{-501\text{ kJ mol}^{-1}}$$

5.2 For the reaction

$$N_2(g)+3H_2(g)\rightarrow 2NH_3(g)\qquad \Delta G^{\ominus}=2\Delta G_f^{\ominus}(NH_3,g)$$

(a) $\Delta G^{\ominus}(500\text{ K})=\tau\,\Delta G^{\ominus}(\mathcal{T})+(1-\tau)\,\Delta H^{\ominus}(\mathcal{T})$ [Problem 5.1, $\tau=T/\mathcal{T}$]

$$=\frac{500\text{ K}}{298.15\text{ K}}\times 2\times(-16.45\text{ kJ mol}^{-1})+\left(1-\frac{500\text{ K}}{298.15\text{ K}}\right)$$

$$\times 2\times(-46.11\text{ kJ mol}^{-1})$$

$$=-55.\overline{17}+62.\overline{43}\text{ kJ mol}^{-1}=\underline{+7.\overline{26}\text{ kJ mol}^{-1}}$$

(b) $$\Delta G^{\ominus}(1000\text{ K})=\frac{1000\text{ K}}{298.15}\times 2\times(-16.45\text{ kJ mol}^{-1})+\left(1-\frac{1000\text{ K}}{298.15\text{ K}}\right)$$

$$\times 2\times(-46.11\text{ kJ mol}^{-1})$$

$$=-110.\overline{35}+217.\overline{09}\text{ kJ mol}^{-1}=\underline{+106.\overline{74}\text{ kJ mol}^{-1}}$$

5.3 $\Delta G^{\ominus}(37\,°\text{C})=\tau\,\Delta G^{\ominus}(\mathcal{T})+(1-\tau)\,\Delta H^{\ominus}(\mathcal{T})$ [Problem 5.1, $\tau=T/\mathcal{T}$]

$$=\frac{310\text{ K}}{298.15\text{ K}}\times(-5798\text{ kJ mol}^{-1})+\left(1-\frac{310\text{ K}}{298.15\text{ K}}\right)$$

$$\times(-5645\text{ kJ mol}^{-1})$$

$$=-5804\text{ kJ mol}^{-1}$$

The difference is

$$\Delta G^{\ominus}(37\,°\text{C}) - \Delta G^{\ominus}(T) = -5804 - (-5798)\ \text{kJ mol}^{-1} = \underline{-6\ \text{kJ mol}^{-1}}$$

Therefore, an additional 6 kJ mol^{-1} of non-expansion work may be done at the higher temperature.

5.4 $\ln \gamma = \int_0^p \left(\frac{Z-1}{p}\right) \mathrm{d}p$ [17]

We draw up the following table:

p/atm	1	4	7	10	40	70	100
$10^3\left(\frac{Z-1}{p}\right)\Big/\text{atm}^{-1}$	−2.99	−3.01	−3.03	−3.04	−3.17	−3.19	−3.13

The points are plotted in Fig. 5.1. The shaded area is −0.313, so at 100 atm

$\gamma = \mathrm{e}^{-0.313} = 0.73$

and the fugacity of oxygen is 100 atm × 0.73 = $\underline{73\ \text{atm}}$

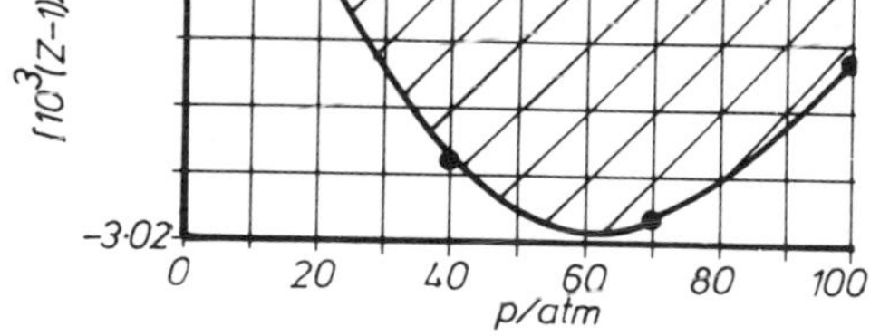

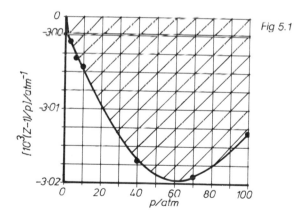

Fig 5.1

5.5 At constant volume, $\mathrm{d}U = C_V\,\mathrm{d}T$. Moreover, $\mathrm{d}S = \mathrm{d}q_{\text{rev}}/T = C_V\,\mathrm{d}T/T$. Therefore,

$$\left(\frac{\partial U}{\partial S}\right)_V = C_V\,\mathrm{d}T/(C_V\,\mathrm{d}T/T) = T$$

We can ensure that the entropy in constant by considering a reversible adiabatic change. Then

$$\mathrm{d}U = -p\,\mathrm{d}V$$

Hence $\left(\frac{\partial U}{\partial V}\right)_S = -p$

5.6 There are two routes. Either use $H(p, S)$ is a state function, and $A(V, T)$ is a state function, and proceed as in Section 5.1:

$$\mathrm{d}H = \mathrm{d}U + p\,\mathrm{d}V + V\,\mathrm{d}p = (T\,\mathrm{d}S - p\,\mathrm{d}V) + p\,\mathrm{d}V + V\,\mathrm{d}p$$

$$= V\mathrm{d}p + T\,\mathrm{d}S$$

But as $\mathrm{d}H$ is exact,

$$\left(\frac{\partial V}{\partial S}\right)_p = \left(\frac{\partial T}{\partial p}\right)_S$$

Similarly, $\mathrm{d}A = -S\,\mathrm{d}T - p\,\mathrm{d}V$, and is exact.

Therefore,

$$\left(\frac{\partial S}{\partial V}\right)_T = \left(\frac{\partial p}{\partial T}\right)_V$$

Alternatively

$$\left(\frac{\partial S}{\partial V}\right)_T = \left(\frac{\partial S}{\partial p}\right)_T\left(\frac{\partial p}{\partial V}\right)_T = -\left(\frac{\partial V}{\partial T}\right)_p\left(\frac{\partial p}{\partial V}\right)_T \text{ [7]}$$

$$= +1\Big/\left(\frac{\partial T}{\partial p}\right)_V \text{ [chain relation]} = \left(\frac{\partial p}{\partial T}\right)_V \text{ [inversion]}$$

5.7 $$\left(\frac{\partial p}{\partial S}\right)_V = -\left(\frac{\partial T}{\partial V}\right)_S = 1\Big/\left(\frac{\partial S}{\partial T}\right)_V\left(\frac{\partial V}{\partial S}\right)_T \text{ [Maxwell, chain relation]}$$

$$= \left(\frac{\partial S}{\partial V}\right)_T\Big/\left(\frac{\partial S}{\partial T}\right)_V \text{ [inversion]}$$

$$= \left(\frac{\partial p}{\partial T}\right)_V\Big/\left(\frac{\partial S}{\partial U}\right)_V\left(\frac{\partial U}{\partial T}\right)_V \text{ [Maxwell]}$$

$$= -\left(\frac{\partial p}{\partial V}\right)_T\left(\frac{\partial V}{\partial T}\right)_p \Big/ \left(\frac{\partial S}{\partial U}\right)_V\left(\frac{\partial U}{\partial T}\right)_V \quad \text{[chain relation]}$$

$$= \frac{-\left(\frac{\partial V}{\partial T}\right)_p\left(\frac{\partial U}{\partial S}\right)_V}{\left(\frac{\partial V}{\partial p}\right)_T\left(\frac{\partial U}{\partial T}\right)_V} = \frac{\alpha T}{\kappa C_V} \quad [(\partial U/\partial S)_V = T]$$

$$\left(\frac{\partial V}{\partial S}\right)_p = \left(\frac{\partial T}{\partial p}\right)_S \quad \text{[Maxwell]}$$

$$= -\left(\frac{\partial S}{\partial p}\right)_T\left(\frac{\partial T}{\partial S}\right)_p \quad \text{[chain]}$$

$$= \left(\frac{\partial V}{\partial T}\right)_p\left(\frac{\partial T}{\partial H}\right)_p\left(\frac{\partial H}{\partial S}\right)_p \quad \text{[Maxwell]}$$

$$= \left(\frac{\partial V}{\partial T}\right)_p\left(\frac{\partial H}{\partial S}\right)_p \Big/ \left(\frac{\partial H}{\partial T}\right)_p \quad \text{[inversion]}$$

$$= \frac{\alpha VT}{C_p} \quad [(\partial H/\partial S)_p = T, \text{ by analogy with } (\partial U/\partial S)_V = T]$$

5.8 $\left(\frac{\delta S}{\delta V}\right)_T = \left(\frac{\delta p}{\delta T}\right)_V$ [Problem 5.6] $= \left(\frac{\delta}{\delta T}\left(\frac{nRT}{V}\right)\right)_V = \frac{nR}{V}$

Therefore

$$\mathrm{d}S = nR\frac{\mathrm{d}V}{V} = nR\,\mathrm{d}\ln V$$

Hence, $S \propto nR \ln V$

5.9 $\mathrm{d}H = T\,\mathrm{d}S + V\,\mathrm{d}p$

$\mathrm{d}H = \left(\frac{\delta H}{\delta S}\right)_p \mathrm{d}S + \left(\frac{\delta H}{\delta p}\right)_S \mathrm{d}p \quad [H = H(p, S)]$ — compare

Thus, $\left(\frac{\delta H}{\delta S}\right)_p = T, \left(\frac{\delta H}{\delta p}\right)_S = V$ [dH exact]

Furthermore,

$$\left(\frac{\partial H}{\partial p}\right)_T = \left(\frac{\partial H}{\partial S}\right)_p\left(\frac{\partial S}{\partial p}\right)_T + \left(\frac{\partial H}{\partial p}\right)_S \quad \text{[Relation 1, Box 3.1]}$$

$$= T\left(\frac{\partial S}{\partial p}\right)_T + V$$

$$= -T\left(\frac{\partial V}{\partial T}\right)_p + V \quad \text{[Maxwell]}$$

(a) For $pV = nRT$

$$\left(\frac{\partial V}{\partial T}\right)_p = \frac{nR}{p}, \text{ hence } \left(\frac{\partial H}{\partial p}\right)_T = \frac{-nRT}{p} + V = \underline{0}$$

(b) For $p = \frac{nRT}{V-nb} - \frac{an^2}{V^2}$ [Table 1.5]

$$T = \frac{p(V-nb)}{nR} + \frac{na(V-nb)}{RV^2}$$

$$\left(\frac{\partial T}{\partial V}\right)_p = \frac{p}{nR} + \frac{na}{RV^2} - \frac{2na(V-nb)}{RV^3}$$

Therefore

$$\left(\frac{\partial H}{\partial p}\right)_T = -T\Big/\left(\frac{\partial T}{\partial V}\right)_p + V \text{ [inversion]}$$

$$= \frac{-T}{\frac{p}{nR} + \frac{na}{RV^2} - \frac{2na(V-nb)}{RV^3}} + V$$

$$= \underline{\frac{nb - (2na/RT)\lambda^2}{1 - (2na/RTV)\lambda^2}, \ \lambda = 1 - \frac{nb}{V}}$$

When $b/V_m \ll 1$, $\lambda \approx 1$ and

$$\frac{2na}{RTV} = \frac{2na}{RT} \cdot \frac{1}{V} \approx \frac{2na}{RT}\frac{p}{nRT} = \frac{2pa}{R^2T^2}$$

Therefore,

$$\left(\frac{\partial H}{\partial p}\right)_T \approx \frac{nb - 2na/RT}{1 - (2pa/R^2T^2)}$$

For argon, $a = 1.345 \text{ L}^2 \text{ atm mol}^{-2}$, $b = 3.219 \times 10^{-2} \text{ L mol}^{-1}$,

$$\frac{2na}{RT} = \frac{2 \times 10.0 \text{ atm} \times 1.345 \text{ L}^2 \text{ atm mol}^{-2}}{8.206 \times 10^{-2} \text{ L atm K}^{-1} \text{ mol}^{-1} \times 298 \text{ K}} = 0.11 \text{ L}$$

$$\frac{2pa}{R^2T^2} = \frac{2\times 1.0\ \text{mol}\times 1.345\ \text{L}^2\ \text{atm mol}^{-2}}{(8.206\times 10^{-2}\ \text{L atm K}^{-1}\ \text{mol}^{-1}\times 298\ \text{K})^2} = 0.045$$

Hence,

$$\left(\frac{\partial H}{\partial p}\right)_T \approx \frac{(3.22\times 10^{-2} - 0.11)\ \text{L}}{1-0.045} = -0.083\ \text{L} = \underline{-8.4\ \text{J atm}^{-1}}$$

$$\Delta H \approx \left(\frac{\partial H}{\partial p}\right)_T \Delta p \approx -8.2\ \text{J atm}^{-1}\times 1\ \text{atm} = \underline{-8\ \text{J}}$$

5.10 $\pi_T = T\left(\frac{\partial p}{\partial T}\right)_V - p$ [4]

$$p = \frac{RT}{V_m} + \frac{BRT}{V_m^2}\ \text{[given]}$$

$$\left(\frac{\partial p}{\partial T}\right)_V = \frac{R}{V_m} + \frac{BR}{V_m^2} + \frac{RT}{V_m^2}\left(\frac{\partial B}{\partial T}\right)_V = \frac{p}{T} + \frac{RT}{V_m^2}\left(\frac{\partial B}{\partial T}\right)_V$$

Hence,

$$\pi_T = \frac{RT^2}{V_m^2}\left(\frac{\partial B}{\partial T}\right)_V \approx \frac{RT^2 \Delta B}{V_m^2\ \Delta T}$$

For $V_m \approx RT/p$, $\underline{\pi_T \approx \frac{p^2}{R}\cdot\frac{\Delta B}{\Delta T}}$

From the data, $\Delta B = -15.6 - (-28.0)\ \text{cm}^3\ \text{mol}^{-1} = +12.4\ \text{cm}^3\ \text{mol}^{-1}$

Hence, (a) $\pi_T = \frac{(1.0\ \text{atm})^2\times(12.4\times 10^{-3}\ \text{L mol}^{-1})}{8.206\times 10^{-2}\ \text{L atm K}^{-1}\ \text{mol}^{-1}\times 50\ \text{K}} = \underline{3.0\times 10^{-3}\ \text{atm}}$

(b) $\pi_T \propto p^2$; so at $p = 10.0$ atm, $\pi_T = \underline{0.30\ \text{atm}}$

5.11 $C_V = \left(\frac{\partial U}{\partial T}\right)_V$ and $C_p = \left(\frac{\partial H}{\partial T}\right)_p$

(a) $\left(\frac{\partial C_V}{\partial V}\right)_T = \frac{\partial^2 U}{\partial V\,\partial T} = \frac{\partial^2 U}{\partial V\,\partial T} = \left(\frac{\partial}{\partial T}\left(\frac{\partial U}{\partial V}\right)_T\right)_V = 0\ [\pi_T = 0]$

$$\left(\frac{\partial C_V}{\partial p}\right)_T = \frac{\partial^2 U}{\partial p\,\partial T} = \frac{\partial^2 U}{\partial T\,\partial p} = \left(\frac{\partial}{\partial T}\left(\frac{\partial U}{\partial p}\right)_T\right)_V$$

$$=\left(\frac{\partial}{\partial T}\left(\frac{\partial U}{\partial V}\right)_T\left(\frac{\partial V}{\partial p}\right)_T\right)_V=0\ [\pi_T=0]$$

Since $C_p=C_V+R$

$$\left(\frac{\partial C_p}{\partial x}\right)_T=\left(\frac{\partial C_V}{\partial x}\right)_T \text{ for } x=p \text{ or } V$$

(*b*) $$\left(\frac{\partial C_V}{\partial V}\right)_T=\frac{\partial^2 U}{\partial T\,\partial V}=\left(\frac{\partial \pi_T}{\partial T}\right)_V \text{ [above]}$$

$$=\left(\frac{\partial}{\partial T}\frac{RT^2}{V_\mathrm{m}^2}\left(\frac{\partial B}{\partial T}\right)_V\right)_V \text{ [Problem 5.10]}$$

$$=\frac{2RT}{V_\mathrm{m}^2}\left(\frac{\partial B}{\partial T}\right)_V+\frac{RT^2}{V_\mathrm{m}^2}\left(\frac{\partial^2 B}{\partial T^2}\right)_V$$

$$=\underline{\frac{RT}{V_\mathrm{m}^2}\left(\frac{\partial^2(BT)}{\partial T^2}\right)_V}$$

5.12 $\mu_\mathrm{J}=\left(\frac{\partial T}{\partial V}\right)_U,\ C_V=\left(\frac{\partial U}{\partial T}\right)_V$

$$\mu_\mathrm{J}C_V=\left(\frac{\partial T}{\partial V}\right)_U\left(\frac{\partial U}{\partial T}\right)_V=-1\Big/\left(\frac{\partial V}{\partial U}\right)_T \text{ [chain relation]}$$

$$=-\left(\frac{\partial U}{\partial V}\right)_T \text{ [inversion]}=p-T\left(\frac{\partial p}{\partial T}\right)_V \text{ [4]}$$

$$\left(\frac{\partial p}{\partial T}\right)_V=-1\Big/\left(\frac{\partial T}{\partial V}\right)_p\left(\frac{\partial V}{\partial p}\right)_T \text{ [chain relation]}$$

$$=-\left(\frac{\partial V}{\partial T}\right)_p\Big/\left(\frac{\partial V}{\partial p}\right)_T=\frac{\alpha}{\kappa_T}$$

Therefore

$\underline{\mu_\mathrm{J}C_V=p-\alpha T/\kappa_T}$

5.13 $\pi_T=T\left(\frac{\partial p}{\partial T}\right)_V-p$ [4]

$$p=\frac{nRT}{V-nb}\mathrm{e}^{-an/RTV} \text{ [Table 1.5]}$$

$$T\left(\frac{\partial p}{\partial T}\right)_V=\frac{nRT}{V-nb}\mathrm{e}^{-an/RTV}+\frac{na}{RTV}\cdot\frac{nRT}{V-nb}\mathrm{e}^{-an/RTV}$$

$$=p+\frac{nap}{RTV}$$

Hence, $\underline{\pi_T=\dfrac{nap}{RTV}}$

$\pi_T\to 0$ as $p\to 0$, $V\to\infty$, $a\to 0$, $T\to\infty$. The fact that $\pi_T>0$ (because $a>0$) is consistent with a representing attractive contributions, since it implies that $(\partial U/\partial V)_T>0$ and the internal energy rises as the gas expands (so decreasing the average attractive interactions).

5.14 $\mathrm{d}G=\left(\dfrac{\partial G}{\partial p}\right)_T\mathrm{d}p=V\,\mathrm{d}p$

$\left(\dfrac{\partial V}{\partial p}\right)_T=-\kappa_T V$ [given], so $\mathrm{d}\ln V=-\kappa\,\mathrm{d}p$

Hence, the volume varies with pressure as

$$\int \mathrm{d}\ln V=-\kappa_T\int \mathrm{d}p$$

or

$V=V_0\,\mathrm{e}^{-\kappa_T(p-p_\mathrm{i})}$ [$V=V_0$ when $p=p_\mathrm{i}$]

Hence

$$\int_\mathrm{i}^\mathrm{f}\mathrm{d}G=\int V\,\mathrm{d}p=V_0\int_{p_\mathrm{i}}^{p_\mathrm{f}}\mathrm{e}^{-\kappa_T(p-p_\mathrm{i})}\,\mathrm{d}p$$

$$G(p_\mathrm{f})=G(p_\mathrm{i})+V_0\frac{1-\mathrm{e}^{-\kappa_T(p_\mathrm{f}-p_\mathrm{i})}}{\kappa_T}=G(p_\mathrm{i})+V_0\frac{1-\mathrm{e}^{-\kappa_T\Delta p}}{\kappa_T}$$

If $\kappa_T\Delta p\ll 1$, $1-\mathrm{e}^{-\kappa_T\Delta p}\approx 1-(1-\kappa_T\Delta p+\frac{1}{2}\kappa_T^2\Delta p^2)=\kappa_T\Delta p-\frac{1}{2}\kappa_T^2\Delta p^2$

Hence

$\underline{G'=G+V_0\,\Delta p(1-\frac{1}{2}\kappa_T\Delta p)}$

For the compression of copper, the change in molar Gibbs function is

$$\Delta G_{\mathrm{m}} = V_{\mathrm{m}}\,\Delta p(1-\tfrac{1}{2}\kappa_T\,\Delta p) = \frac{M\,\Delta p}{\rho}(1-\tfrac{1}{2}\kappa_T\,\Delta p)$$

$$= \frac{63.54\ \mathrm{g\ mol^{-1}}}{8.93\times10^{6}\ \mathrm{g\ m^{-3}}}\times 500\times 1.013\times10^{5}\ \mathrm{Pa}\times(1-\tfrac{1}{2}\kappa_T\,\Delta p)$$

$$= 360.\overline{4}\ \mathrm{J}\times(1-\tfrac{1}{2}\kappa_T\,\Delta p)$$

If we take $\kappa_T = 0$ (incompressible), $\Delta G_{\mathrm{m}} = +360$ J. For its actual value

$$\tfrac{1}{2}\kappa_T\,\Delta p = \tfrac{1}{2}\times 0.8\times10^{-6}\ \mathrm{atm^{-1}}\times 500\ \mathrm{atm} = 2\times10^{-4}$$

$$1-\tfrac{1}{2}\kappa_T\,\Delta p = 0.9998$$

Hence ΔG_{m} differs from the simpler version by only 2 parts in 10^{-4} (0.02 per cent).

5.15 $\left(\dfrac{\partial}{\partial T}\left(\dfrac{\Delta G}{T}\right)\right)_b = \dfrac{-\Delta H}{T^2}$ [8a]

(a) $$\int \mathrm{d}\left(\frac{\Delta G}{T}\right) = -\int \frac{\Delta H\,\mathrm{d}T}{T^2} \approx -\Delta T\int\frac{\mathrm{d}T}{T^2}\quad [\Delta H\ \text{constant}]$$

$$\frac{\Delta G'}{T'} - \frac{\Delta G}{T} = \Delta H\left(\frac{1}{T'}-\frac{1}{T}\right)$$

$$\Delta G' = \frac{T'}{T}\Delta G + \left(1-\frac{T'}{T}\right)\Delta H$$

$$= \underline{\tau\,\Delta G + (1-\tau)\,\Delta H}\ \text{with}\ \tau = T'/T$$

(b) $\Delta H(T'') = \Delta H(T) + (T''-T)\,\Delta C_p$ [given]

$$\frac{\Delta G'}{T'} - \frac{\Delta G}{T} = -\Delta H\int_T^{T'}\frac{\mathrm{d}T''}{T''^2} - \Delta C_p\int_T^{T'}\frac{(T''-T)\,\mathrm{d}T''}{T''^2}$$

$$= \left(\frac{1}{T'}-\frac{1}{T}\right)\Delta H - \Delta C_p\ln\frac{T'}{T} - T\,\Delta C_p\left(\frac{1}{T'}-\frac{1}{T}\right)$$

Therefore, with $\tau = T'/T$

$$\Delta G' = \tau\,\Delta G + (1-\tau)\,\Delta H - T'\,\Delta C_p\ln\tau - T\,\Delta C_p(1-\tau)$$

$$= \underline{\tau\,\Delta G + (1-\tau)(\Delta H - T\,\Delta C_p) - T'\,\Delta C_p\ln\tau}$$

5.16 $\kappa_S = -\frac{1}{V}\left(\frac{\partial V}{\partial p}\right)_S = 1\Big/V\left(\frac{\partial p}{\partial V}\right)_S$

For a reversible adiabatic change, $pV^\gamma = \text{const}$,

$$\left(\frac{\partial p}{\partial V}\right)_S = \left(\frac{\partial}{\partial V}\frac{\text{const}}{V^\gamma}\right)_S = -\gamma\frac{\text{const}}{V^{\gamma+1}} = \frac{-\gamma p}{V}$$

Therefore,

$$\kappa_S = \frac{1}{V\left(\frac{-\gamma p}{V}\right)} = \frac{-1}{\gamma p}$$

Hence, $\underline{\gamma p \kappa_S = -1}$

5.17 $\mathrm{d}S = \left(\frac{\partial S}{\partial T}\right)_V \mathrm{d}T + \left(\frac{\partial S}{\partial V}\right)_T \mathrm{d}V \; [S = S(V, T)]$

$$T\,\mathrm{d}S = T\left(\frac{\partial S}{\partial T}\right)_V \mathrm{d}T + T\left(\frac{\partial S}{\partial V}\right)_T \mathrm{d}V$$

Now, $\left(\frac{\partial S}{\partial T}\right)_V = \left(\frac{\partial S}{\partial U}\right)_V\left(\frac{\partial U}{\partial T}\right)_V = \frac{1}{T}\times C_V$

$$\left(\frac{\partial S}{\partial V}\right)_T = \left(\frac{\partial p}{\partial T}\right)_V \; \text{[Maxwell]}$$

Hence, $\underline{T\,\mathrm{d}S = C_V\,\mathrm{d}T + T\left(\frac{\partial p}{\partial T}\right)_V \mathrm{d}V}$

For a reversible, isothermal expansion, $T\,\mathrm{d}S = \mathrm{d}q_{\mathrm{rev}}$; therefore

$$\mathrm{d}q_{\mathrm{rev}} = T\left(\frac{\partial p}{\partial T}\right)_V \mathrm{d}V = \frac{nRT}{V-nb}\mathrm{d}V$$

$$q_{\mathrm{rev}} = nRT\int_{\mathrm{i}}^{\mathrm{f}}\frac{\mathrm{d}V}{V-nb} = \underline{nRT\ln\left(\frac{V_{\mathrm{f}}-nb}{V_{\mathrm{i}}-nb}\right)}$$

5.18 $\mathrm{d}S = \left(\frac{\partial S}{\partial T}\right)_p \mathrm{d}T + \left(\frac{\partial S}{\partial p}\right)_T \mathrm{d}p \; [S = S(p, T)]$

$$T\,dS = T\left(\frac{\partial S}{\partial T}\right)_p dT + T\left(\frac{\partial S}{\partial p}\right)_T dp$$

Use $\left(\frac{\partial S}{\partial T}\right)_p = \left(\frac{\partial S}{\partial H}\right)_p \left(\frac{\partial H}{\partial T}\right)_p = \frac{1}{T}\times C_p$

$\left(\frac{\partial S}{\partial p}\right)_T = -\left(\frac{\partial V}{\partial T}\right)_p$ [Maxwell]

Hence $T\,dS = C_p\,dT - T\left(\frac{\partial V}{\partial T}\right)_p dp = \underline{C_p\,dT - \alpha TV\,dp}$

For reversible, isothermal compression, $T\,dS = dq_{\text{rev}}$, $dT = 0$; hence

$dq_{\text{rev}} = -\alpha TV\,dp$

$\underline{q_{\text{rev}} = -\alpha TV\,\Delta p}$ if the substance is incompressible.

For mercury,

$q_{\text{rev}} = -1.82\times10^{-4}\,\text{K}^{-1}\times273\,\text{K}\times1.00\times10^{-4}\,\text{m}^3\times1.0\times10^8\,\text{Pa}$

$= \underline{-0.50\,\text{kJ}}$

5.19 $G' = G + \int_0^p V\,dp$

$= G + V_0\int_0^p e^{-p/p^*}\,dp$

$= \underline{G + p^* V_0(1 - e^{-p/p^*})}$

Since $e^{-p/p^*} < 1$ if $p > 0$, $G' > G$. Therefore, when the pressure is relaxed, the spontaneous direction of change is expansion.

5.20 $\ln\gamma = \int_0^p \left(\frac{Z-1}{p}\right) dp$

$$Z = 1 + \frac{B}{V_m} + \frac{C}{V_m^2} = 1 + B'p + C'p^2 + \cdots$$

with $B' = \frac{B}{RT}$, $C' = \frac{C - B^2}{R^2T^2}$ [Problem 1.15]

$$\frac{Z-1}{p} = B' + C'p + \cdots$$

Therefore,

$$\ln\gamma=\int_0^p B'\,\mathrm{d}p+\int_0^p C'p\,\mathrm{d}p+\cdots$$

$$=B'p+\tfrac{1}{2}C'p^2+\cdots$$

$$=\frac{Bp}{RT}+\frac{(C-B^2)p^2}{2R^2T^2}+\cdots$$

For argon,

$$\frac{Bp}{RT}=\frac{-21.13\times10^{-3}\,\mathrm{L\,mol^{-1}}\times1.00\,\mathrm{atm}}{8.206\times10^{-2}\,\mathrm{L\,atm\,K^{-1}\,mol^{-1}}\times273\,\mathrm{K}}=-9.43\times10^{-4}$$

$$\frac{(C-B^2)p^2}{2R^2T^2}=\frac{\{1.054\times10^{-3}\,\mathrm{L^2\,mol^{-2}}-(-21.13\times10^{-3}\,\mathrm{L\,mol^{-1}})^2\}\times1.00\,\mathrm{atm}}{2\times(8.206\times10^{-2}\,\mathrm{L\,atm\,K^{-1}\,mol^{-1}}\times273\,\mathrm{K})^2}$$

$$=6.05\times10^{-7}$$

Therefore,

$$\ln\gamma=-9.43\times10^{-4}+6.05\times10^{-7}=-9.42\times10^{-4}$$

$$\gamma=0.9991$$

Hence $f=1.00\,\mathrm{atm}\times0.9998=\underline{0.999\overline{1}\,\mathrm{atm}}$

5.21 The equation of state

$$\frac{pV_m}{RT}=1+\frac{BT}{V_m}$$

solves to $V_m=\dfrac{RT}{2p}\left\{1+\left(1+\dfrac{4pB}{R}\right)^{1/2}\right\}$

so

$$\frac{Z-1}{p}=\frac{pV_m/RT-1}{p}=\frac{BT}{pV_m}$$

$$=\frac{2B/R}{1+\left(1+\dfrac{4pB}{R}\right)^{1/2}}$$

$$\ln\gamma=\int_0^p\left(\frac{Z-1}{p}\right)\mathrm{d}p=\frac{2B}{R}\int_0^p\frac{\mathrm{d}p}{1+\left(1+\dfrac{4pB}{R}\right)^{1/2}}$$

$$= \int_2^a \left(\frac{a-1}{a}\right) \mathrm{d}a \qquad a = 1 + \left(1 + \frac{4pB}{R}\right)^{1/2}$$

$$= a - 2 - \ln \tfrac{1}{2}a$$

$$= \left(1 + \frac{4pB}{R}\right)^{1/2} - 1 - \ln \frac{1}{2}\left(1 + \frac{4pB}{R}\right)^{1/2}$$

Hence

$$\gamma = \frac{2\mathrm{e}^{(1+4pB/R)^{1/2}-1}}{1+(1+4pB/R)^{1/2}}$$

This function is plotted in Fig. 5.2. When $4pB/R \ll 1$,

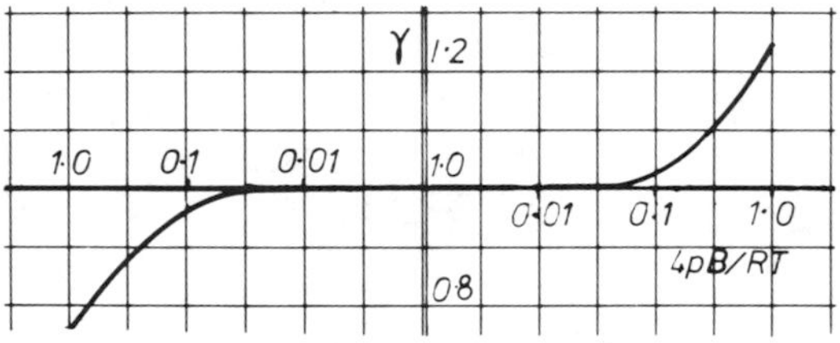

Fig 5.2

$\mathrm{e}^x \approx 1 + x$, $(1+x)^{1/2} \approx 1 + \tfrac{1}{2}x$, and $(1+x)^{-1} \approx 1 - x$. Then

$$\gamma \approx 1 + \frac{pB}{R}$$

6. Changes of state: physical transformations of pure substances

Exercises

6.1 $p = p^* \mathrm{e}^{-C}$, $C = \dfrac{\Delta H_{\mathrm{vap}}}{R}\left(\dfrac{1}{T} - \dfrac{1}{T^*}\right)$ [8b]

$$\ln \frac{p^*}{p} = C$$

$$\frac{1}{T} = \frac{1}{T^*} + \frac{R}{\Delta H_{\mathrm{vap}}} \ln \frac{p^*}{p}$$

$$= \frac{1}{297.25\ \mathrm{K}} + \frac{8.314\ \mathrm{J\ K^{-1}\ mol^{-1}}}{28.7 \times 10^3\ \mathrm{J\ mol^{-1}}} \ln \frac{400\ \mathrm{Torr}}{500\ \mathrm{Torr}}$$

$$= 3.30\bar{0} \times 10^{-3}\ \mathrm{K^{-1}}$$

Hence $T = \underline{303\ \mathrm{K}}$

6.2 $\dfrac{\mathrm{d}p}{\mathrm{d}T} = \dfrac{\Delta S_{\mathrm{m}}}{\Delta V_{\mathrm{m}}}$ [4]

$$\Delta S_{\mathrm{fus}} = \Delta V_{\mathrm{m}} \times \left(\frac{\mathrm{d}p}{\mathrm{d}T}\right) = (163.3 - 161.0) \times 10^{-6}\ \mathrm{m^3\ mol^{-1}}$$

$$\times \frac{(100 - 1) \times 1.013 \times 10^5\ \mathrm{Pa}}{(351.26 - 350.75)\ \mathrm{K}}$$

$$= \underline{+45.2\bar{3}\ \mathrm{J\ K^{-1}\ mol^{-1}}}$$

$$\Delta H_{\mathrm{fus}} = T_{\mathrm{f}}\,\Delta S = 350.75\ \mathrm{K} \times 45.23\ \mathrm{J\ K^{-1}\ mol^{-1}}$$

$$= \underline{+16\ \mathrm{kJ\ mol^{-1}}}$$

6.3 $\dfrac{\mathrm{d}\ln p}{\mathrm{d}T} = \dfrac{\Delta H_{\mathrm{vap}}}{RT^2}$ [8a]

$$\frac{d\ln p}{dT}=\frac{2501.8}{T^2/\text{K}}=\frac{2501.8\ \text{K}}{T^2}$$

Therefore,

$$\Delta H_{\text{vap}}=2501.8\ \text{K}\times R$$

$$=2501.8\ \text{K}\times 8.314\ \text{J K}^{-1}\,\text{mol}^{-1}=\underline{+20.80\ \text{kJ mol}^{-1}}$$

6.4 $w=\gamma\,\Delta\sigma$ [10]

$$=7.20\times10^{-2}\ \text{N m}^{-1}\times(2500-150)\times10^{-4}\ \text{m}^2\ \text{[Table 6.1]}$$

$$=\underline{16.9\ \text{mJ}}$$

6.5 $\gamma=\frac{1}{2}h\rho g r$ [15]

$$=\tfrac{1}{2}\times1.20\times10^{-2}\ \text{m}\times871\ \text{kg m}^{-3}\times9.81\ \text{m s}^{-2}\times4.0\times10^{-4}\ \text{m}$$

$$=\underline{2.0\bar{5}\times10^{-2}\ \text{N m}^{-1}}\qquad[1\ \text{N}=1\ \text{kg m s}^{-2}]$$

6.6 $p=p^*\,e^{2\gamma V_{\text{m}}/rRT}$ [13a]

$$r=\frac{2\gamma V_{\text{m}}}{RT}\left(\ln\frac{p}{p^*}\right)^{-1}=\frac{2\gamma M}{\rho RT}\left(\ln\frac{p}{p^*}\right)^{-1}$$

$$=\frac{2\times2.70\times10^{-2}\ \text{N m}^{-1}\times153.81\times10^{-3}\ \text{kg mol}^{-1}}{1600\ \text{kg m}^{-3}\times8.314\ \text{J K}^{-1}\text{mol}^{-1}\times293\ \text{K}}\left(\ln\frac{87.95\ \text{Torr}}{87.05\ \text{Torr}}\right)^{-1}$$

$$=\underline{207\ \text{nm}}$$

6.7 $\Delta T\approx\dfrac{\Delta V_{\text{fus}}}{\Delta S_{\text{fus}}}\times\Delta p$ [4]

$$\approx\frac{T_{\text{f}}\,\Delta V_{\text{fus}}}{\Delta H_{\text{fus}}}\times\Delta p=\frac{T_{\text{f}}\,\Delta pM}{\Delta H_{\text{fus}}}\,\Delta(1/\rho)\qquad[V_{\text{m}}=M/\rho]$$

$$\approx\frac{278.6\ \text{K}\times999\times1.013\times10^5\ \text{Pa}\times78.12\times10^{-3}\ \text{kg mol}^{-1}}{10.59\times10^3\ \text{J mol}^{-1}}$$

$$\times\left(\frac{1}{879\ \text{kg m}^{-3}}-\frac{1}{891\ \text{kg m}^{-3}}\right)$$

$$\approx3.18\ \text{K}$$

Therefore, at 1000 atm, $T_{\text{f}}\approx278.6+3.18=\underline{281.8\ \text{K}}$ (8.7 °C)

6.8 $\dfrac{dn}{dt}=\dfrac{dq/dt}{\Delta H_{vap}}=\dfrac{1.2\times10^3\ \mathrm{W\ m^{-2}}\times50\ \mathrm{m^2}}{44.0\times10^3\ \mathrm{J\ mol^{-1}}}$

$$=1.4\ \mathrm{mol\ s^{-1}}$$

$$\frac{dm}{dt}=1.4\ \mathrm{mol\ s^{-1}}\times18.02\ \mathrm{g\ mol^{-1}}=\underline{25\ \mathrm{g\ s^{-1}}}$$

6.9 $n=\dfrac{pV}{RT},\ n=\dfrac{m}{M},\ V=75\ \mathrm{m^3}$

$$m=\frac{pVM}{RT}$$

(a) $m=\dfrac{24\ \mathrm{Torr}\times75\times10^3\ \mathrm{L^3}\times18.02\ \mathrm{g\ mol^{-1}}}{62.364\ \mathrm{L\ Torr\ K^{-1}\ mol^{-1}}\times298.15\ \mathrm{K}}=\underline{1.7\ \mathrm{kg}}$

(b) $m=\dfrac{98\ \mathrm{Torr}\times75\times10^3\ \mathrm{L^3}\times78.11\ \mathrm{g\ mol^{-1}}}{62.364\ \mathrm{L\ Torr\ K^{-1}\ mol^{-1}}\times298.15\ \mathrm{K}}=\underline{31\ \mathrm{kg}}$

(c) $m=\dfrac{1.7\times10^{-3}\ \mathrm{Torr}\times75\times10^3\ \mathrm{L^3}\times200.59\ \mathrm{g\ mol^{-1}}}{62.364\ \mathrm{L\ Torr\ K^{-1}\ mol^{-1}}\times298.15\ \mathrm{K}}=\underline{1.4\ \mathrm{kg}}$

[The mercury is assumed to be present as a monatomic vapor.]

6.10 The vapor pressure of ice at −5 °C is 3.9×10^{-3} atm, or 3 Torr. Therefore, the first will sublime. A partial pressure of 3 Torr or more will ensure that the frost remains.

6.11 The volume decreases as the vapor is cooled from 400 K to 373 K. At the latter temperature the vapor condenses to a liquid and (if 1 atm pressure is maintained) there is a large decrease in volume. The liquid cools with only a small decrease in volume until the temperature reaches 273 K, when it freezes. The direction of the slope of the solid/liquid curve shows that the volume of the sample will then increase if the pressure is maintained. Ice remains at 260 K. There will be a pause in the rate of cooling at 373 K (about 40 kJ mol^{-1} of energy is released as heat) and a pause at 273 K (when about 6 kJ mol^{-1} is released).

6.12 Cooling from 400 K will cause the contraction of the gaseous sample until 273.16 K is reached, when the volume decreases by a large amount and solid ice is formed directly; liquid water may also form in equilibrium with the vapor and the solid.

6.13 See Fig. 6.1. (a) The gas expands. (b) The sample contracts but remains gaseous because 320 K is greater than the critical temperature. (c) The gas contracts and forms a liquid without the appearance of a discernable surface. (d) The volume increases as the pressure on the liquid is reduced. (e) The liquid cools, then freezes, contracting as it does so. (f) The solid expands slightly as the pressure is reduced and sublimes when the pressure reaches about 5 atm. (g) The gas expands as it is heated at constant pressure.

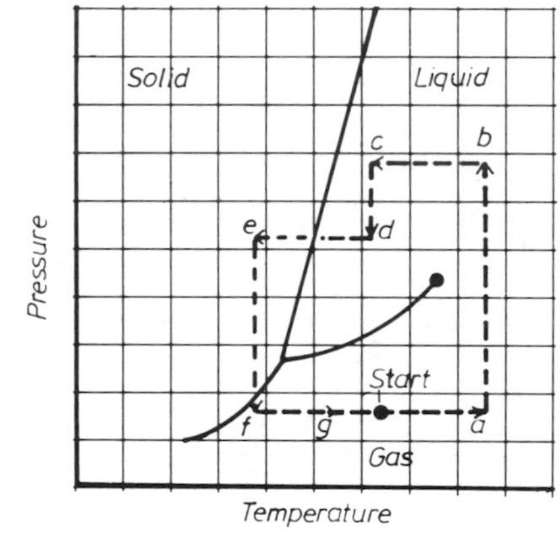

Fig 6.1

6.14 $p = p^* \, e^{2\gamma V_m / rRT}$ [13a]

$= p^* \, e^{2\gamma M / r\rho RT}$ $[V_m = M/\rho]$

$$\frac{2\gamma M}{\rho RT} = \frac{2 \times 2.9 \times 10^{-2}\ \mathrm{N\,m^{-1}} \times 78.11\ \mathrm{g\,mol^{-1}}}{0.879 \times 10^6\ \mathrm{g\,m^{-3}} \times 8.314\ \mathrm{J\,K^{-1}\,mol^{-1}} \times 298.15\ \mathrm{K}}$$

$$= 2.0\bar{8} \times 10^{-9}\ \mathrm{m}$$

(a) $$\frac{2\gamma M}{r\rho RT} = \frac{2.0\bar{8} \times 10^{-9}\ \mathrm{m}}{10 \times 10^{-6}\ \mathrm{m}} = 2.0\bar{8} \times 10^{-4}$$

$p = p^* \, e^{2.0\bar{8} \times 10^{-4}} = \underline{1.0002p^*}$

(b) $$\frac{2\gamma M}{r\rho RT} = \frac{2.08 \times 10^{-9}\ \mathrm{m}}{0.10 \times 10^{-6}\ \mathrm{m}} = 0.020\bar{8}$$

$p = p^* \, e^{0.020\bar{8}} = \underline{1.02p^*}$

Problems

6.1 $\dfrac{dp}{dT}=\dfrac{\Delta S_{vap}}{\Delta V_{vap}}=\dfrac{\Delta H_{vap}}{T_b\,\Delta V_{vap}}$ [7]

$$=\frac{14.4\times10^3\ \text{J mol}^{-1}}{180\ \text{K}\times(14.5\times10^{-3}-1.15\times10^{-4})\ \text{m}^3\ \text{mol}^{-1}}=\underline{+5.56\ \text{kPa K}^{-1}}$$

$$\frac{dp}{dT}=\frac{\Delta H_{vap}}{RT^2}p \qquad [8a,\ d\ln p=dp/p]$$

$$=\frac{14.4\times10^3\ \text{J mol}^{-1}\times1.013\times10^5\ \text{Pa}}{8.314\ \text{J K}^{-1}\ \text{mol}^{-1}\times(180\ \text{K})^2}=\underline{+5.42\ \text{kPa K}^{-1}}$$

The percentage error is <u>2.5 per cent</u>

6.2 (a) $\left(\dfrac{\partial\mu(l)}{\partial T}\right)_p-\left(\dfrac{\partial\mu(s)}{\partial T}\right)_p=-S_m(l)+S_m(s)$ [Section 6.5]

$$=-\Delta S_{fus}=\frac{-\Delta H_{fus}}{T_f}$$

$$=\frac{-6.01\ \text{kJ mol}^{-1}}{273.15\ \text{K}}=\underline{-22.0\ \text{J K}^{-1}\ \text{mol}^{-1}}$$

(b) $\left(\dfrac{\partial m(g)}{\partial T}\right)_p-\left(\dfrac{\partial m(l)}{\partial T}\right)_p=-S_m(g)+S_m(l)$

$$=-\Delta S_{vap}=\frac{-\Delta H_{vap}}{T_b}$$

$$=\frac{-40.6\ \text{kJ mol}^{-1}}{373.15\ \text{K}}=\underline{-109.0\ \text{J K}^{-1}\ \text{mol}^{-1}}$$

$$\Delta\mu\approx\left(\frac{\partial m}{\partial T}\right)_p\Delta T=-S_m\,\Delta T\ [1]$$

$$\Delta\mu(l)-\Delta\mu(s)=\mu(l,5\,°\text{C})-\mu(l,0\,°\text{C})-\mu(s,-5\,°\text{C})+\mu(s,0\,°\text{C})$$

$$=\mu(l,-5\,°\text{C})-\mu(s,-5\,°\text{C})[\mu(l,0\,°\text{C})=\mu(s,0\,°\text{C})]$$

$$\approx-\{S_m(l)-S_m(s)\}\,\Delta T\approx\Delta S_{fus}\,\Delta T$$

$$=-5\ \text{K}\times-22.0\ \text{J K}^{-1}\ \text{mol}^{-1}=\underline{+1\bar{1}0\ \text{J mol}^{-1}}$$

Since $\mu(l, -5\,°\mathrm{C}) > \mu(s, -5\,°\mathrm{C})$, there is a thermodynamic tendency to freeze.

6.3 (a) $\left(\dfrac{\partial \mathrm{m}(l)}{\partial p}\right)_T - \left(\dfrac{\partial m(s)}{\partial p}\right)_T = V_{\mathrm{m}}(l) - V_{\mathrm{m}}(s)$ [2]

$$= M\,\Delta\left(\frac{1}{\rho}\right) = 18.02\ \mathrm{g\ mol^{-1}} \times \left(\frac{1}{1.000\ \mathrm{g\ cm^{-3}}} - \frac{1}{0.917\ \mathrm{g\ cm^{-3}}}\right)$$

$$= \underline{-1.63\ \mathrm{cm^3\ mol^{-1}}}$$

(b) $\left(\dfrac{\partial \mathrm{m}(g)}{\partial p}\right)_T - \left(\dfrac{\partial m(l)}{\partial p}\right)_T = V_{\mathrm{m}}(g) - V_{\mathrm{m}}(l)$

$$= 18.02\ \mathrm{g\ mol^{-1}} \times \left(\frac{1}{0.598\ \mathrm{g\ L^{-1}}} - \frac{1}{0.958 \times 10^3\ \mathrm{g\ L^{-1}}}\right)$$

$$= \underline{+30.1\ \mathrm{L\ mol^{-1}}}$$

At $1.\bar{0}$ atm and 100 °C, $\mu(l) = \mu(g)$; therefore, at 1.2 atm and 100 °C

$$\mu(g) - \mu(l) \approx \Delta V_{\mathrm{vap}}\,\Delta T = \text{[as in Problem 6.2]}\ 30.1 \times 10^{-3}\ \mathrm{m^3\ mol^{-1}} \times 0.2 \times 1.013 \times 10^5\ \mathrm{Pa}$$

$$\approx \underline{+0.6\ \mathrm{kJ\ mol^{-1}}}$$

Since $\mu(g) > \mu(l)$, the gas tends to condense into a liquid.

6.4 $\dfrac{\mathrm{d}p}{\mathrm{d}T} = \dfrac{\Delta S}{\Delta V}\ [4] = \dfrac{\Delta H}{T\,\Delta V}$

$$\Delta T \approx \frac{T\,\Delta V}{\Delta H} \times \Delta p,\quad \Delta p = \rho g h$$

Therefore,

$$\Delta T = \frac{T\rho g h\,\Delta V}{\Delta H}$$

$$= \frac{234.3\ \mathrm{K} \times 13.6 \times 10^3\ \mathrm{kg\ m^{-3}} \times 9.81\ \mathrm{m\ s^{-2}} \times 10\ \mathrm{m} \times 0.517 \times 10^{-6}\ \mathrm{m^3\ mol^{-1}}}{2.292 \times 10^3\ \mathrm{J\ mol^{-1}}}$$

$$= 0.070\ \mathrm{K}$$

Therefore, the freezing point changes to $\underline{234.4\ \mathrm{K}}$

6.5 At equilibrium, $n_1 = \dfrac{p_1 V}{RT}$, $q = -n_1\,\Delta H_{\mathrm{vap}}$, $\Delta T = \dfrac{q}{C_p}$

Therefore,

$$\Delta T = \frac{-p_1 V \Delta H_{vap}}{RTC_p}$$

$$= \frac{-23.8\,\text{Torr} \times 50.0\,\text{L} \times 44.0 \times 10^3\,\text{J mol}^{-1}}{62.364\,\text{L Torr K}^{-1}\,\text{mol}^{-1} \times 298.15\,\text{K} \times 75.5\,\text{J K}^{-1}\,\text{mol}^{-1} \times \dfrac{250\,\text{g}}{18.02\,\text{g mol}^{-1}}}$$

$$= -2.7\,\text{K}$$

The final temperature will be about 22 °C

6.6 $\dfrac{d\ln p}{dT} = \dfrac{\Delta H_{vap}}{RT^2}$ [8a],

$$\ln p = \text{constant} - \frac{\Delta H_{vap}}{RT}$$

Therefore, plot $\ln p$ against $1/T$ and identify $-\Delta H_{vap}/R$ as its slope. Construct the following table:

θ/°C	0	20	40	50	70	80	90	100
T/K	273	293	313	323	343	353	363	373
1000 K/T	3.66	3.41	3.19	3.10	2.92	2.83	2.75	2.68
$\ln p$/Torr	2.67	3.87	4.89	5.34	6.15	6.51	6.84	7.16

The points are plotted in Fig. 6.2. The slope is -4546, so

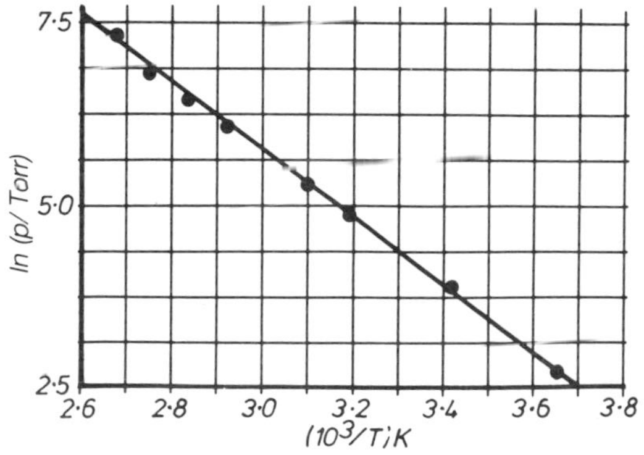

Fig 6.2

$$\frac{-\Delta H_{vap}}{R} = -4546, \text{ or } \Delta H_{vap} = \underline{+37.8 \text{ kJ mol}^{-1}}$$

the normal boiling point is reached at $p = 760$ Torr, which occurs at $1000\ \text{K}/T = 2.80$, so $T_b = 357$ K (84 °C).
[Alternatively, do a least-squares fit of $\ln p$ to $1/T$ using the procedure outlined in the Appendix.]

6.7 Adapt the procedure in Problem 6.6, but note that $T_b = \underline{227.5\ °\text{C}}$ is obvious from the raw data. Draw up the following table:

θ/°C	57.4	100.4	133.0	157.3	203.5	227.5
T/K	330.6	373.6	406.2	430.5	476.7	500.7
1000 K/T	3.02	2.68	2.46	2.32	2.10	2.00
$\ln p$/Torr	0.00	2.30	3.69	4.61	5.99	6.63

The points are plotted in Fig. 6.3. The slope is -6.6×10^3, so $\dfrac{-\Delta H_{vap}}{R} = -6.6 \times 10^3$ K, implying that $\Delta H_{vap} = \underline{+55 \text{ kJ mol}^{-1}}$

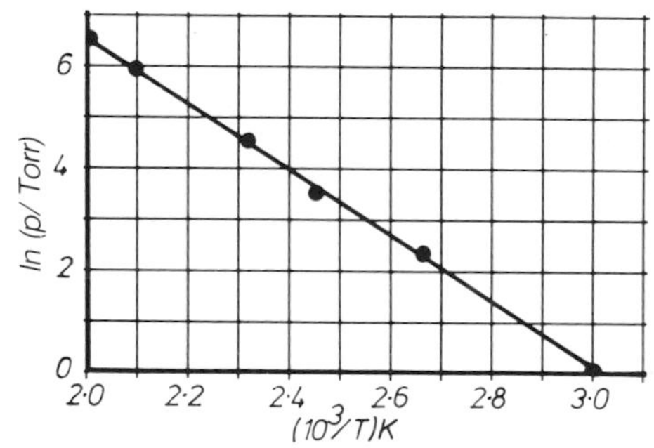

Fig 6.3

6.8 (a) Solid–liquid boundary:

$$p = p^* + \frac{\Delta H_{fus}}{\Delta V_{fus}} \ln \frac{T}{T^*} \quad [6a]$$

(b) liquid–vapor boundary:

$$p = p^* \, e^{-C}, \; C = \frac{\Delta H_{vap}}{R}\left(\frac{1}{T} - \frac{1}{T^*}\right) \; [8b]$$

(c) solid–vapor boundary

$$p = p^* \, e^{-C}, \; C = \frac{\Delta H_{sub}}{R}\left(\frac{1}{T} - \frac{1}{T^*}\right) \; [9b]$$

We need $\Delta H_{sub} = \Delta H_{fus} + \Delta H_{vap} = 41.4 \text{ kJ mol}^{-1}$

$$\Delta V_{fus} = M\left(\frac{1}{\rho(l)} - \frac{1}{\rho(s)}\right) = \frac{78.11 \text{ g mol}^{-1}}{\text{g cm}^{-3}} \times \left(\frac{1}{0.879} - \frac{1}{0.891}\right)$$

$$= +1.19\overline{7} \text{ cm}^3 \text{ mol}^{-1}$$

$$\text{(a)} \; p = p^* + \frac{10.6 \times 10^3 \text{ J mol}^{-1}}{1.19\overline{7} \times 10^{-6} \text{ m}^3 \text{ mol}^{-1}} \ln \frac{T}{T^*}$$

$$= p^* + 8.85\overline{5} \times 10^9 \text{ Pa} \ln \frac{T}{T^*}$$

$$= p^* + 6.64 \times 10^7 \text{ Torr} \ln \frac{T}{T^*} \; [1 \text{ Torr} = 133.322 \text{ Pa}]$$

This line is plotted as *a* in Fig. 6.4, starting at $(p^*, T^*) = (36 \text{ Torr}, 5.50\,°\text{C}$ $[278.65 \text{ K}])$.

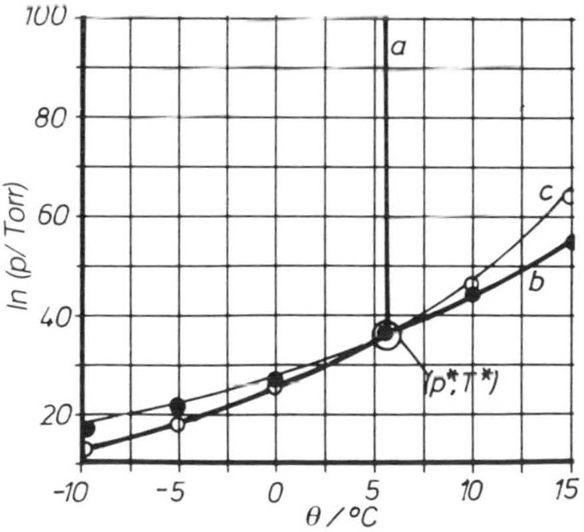

Fig 6.4

(b) $C = \dfrac{30.8 \times 10^3\ \text{J mol}^{-1}}{8.314\ \text{J K}^{-1}\ \text{mol}^{-1}} \times \left(\dfrac{1}{T} - \dfrac{1}{T^*}\right)$

$$= 37\overline{05}\ \text{K} \times \left(\frac{1}{T} - \frac{1}{T^*}\right)$$

The points are plotted as line *b* in Fig. 6.4, starting from $(p^*, T^*) = (36\ \text{Torr}, 5.50\ °\text{C}\ [278.65\ \text{K}])$.

(c) $C = \dfrac{41.4 \times 10^3\ \text{J mol}^{-1}}{8.314\ \text{J K}^{-1}\ \text{mol}^{-1}} \times \left(\dfrac{1}{T} - \dfrac{1}{T^*}\right) = 49\overline{80}\ \text{K} \times \left(\dfrac{1}{T} - \dfrac{1}{T^*}\right)$

These points are plotted as line *c* in Fig. 6.4, starting at (36 Torr, 5.50 °C).

6.9 For a droplet of radius a, the surface area is $4\pi a^2$ and the volume is $\frac{4}{3}\pi a^3$. The area occupied by a molecule of radius r is πr^2 and the volume it occupies is $\frac{4}{3}\pi r^3$. The total number on the surface is therefore $4\pi a^2/\pi r^2 = 4a^2/r^2$, and the total number in the droplet is $\frac{4}{3}\pi a^3/\frac{4}{3}\pi r^3 = a^3/r^3$. Hence

$$\frac{\text{Number on surface}}{\text{Number in droplet}} = \frac{4a^2/r^2}{a^3/r^3} = \frac{4r}{a}$$

$$= \frac{4 \times 120\ \text{pm}}{a} = \frac{4.8 \times 10^{-10}\ \text{m}}{a}$$

(a) $a = 10^{-5}\ \text{mm}$, ratio $= \dfrac{4.8 \times 10^{-10}\ \text{m}}{10^{-8}\ \text{m}} = \underline{5 \times 10^{-2}}$ (1 in 20)

(b) $a = 10^{-2}\ \text{mm}$, ratio $= \dfrac{4.8 \times 10^{-10}\ \text{m}}{10^{-5}\ \text{m}} = \underline{5 \times 10^{-5}}$ (1 in 20 000)

(c) $a = 1\ \text{mm}$, ratio $= \dfrac{4.8 \times 10^{-10}\ \text{m}}{10^{-3}\ \text{m}} = \underline{5 \times 10^{-7}}$ (1 in 2 million)

6.10 $\Delta A = \gamma\, \Delta\sigma$ [11]

Initial volume $= \dfrac{m}{\rho}$ with $m = 100\ \text{g}$ and $\rho = 0.88\ \text{g cm}^{-3}$. The volume of the N droplets is $N \times \frac{4}{3}\pi r^3$, so

$$N \times \tfrac{4}{3}\pi r^3 = \frac{m}{\rho}, \text{ implying that } N = \frac{3m}{4\pi\rho r^3}$$

$$\text{Surface area of droplets} = N \times 4\pi r^2 = \frac{3m}{\rho r}$$

Surface area of initial sample is negligible. Therefore $\Delta\sigma \approx 3m/\rho r$, so

$$\Delta A \approx \frac{3m\gamma}{\rho r}$$

$$\approx \frac{3 \times 100\,\text{g} \times 2.8 \times 10^{-2}\,\text{N m}^{-1}}{0.88 \times 10^{6}\,\text{g m}^{-3} \times 1.0 \times 10^{-6}\,\text{m}} = \underline{9.5\,\text{J}}$$

The minimum work required to achieve dispersal is $w = \Delta A$, or $\underline{9.5\,\text{J}}$.

6.11 $h = \dfrac{2\gamma}{\rho g r}$ [15]

$$= \frac{2 \times 2.189 \times 10^{-2}\,\text{N m}^{-1}}{0.780 \times 10^{3}\,\text{kg m}^{-3} \times 9.81\,\text{m s}^{-2} \times 0.10 \times 10^{-3}\,\text{m}}$$

$$= 5.7\bar{2} \times 10^{-2}\,\text{m} = \underline{5.7\,\text{cm}}$$

$$\text{Pressure} = \frac{2\gamma}{r}\ [12]$$

$$= \frac{2 \times 2.189 \times 10^{-2}\,\text{N m}^{-1}}{0.10 \times 10^{-3}\,\text{m}} = \underline{0.44\,\text{kPa}}\ (3.3\ \text{Torr})$$

6.12 The surface is curved only in the radial direction, the circumferential direction being essentially flat (Fig. 6.5). Hence the pressure difference is γ/r in place of $2\gamma/r$, where $2r$ is the width of the separation of rod and tube.

Fig 6.5

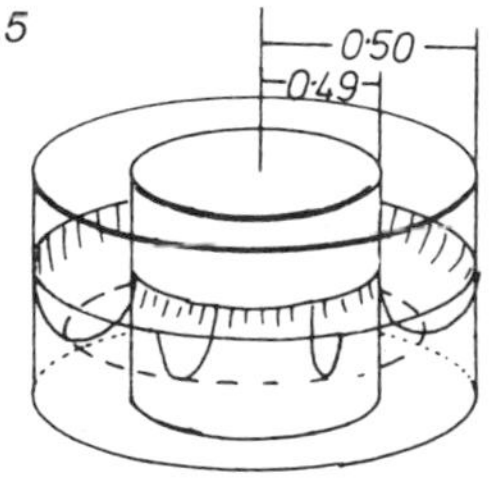

Hence

$$h=\frac{\gamma}{\rho g r}, \quad r=5.0\times10^{-3}\text{ cm}$$

$$=\frac{7.28\times10^{-2}\text{ N m}^{-1}}{0.998\times10^{3}\text{ kg m}^{-3}\times9.81\text{ m s}^{-2}\times5.0\times10^{-5}\text{ m}}$$

$$=0.15\text{ m}=\underline{15\text{ cm}}$$

6.13 $\left(\frac{\partial\,\Delta A}{\partial p}\right)_T=\left(\frac{\partial A_\beta}{\partial p}\right)_T-\left(\frac{\partial A_\alpha}{\partial p}\right)_T=-V_\beta+V_\alpha$ [Example 5.2]

Therefore, if $V_\beta=V_\alpha$, ΔA is independent of pressure.

6.14 $\mathrm{d}H=C_p\,\mathrm{d}T+V\,\mathrm{d}p$, implying that $\mathrm{d}\,\Delta H=\Delta C_p\,\mathrm{d}T+\Delta V\,\mathrm{d}p$

However, along a phase boundary dp and dT are related by

$$\frac{\mathrm{d}p}{\mathrm{d}T}=\frac{\Delta H}{T\,\Delta V}\ [5]$$

Therefore,

$$\mathrm{d}\,\Delta H=\left(\Delta C_p+\Delta V\times\frac{\Delta H}{T\,\Delta V}\right)\mathrm{d}T=\left(\Delta C_p+\frac{\Delta H}{T}\right)\mathrm{d}T \text{ and } \frac{\mathrm{d}H}{\mathrm{d}T}=\Delta C_p+\frac{\Delta H}{T}$$

Then, since

$$\frac{\mathrm{d}}{\mathrm{d}T}\left(\frac{\Delta H}{T}\right)=\frac{1}{T}\frac{\mathrm{d}\Delta H}{\mathrm{d}T}-\frac{\Delta H}{T^2}=\frac{1}{T}\left(\frac{\mathrm{d}\Delta H}{\mathrm{d}T}-\frac{\Delta H}{T}\right)$$

substituting the first result gives

$$\frac{\mathrm{d}}{\mathrm{d}T}\left(\frac{\Delta H}{T}\right)=\frac{\Delta C_p}{T}$$

Therefore, $\mathrm{d}\left(\frac{\Delta H}{T}\right)=\frac{\Delta C_p\,\mathrm{d}T}{T}=\underline{\Delta C_p\,\mathrm{d}\ln T}$

6.15 Amount of gas $=\frac{PV}{RT}$, amount of vapor $=\frac{m}{M}$

$$\text{Mole fraction of vapor} = \frac{m/M}{m/M + PV/RT}$$

$$\text{Partial pressure of vapor} = p = \frac{m/M}{m/M + PV/RT} \times P$$

$$= \frac{P(mRT/PVM)}{(mRT/PVM)+1}$$

$$= \frac{mPA}{mA+1}, \quad A = \frac{RT}{PVM}$$

For geraniol, $M = 154.2\ \text{g mol}^{-1}$, $T = 383\ \text{K}$, $V = 5.00\ \text{L}$, $P = 1.00\ \text{atm}$, and $m = 0.32\ \text{g}$, so

$$A = \frac{8.206 \times 10^{-2}\ \text{L atm K}^{-1}\ \text{mol}^{-1} \times 383\ \text{K}}{1.00\ \text{atm} \times 5.00\ \text{L} \times 154.2 \times 10^{-3}\ \text{kg mol}^{-1}} = 40.7\bar{6}\ \text{kg}^{-1}$$

Therefore,

$$p = \frac{0.32\ \text{g} \times 760\ \text{Torr} \times 40.7\bar{6}\ \text{kg}^{-1}}{0.32\ \text{g} \times 40.7\bar{6}\ \text{kg}^{-1} + 1} = \underline{9.8\ \text{Torr}}$$

6.16 $P = P_0\,e^{-Mgh/RT}$ [Problem 1.17]

$$p = p^*\,e^{-C} \qquad C = \frac{\Delta H_{\text{vap}}}{R}\left(\frac{1}{T} - \frac{1}{T^*}\right) \qquad [8b]$$

let $T^* = T_b$, the normal boiling point; then $p^* = 1\ \text{atm}$. Let $T = T_h$, the boiling point at the altitude h. Take $P_0 = 1\ \text{atm}$. The vapor pressure (p) is equal to the ambient pressure when $p(T) = P(h)$, and when this is so, $T = T_h$. Therefore, since $P_0 = p^*$, $p(T) = P(h)$ implies that

$$e^{-Mgh/RT} = \exp\left\{-\frac{\Delta H_{\text{vap}}}{R}\left(\frac{1}{T_h} - \frac{1}{T_b}\right)\right\}$$

It follows that

$$\frac{1}{T_h} = \frac{1}{T_b} + \frac{Mgh}{T\,\Delta H_{\text{vap}}}$$

where T is the ambient temperature and M the molar mass of the air.

For water at 3000 m, using $M = 29\ \text{g mol}^{-1}$

$$\frac{1}{T_h}=\frac{1}{373\ \text{K}}+\frac{29\times10^{-3}\ \text{kg mol}^{-1}\times9.81\ \text{m s}^{-2}\times3.000\times10^{3}\ \text{m}}{293\ \text{K}\times40.7\times10^{3}\ \text{J mol}^{-1}}$$

$$=\frac{1}{373\ \text{K}}+\frac{1}{1.39\bar{7}\times10^{4}\ \text{K}}$$

Hence, $T_h=\underline{363\ \text{K}}$ (90 °C).

6.17 (a) From trigonometry and Fig. 6.6,

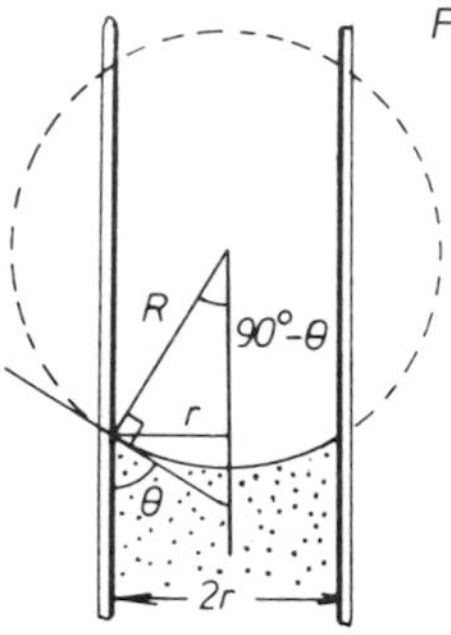

Fig 6.6

$$\frac{r}{R}=\sin(90°-\theta)=\cos\theta,\ \text{implying that}\ R=\frac{r}{\cos\theta}$$

Use this R in the Laplace equation for the pressure ($2\gamma/R$), and by repetition of the argument in the text [Section 6.8], arrive at

$$h=\frac{2\gamma}{\rho gR}=\frac{2\gamma\cos\theta}{\rho gr}$$

(b) The force *upward* on the liquid is $2\pi r\gamma\cos\theta$ (since γ is the force per unit length, $2\pi r$ is the circumference of the liquid-tube contact, and $\cos\theta$ the component of force vertically). The force downward is $\pi r^2h\times\rho g$ (since πr^2h is the volume of the liquid in the capillary and ρ is its density). Hence, when the two forces are in equilibrium,

$$2\pi r\gamma\cos\theta=\pi r^2h\rho g$$

which solves to

$$h=\frac{2\gamma\cos\theta}{\rho gr}$$

as before.

6.18 $d\mu = -S\,dT + \gamma\,d\sigma + V\,dp$

$= V\,dp + \gamma\,d\sigma$ if T is constant.

Therefore, since $d\mu$ is an exact differential,

$$\underline{\left(\frac{\partial V}{\partial \sigma}\right)_{p,T} = \left(\frac{\partial \gamma}{\partial p}\right)_{\sigma,T}}$$

For a spherical droplet, $V = \frac{4}{3}\pi r^3$ and $\sigma = 4\pi r^2$. Hence,

$$\frac{dV}{d\sigma} = \frac{dV}{dr} \times \frac{dr}{d\sigma} = \left(\frac{dV}{dr}\right) \Big/ \left(\frac{d\sigma}{dr}\right) = \frac{4\pi r^2}{8\pi} = \frac{1}{2}r$$

Therefore,

$$\left(\frac{\partial \gamma}{\partial p}\right)_{\sigma,T} = \frac{1}{2}r, \text{ implying that } d\gamma = \frac{1}{2}r\,dp$$

which integrates to

$$\gamma = \frac{1}{2}r(p_{in} - p_{out}), \text{ implying that } \underline{p_{in} - p_{out} = \frac{2\gamma}{r}}$$

6.19 $\frac{d}{dt}(mv) = F$ [Newton's second law]. Both m and F depend on the time, and we can write

$m = \text{volume} \times \text{density} = (\pi r^2 \delta) \times \rho$

$F = 2 \times \text{circumference} \times \text{surface tension} = 4\pi r\gamma$

Hence,

$$\frac{d}{dt}(\pi r^2 \delta \rho v) = 4\pi r\gamma, \text{ or } \frac{d}{dt}(r^2 v) = \frac{4r\gamma}{\rho\delta}$$

If we neglect acceleration,

$$\frac{d}{dt}(r^2 v) \approx 2rv\frac{dr}{dt} = 2rv^2 = \frac{4r\gamma}{\rho\delta}$$

Therefore, $\underline{v = \left(\frac{2\gamma}{\delta\rho}\right)^{1/2}}$

When $\gamma \approx 2.6 \times 10^{-2}\ \text{N m}^{-1}$, estimating $\delta \approx 0.01$ mm, and $\rho \approx 1\ \text{g cm}^{-3}$

$$v \approx \left(\frac{2 \times 2.6 \times 10^{-2}\ \text{N m}^{-1}}{0.01 \times 10^{-3}\ \text{m} \times 1 \times 10^{3}\ \text{kg m}^{-3}}\right)^{1/2} \approx \underline{2\ \text{m s}^{-1}}$$

7. Changes of state: physical transformations of simple mixtures

Exercises

7.1 Let A denotes acetone and C chloroform. Then

$$n_A M_A + n_C M_C = m \qquad \text{(a)}$$

where m is the mass of the sample. We also know that

$$x_A = \frac{n_A}{n_A + n_C}, \text{ imply that } (x_A - 1)n_A + x_A n_C = 0$$

and hence that

$$-x_C n_A + x_A n_C = 0 \qquad \text{(b)}$$

On solving (a) and (b), we find

$$n_A = \frac{x_A}{x_C} \times n_C, \; n_C = \frac{m x_C}{x_A M_A + x_C M_C}$$

Since $x_C = 0.4693$, $x_A = 1 - x_C = 0.5307$,

$$n_C = \frac{0.4693 \times 1000 \text{ g}}{(0.5307 \times 58.08 + 0.4693 \times 119.37) \text{ g mol}^{-1}} = 5.404 \text{ mol}$$

$$n_A = \frac{0.5307}{0.4693} \times 5.404 = 6.111 \text{ mol}$$

The total volume, $V = n_A V_A + n_B V_B$, is therefore

$$V = 6.111 \text{ mol} \times 74.166 \text{ cm}^3 \text{ mol}^{-1} + 5.404 \times 80.235 \text{ cm}^3 \text{ mol}^{-1}$$

$$= \underline{886.8 \text{ cm}^3}$$

7.2 Check whether p_B/x_B is equal to a constant (K_B):

x	0.005	0.012	0.019
p/x	6×10^3	6.4×10^3	6.4×10^3 kPa

Hence, $K_B \approx \underline{6.4 \times 10^3 \text{ kPa}}$

7.3 $m(\mathrm{GeCl_4}) = 1000\ \mathrm{g}$, corresponding to

$$n(\mathrm{GeCl_4}) = \frac{1000\ \mathrm{g}}{214.39\ \mathrm{g\ mol^{-1}}} = 4.664\ \mathrm{mol},\ n(\mathrm{HCl}) = 0.10\ \mathrm{mol}$$

Therefore, $x = \dfrac{0.10\ \mathrm{mol}}{0.10\ \mathrm{mol} + 4.664\ \mathrm{mol}} = 0.021\bar{0}$

and from $K = 6.4\ \mathrm{kPa}$ (Exercise 7.2),

$$p = 0.021\bar{0} \times 6.4\ \mathrm{kPa} = \underline{13\bar{4}\ \mathrm{Pa}}$$

7.4 $p = p_A + p_B = x_A p_A^* + x_B p_B^* = x_A p_A^* + (1 - x_A) p_B^*$ [20b], hence

$$x_A = \frac{p - p_B^*}{p_A^* - p_B^*}$$

For boiling under 0.50 atm (380 Torr) pressure, the combined vapor pressure must be 380 Torr, hence

$$x_A = \frac{380 - 150}{400 - 150} = \underline{0.920},\ x_B = \underline{0.080}$$

The composition of the vapor is given by [21b].

$$y_A = \frac{x_A p_A^*}{p_B^* + (p_A^* - p_B^*)x_A} = \frac{0.920 \times 400}{150 + (400 - 150) \times 0.920} = \underline{0.968}$$

and $y_B = 1 - 0.968 = \underline{0.032}$

7.5 $K_b = \dfrac{RT^{*2}M}{\Delta H_{\mathrm{vap}}}$ [15a]

$$= \frac{8.314\ \mathrm{J\ K^{-1}\ mol^{-1}} \times (349.9\ \mathrm{K})^2 \times 153.81\ \mathrm{g\ mol^{-1}}}{30.0 \times 10^3\ \mathrm{J\ mol^{-1}}}$$

$$= \underline{5.22\ \mathrm{K/(mol\ kg^{-1})}}$$

$$K_f = \frac{RT^{*2}M}{\Delta H_{\mathrm{fus}}}$$

$$= \frac{8.314\ \mathrm{J\ K^{-1}\ mol^{-1}} \times (250.3\ \mathrm{K})^2 \times 153.81 \times 10^{-3}\ \mathrm{kg\ mol^{-1}}}{2.47 \times 10^3\ \mathrm{J\ mol^{-1}}}$$

$$= \underline{32\ \mathrm{K/(mol\ kg^{-1})}}$$

7.6 Let B denote the benzene and A the solute, then

$$p_B = x_B p_B^* \text{ and } x_B = \frac{n_B}{n_A + n_B}$$

Hence $p_B = \dfrac{n_B p_B^*}{n_A + n_B}$

which solves to

$$n_A = \frac{n_B(p_B^* - p_B)}{p_B}$$

Then, since $n_A = m_A/M_A$, where m_A is the mass of A present,

$$M_A = \frac{m_A p_B}{m_B(p_B^* - p_B)} = \frac{m_A M_B p_B}{m_B(p_B^* - p_B)}$$

From the data,

$$M_A = \frac{19.0\text{ g} \times 78.11\text{ g mol}^{-1} \times 386\text{ Torr}}{500\text{ g} \times (400 - 386)\text{ Torr}}$$

$$= \underline{82\text{ g mol}^{-1}}$$

7.7 $\ln x_B = \dfrac{-\Delta H_{fus}}{R}\left(\dfrac{1}{T} - \dfrac{1}{T^*}\right)$ [17]

$$\frac{1}{T} = \frac{1}{T^*} - \frac{R}{\Delta H_{fus}} \ln x_B$$

Therefore, with $x_B = 0.905$, $T^* = 278.65$ K, and $\Delta H_{fus} = +10.59$ kJ mol^{-1},

$$\frac{1}{T} = \frac{1}{278.65\text{ K}} - \frac{8.314\text{ J K}^{-1}\text{ mol}^{-1}}{10.59 \times 10^3\text{ J mol}^{-1}} \times \ln 0.905$$

$$= \underline{272.70\text{ K}}\ (-0.45\ ^\circ\text{C})$$

7.8 $\Delta T = K_f m_B$ [16b]

$$m_B\text{ [molality of B]} = \frac{100\text{ g}}{M \times 750\text{ g}} = \frac{0.133\bar{3}}{M}$$

$$\Delta T = \frac{0.133\bar{3}\ K_f}{M}, \text{ implying that } M = \frac{0.133\bar{3}\ K_f}{\Delta T}$$

Then, since $K_f = 30\ \text{K}/(\text{mol kg}^{-1}) = 30\ \text{K kg mol}^{-1}$ [Table 8.2],

$$M = \frac{0.1333 \times 30\ \text{K kg mol}^{-1}}{10.5\ \text{K}} = 0.381\ \text{kg mol}^{-1}$$

$= \underline{381\ \text{g mol}^{-1}}$

7.9 $\Pi V = n_B RT$ [19a] with $n_B/V \approx m_B \rho^{\ominus}$ for dilute solutions, with $\rho^{\ominus} = 10^3\ \text{kg m}^{-3}$

$$\Delta T = K_f m_B\ [16b] \approx K_f \times \frac{\Pi}{RT\rho^{\ominus}}$$

Therefore, with $K_f = 1.86\ \text{K}/(\text{mol kg}^{-1}) = 1.86\ \text{K kg mol}^{-1}$ [Table 8.2]

$$\Delta T \approx \frac{1.86\ \text{K kg mol}^{-1} \times 120 \times 10^3\ \text{Pa}}{8.314\ \text{J K}^{-1}\ \text{mol}^{-1} \times 300\ \text{K} \times 10^3\ \text{kg m}^{-3}} = 0.089\ \text{K}$$

Therefore, the solution will freeze at about $\underline{-0.09\ °\text{C}}$

7.10 $p_A = y_A p = 0.350p = x_A p_A^* = x_A \times 575\ \text{Torr}$

$p_B = y_B p = (1 - y_A)p - 0.650p = x_B p_B^* = (1 - x_A) \times 390\ \text{Torr}$

Therefore,

$$\frac{y_A p}{y_B p} = \frac{x_A p_A^*}{x_B p_B^*}$$

Hence

$$\frac{0.350}{0.650} = \frac{575 x_A}{390(1 - x_A)}$$

which solves to

$$x_A = \underline{0.268},\ x_B = 1 - x_A = \underline{0.732}$$

and

$$0.350p = x_A p_A^*$$

implies $p = \dfrac{x_A p_A^*}{0.350} = \dfrac{0.268 \times 575\ \text{Torr}}{0.350} = \underline{440\ \text{Torr}}$

7.11 $\Delta G_{\text{mix}} = nRT\{x_A \ln x_A + x_B \ln x_B\}$ [7]

$x_A = x_B = 0.5,\ n = pV/RT$

Therefore,

$$\begin{aligned}\Delta G_{\text{mix}} &= pV \times \{\tfrac{1}{2}\ln\tfrac{1}{2} + \tfrac{1}{2}\ln\tfrac{1}{2}\} = -pV\ln 2 \\ &= -1.0 \times 1.013 \times 10^5\ \text{Pa} \times 5.0 \times 10^{-3}\ \text{m}^3 \times \ln 2 \\ &= -3.5 \times 10^2\ \text{J} = \underline{-0.35\ \text{kJ}}\end{aligned}$$

$$\Delta S_{\text{mix}} = -nR\{x_A \ln x_A + x_B \ln x_B\} = \frac{-\Delta G_{\text{mix}}}{T}\ [8]$$

$$= \frac{-0.35\ \text{kJ}}{298\ \text{K}} = \underline{+1.2\ \text{J K}^{-1}}$$

7.12 $\Delta S_{\text{mix}} = -nR\sum_J x_J \ln x_J$ [8]

Therefore, for molar amounts,

$$\begin{aligned}\Delta S_{\text{mix}} &= -R\sum_J x_J \ln x_J \\ &= -R(0.782\ln 0.782 + 0.209\ln 0.209 \\ &\quad + 0.009\ln 0.009 + 0.0003\ln 0.0003) \\ &= 0.564R = \underline{+4.7\ \text{J K}^{-1}\ \text{mol}^{-1}}\end{aligned}$$

7.13 $\Delta G_{\text{mix}} = nRT\sum_J x_J \ln x_J$ [7]

$$\Delta S_{\text{mix}} = -nR\sum_J x_J \ln x_J\ [8] = \frac{-\Delta G_{\text{mix}}}{T}$$

$$\left.\begin{aligned} n(\text{Hex}) &= \frac{500\ \text{g}}{86.17\ \text{g mol}^{-1}} = 5.80\bar{2}\ \text{mol} \\ n(\text{Hep}) &= \frac{500\ \text{g}}{100.20\ \text{g mol}^{-1}} = 4.99\bar{0}\ \text{mol}\end{aligned}\right\}\ n = \overline{10}.792\ \text{mol}$$

Hence $x(\text{Hex}) = \dfrac{5.80\bar{2}\ \text{mol}}{10.79\bar{2}\ \text{mol}} = 0.538$

$$x(\text{Hep})=\frac{4.99\bar{0}\text{ mol}}{10.79\bar{2}\text{ mol}}=0.462$$

Therefore,

$$\Delta G_{\text{mix}}=10.79\bar{2}\text{ mol}\times 8.314\text{ J K}^{-1}\text{ mol}^{-1}\times 298.15\text{ K}$$
$$\times(0.538\ln 0.538+0.462\ln 0.462)$$
$$=\underline{-18.5\text{ kJ}}$$

$$\Delta S_{\text{mix}}=\frac{+18.4\bar{6}\text{ kJ}}{298.15\text{ K}}=\underline{+61.9\text{ J K}^{-1}}$$

7.14 The greatest enthalpy of mixing occurs for $x_A=x_B=\frac{1}{2}$ [Example 7.4]. Therefore, mix equal mole fractions, or masses in the ratio

$$\frac{m(\text{Hex})}{m(\text{Hep})}=\frac{M(\text{Hex})}{M(\text{Hep})}=\frac{86.17\text{ g mol}^{-1}}{100.20\text{ g mol}^{-1}}=\underline{0.8600}$$

7.15 $p=xK$ [12], $K=1.25\times 10^6$ Torr

$$x=\frac{n(CO_2)}{n(CO_2)+n(H_2O)}\approx\frac{n(CO_2)}{n(H_2O)}$$

Therefore,

$$n(CO_2)\approx xn(H_2O)\text{ with }n(H_2O)=\frac{10^3\text{ g}}{18.02\text{ g mol}^{-1}}\text{ and }x=\frac{p}{K}$$

Hence

$$n(CO_2)\approx\frac{10^3\text{ g}}{18.02\text{ g mol}^{-1}}\times\frac{p}{1.26\times 10^6\text{ Torr}}$$
$$\approx 4.4\times 10^{-5}\text{ mol}\times(p/\text{Torr})$$

(a) $p=0.10$ atm $=76$ Torr,

hence $n(CO_2)=4.4\times 10^{-5}\text{ mol}\times 76=3.4\times 10^{-3}$ mol. The solution is therefore $\underline{3.4\text{ mmol kg}^{-1}}$ in CO_2.

(b) $p=1.0$ atm; since $n\propto p$, the solution is $\underline{34\text{ mmol kg}^{-1}}$ in CO_2.

7.16 $K(N_2)=6.51\times 10^7$ Torr and $K(O_2)=3.30\times 10^7$ Torr. Therefore, as in Exercise 7.15, the amount of dissolved gas in 1 kg of water is

$$n(N_2)=\frac{10^3\ \text{g}}{18.02\ \text{g mol}^{-1}}\times\frac{p(N_2)}{6.51\times10^7\ \text{Torr}}=8.52\times10^{-7}\ \text{mol}\times(p/\text{Torr})$$

For $p(N_2)=xp$ and $p=760$ Torr

$$n(N_2)=8.52\times10^{-7}\ \text{mol}\times x\times760=6.48x\times10^{-4}\ \text{mol}$$

and with $x=0.782$,

$$n(N_2)=0.782\times6.48\times10^{-4}\ \text{mol}=5.1\times10^{-4}\ \text{mol}$$
$$=0.51\ \text{mmol}$$

The molality of the solution is therefore approximately $\underline{5.1\times10^{-4}\ \text{mol kg}^{-1}}$

Similarly, for oxygen,

$$n(O_2)=\frac{10^3\ \text{g}}{18.02\ \text{g mol}^{-1}}\times\frac{p(O_2)}{3.30\times10^7\ \text{Torr}}=1.68\times10^{-6}\ \text{mol}\times(p/\text{Torr})$$

For $p(O_2)=xp$ and $p=760$ Torr

$$n(O_2)=1.68\times10^{-6}\ \text{mol}\times x\times760=1.28\ \text{mmol}\times x$$

and when $x=0.209$, $n(O_2)\approx0.27$ mmol. Hence the solution will be $\underline{0.27\ \text{mmol kg}^{-1}}$ in O_2.

7.17 Use the result established in Example 7.14 that the amount of CO_2 in 1 kg of water is given by

$$n(CO_2)=4.4\times10^{-5}\ \text{mol}\times(p/\text{Torr})$$

and substitute $p\approx5.0\times760\ \text{Torr}=3.8\times10^3$ Torr, to give

$$n(CO_2)=4.4\times10^{-5}\ \text{mol}\times3.8\times10^3=0.17\ \text{mol}$$

Hence, the molality of the solution is about $\underline{0.17\ \text{mol kg}^{-1}}$ and the molar concentration about 0.17 M.

7.18 $$\Delta T=K_f m_B=1.86\ \text{K kg mol}^{-1}\times\frac{7.5\ \text{g}}{342.3\ \text{g mol}^{-1}}\Big/0.25\ \text{kg}$$
$$=0.16\ \text{K}$$

Hence, the freezing point will be approximately $\underline{-0.16\ °\text{C}}$

7.19 $$\ln x_B=\frac{\Delta H_{\text{fus}}}{R}\left(\frac{1}{T^*}-\frac{1}{T}\right)$$ [17; B, the solute, is anthracene]

$$= \frac{28.8 \times 10^{3}\ \mathrm{J\ mol^{-1}}}{8.314\ \mathrm{J\ K^{-1}\ mol^{-1}}} \times \left(\frac{1}{490.\overline{15}\ \mathrm{K}} - \frac{1}{298.\overline{15}\ \mathrm{K}}\right)$$

$$= -4.55$$

Therefore, $x_B = e^{-4.55} = 0.0106$

Since $x_B \ll 1$, $x(\text{anthracene}) \approx \dfrac{n(\text{anthracene})}{n(\text{benzene})}$

Therefore, in 1 kg of benzene,

$$n(\text{anthr.}) \approx x(\text{anthr.}) \times \frac{1000\ \mathrm{g}}{78.11\ \mathrm{g\ mol^{-1}}}$$

$$\approx 0.0106 \times 12.80\ \mathrm{mol} = 0.136\ \mathrm{mol}$$

The molality of the solution is therefore $0.136\ \mathrm{mol\ kg^{-1}}$. Since $M = 178\ \mathrm{g\ mol^{-1}}$, 0.136 mol corresponds to $\underline{24\ \text{g anthracene}}$ in 1 kg of benzene.

7.20 $\ln x_B = \dfrac{\Delta H_{\text{fus}}}{R}\left(\dfrac{1}{T^*} - \dfrac{1}{T}\right)$ [17; B, the solute, is lead]

$$= \frac{5.2 \times 10^{3}\ \mathrm{J\ mol^{-1}}}{8.314\ \mathrm{J\ K^{-1}\ mol^{-1}}} \times \left(\frac{1}{600\ \mathrm{K}} - \frac{1}{553\ \mathrm{K}}\right)$$

$= -0.088\overline{6}$, implying that $x_B = \underline{0.92}$

$x_B = \dfrac{n(\text{Pb})}{n(\text{Pb}) + n(\text{Bi})}$, implying that $n(\text{Pb}) = \dfrac{x_B n(\text{Bi})}{1 - x_B}$

For 1 kg of bismuth, $n(\text{Bi}) = \dfrac{1000\ \mathrm{g}}{208.98\ \mathrm{g\ mol^{-1}}} = 4.785\ \mathrm{mol}$

Hence, the amount of lead that dissolves in 1 kg of bismuth is

$$n(\text{Pb}) = \frac{0.92 \times 4.785\ \mathrm{mol}}{1 - 0.92} = 55\ \mathrm{mol},\ \text{or}\ \underline{11\ \mathrm{kg}}$$

7.21 $\Pi V = n_B RT$, so $\Pi = \dfrac{mRT}{MV} = \dfrac{cRT}{M}$, $c = m/V$

$\Pi = \rho g h$ [hydrostatic pressure], so

$$h = \left(\frac{RT}{\rho g M}\right) c$$

Hence, plot h against c and identify the slope as $RT/\rho gM$. Fig. 7.1 shows the plot of the data. The slope of the line is 0.29, so

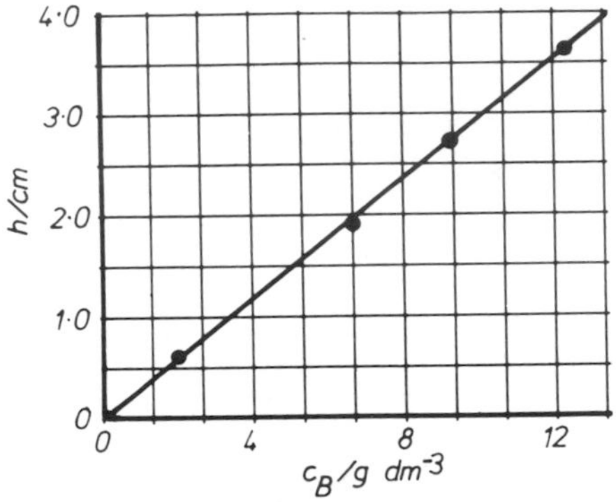

Fig 7.1

$$\frac{RT}{\rho gM}=\frac{0.29\ \text{cm}}{\text{g L}^{-1}}=0.29\ \text{cm L g}^{-1}=0.29\times10^{-2}\ \text{m}^4\ \text{kg}^{-1}$$

$$\text{Therefore, } M=\frac{RT}{\rho g\times0.29\times10^{-2}\ \text{m}^4\ \text{kg}^{-1}}$$

$$=\frac{8.314\ \text{J K}^{-1}\ \text{mol}^{-1}\times298.15\ \text{K}}{1.004\times10^3\ \text{kg m}^{-3}\times9.81\ \text{m s}^{-2}\times0.29\times10^{-2}\ \text{m}^4\ \text{kg}^{-1}}$$

$$=\underline{87\ \text{kg mol}^{-1}}$$

7.22 Proceed as in Exercise 7.21. The data are plotted in Fig. 7.2, and the slope of the line is 1.78. Therefore

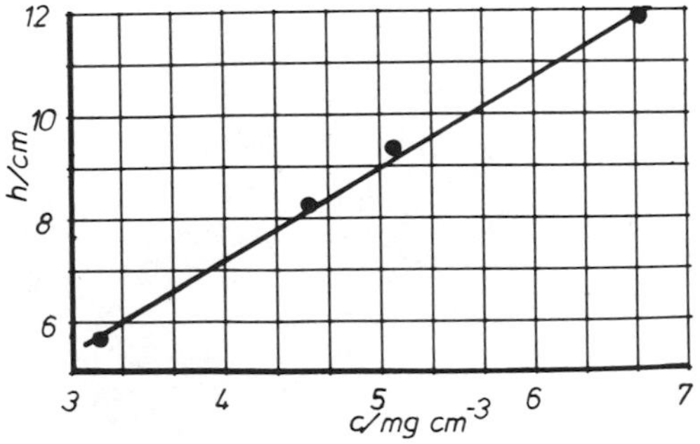

Fig 7.2

$$M = \frac{8.314\ \mathrm{J\ K^{-1}\ mol^{-1}} \times 293.15\ \mathrm{K}}{1.000 \times 10^3\ \mathrm{kg\ m^{-3}} \times 9.81\ \mathrm{m\ s^{-2}} \times 1.78 \times 10^{-2}\ \mathrm{m^4\ kg^{-1}}}$$

$$= \underline{14\ \mathrm{kg\ mol^{-1}}}$$

7.23 The data are plotted in Fig. 7.3. From the graph, the vapor in equilibrium with a liquid of composition (a) $x_T = 0.25$ has $\underline{y_T = 0.36}$, (b) $x_O = 0.25$ has $\underline{y_T = 0.82}$

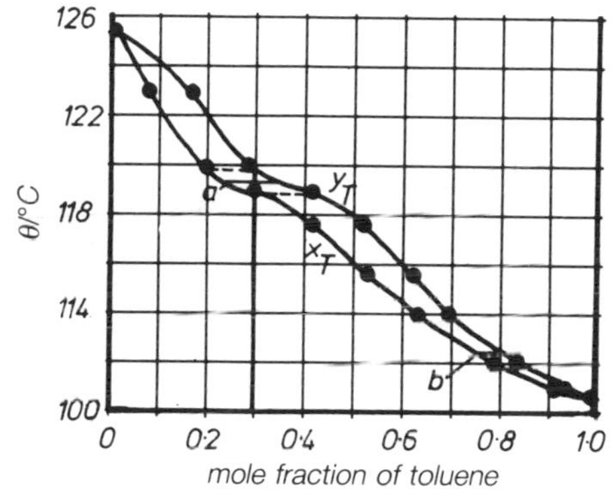

Fig 7.3

Problems

7.1 $p_A = y_A p$ and $p_B = y_B p$ [Dalton's law]. Hence, draw up the following table:

p_A/kPa	0	1.399	3.566	5.044	6.996	7.940	9.211	10.105	11.287	12.295
x_A	0	0.0898	0.2476	0.3577	0.5194	0.6036	0.7188	0.8019	0.9105	1
y_A	0	0.0410	0.1154	0.1762	0.2772	0.3393	0.4450	0.5435	0.7284	1

p_B/kPa	0	4.209	8.487	11.487	15.462	18.243	23.582	27.334	32.722	36.066
x_B	0	0.0895	0.1981	0.2812	0.3964	0.4806	0.6423	0.7524	0.9102	1
y_B	0	0.2716	0.4565	0.5550	0.6607	0.7228	0.8238	0.8846	0.9590	1

The data are plotted in Fig. 7.4. The Henry's law constants are given by

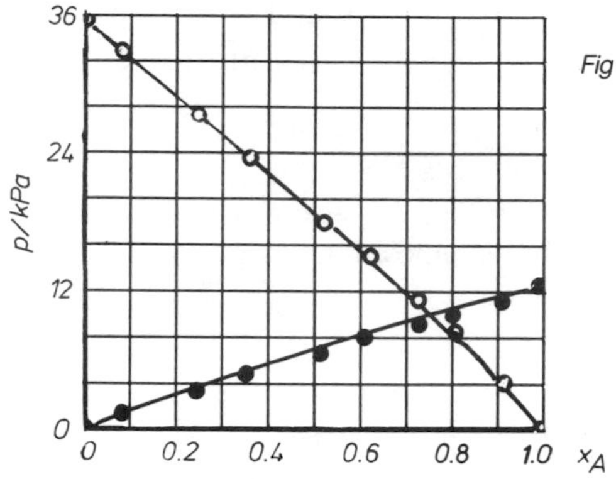

Fig 7.4

$$K_A = \frac{p_A}{x_A} = \underline{15.58\ \text{kPa}}\ \text{from the point at}\ x_A = 0.0898$$

$$K_B = \frac{p_B}{x_B} = \underline{47.03\ \text{kPa}}\ \text{from the point at}\ x_B = 0.0895$$

7.2 $V_A = \left(\frac{\partial V}{\partial n_A}\right)_{n_B} = \left(\frac{\partial V}{\partial m}\right)_{n(H_2O)}\ \text{mol}^{-1}$ with $m \equiv m/(\text{mol kg}^{-1})$

$$= (16.62 + \tfrac{3}{2} \times 1.77 \times m^{1/2} + 2 \times 0.12m)\ \text{cm}^3\ \text{mol}^{-1}$$

$$= \underline{17.5\ \text{cm}^3\ \text{mol}^{-1}}\ \text{when}\ m = 0.100$$

For a solution consisting of 0.100 mol NaCl and 1.00 kg of water, corresponding to 55.49 mol H_2O, the total volume is given both by

$$V = 1003 + 16.62 \times 0.100 \times 1.77 \times (0.100)^{3/2} + 0.12 \times (0.100)^2\ \text{cm}^3$$

$$= 1004.7\ \text{cm}^3$$

and by

$$V = n(\text{NaCl})V_{\text{NaCl}} + n(H_2O)V_{H_2O}$$

$$= 0.100\ \text{mol} \times 17.5\ \text{cm}^3\ \text{mol}^{-1} + 55.49\ \text{mol} \times V_{H_2O}$$

Therefore,

$$V_{H_2O} = \frac{1004.7\ \text{cm}^3 - 1.75\ \text{cm}^3}{55.49\ \text{mol}} = \underline{18.1\ \text{cm}^3\ \text{mol}^{-1}}$$

7.3 $V_{\text{salt}} = \left(\frac{\partial V}{\partial m}\right)_{H_2O}\ \text{mol}^{-1}$ [Problem 7.2]

$$= 69.38(m - 0.07)\ \mathrm{cm^3\,mol^{-1}} \text{ with } m \equiv m/(\mathrm{mol\,kg^{-1}})$$

Therefore, at $m = 0.050\ \mathrm{mol\,kg^{-1}}$, $V_{\mathrm{salt}} = \underline{-1.4\ \mathrm{cm^3\,mol^{-1}}}$

The total volume at this molality is

$$V = 1000.21 + 34.69 \times (0.02)^2\ \mathrm{cm^3} = 1001.20\ \mathrm{cm^3}$$

Hence, as in Problem 7.2,

$$V(\mathrm{H_2O}) = \frac{1001.20\ \mathrm{cm^3} - 0.050\ \mathrm{mol} \times (-1.4\ \mathrm{cm^3\,mol^{-1}})}{55.49\ \mathrm{mol}}$$

$$= \underline{18.04\ \mathrm{cm^3\,mol^{-1}}}$$

7.4 Rework the derivation in the Further Information section of Chapter 7 with

$$w = \frac{100 m_{\mathrm{B}}}{m_{\mathrm{A}} + m_{\mathrm{B}}} \qquad \rho = \frac{m_{\mathrm{A}} + m_{\mathrm{B}}}{V} \qquad n_{\mathrm{A}} = \frac{m_{\mathrm{A}}}{M_{\mathrm{A}}}$$

The procedure runs as follows:

$$V_{\mathrm{A}} = \left(\frac{\partial V}{\partial n_{\mathrm{A}}}\right)_{n_{\mathrm{B}}} = \left(\frac{\partial V}{\partial m_{\mathrm{A}}}\right)_{\mathrm{B}} M_{\mathrm{A}}$$

$$= \frac{\partial}{\partial m_{\mathrm{A}}}\left(\frac{m_{\mathrm{A}} + m_{\mathrm{B}}}{\rho}\right) \times M_{\mathrm{A}}$$

$$= \frac{M_{\mathrm{A}}}{\rho} + (m_{\mathrm{A}} + m_{\mathrm{B}}) M_{\mathrm{A}} \frac{\partial}{\partial m_{\mathrm{A}}} \frac{1}{\rho}$$

$$\frac{\partial}{\partial m_{\mathrm{A}}} \frac{1}{\rho} = \left(\frac{\partial w}{\partial m_{\mathrm{A}}}\right) \frac{\partial}{\partial w} \frac{1}{\rho} = \frac{-w}{m_{\mathrm{A}} + m_{\mathrm{B}}} \frac{\partial}{\partial w} \frac{1}{\rho}$$

Therefore,

$$V_{\mathrm{A}} = \frac{M_{\mathrm{A}}}{\rho} - w M_{\mathrm{A}} \frac{\partial}{\partial w} \frac{1}{\rho}$$

and hence

$$\frac{1}{\rho} = \frac{V_{\mathrm{A}}}{M_{\mathrm{A}}} + w \frac{\mathrm{d}}{\mathrm{d}w}\left(\frac{1}{\rho}\right)$$

Therefore, plot $1/\rho$ against w and extrapolate the tangent to $w = 0$ to obtain $V_{\mathrm{A}}/M_{\mathrm{A}}$. For the actual procedure, draw up the following table:

w	2.162	10.98	20.80	30.00	39.2	51.68
$\rho/(\mathrm{g\ cm^{-3}})$	1.01	1.06	1.12	1.18	1.24	1.32
$1/(\rho/\mathrm{g\ cm^{-3}})$	0.990	0.943	0.893	0.847	0.806	0.758

w	62.64	71.57	82.33	93.40	99.60
$\rho/(\mathrm{g\ cm^{-3}})$	1.38	1.42	1.46	1.49	1.51
$1/(\rho/\mathrm{g\ cm^{-3}})$	0.725	0.704	0.685	0.671	0.662

The graph of $1/\rho$ against w is shown in Fig. 7.5. Tangents have been drawn at

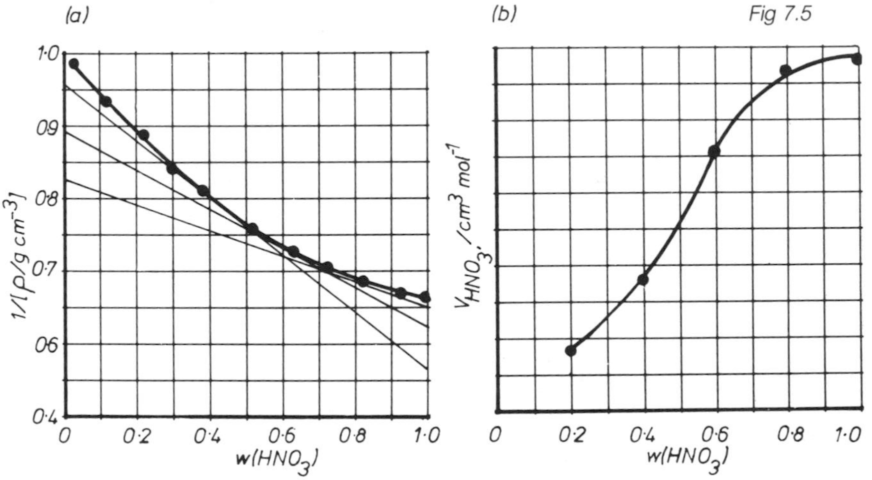

four values of w, and V_A/M_A (with A denoting H_2O) read off from the intercepts at $w=0$ and V_B/M_B (with B denoting HNO_3) from the intercepts at $w=100$. We can then draw up the following table using $M_A = 18.02\ \mathrm{g\ mol^{-1}}$ and $M_B = 63.02\ \mathrm{g\ mol^{-1}}$:

w	20	40	60	80
$(V_A/M_A)\ \mathrm{g\ cm^3}$	0.975	0.965	0.900	0.825
$(V_B/M_B)\ \mathrm{g\ cm^3}$	0.535	0.565	0.620	0.655
$V_A/(\mathrm{cm^3\ mol^{-1}})$	17.6	17.4	16.2	14.9
$V_B/(\mathrm{cm^3\ mol^{-1}})$	33.7	35.6	39.1	41.3

The partial molar volume of HNO_3 (the value of V_B) is plotted in Fig. 7.5b.

7.5 Use the same procedure as in Problem 7.4, and begin by drawing up the following table:

w	5	10	15	20
$\rho/(\text{g cm}^{-3})$	1.051	1.107	1.167	1.230
$1/(\rho/\text{g cm}^{-3})$	0.951	0.903	0.857	0.813

The values of $1/\rho$ are plotted against w in Fig. 7.6. The intercept at $w = 100$ is

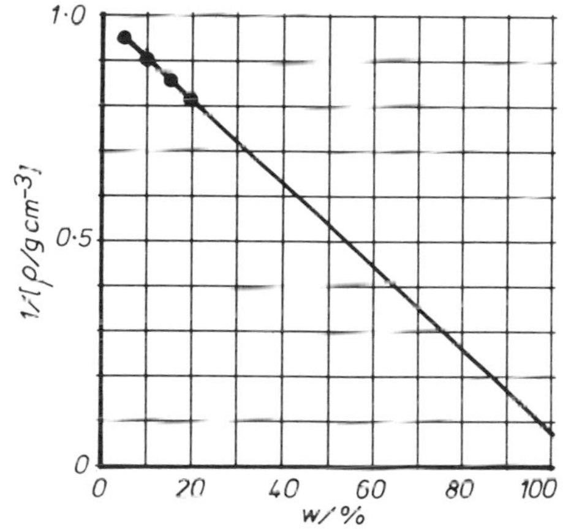

Fig 7.6

the value of $V(\text{CuSO}_4)/M(\text{CuSO}_4)$; within the precision of the plot, all four intercepts are coincident at 0.075, and so

$$V(\text{CuSO}_4) = 0.075\ \text{g}^{-1}\,\text{cm}^3 \times 159.6\ \text{g mol}^{-1} = \underline{12.0\ \text{cm}^3\,\text{mol}^{-1}}$$

7.6 Let E denote ethanol and W denote water; then

$$V = n_E V_E + n_W V_W$$

For a 50 per cent mixture by mass, $m_E = m_W$, implying that

$$n_E M_E = n_W M_W, \text{ or } n_W = \frac{n_E M_E}{M_W}$$

Hence,

$$V = n_E V_E + \frac{n_E M_E V_W}{M_W}$$

which solves to

$$n_E = \frac{V}{V_E + \dfrac{M_E V_W}{M_W}} \qquad n_W = \frac{M_E V}{V_E M_W + M_E V_W}$$

Furthermore,

$$x_E = \frac{n_E}{n_E + n_W} = \frac{1}{1 + \dfrac{M_E}{M_W}}$$

Since $M_E = 46.07\ \text{g mol}^{-1}$ and $M_W = 18.02\ \text{g mol}^{-1}$, $M_E/M_W = 2.557$. Therefore
$x_E = 0.2811$, $x_W = 1 - x_E = 0.7189$.

At this composition
$V_E = 56.0\ \text{cm}^3\ \text{mol}^{-1}$ $\quad V_W = 17.5\ \text{cm}^3\ \text{mol}^{-1}$ [Fig. 7.1 of the text]

Therefore,

$$n_E = \frac{100\ \text{cm}^3}{56.0\ \text{cm}^3\ \text{mol}^{-1} + 2.557 \times 17.5\ \text{cm}^3\ \text{mol}^{-1}} = 0.993\ \text{mol}$$

$$n_W = 2.557 \times 0.993\ \text{mol} = 2.54\ \text{mol}$$

These two amounts correspond to 45.7 g ethanol and 45.7 g water. In terms of volumes of the pure liquids, mix $\underline{57.6\ \text{cm}^3}$ of ethanol and $\underline{45.7\ \text{cm}^3}$ of water.

The change in volume on adding a virtually infinitesimal amount of ethanol is

$$\Delta V \approx V_E\, \Delta n_E \approx 56.0\ \text{cm}^3\ \text{mol}^{-1} \times \frac{1.00\ \text{cm}^3 \times 0.789\ \text{g cm}^{-3}}{46.07\ \text{g mol}^{-1}}$$

$$= \underline{0.96\ \text{cm}^3}$$

7.7 Proceed as explained in the Further Information section. Plot V_m against x_C, extrapolate the tangents, and obtain V_C from the intercept at $x_C = 1$ and V_A from the intercept at $x_C = 0$. The volumes are plotted in Fig. 7.7a and the intercepts are as follows:

x_C	0.0	0.2	0.4	0.6	0.8	1.0
$V_A/(\text{cm}^3\ \text{mol}^{-1})$	73.99	74.03	74.11	73.96	73.50	72.74
$V_B/(\text{cm}^3\ \text{mol}^{-1})$	80.85	80.53	80.31	80.37	80.60	80.66

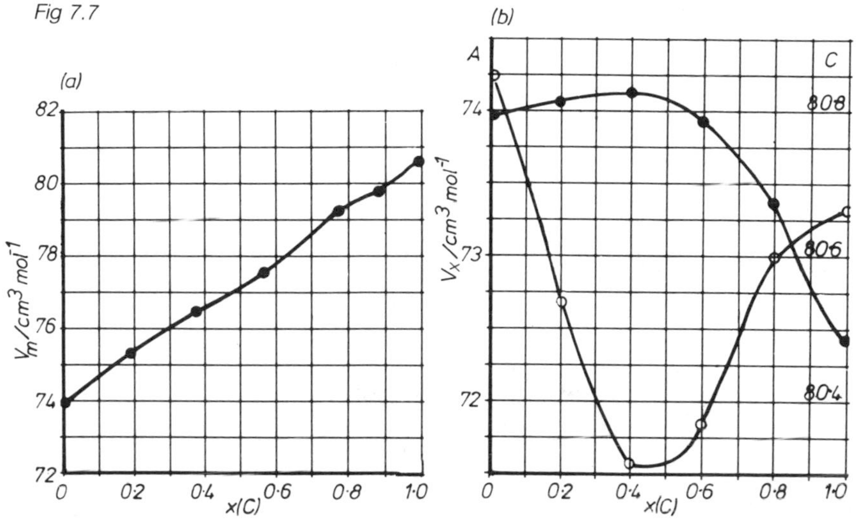

These points are plotted in Fig. 7.7b.

7.8 We find a sequence of changes that achieve the overall change specified in the questions, viz:

(1) Expansion of nitrogen to the same pressure as the hydrogen.

(2) Mixing.

(3) Compression of mixture to the original volume.

(1) $G(N_2, 1.0\text{ atm}) = G(N_2, 3.0\text{ atm}) + n(N_2)RT \ln \dfrac{1.0\text{ atm}}{3.0\text{ atm}}$

(2) $\Delta G_{\text{mix}} = nRT\{x(N_2)\ln x(N_2) + x(H_2)\ln x(H_2)\}$

$$= nRT\{\tfrac{3}{4}\ln\tfrac{3}{4} + \tfrac{1}{4}\ln\tfrac{1}{4}\} = -0.562nRT$$

(3) Since $p_f = 2.0$ atm,

$$G(\text{mixture}, 2.0\text{ atm}) = G(\text{mixture}, 1.0\text{ atm}) + nRT\ln 2$$

The overall change is therefore

$$\Delta G = n(N_2)RT\ln\tfrac{1}{3} - 0.562nRT + nRT\ln 2$$

The amounts are obtained from the perfect gas law:

$$n(N_2) = \frac{p_i(N_2)V_i}{RT} \qquad n = \frac{pV}{RT}$$

Therefore,

$$\begin{aligned}\Delta G &= p_i(N_2)V_i \ln \tfrac{1}{3} - 0.562pV + pV\ln 2 \\ &= -p_i(N_2)V_i \ln 3 + (\ln 2 - 0.562)pV \\ &= -3.0\times 1.013\times 10^5\ \text{Pa}\times 2.5\times 10^{-3}\ \text{m}^3\times \ln 3 \\ &\quad + (\ln 2 - 0.562)\times 2.0\times 1.013\times 10^5\ \text{Pa}\times 5.0\times 10^{-3}\ \text{m}^3 \\ &= -835\ \text{J} + 133\ \text{J} = \underline{-0.70\ \text{kJ}}\end{aligned}$$

7.9 $\Delta T = K_f m_B$ with $K_f = 40\ \text{K}/(\text{mol kg}^{-1})$

$M(CF_3(CF_2)_3CF_3) = 288.05\ \text{g mol}^{-1}$, $M(CF_3(CF_2)_4CF_3) = 338.06\ \text{g mol}^{-1}$

The amounts corresponding to 1.00 g are therefore

$$n(CF_3(CF_2)_3CF_3) = 3.47\overline{2}\ \text{mmol},\quad n(CF_3(CF_2)_4CF_3) = 2.95\overline{8}\ \text{mmol}$$

The molalities of the solutions formed by dissolving these amounts in 100.0 g of solvent (camphor) are therefore

$$m(CF_3(CF_2)_3CF_3) = 34.7\overline{2}\ \text{mmol kg}^{-1},\quad m(CF_3(CF_2)_4CF_3) = 29.5\overline{8}\ \text{mmol kg}^{-1}$$

The resulting freezing point depressions are therefore

$$\Delta T = 34.7\overline{2}\ \text{mmol kg}^{-1}\times 40\ \text{K}/(\text{mol kg}^{-1}) = 1.4\ \text{K}$$

$$\Delta T = 29.5\overline{8}\ \text{mmol kg}^{-1}\times 40\ \text{K}/(\text{mol kg}^{-1}) = 1.2\ \text{K}$$

The temperature measurement must therefore be able to distinguish between these two depressions, which suggests a precision of no less than $\underline{\pm 0.05\ \text{K}}$

7.10 $\Delta T = \dfrac{RT_f^2 x_B}{\Delta H_{fus}}$ [16a], $x_B \approx \dfrac{n_B}{n(CH_3COOH)} = \dfrac{n_B M(CH_3COOH)}{1000\ \text{g}}$

Hence $\Delta T = \dfrac{n_B MRT_f^2}{\Delta H_{fus}\times 1000\ \text{g}} = \dfrac{m_B MRT_f^2}{\Delta H_{fus}}$ [m_B: molality of solution]

$$= m_B \times \frac{60.05\ \text{g mol}^{-1}\times 8.314\ \text{J K}^{-1}\ \text{mol}^{-1}\times (290\ \text{K})^2}{11.4\times 10^3\ \text{J mol}^{-1}}$$

$$= 3.68\ \text{K}\times m_B/(\text{mol kg}^{-1})$$

where m_B is the apparent molality, which we write νm_B° where ν is the number of ions per formula unit. We can draw up the following table from the data.

$m^\circ/(\text{mol kg}^{-1})$	0.015	0.037	0.077	0.295	0.602
$\Delta T/\text{K}$	0.115	0.295	0.470	1.381	2.67
$m/(\text{mol kg}^{-1})$	0.0312	0.0802	0.128	0.375	0.726
$\nu = m/m^\circ$	2.1	2.2	1.7	1.3	1.2

See the original reference for further information about the interpretation of the data.

7.11 $m_B = \frac{\Delta T}{K_f} = \frac{0.0703\ \text{K}}{1.86\ \text{K/(mol kg}^{-1})} = 0.0378\ \text{mol kg}^{-1}$

Since the solution molality is nominally $0.0096\ \text{mol kg}^{-1}$ in $Th(NO_3)_4$, each formula unit supplies $0.0378/0.0096 \approx 4$ ions. (More careful data, as described in the original reference gives $\nu \approx 5$ to 6.)

7.12 On a Raoult's law basis, $a = p/p^*$, $a = \gamma x$, and $\gamma = p/xp^*$. On a Henry's law basis, $a = p/K$, and $\gamma = p/xK$. Therefore, plot the data and extrapolate the low concentration data to determine K. The data are plotted in Fig. 7.8,

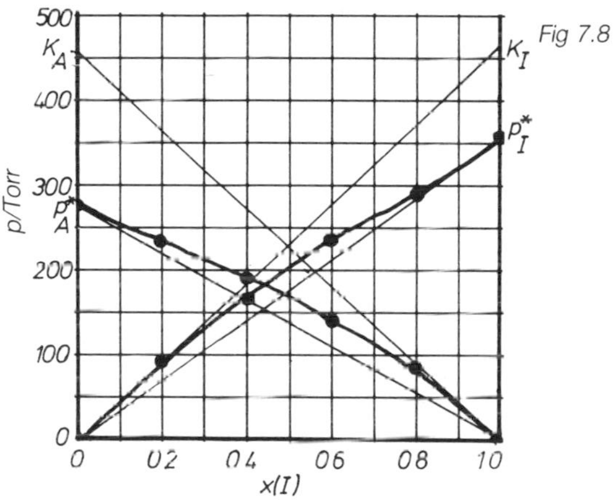

which gives $K_I = 465$ Torr. Then draw up the following table:

x_I	0	0.2	0.4	0.6	0.8	1.0	
p_I/Torr	0	92	165	230	290	353‡	
p_A/Torr	280†	230	185	135	80	0	
$\gamma_I(R)$	—	1.303	1.169	1.086	1.027	1.000	$[p_I/x_Ip_I^*]$
$\gamma_A(R)$	1.000	1.027	1.101	1.205	1.429	—	$[p_A/x_Ap_A^*]$
$\gamma_I(H)$	1.000	0.929	0.887	0.824	0.780	0.759	$[p_I/x_IK_I]$

† The value of p_A^*; ‡ the value of p_I^*.

7.13 The data are plotted in Fig. 7.9. The regions where the vapor pressure curves showed approximate straight lines are denoted R for Raoult and H for Henry. A and B denote acetic acid and benzene respectively. As in Problem

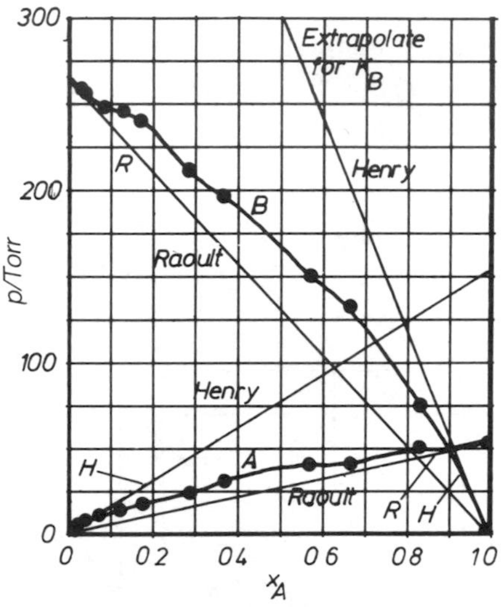

Fig 7.9

7.12, we need to form $\gamma_A = p_A/x_A p_A^*$ and $\gamma_B = p_B/x_B p_B^*$ for the Raoult's law activity coefficients and $\gamma_B = p_B/x_B K$ for the activity coefficient of benzene on a Henry's law basis, with K determined by extrapolation. We use $p_A^* = 55$ Torr, $p_B^* = 264$ Torr, and $K_B = 600$ Torr to draw up the following table:

x_A	0	0.2	0.4	0.6	0.8	1.0	
p_A/Torr	0	20	30	38	50	55	
p_B/Torr	264	228	190	150	93	0	
a_A(R)	0	0.36	0.55	0.69	0.91	1.00	$[p_A/p_A^*]$
a_B(R)	1.00	0.86	0.72	0.57	0.35	0	$[p_B/p_B^*]$
γ_A(R)	—	1.82	1.36	1.15	1.14	1.00	$[p_A/x_A p_A^*]$
γ_B(R)	1.00	1.08	1.20	1.42	1.76	—	$[p_B/x_B p_B^*]$
a_B(H)	0.44	0.38	0.32	0.25	0.16	0	$[p_B/K_B]$
γ_B(H)	0.44	0.48	0.53	0.63	0.78	1.00	$[p_B/x_B K_B]$

Since $G^E = RT(x_A \ln \gamma_A + x_B \ln \gamma_B)$ [as in eqn 14] we can draw up the following table from the information above and $RT = 2.48$ kJ mol^{-1}:

x_A	0	0.2	0.4	0.6	0.8	1.0
$x_A \ln \gamma_A$	0	0.12	0.12	0.08	0.10	0
$x_B \ln \gamma_B$	0	0.06	0.11	0.14	0.11	0
$G^E/(\text{kJ mol}^{-1})$	0	0.45	0.57	0.55	0.52	0

7.14 $G^E = RTx(1-x)\{0.4857 - 0.1077(2x-1) + 0.0191(2x-1)^2\}$

with $x = 0.25$ gives $G^E = 0.1021RT$. Therefore,

$$\Delta G_{\text{mix}} = nRT(x_A \ln x_A + x_B \ln x_B) + nG^E$$
$$= nRT(0.25 \ln 0.25 + 0.75 \ln 0.75) + nG^E$$
$$= -0.562nRT + 0.1021nRT = -0.460nRT$$

Since $n = 4$ mol and $RT = 8.314 \text{ J K}^{-1} \text{ mol}^{-1} \times 303.15 \text{ K} = 2.52 \text{ kJ mol}^{-1}$,

$\Delta G_{\text{mix}} = -0.460 \times 4 \text{ mol} \times 2.52 \text{ kJ mol}^{-1} = \underline{-4.6 \text{ kJ}}$

7.15 $\mu_A = \left(\frac{\partial G}{\partial n_A}\right)_{n_B} = \mu_A^{\circ} + \left(\frac{\partial}{\partial n_A}(nG^E)\right)_{n_B}$ [μ_A° from ideal value]

$$\left(\frac{\partial nG^E}{\partial n_A}\right)_{n_B} = G^E + n\left(\frac{\partial G^E}{\partial n_A}\right)_{n_B}$$
$$= G^E + n\left(\frac{\partial x_A}{\partial n_A}\right)_B \left(\frac{\partial G^E}{\partial x_A}\right)_B$$
$$= G^E + n \times \frac{x_B}{n} \times \left(\frac{\partial G^E}{\partial x_A}\right)_B \quad [\partial x_A/\partial n_A = x_B/n]$$
$$= gRTx_A(1-x_A) + (1-x_A)gRT(1-2x_A)$$
$$= gRT(1-x_A)^2 = gRTx_B^2$$

Therefore, $\underline{\mu_A = \mu_A^{\ominus} + RT \ln x_A + gRTx_B^2}$

7.16 $x_A \, d\mu_A + x_B \, d\mu_B = 0$ [6]

Therefore,

$$x_A\left(\frac{\partial m_A}{\partial x_A}\right)_{p,T} + x_B\left(\frac{\partial m_B}{\partial x_A}\right)_{p,T} = 0 \text{ [divide through by } dx_A]$$

and so

$$x_A\left(\frac{\partial m_A}{\partial x_A}\right)_{p,T} - x_B\left(\frac{\partial m_B}{\partial x_B}\right)_{p,T} = 0 \; [dx_B = -dx_A \text{ as } x_A + x_B = 1]$$

which implies that

$$\left(\frac{\partial m_A}{\partial \ln x_A}\right)_{p,T} = \left(\frac{\partial m_B}{\partial \ln x_B}\right)_{p,T} \quad [\mathrm{d}\ln x = \mathrm{d}x/x]$$

Then, since $\mu = \mu^{\ominus} + RT\ln f/p^{\ominus}$,

$$\left(\frac{\partial \ln f_A}{\partial \ln x_A}\right)_{p,T} = \left(\frac{\partial \ln f_B}{\partial \ln x_B}\right)_{p,T}$$

On replacing f by p,

$$\left(\frac{\partial \ln p_A}{\partial \ln x_A}\right)_{p,T} = \left(\frac{\partial \ln p_B}{\partial \ln x_B}\right)_{p,T}$$

If A satisfies Raoult's law, we can write $p_A = x_A p_A^*$, which implies that

$$\left(\frac{\partial \ln p_A}{\partial \ln x_A}\right)_{p,T} = \frac{\partial \ln x_A}{\partial \ln x_A} + \frac{\partial \ln p_A^*}{\partial \ln x_A} = 1 + 0$$

Therefore,

$$\left(\frac{\partial \ln p_B}{\partial \ln x_B}\right)_{p,T} = 1$$

which is satisfied if $p_B = x_B p_B^*$ [by integration]. Hence, if A satisfies Raoult's law, then so does B.

7.17 $n_A\,\mathrm{d}V_A + n_B\,\mathrm{d}V_B = 0$ [6]

Hence

$$\frac{n_A}{n_B}\mathrm{d}V_A = -\mathrm{d}V_B$$

Therefore, by integration,

$$V_B(x_A) - V_B(0) = -\int_{V_A(0)}^{V_A(x_A)} \frac{n_A}{n_B}\mathrm{d}V_A = -\int_{V_A(0)}^{V_A(x_A)} \frac{x_A\,\mathrm{d}V_A}{1-x_A}$$

Therefore,

$$V_B(x_A, x_B) = V_B(0, 1) + \int_{V_A(0)}^{V_A(x_A)} \frac{x_A\,\mathrm{d}V_A}{1-x_A}$$

We should now plot $x_A/(1-x_A)$ against V_A and estimate the integral. For the present purpose we integrate up to $V_A(0.5, 0.5) = 74.06\ \mathrm{cm^3\,mol^{-1}}$ [Fig. 7.7], and use the data in Problem 7.7 to construct the following table:

$V_A/(\text{cm}^3\,\text{mol}^{-1})$	74.11	73.96	73.50	72.74
x_A	0.60	0.40	0.20	0
$x_A/(1-x_A)$	1.50	0.67	0.25	0

The points are plotted in Fig. 7.10, and the area required is 0.30. Hence,

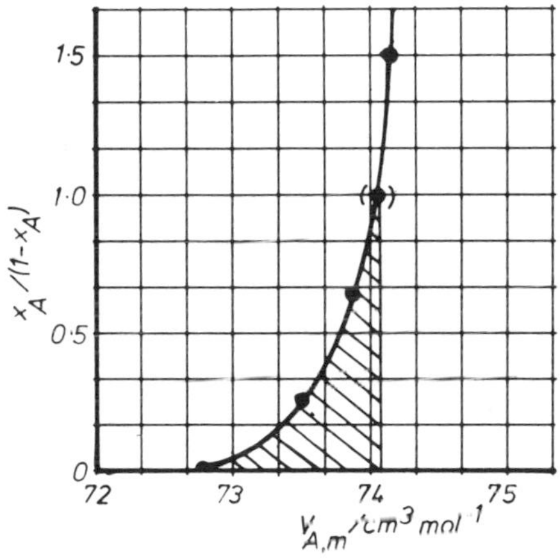

Fig 7.10

$$V(\text{CHCl}_3;\,0.5,\,0.5) = 80.66\ \text{cm}^3\,\text{mol}^{-1} - 0.30\ \text{cm}^3\,\text{mol}^{-1}$$
$$= \underline{80.36\ \text{cm}^3\,\text{mol}^{-1}}$$

7.18 $\ln x_A = \dfrac{-\Delta G_{\text{fus}}}{RT}$ [Section 7.5]

$$\frac{d\ln x_A}{dT} = -\frac{1}{R}\frac{d}{dT}\left(\frac{\Delta G_{\text{fus}}}{T}\right) = \frac{\Delta H_{\text{fus}}}{RT^2} \text{ [Gibbs-Helmholtz equation]}$$

$$\int_1^{x_A} d\ln x_A = \int_{T^*}^{T} \frac{\Delta H_{\text{fus}}\,dT}{RT^2} \approx \frac{\Delta H_{\text{fus}}}{R}\int_{T^*}^{T}\frac{dT}{T^2}$$

$$\underline{\ln x_A = \frac{-\Delta H_{\text{fus}}}{R}\left(\frac{1}{T} - \frac{1}{T^*}\right)}$$

The approximations $\ln x_A \approx -x_B$ and $T \approx T^*$ then lead to eqns 15 and 16, as in the text.

7.19 $\phi = -\dfrac{\ln a_A}{r}$ (a)

Therefore, $d\phi = -\dfrac{1}{r}\,d\ln a_A + \dfrac{1}{r^2}\ln a_A\,dr$

$d\ln a_A = \dfrac{1}{r}\ln a_A\,dr - r\,d\phi$ (b)

From the Gibbs-Duhem equation, $x_A\,d\mu_A + x_B\,d\mu_B = 0$, which implies that (since $\mu = \mu^\ominus + RT\ln a$)

$$d\ln a_B = -\frac{x_A}{x_B}\,d\ln a_A = -\frac{d\ln a_A}{r}$$

$$= -\frac{1}{r^2}\ln a_A\,dr + d\phi \qquad \text{[from (b)]}$$

$$= \frac{1}{r}\phi\,dr + d\phi \qquad \text{[from (a)]}$$

$$= \phi\,d\ln r + d\phi$$

Subtract $d\ln r$ from both sides, to obtain

$$d\ln\frac{a_B}{r} = (\phi - 1)\,d\ln r + d\phi = \frac{(\phi - 1)}{r}\,dr + d\phi$$

Then, by integration,

$$\ln\frac{a_B}{r} = \underline{\phi - \phi(0) + \int_0^r \left(\frac{\phi - 1}{r}\right) dr}$$

7.20 As in the argument leading to eqn 18 of the text, at equilibrium

$$\mu_A^*(p) = \mu_A(x_A, p + \Pi)$$

which implies that, with $\mu = \mu^* + RT\ln a$ for a real solution,

$$\mu_A^*(p) = \mu_A^*(p + \Pi) + RT\ln a_A$$

$$= \mu_A^*(p) + \int_p^{p+\Pi} V_m\,dp + RT\ln a_A$$

and hence that

$$\int_{p}^{p+\Pi} V_\mathrm{m}\,\mathrm{d}p = -RT\ln a_\mathrm{A}$$

For an incompressible solution, the integral evaluates to ΠV_m, so

$$\Pi V_\mathrm{m} = -RT\ln a_\mathrm{A}$$

In terms of the osmotic coefficient ϕ [Problem 7.19]

$$\Pi V_\mathrm{m} = r\phi RT \qquad r = \frac{x_\mathrm{B}}{x_\mathrm{A}} = \frac{n_\mathrm{B}}{n_\mathrm{A}}$$

For a dilute solution,

$$r \approx \frac{n_\mathrm{B}}{n_\mathrm{A}} \text{ and } n_\mathrm{A}V_\mathrm{m} \approx V$$

Hence

$$\Pi V = n_\mathrm{B}\phi RT$$

and therefore, with $[\mathrm{B}] = n_\mathrm{B}/V$

$$\underline{\Pi = \phi[\mathrm{B}]RT}$$

8. Changes of state: the phase rule

Exercises

8.1 (a) Salt, water; $C = \underline{2}$

(b) Na^+, H^+, $H_2PO_4^-$, HPO_4^{2-}, PO_4^{3-}, H_2O, OH^- giving 7 species. There are also three equilibria, namely

$$H_2PO_4^- \rightleftharpoons H^+ + HPO_4^{2-}$$

$$HPO_4^{2-} \rightleftharpoons H^+ + PO_4^{3-}$$

$$H^+ + OH^- \rightleftharpoons H_2O$$

(These could all be written as Brønsted equilibria without changing the conclusions.) There are also two conditions of electrical neutrality, namely

$$[Na^+] = [\text{phosphates}], \; [H^+] = [OH^-] + [\text{phosphates}]$$

where $[\text{phosphates}] = [H_2PO_4^-] + 2[HPO_4^{2-}] + 3[PO_4^{3-}]$
Hence, the number of independent components is

$$C = 7 - (3 + 2) = \underline{2}$$

(c) Al^{3+}, H^+, $AlCl_3$, $Al(OH)_3$, OH^-, Cl^-, H_2O giving 7 species. There are also three equilibria:

$$AlCl_3 + 3H_2O \rightleftharpoons Al(OH)_3 + 3HCl$$

$$AlCl_3 \rightleftharpoons Al^{3+} + 3Cl^-$$

$$H_2O \rightleftharpoons H^+ + OH^-$$

and one condition of electrical neutrality:

$$[H^+] + 3[Al^{3+}] = [OH^-] + [Cl^-]$$

Hence, the number of independent components is

$$C = 7 - (3 + 1) = \underline{3}$$

8.2 $CuSO_4 \cdot 5H_2O(s) \rightleftharpoons CuSO_4(s) + 5H_2O(g)$

We must specify 'H_2O' for the gas phase and '$CuSO_4 \cdot 5H_2O$' for the solid phase; $CuSO_4$ is then fixed by the equilibrium. Hence $\underline{C = 2 \text{ and } P = 2}$ (s and g).

8.3 $NH_4Cl(s) \rightleftharpoons NH_3(g) + HCl(g)$.

For this system $\underline{C=1}$ [Section 8.1] and $\underline{P=2}$ (s and g). If ammonia is added before heating, $\underline{C=2}$ [because NH_4Cl, NH_3 are now independent] and $P=2$ (s and g).

8.4 The two components are Na_2SO_4 and H_2O (proton transfer equilibria to give HSO_4^- etc. do not change the number of independent components [Exercise 8.1]) so $\underline{C=2}$. There are three phases present (solid salt, liquid solution, vapor), so $\underline{P=3}$. The variance is

$$F = C - P + 2 = 2 - 3 + 2 = \underline{1}$$

If the pressure is changed, the temperature must be changed to maintain the equilibrium.

8.5 Still $\underline{C=2}$ (Na_2SO_4, H_2O) but now there is no solid phase present, so $\underline{P=2}$ (liquid solution, vapor) and the variance is $F = 2 - 2 + 2 = \underline{2}$. We are free to change the amount of dissolved salt and the pressure, but the temperature must be changed to maintain equilibrium between the two phases.

8.6 See Fig. 8.1.

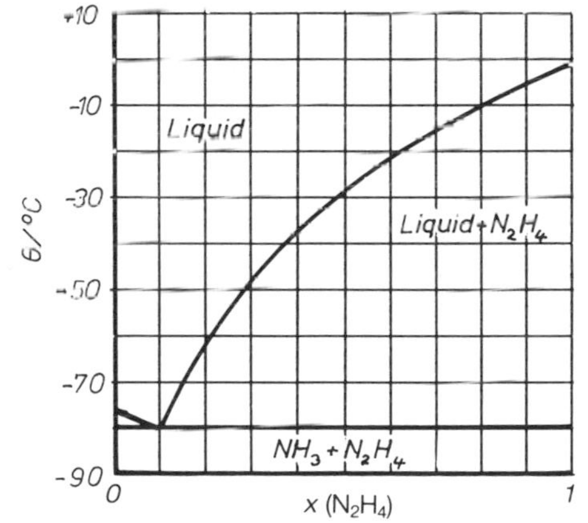

Fig 8.1

8.7 Refer to Fig. 8.8 of the text. At b_3 there are two phases with compositions $x_A = 0.18$ and $x_A = 0.70$; their abundances are in the ratio 0.13 [lever rule]. Since $C=2$ and $P=2$ we have $F=2$ (such as p and x). On heating, the phases merge, and the single-phase region is encountered. Then $F=3$ (such as p, T, and x). The liquid comes into equilibrium with its vapor when the isopleth cuts the phase line. At this temperature, and for all points up to b_1, $C=2$ and $P=2$, implying that $F=2$ (for example p, x). The whole sample is a vapor above b_1.

8.8 The phase diagram should be labeled as in Fig. 8.2. (a) Solid Ag with

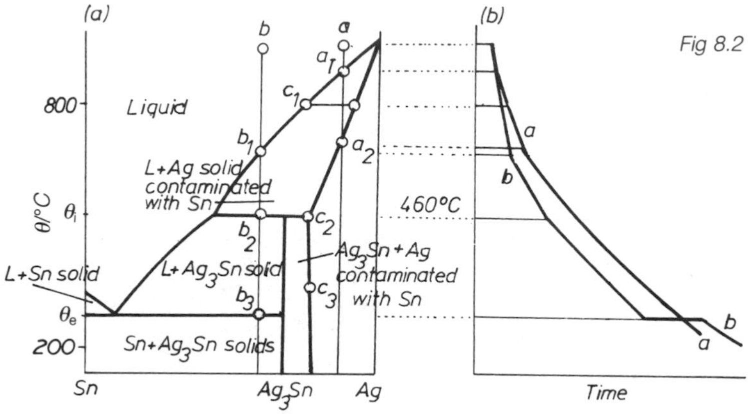

dissolved Sn begins to precipitate at a_1, and the sample solidifies completely at a_2. (b) Solid Ag with dissolved Sn begins to precipitate at b_1, and the liquid becomes richer in Sn. The peritectic reaction occurs at b_2, and as cooling continues Ag_3Sn is precipitated and the liquid becomes richer in Sn. At b_3 the system has its eutectic composition (e) and freezes without further change.

8.9 The incongruent melting point [Section 8.5] is marked as θ_i in Fig. 8.2a ($\theta_i = 460\,°C$). The composition of the eutectic is e, and corresponds to 4 per cent by mass of silver. It melts at $\theta_e = 215\,°C$.

8.10 The cooling curves are shown in Fig. 8.2b. Note the eutectic halt for the isopleth b.

8.11 Refer to Fig. 8.2a.

(a) The solubility of silver in tin at 800 °C is determined by the point c_1 [at higher proportions of silver, the system separates into two phases]. The point c_1 corresponds to 80 per cent silver by mass.

(b) See point c_2. The compound Ag_3Sn decomposes at this temperature.

(c) The solubility of Ag_3Sn in silver is given by point c_3 at 300 °C.

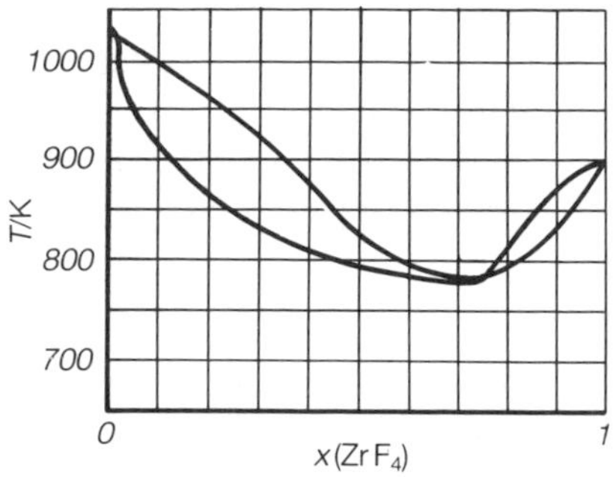

Fig 8.3

8.12 The phase diagram is shown in Fig. 8.3. A solid solution with $x(ZrF_4) = 0.21$ appears at 875 °C. The solid solution continues to form, and its ZrF_4 content increases until it reaches $x(ZrF_4) = 0.40$ at 820 °C. At that temperature, the entire sample is solid.

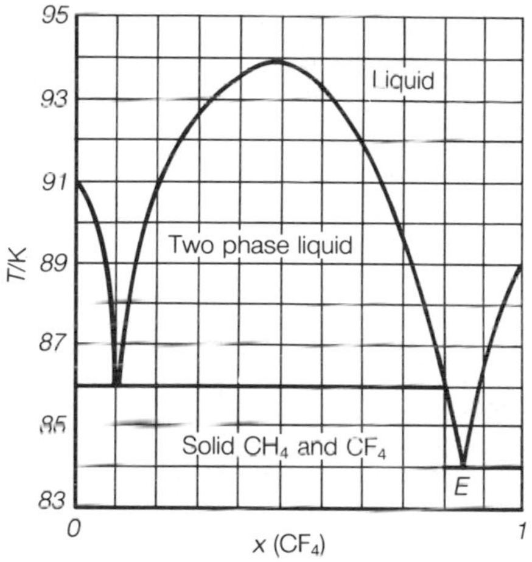

Fig 8.4

8.13 The phase diagram is drawn in Fig. 8.4.

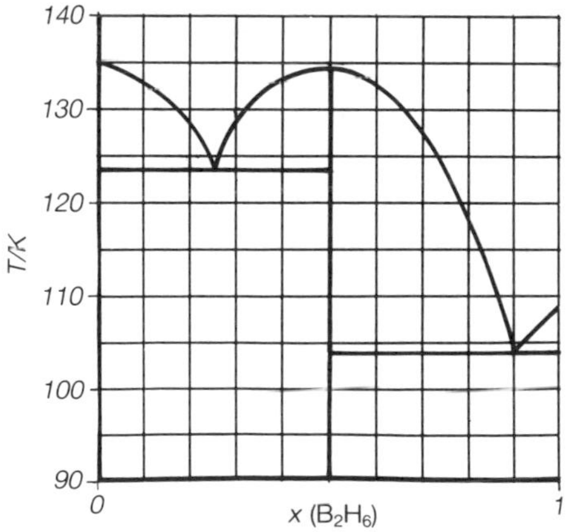

Fig 8.5

8.14 The phase diagram is shown in Fig. 8.5. The solid compound begins to crystallize at 120 K. The liquid becomes progressively richer in diborane until the liquid composition reaches 0.90 at 104 K. At that point the liquid disappears as heat is removed. Below 104 K the system is a mixture of solid compound and solid diborane.

Fig 8.6

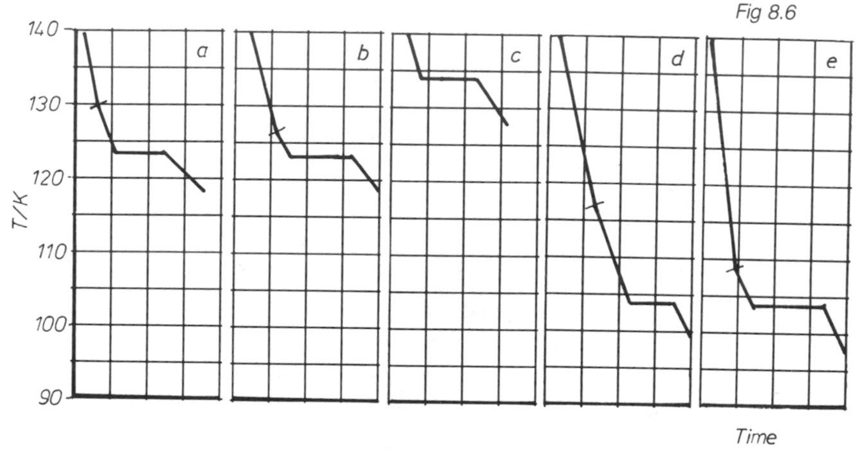

8.15 The cooling curves are sketched in Fig. 8.6.

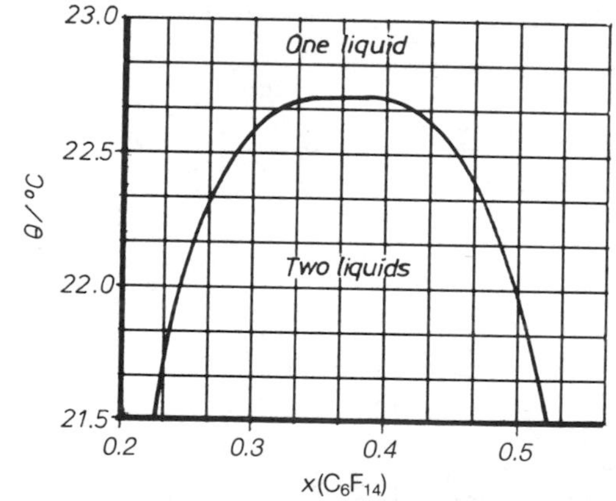

Fig 8.7

8.16 The phase diagram is sketched in Fig. 8.7. (a) The mixture has a single liquid phase at all compositions. (b) When the composition reaches $x(C_6F_{14}) =$ 0.25 the mixture separates into two liquid phases of compositions $x = 0.25$ and 0.48. The relative amounts of the two phases change until the composition reaches $x = 0.48$. At all mole fractions greater than 0.48 in C_6F_{14} the mixture forms a single liquid phase.

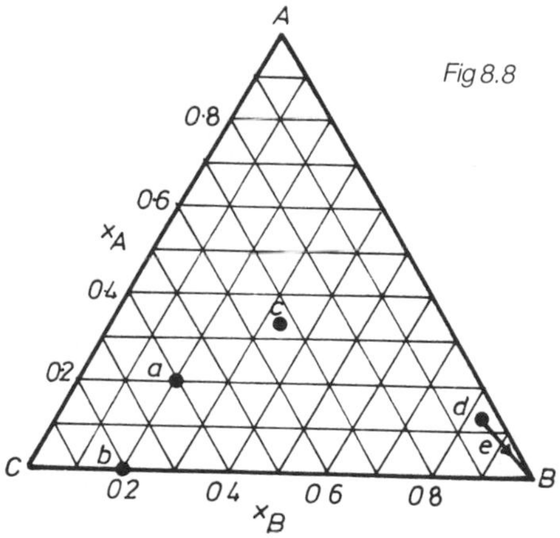

8.17 The features are plotted in Fig. 8.8 using the instructions given in Section 8.7 [see Example 8.5].

8.18 We first convert the mass percentage compositions to mole fractions using $M(\mathrm{NaCl}) = 58.4\ \mathrm{g\ mol^{-1}}$, $M(\mathrm{H_2O}) = 18.0\ \mathrm{g\ mol^{-1}}$, and $M(\mathrm{Na_2SO_4 \cdot 10H_2O}) = 322.2\ \mathrm{g\ mol^{-1}}$. Thus, in a sample of total mass 100 g,

$$n(\mathrm{NaCl}) = \frac{0.25 \times 100\ \mathrm{g}}{58.4\ \mathrm{g\ mol^{-1}}} = 0.43\ \mathrm{mol}$$

$$n(\mathrm{H_2O}) = \frac{0.50 \times 100\ \mathrm{g}}{18.0\ \mathrm{g\ mol^{-1}}} = 2.8\ \mathrm{mol}$$

$$n(\mathrm{Na_2SO_4 \cdot 10H_2O}) = \frac{0.25 \times 100\ \mathrm{g}}{322.2\ \mathrm{g\ mol^{-1}}} = 0.078\ \mathrm{mol}$$

(a) These amounts corresponds to the mole fractions

$$x(\mathrm{NaCl}) = 0.13,\ x(\mathrm{H_2O}) = 0.85,\ x(\mathrm{Na_2SO_4 \cdot 10H_2O}) = 0.024$$

and corresponds to the point *d* in Fig. 8.8 where A = NaCl, B = H_2O, and C = $Na_2SO_4 \cdot 10H_2O$. (b) In this calculation, the 'water' apex is the one marked B; hence the line labeled *e* is followed as water is added.

8.19 The composition (W, C, A) = (2.3 g, 9.2 g, 3.1 g) corresponds to (0.128 mol, 0.077 mol, 0.052 mol) [using $M = 18.02$, 119.4, and 60.5 $\mathrm{g\ mol^{-1}}$ respectively]. The mole fractions corresponding to this composition are therefore (0.50, 0.30, 0.20). The point lies at q in Fig. 8.17 of the text, the intersection of the broken line and the third tie-line. The point q lies in the two-phase region of the diagram. The two phases have compositions given by the points at the ends of the tie-lines, namely (0.06, 0.82, 0.12) and (0.62, 0.16, 0.22). Their relative abundances are given by the level rule as 0.27. (c) When water is added, the composition moves along the line joining the point q to the W apex. When $x(H_2O) = 0.79$, the system enters the single-phase region. (b) When acetic acid is added to the original mixture, it becomes a single-phase system when $x(CH_3COOH) = 0.35$, the point a_3 in the diagram.

8.20 The positions of the four points are shown in Fig. 8.9, which is a

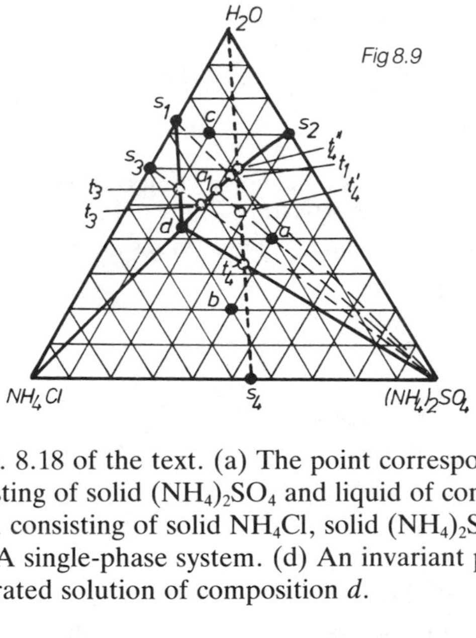

reproduction of Fig. 8.18 of the text. (a) The point corresponds to a two-phase system consisting of solid $(NH_4)_2SO_4$ and liquid of composition a_1. (b) A three-phase system, consisting of solid NH_4Cl, solid $(NH_4)_2SO_4$, and liquid of composition d. (c) A single-phase system. (d) An invariant point: the system consists of the saturated solution of composition d.

8.21 Refer to Fig. 8.9. Solubilities are given by the compositions at which binary system just fails to become a two-phase system. These are the points (a) s_1, corresponding to $x(NH_4Cl) = 0.26$ and (b) s_2, corresponding to $x((NH_4)_2SO_4) = 0.30$. Convert to mol kg^{-1} by taking $n(H_2O) = 55.45$ mol and noting that $M(NH_4Cl) = 53.49$ g mol^{-1} and $M((NH_4)_2SO_4) = 132.14$ g mol^{-1}. Since $x(s) = n(s)/\{n(s) + n(S)\}$,

$$n(s) = \frac{x(s)n(S)}{1 - x(s)}$$

Therefore,

(a) $n(NH_4Cl) = 19.5$ mol, (b) $n((NH_4)_2SO_4) = 23.8$ mol

and the solubilities of the chloride and the sulfate are 19.5 mol kg^{-1} and 23.8 mol kg^{-1} respectively.

8.22 Refer to Fig. 8.9.

(a) Initially the system is at s_3 (for example). It consists of a saturated solution of composition s_1 and excess chloride. Addition of sulfate leads to a single-phase system when the composition reaches t_3. The sulfate continues to dissolve until t_3' is reached; after that, the two-phase region is reached and further sulfate remains undissolved.

(b) The composition consists of 0.47 mol NH_4Cl and 0.55 mol $(NH_4)_2SO_4$, with mole fractions 0.45 and 0.55 respectively. This composition corresponds to the point s_4. Addition of water moves the system along the line s_4, t_4. Three phases (solid chloride, solid sulfate, and unsaturated solution d) survive until s_4 is passed. Then the two-phase region is entered and there are present the solid sulfate and a liquid of composition that changes from d toward t_4''. For instance, when the overall composition is t_4', the liquid composition is a_1. At t_4'' the single-phase region is entered and the solution from then on becomes progressively more dilute.

8.23 The phase diagram is shown in Fig. 8.10.

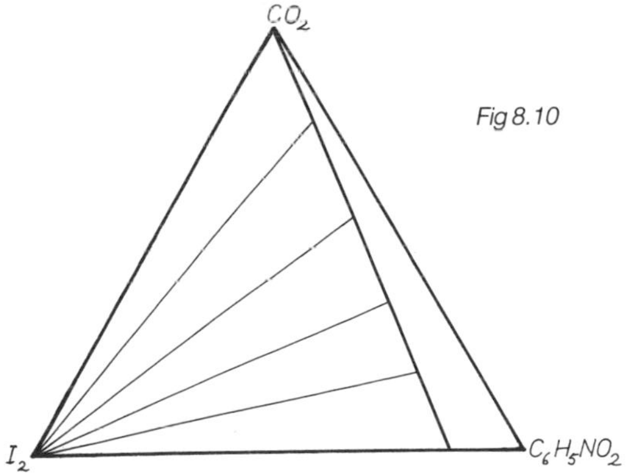

Fig 8.10

Problems

8.1 $F = C - P + 2$, with $C = 1$. At the transition point $P = 3$ (s, l, and g) for melting and $P = 3$ (l, l', and g) at the transition. Hence, $F = 1 - 3 + 2 = 0$ for both.

8.2 The data are plotted in Fig. 8.11. (a) At $x(\text{MgO})=0.3$, solid and liquid are in equilibrium at 2150 °C. (b) From the tie-line at 2200 °C, the liquid

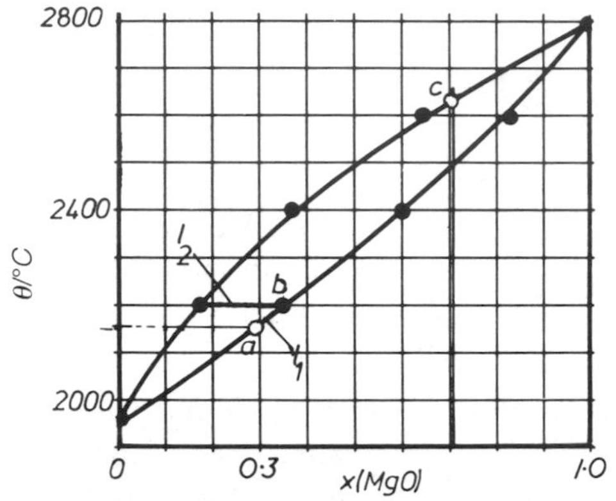

Fig 8.11

composition is $y(\text{MgO})=\underline{0.18}$ and the solid $x(\text{MgO})=\underline{0.35}$. The proportions of the two phases are given by the lever rule, and solid/liquid$=\underline{0.42}$. (c) Solidification begins at point c, corresponding to $\underline{2650\ °\text{C}}$.

8.3 The temperature–composition lines can be calculated from the formula for the depression of freezing point (Chapter 7):

$$\Delta T \approx \frac{RT^{*2}x_B}{\Delta H_{\text{fus}}}$$

For bismuth

$$\frac{RT^{*2}}{\Delta H_{\text{fus}}}=\frac{8.314\ \text{J K}^{-1}\ \text{mol}^{-1}\times(544.5\ \text{K})^2}{10.88\times10^3\ \text{J mol}^{-1}}=227\ \text{K}$$

For cadmium

$$\frac{RT^{*2}}{\Delta H_{\text{fus}}}=\frac{8.314\ \text{J K}^{-1}\ \text{mol}^{-1}\times(594\ \text{K})^2}{6.07\times10^3\ \text{J mol}^{-1}}=483\ \text{K}$$

We can use these constants to construct the following tables:

$x(\text{Cd})$	0.1	0.2	0.3	0.4
$\Delta T/\text{K}$	22.7	45.4	68.1	90.8 $[\Delta T=x(\text{Cd})\times 227\ \text{K}]$
T_f/K	522	499	476	454 $[T_f=T_f^*-\Delta T]$

x(Bi)	0.1	0.2	0.3	0.4
ΔT/K	48.3	96.6	145	193 [$\Delta T = x(\text{Bi}) \times 483$ K]
T_f	546	497	449	401 [$T_f = T_f^* - \Delta T$]

These points are plotted in Fig. 8.12a.

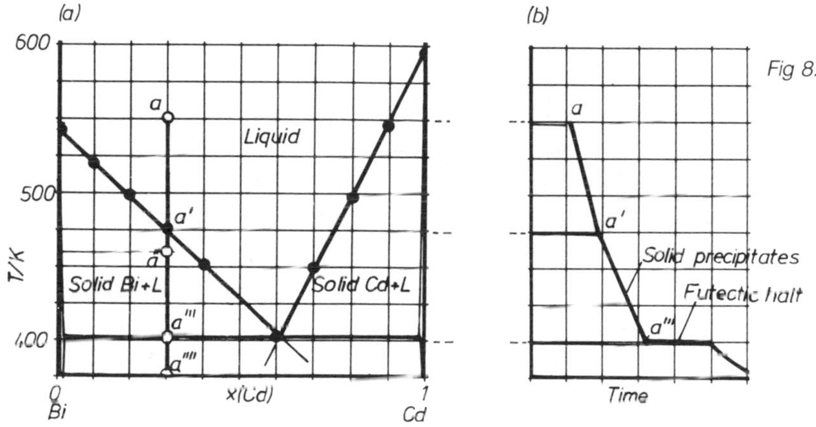

Fig 8.12

Liquid at a cools without separation of a solid until a' is reached (at 475 K). Solid Bi then separates, and the liquid becomes richer in Cd. At a''' (400 K) the composition is pure solid Bi + liquid of composition $x(\text{Bi}) = 0.4$. The whole mass then solidifies to solid Bi + solid Cd. (a) At 460 K (point a''), liquid/solid = 5 [lever rule]. (b) At 350 K (point a''') there is no liquid. The cooling curve is shown in Fig. 8.12b.

8.4 The data are plotted in Fig. 8.13. From the upper and lower extremes of the two-phase region we find $T_{uc} = 122\,°\text{C}$ and $T_{lc} = 8\,°\text{C}$. According to the phase diagram, miscibility is complete up to point a. Therefore, before that point is reached, $P = 1$, $C = 2$, implying that $F = 3$ (p, T, and x). Two phases occur at a corresponding to $w(\text{toluidine}) = 0.18$ and 0.84. At that point, $P = 2$, $C = 2$, and $F = 2$ (p, or x or T). At the point a' there are two phases of composition $w = 0.18$ and 0.84. They are present in the ratio $(a'' - a')/(a' - a) = 2$ with the former dominant. At a'' there are still two phases with those compositions, but the former ($w = 0.18$) is present only as a trace. One more drop takes the system into the one-phase region.

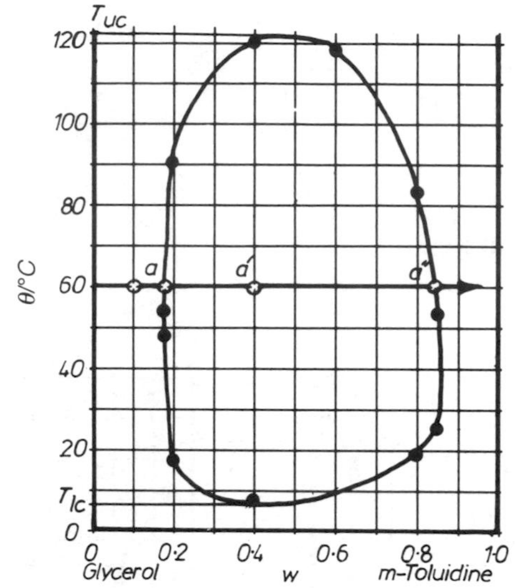

Fig 8.13

8.5 The phase diagram is drawn in Fig. 8.14. The composition points fall on the dotted line. The first solid to appear in $(NH_4)_2SiF_6$. When the water content reaches 70.4 per cent by mass, both $(NH_4)_2SiF_6$ and the double salt crystallize as more water is removed. The solution concentration remains constant until the H_2O disappears.

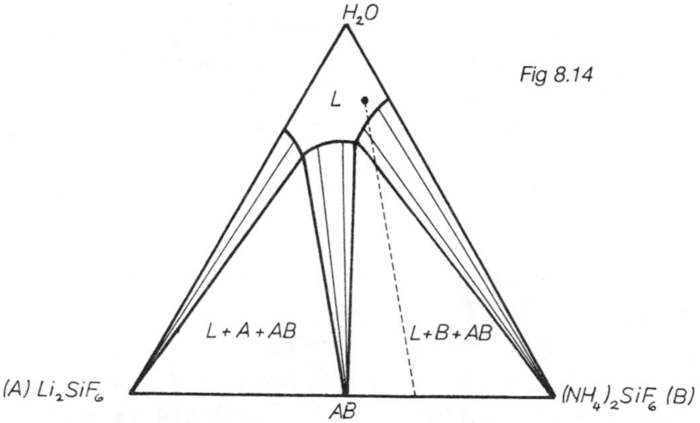

Fig 8.14

8.6 The information has been used to construct the phase diagram in Fig. 8.15a. In $MgCu_2$ the mass percentage of Mg is $100 \times 24.3/(24.3 + 127) = 16$, and in Mg_2Cu it is $100 \times 48.6/(48.6 + 63.5) = 43$. The initial point is a_1, corresponding to a liquid single-phase system. At a_2 (at 770 °C) $MgCu_2$ begins

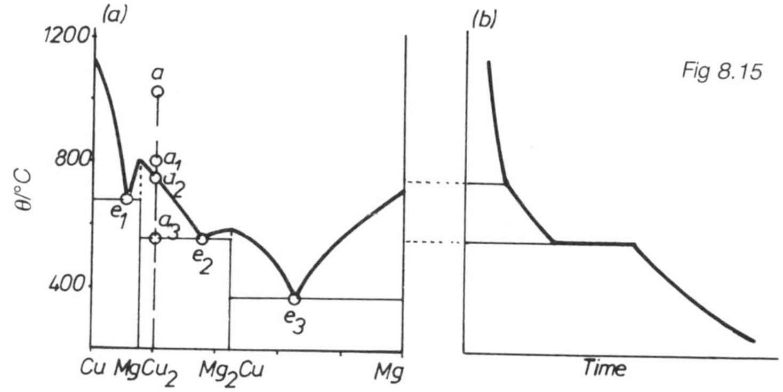

Fig 8.15

to come out of solution and the liquid becomes richer in Mg, moving toward e_2. At a_3 there is solid $MgCu_2$ + liquid of composition e_2 (33 per cent by mass of Mg). This solution freezes without further change. The cooling curve will resemble that shown in Fig. 8.15b.

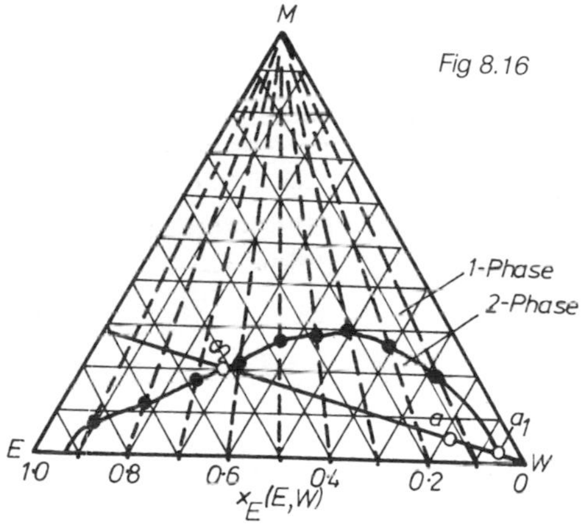

Fig 8.16

8.7 The points are plotted in Fig. 8.16. Note that addition of M preserves the E/W ratio. The composition (M, E, W) = (5 g, 30 g, 50 g) corresponds to (0.156 mol, 0.405 mol, 2.775 mol) since the molar masses are (32.04, 74.12, 18.02) g mol^{-1}. The mole fraction composition is therefore (0.047, 0.121, 0.832), which is point a in Fig. 8.16. This point lies in the two-phase region. The line $w-a$ corresponds to constant M/E ratio. When either point a_1 or a_2 is reached, the single-phase region is entered. These two points correspond to the compositions $a_1 = (0.02, 0.05, 0.93)$ and $a_2 = (0.20, 0.52, 0.28)$. Since n_E

and n_M remains constant at 0.156 mol and 0.405 mol respectively, we require $n_W = 7.3$ mol, or 131 g. Hence, 81 g of water must be added.

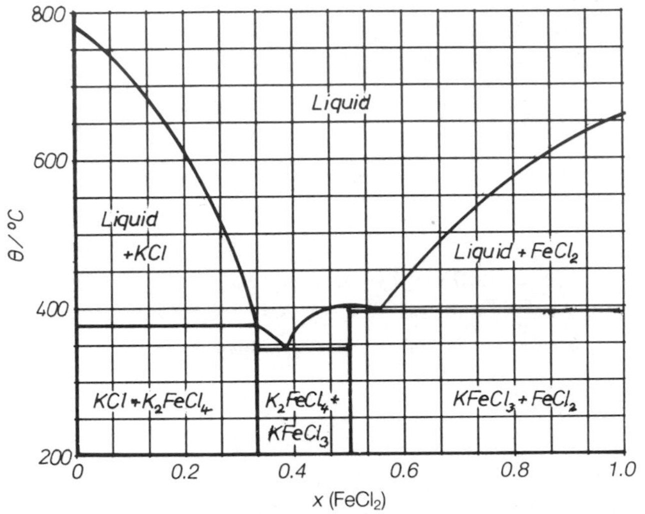

Fig 8.17

8.8 The data are plotted in Fig. 8.17. At 360 °C, $K_2FeCl_4(s)$ appears. The solution becomes richer in $FeCl_2$ until the temperature reaches 351 °C, at which point $KFeCl_3(s)$ also appears. Below 351 °C the system is a mixture of $K_2FeCl_4(s)$ and $KFeCl_3(s)$.

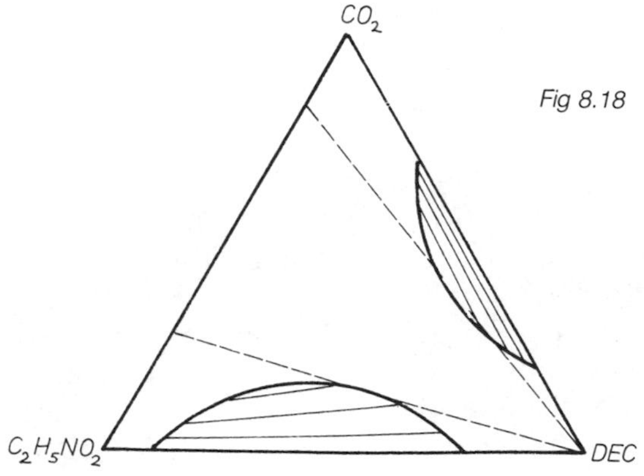

Fig 8.18

8.9 (a) The phase diagram is shown in Fig. 8.18. (b) The triangular area enclosed by the two dotted lines is spanned by $x(C_2H_5NO_2)=0.29$ and 0.83, and cannot be left by adding DEC since all composition points move toward the DEC apex as DEC is added.

8.10 Let α and β constitute an isolated system, but be in thermal contact with each other. When an amount of energy dq flows from α to β the change in entropy is

$$dS=\frac{dq}{T_\alpha}-\frac{dq}{T_\beta}=0 \text{ only if } T_\alpha=T_\beta$$

Consider an isolated system divided internally by a partition. The condition for equilibrium overall is $(dU)_{S,V}=0$. The total contribution to dU at constant entropy (only work being exchanged) and constant overall volume (only internal motion of the partition) is

$$dU=-p_\alpha\,dV+p_\beta\,dV=0 \text{ only if } p_\alpha=p_\beta$$

8.11 Refer to Fig. 8.19. From the properties of similar triangles (using ~ to

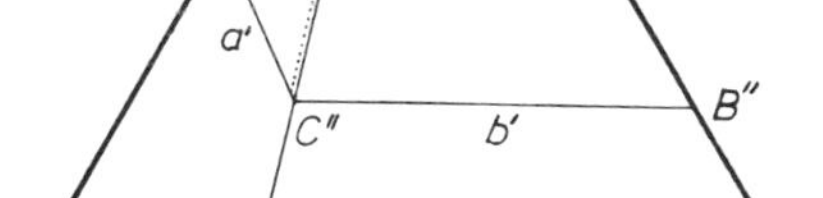

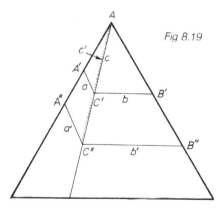

Fig 8.19

denote similarity)

$$AA'C \sim AA''C'' \text{ implying that } \frac{a}{c}=\frac{a'}{c'}$$

and hence $\dfrac{a}{a'} = \dfrac{c}{c'}$

$AB'C' \sim AB''C''$ implying that $\dfrac{b}{c} = \dfrac{b'}{c'}$,

and hence $\dfrac{b}{b'} = \dfrac{c}{c'}$

It follows that $\dfrac{a}{a'} = \dfrac{b}{b'}$, implying that $\underline{\dfrac{a}{b} = \dfrac{a'}{b'}}$

9. Changes of state: chemical reactions

Exercises

9.1 $\Delta G^{\ominus} = -RT\ln K$ [5a]

$$= -8.314\ \mathrm{J\,K^{-1}\,mol^{-1}} \times 400\ \mathrm{K} \times \ln 2.07$$

$$= \underline{-2.42\ \mathrm{kJ\,mol^{-1}}}$$

9.2 $K = \mathrm{e}^{-\Delta G^{\ominus}/RT}$ [5a]

$$= \mathrm{e}^{+3.67\times10^{3}\ \mathrm{J\,mol^{-1}}/8.314\ \mathrm{J\,K^{-1}\,mol^{-1}}\times 400\ \mathrm{K}} = \underline{3.01}$$

9.3 $\dfrac{\Delta G^{\ominus\prime}}{T'} - \dfrac{\Delta G^{\ominus}}{T} = \Delta H^{\ominus}\left(\dfrac{1}{T'} - \dfrac{1}{T}\right)$ [Gibbs-Helmholtz]

and

$$\ln K' - \ln K = -\frac{\Delta H^{\ominus}}{R}\left(\frac{1}{T'} - \frac{1}{T}\right) \text{ [11b]}$$

$K' = 1$ implies $\ln K' = 0$, which implies that $\Delta G^{\ominus\prime} = 0$, which occurs when

$$\frac{-\Delta G^{\ominus}}{T} = \Delta H^{\ominus}\left(\frac{1}{T'} - \frac{1}{T}\right)$$

or $$\frac{1}{T'} = \frac{1}{T} - \frac{\Delta G^{\ominus}}{T\,\Delta H^{\ominus}} = \frac{1}{T}\left(1 - \frac{\Delta G^{\ominus}}{\Delta H^{\ominus}}\right)$$

$$= \frac{1}{1280\ \mathrm{K}}\left(1 - \frac{33\ \mathrm{kJ\,mol^{-1}}}{224\ \mathrm{kJ\,mol^{-1}}}\right) = 6.66\times10^{-4}\ \mathrm{K^{-1}}$$

Hence, $T' = \underline{1500\ \mathrm{K}}$

9.4 $\ln K = -1.04 - \dfrac{1088\ \mathrm{K}}{T} + \dfrac{1.51\times10^{5}\ \mathrm{K^2}}{T^2}$

$$\frac{\mathrm{d}\ln K}{\mathrm{d}(1/T)} = \frac{-\Delta H^{\ominus}}{R} \text{ [11b]}$$

Therefore,

$$\frac{-\Delta H^{\ominus}}{R} = -1088\ \text{K} + \frac{2\times 1.51\times 10^{5}\ \text{K}^{2}}{T}$$

Therefore, at 400 K

$$\Delta H^{\ominus} = \left(1088\ \text{K} - \frac{3.02\times 10^{5}\ \text{K}^{2}}{400\ \text{K}}\right)\times 8.314\ \text{J K}^{-1}\ \text{mol}^{-1}$$

$$= \underline{+2.77\ \text{kJ mol}^{-1}}$$

$$\Delta G^{\ominus} = -RT\ln K$$

$$= RT\times\left(1.04 + \frac{1088\ \text{K}}{T} - \frac{1.51\times 10^{5}\ \text{K}^{2}}{T^{2}}\right)$$

$$= RT\times\left(1.04 + \frac{1088\ \text{K}}{400\ \text{K}} - \frac{1.51\times 10^{5}\ \text{K}^{2}}{(400\ \text{K})^{2}}\right) = +9.37\ \text{kJ mol}^{-1}$$

$$= \Delta H^{\ominus} = T\Delta S^{\ominus}$$

Therefore,

$$\Delta S^{\ominus} = \frac{\Delta H^{\ominus} - \Delta G^{\ominus}}{T} = \frac{2.77\ \text{kJ mol}^{-1} - 9.37\ \text{kJ mol}^{-1}}{400\ \text{K}}$$

$$= \underline{-16.5\ \text{J K}^{-1}\ \text{mol}^{-1}}$$

9.5 $p_{\text{B}} = x_{\text{B}}p$ [B denotes borneol]

$$= \frac{0.15\ \text{mol}}{0.15\ \text{mol} + 0.30\ \text{mol}}\times 600\ \text{Torr} = 200\ \text{Torr}$$

$p_{\text{I}} = p - p_{\text{B}}$ [I denotes isoborneol] $= 400$ Torr

$$Q = \frac{p_{\text{I}}}{p_{\text{B}}} = 2.00$$

$\Delta G_{\text{r}} = \Delta G^{\ominus} + RT\ln Q$ [4]

$$= +9.4\ \text{kJ mol}^{-1} + 8.314\ \text{J K}^{-1}\ \text{mol}^{-1}\times 503\ \text{K}\times\ln 2.00$$

$$= \underline{+12.3\ \text{kJ mol}^{-1}}$$

9.6 $\text{U}(s) + \tfrac{3}{2}\text{H}_2(g) \rightleftharpoons \text{UH}_3(s)$

$\ln K = \ln(p/p^{\ominus})^{-3/2} = -\tfrac{3}{2}\ln p/p^{\ominus}$

$$\Delta G^{\ominus} = -RT \ln K = \tfrac{3}{2}RT \ln p/p^{\ominus}$$

$$= \tfrac{3}{2} \times 8.314\ \text{J K}^{-1}\ \text{mol}^{-1} \times 500\ \text{K} \times \ln \frac{1.04\ \text{Torr}}{750\ \text{Torr}}\ [p^{\ominus} = 1\ \text{bar} \approx 1\ \text{atm}]$$

$$= \underline{-41.0\ \text{kJ mol}^{-1}}$$

9.7 $K_x \propto p^{-\nu}$ [10]

(a) $\nu = 1 + 1 - 1 = 1$, so $\underline{K_x' = \tfrac{1}{2}K_x}$

(b) $\nu = 1 + 1 - 1 - 1 = 0$, so $\underline{K_x' = K_x}$

9.8 $K = \dfrac{p_{\text{I}}}{p_{\text{B}}} = \dfrac{x_{\text{I}}}{x_{\text{B}}}\ [p_{\text{I}} = x_{\text{I}}p,\ p_{\text{B}} = x_{\text{B}}p] = \dfrac{1 - x_{\text{B}}}{x_{\text{B}}}$

Hence, $x_{\text{B}} = \dfrac{1}{1+K} = \dfrac{1}{1 + 0.106} = 0.904$

$$x_{\text{I}} = 0.096$$

The initial amounts of the isomers are

$$n_{\text{B}} = \frac{7.50\ \text{g}}{M},\ n_{\text{I}} = \frac{140\ \text{g}}{M},\ n = \frac{21.5\bar{0}\ \text{g}}{M}$$

The total amount remains the same, but at equilibrium

$$\frac{n_{\text{B}}}{n} = x_{\text{B}} = 0.904,\ n_{\text{B}} = 0.904 \times \frac{21.5\bar{0}\ \text{g}}{M}$$

The mass of borneol at equilibrium is therefore

$$m_{\text{B}} = n_{\text{B}} \times M = 0.904 \times 21.5\bar{0}\ \text{g} = \underline{19.4\ \text{g}}$$

and the mass of isoborneol is

$$m_{\text{I}} = n_{\text{I}}M = 0.096 \times 21.5\bar{0}\ \text{g} = \underline{2.1\ \text{g}}$$

9.9 Determine whether $\Delta G^{\ominus} < 0$ at 298 K:

(a) $\Delta G^{\ominus}/(\text{kJ mol}^{-1}) = -202.87 - (-95.30 - 16.45) = -91.12$

(b) $\Delta G^{\ominus}/(\text{kJ mol}^{-1}) = 3 \times (-856.64) - 2 \times (-1582.3) = +594.7$

(c) $\Delta G^{\ominus}/(\text{kJ mol}^{-1}) = -100.4 - (-33.56) = -66.8$

(d) $\Delta G^{\ominus}/(\text{kJ mol}^{-1}) = 2 \times (-33.56) - (-166.9) = +99.8$

(e) $\Delta G^{\ominus}/(\text{kJ mol}^{-1}) = -744.53 - (-27.83) - 2 \times (-120.35) = -476.00$

Therefore, (a), (c), and (e) have $K > 1$ at 298 K.

9.10 Determine whether $\Delta H^{\ominus} > 0$ at 298 K using $\Delta H_f^{\ominus}$ values from Table 2.10.

(a) $\Delta H^{\ominus}/(\text{kJ mol}^{-1}) = -314.43 - (-46.11 - 92.31) = -176.01$

(b) $\Delta H^{\ominus}/(\text{kJ mol}^{-1}) = 3 \times (-910.94) - 2 \times (-1675.7) = +618.6$

(c) $\Delta H^{\ominus}/(\text{kJ mol}^{-1}) = -100.0 - (-20.63) = -79.4$

(d) $\Delta H^{\ominus}/(\text{kJ mol}^{-1}) = 2 \times (-20.63) - (-178.2) = +136.9$

(e) $\Delta H^{\ominus}/(\text{kJ mol}^{-1}) = -909.27 - (-39.7) - 2 \times (-187.78) = -494.0$

Since (a), (c), and (e) are exothermic, an increase in temperature favors the reactants; (b) and (d) are endothermic, and an increase in temperature favors the products.

9.11 $\ln \frac{K'}{K} = \frac{\Delta H^{\ominus}}{R}\left(\frac{1}{T} - \frac{1}{T'}\right)$ [12]

Therefore, $\Delta H^{\ominus} = \dfrac{R \ln K'/K}{\dfrac{1}{T} - \dfrac{1}{T'}}$

$T' = 308$ K, hence, with $K'/K = \kappa$

$$\Delta H^{\ominus} = \frac{8.314 \text{ J K}^{-1} \text{ mol}^{-1} \times \ln \kappa}{\dfrac{1}{298 \text{ K}} - \dfrac{1}{308 \text{ K}}} = 76 \text{ kJ mol}^{-1} \times \ln \kappa$$

Therefore

(a) $\kappa = 2$, $\Delta H^{\ominus} = 76 \text{ kJ mol}^{-1} \times \ln 2 = +53 \text{ kJ mol}^{-1}$

(b) $\kappa = \frac{1}{2}$, $\Delta H^{\ominus} = 76 \text{ kJ mol}^{-1} \times \ln \frac{1}{2} = -53 \text{ kJ mol}^{-1}$

9.12 $\Delta G^{\ominus} = -RT \ln K$

$$\Delta G^{\ominus} - \Delta G^{\ominus\prime} = -RT \ln \frac{K}{K'} = -RT \ln 1.1 = -0.24 \text{ kJ mol}^{-1}$$

The percentage error, g, is

$$g = 100 \times \left(\frac{\Delta G^{\ominus} - \Delta G^{\ominus\prime}}{\Delta G^{\ominus}}\right) = \frac{100 \ln K/K'}{\ln K}$$

Suppose $K' = K + \Delta K$, then

$$\ln \frac{K}{K'} = -\ln \frac{K+\Delta K}{K} = -\ln\left(1 + \frac{\Delta K}{K}\right) \approx \frac{-\Delta K}{K}$$

Hence

$$\frac{100\,\Delta K}{K} \approx -g \ln K$$

and the percentage error in K, k, is

$\underline{k \approx -g \ln K} \approx 10\% \times \ln K$

9.13 $\Delta G_r = \Delta G^{\ominus} + RT \ln Q$ [4] for $\frac{1}{2}N_2(g) + \frac{3}{2}H_2(g) \rightarrow NH_3(g)$

$$Q = \frac{p(NH_3)/p^{\ominus}}{(p(N_2)/p^{\ominus})^{1/2}(p(H_2)/p^{\ominus})^{3/2}} = \frac{p(NH_3)p^{\ominus}}{p(N_2)^{1/2}p(H_2)^{3/2}}$$

$$= \frac{4.0}{(3.0)^{1/2}(1.0)^{3/2}} = \frac{4.0}{\sqrt{3.0}}$$

Therefore,

$$\Delta G_r = -16.45\ \mathrm{kJ\ mol^{-1}} + RT \ln \frac{4.0}{\sqrt{3.0}}$$

$$= -16.45\ \mathrm{kJ\ mol^{-1}} + 2.07\ \mathrm{kJ\ mol^{-1}} = \underline{-14.38\ \mathrm{kJ\ mol^{-1}}}$$

Since $\Delta G_r < 0$, the spontaneous direction of reaction is toward products.

9.14 $NH_4Cl(s) \rightleftharpoons NH_3(g) + HCl(g)$

$p = p(NH_3) + p(HCl) = 2p(NH_3)$ $[p(NH_3) = p(HCl)]$

(a) $K_p = \frac{p(NH_3)}{p^{\ominus}} \times \frac{p(HCl)}{p^{\ominus}} = \frac{p(NH_3)^2}{p^{\ominus 2}} = \frac{1}{4}\left(\frac{p}{p^{\ominus}}\right)^2$

At 427 °C (700 K), $K_p = \frac{1}{4} \times \left(\frac{608\ \mathrm{kPa}}{100\ \mathrm{kPa}}\right)^2 = \underline{9.24}$

At 459 °C (732 K), $K_p = \frac{1}{4} \times \left(\frac{1115\ \mathrm{kPa}}{100\ \mathrm{kPa}}\right)^2 = \underline{31.08}$

(b) $\Delta G^{\ominus} = -RT \ln K_p$

$= -8.314\ \mathrm{J\ K^{-1}\ mol^{-1}} \times 700\ \mathrm{K} \times \ln 9.24$

$= \underline{-12.9\ \mathrm{kJ\ mol^{-1}}}$ (at 427 °C)

(c) $\Delta H^{\ominus} \approx \dfrac{R \ln K'/K}{\dfrac{1}{T} - \dfrac{1}{T'}}$ [12, as in Exercise 9.11]

$$\approx \frac{8.314\ \mathrm{J\,K^{-1}\,mol^{-1}} \times \ln \dfrac{31.08}{9.24}}{\dfrac{1}{700\ \mathrm{K}} - \dfrac{1}{732\ \mathrm{K}}} = \underline{+161\ \mathrm{kJ\,mol^{-1}}}$$

(d) $\Delta S^{\ominus} = \dfrac{\Delta H^{\ominus} - \Delta G^{\ominus}}{T} = \dfrac{161\ \mathrm{kJ\,mol^{-1}} - (-12.9\ \mathrm{kJ\,mol^{-1}})}{700\ \mathrm{K}}$

$$= \underline{+248\ \mathrm{J\,K^{-1}\,mol^{-1}}}$$

9.15 $\Delta H^{\ominus} = \dfrac{R \ln K'/K}{\dfrac{1}{T} - \dfrac{1}{T'}}$ [12, as in Exercise 9.11]

$$= \frac{2.303R \lg K'/K}{\dfrac{1}{T} - \dfrac{1}{T'}} = \frac{2.303R(\mathrm{p}K_{\mathrm{w}} - \mathrm{p}K'_{\mathrm{w}})}{\dfrac{1}{T} - \dfrac{1}{T'}}$$

$$= \frac{2.303 \times 8.314\ \mathrm{J\,K^{-1}\,mol^{-1}} \times (14.17 - 13.84)}{\dfrac{1}{293\ \mathrm{K}} - \dfrac{1}{303\ \mathrm{K}}}$$

$$= \underline{+56.1\ \mathrm{kJ\,mol^{-1}}}$$

9.16 $\Delta G^{\ominus} = \Delta H^{\ominus} - T\Delta S^{\ominus} = 0$ when $\Delta H^{\ominus} = T\Delta S^{\ominus}$

Therefore, the decomposition temperature (when $K = 1$) is

$$T = \frac{\Delta H^{\ominus}}{\Delta S^{\ominus}}$$

(a) $CaCO_3(s) \rightarrow CaO(s) + CO_2(g)$

$\Delta H^{\ominus} = -635.09 - 393.51 - (-1206.9)\ \mathrm{kJ\,mol^{-1}} = +178.3\ \mathrm{kJ\,mol^{-1}}$

$\Delta S^{\ominus} = 39.75 + 213.74 - 92.9\ \mathrm{J\,K^{-1}\,mol^{-1}} = +160.6\ \mathrm{J\,K^{-1}\,mol^{-1}}$

$T = \dfrac{178.3 \times 10^3\ \mathrm{J\,mol^{-1}}}{160.6\ \mathrm{J\,K^{-1}\,mol^{-1}}} = \underline{1110\ \mathrm{K}}$ (840 °C)

(b) $CuSO_4 \cdot 5H_2O(s) \rightleftharpoons CuSO_4(s) + 5H_2O(g)$

$\Delta H^{\ominus} = -771.36 + 5 \times (-241.82) - (-2279.7)\ \mathrm{kJ\ mol^{-1}} = +299.2\ \mathrm{kJ\ mol^{-1}}$

$\Delta S^{\ominus} = 109 + 5 \times 188.83 - 300.4\ \mathrm{J\ K^{-1}\ mol^{-1}} = 752.\bar{2}\ \mathrm{J\ K^{-1}\ mol^{-1}}$

Therefore,

$$T = \frac{299.2 \times 10^3\ \mathrm{J\ mol^{-1}}}{752.\bar{2}\ \mathrm{J\ K^{-1}\ mol^{-1}}} = \underline{397\ \mathrm{K}}$$

9.17 $\Delta G^{\ominus}(T) = \Delta H^{\ominus}(0) + T\,\Delta\Phi_0(T)$ [14a]

$\Delta G^{\ominus}(\mathcal{T}) = \Delta H^{\ominus}(0) + \mathcal{T}\,\Delta\Phi_0(\mathcal{T})$

$\Delta G^{\ominus}(T) - \Delta G^{\ominus}(\mathcal{T}) = T\,\Delta\Phi_0(T) - \mathcal{T}\,\Delta\Phi_0(\mathcal{T})$

Therefore,

$$\Delta G^{\ominus}(T) = \Delta G^{\ominus}(\mathcal{T}) + T\,\Delta\Phi_0(T) - \mathcal{T}\,\Delta\Phi_0(\mathcal{T})$$

(a) $N_2(g) + 3H_2(g) \rightarrow 2NH_3(g)$ at 1000 K

$\Delta\Phi_0(1000\ \mathrm{K}) = 2 \times 203.5 - 197.9 - 3 \times 137.0\ \mathrm{J\ K^{-1}\ mol^{-1}} = +201.9\ \mathrm{J\ K^{-1}\ mol^{-1}}$

$\Delta\Phi_0(\mathcal{T}) = 2 \times 159.0 - 162.4 - 3 \times 102.2\ \mathrm{J\ K^{-1}\ mol^{-1}} = +151.0\ \mathrm{J\ K^{-1}\ mol^{-1}}$

$\Delta G^{\ominus}(\mathcal{T}) = 2\Delta G_f^{\ominus}(NH_3, \mathcal{T}) = 2 \times (-16.45\ \mathrm{kJ\ mol^{-1}}) = -32.90\ \mathrm{kJ\ mol^{-1}}$

Therefore,

$$\Delta G^{\ominus}(T) = -32.90\ \mathrm{kJ\ mol^{-1}} + 1000\ \mathrm{K} \times 201.9\ \mathrm{J\ K^{-1}\ mol^{-1}}$$
$$- 298.15\ \mathrm{K} \times 151.0\ \mathrm{J\ K^{-1}\ mol^{-1}} = \underline{+124.0\ \mathrm{kJ\ mol^{-1}}}$$

$$\ln K = \frac{-\Delta G^{\ominus}(T)}{RT} = \frac{-124.10^3\ \mathrm{J\ mol^{-1}}}{8.314 \times 10^3\ \mathrm{J\ mol^{-1}}} = -14.91$$

Therefore, $K = \mathrm{e}^{-14.91} = \underline{3.3 \times 10^{-7}}$ at 1000 K

(b) $CO(g) + H_2O(g) \rightarrow H_2(g) + CO_2(g)$ at 500 K and 2000 K

$\Delta G^{\ominus}(\mathcal{T}) = \Delta G_f^{\ominus}(CO_2, g) - \Delta G_f^{\ominus}(CO, g) - \Delta G_f^{\ominus}(H_2O, g)$

$\qquad = -394.36 - (-137.17) - (-228.57)\ \mathrm{kJ\ mol^{-1}} = -28.62\ \mathrm{kJ\ mol^{-1}}$

$\Delta\Phi_0(T) = \Phi_0(H_2, T) + \Phi_0(CO_2, T) - \Phi_0(CO, T) - \Phi_0(H_2O, T)$

$\Delta\Phi_0(500\ \mathrm{K}) = -116.9 - 199.5 + 183.5 + 172.8\ \mathrm{J\ K^{-1}\ mol^{-1}} = +39.9\ \mathrm{J\ K^{-1}\ mol^{-1}}$

$\Delta\Phi_0(2000\ \mathrm{K}) = -157.6 - 258.8 - 225.9 + 223.1\ \mathrm{J\ K^{-1}\ mol^{-1}} = +65.5\ \mathrm{J\ K^{-1}\ mol^{-1}}$

$\Delta\Phi_0(\mathcal{T}) = -102.2 - 182.3 + 168.4 + 155.5\ \mathrm{J\ K^{-1}\ mol^{-1}} = +39.4\ \mathrm{J\ K^{-1}\ mol^{-1}}$

Therefore,

$$\Delta G^{\ominus}(500\ \text{K}) = -28.62\ \text{kJ mol}^{-1} + 500\ \text{K} + 39.9\ \text{J K}^{-1}\ \text{mol}^{-1}$$
$$- 298.15\ \text{K} \times 39.4\ \text{J K}^{-1}\ \text{mol}^{-1} = \underline{-20.42\ \text{kJ mol}^{-1}}$$

$$\Delta G^{\ominus}(2000\ \text{K}) = -28.62\ \text{kJ mol}^{-1} + 2000\ \text{K} \times 65.5\ \text{J K}^{-1}\ \text{mol}^{-1}$$
$$- 298.15\ \text{K} \times 39.4\ \text{J K}^{-1}\ \text{mol}^{-1} = \underline{+90.63\ \text{kJ mol}^{-1}}$$

Hence, at 500 K

$$\ln K = \frac{-\Delta G^{\ominus}}{RT} = \frac{+20.42 \times 10^{3}\ \text{J mol}^{-1}}{8.314\ \text{J K}^{-1}\ \text{mol}^{-1} \times 500\ \text{K}} = +4.91,\ K = \underline{136}$$

and at 2000 K

$$\ln K = \frac{-\Delta G^{\ominus}}{RT} = \frac{-90.63 \times 10^{3}\ \text{J mol}^{-1}}{8.314\ \text{J K}^{-1}\ \text{mol}^{-1} \times 2000\ \text{K}} = -5.45,\ K = \underline{4.3 \times 10^{-3}}$$

9.18 When [Acid] = [Salt], $\text{p}K_\text{a} = \text{pH}$ [24]

Hence, $\underline{\text{p}K_\text{a} = 5.40}$ and $K_\text{a} = 10^{-5.40} = \underline{4.0 \times 10^{-6}}$

When the solution is [Acid] = 0.015 M

$$\text{pH} = \tfrac{1}{2}\text{p}K_\text{a} - \tfrac{1}{2}\lg[\text{Acid}] \qquad [\text{Example 9.7}]$$
$$= \tfrac{1}{2} \times 5.40 - \tfrac{1}{2} \times (-1.82) = \underline{3.61}$$

9.19 (a) NH_4Cl

In water, the NH_4^+ acts as an acid in the Brønsted equilibrium

$$NH_4^+(aq) + H_2O(l) \rightleftharpoons NH_3(aq) + H_3O^+(aq) \qquad K_\text{a} = \frac{[H_3O^+][NH_3]}{[NH_4^+]}$$

Since $[NH_3] \approx [H_3O^+]$, because the water autoprotolysis can be ignored in the presence of a weak acid (NH_4^+); therefore,

$$K_\text{a} \approx \frac{[H_3O^+]^2}{[NH_4^+]} \approx \frac{[H_3O^+]^2}{S}$$

where S is the nominal concentration of the salt. Therefore,

$$[H_3O^+] \approx (SK_\text{a})^{1/2}$$

and $\text{pH} \approx \tfrac{1}{2}\text{p}K_\text{a} - \tfrac{1}{2}\lg S$

$$\approx \tfrac{1}{2} \times 9.25 - \tfrac{1}{2}\lg 0.10 = \underline{5.13}$$

(b) $NaCH_3CO_2$

The $CH_3CO_2^-$ ion acts as a weak base:

$$CH_3CO_2^-(aq) + H_2O(l) \rightleftharpoons CH_3COOH(aq) + OH^-(aq)$$

$$K_b = \frac{[CH_3COOH][OH^-]}{[CH_3CO_2^-]}$$

Then, since $[CH_3COOH] \approx [OH^-]$ and $[CH_3CO_2^-] \approx S$, the nominal concentration of the salt,

$$K_b \approx \frac{[OH^-]^2}{S}, \text{ implying that } [OH^-] \approx (SK_b)^{1/2}$$

Therefore, $pOH = \tfrac{1}{2}pK_b - \tfrac{1}{2}\lg S$

However, $pH + pOH = pK_w$, so $pH = pK_w - pOH$

$$pK_a + pK_b = pK_w, \text{ so } pK_b = pK_w - pK_a$$

Therefore,

$$pH = pK_w - \tfrac{1}{2}(pK_w - pK_a) + \tfrac{1}{2}\lg S = \tfrac{1}{2}pK_w + \tfrac{1}{2}pK_a + \tfrac{1}{2}\lg S$$
$$= \tfrac{1}{2} \times 14.00 + \tfrac{1}{2} \times 4.75 + \tfrac{1}{2} \times \lg 0.10 = \underline{8.88}$$

(c) $CH_3COOH(aq) + H_2O(l) \rightleftharpoons H_3O^+(aq) + CH_3CO_2^-(aq)$

$$K_a = \frac{[H_3O^+][CH_3CO_2^-]}{[CH_3COOH]}$$

Since we can ignore the water autoprotolysis, $[H_3O^+] \approx [CH_3CO_2^-]$, so

$$K_a \approx \frac{[H_3O^+]^2}{A}$$

where $A = [CH_3COOH]$, the nominal acid concentration [the ionization is small]. Therefore,

$$[H_3O^+] \approx (AK_a)^{1/2}, \text{ implying that } pH \approx \tfrac{1}{2}pK_a - \tfrac{1}{2}\lg A$$

Hence,

$$pH \approx \tfrac{1}{2} \times 4.75 - \tfrac{1}{2}\lg 0.100 = \underline{2.88}$$

9.20 The pH of a solution in which the nominal salt concentration is S is

$$pH = \tfrac{1}{2}pK_w + \tfrac{1}{2}pK_a + \tfrac{1}{2}\lg S \quad \text{[Exercise 9.19b]}$$

The volume of the solution at the equivalence point is

$$V = 25.00\ \text{mL} + 25.00\ \text{mL} \times \frac{0.100\ \text{M}}{0.150\ \text{M}} = 41.67\ \text{mL}$$

and the concentration of salt is

$$S = 0.100(\text{M}) \times \frac{25.00\ \text{mL}}{41.67\ \text{mL}} = 0.0600(\text{M})$$

Hence, with $\text{p}K_a = 3.86$,

$$\text{pH} = \tfrac{1}{2} \times 14.00 + \tfrac{1}{2} \times 3.86 + \tfrac{1}{2} \times \lg 0.0600 = \underline{8.3}$$

9.21 One procedure is to plot eqn 22, as in Fig. 9.6 of the text. An alternative procedure is to estimate some of the points using the expressions given in Fig. 9.7 of the text. Initially only the salt is present, and we use eqn 25a [as in Exercise 9.20]:

$$\text{pH} = \tfrac{1}{2}\text{p}K_a + \tfrac{1}{2}\text{p}K_w + \tfrac{1}{2} \lg S,\ \lg S = -1.00$$
$$= \tfrac{1}{2}(4.75 + 14.00 - 1.00) = 8.88 \qquad \text{(a)}$$

When $A \approx S$, use the Henderson–Hasselbalch equation (eqn 24):

$$\text{pH} = \text{p}K_a - \lg \frac{A}{S} = 4.75 - \lg \frac{A}{0.10}$$
$$= 3.75 - \lg A\ . \qquad \text{(b)}$$

When so much acid has been added that $A \gg S$, use the 'weak acid alone' formula, eqn 23:

$$\text{pH} = \tfrac{1}{2}\text{p}K_a - \tfrac{1}{2} \lg A \qquad \text{(a)}$$

We can draw up the following table:

A	0	0.06	0.08	0.10	0.12	0.14	0.6	0.8	1.0
pH	8.88	4.97	4.85	4.75	4.67	4.60	2.49	2.43	2.33
Formula	(a)			(b)				(c)	

The results are plotted in Fig. 9.1.

9.22 We require $\text{p}K_a \approx \text{pH(buffer)}$ [Example 9.12]. Therefore, (a) for $\text{pH} \approx 2.2$ use $Na_2HPO_4 + H_3PO_4$ since

$$H_3PO_4 + H_2O \rightleftharpoons H_3O^+ + H_2PO_4^- \qquad \text{p}K_a = 2.12$$

(b) for $\text{pH} \approx 7$ use $NaH_2PO_4 + Na_2HPO_4$ since

$$H_2PO_4^- + H_2O \rightleftharpoons H_3O^+ + HPO_4^{2-} \qquad \text{p}K_a = 7.2$$

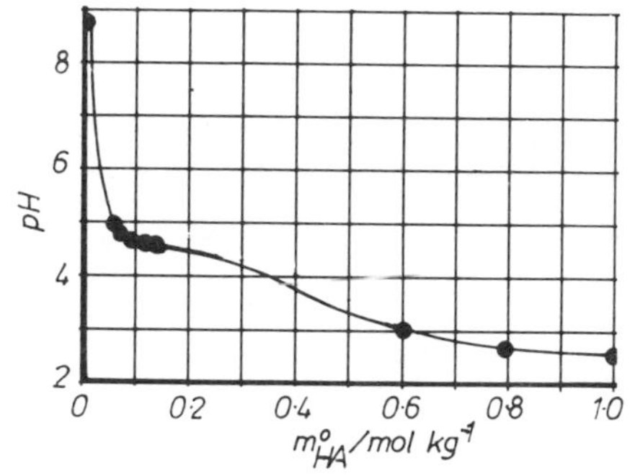

Fig 9.1

Problems

9.1 $U(s)+\frac{3}{2}H_2(g) \rightleftharpoons UH_3(s) \quad K=(p/p^{\ominus})^{-3/2}$

$$\Delta H_f^{\ominus}=RT^2\frac{d\ln K}{dT}=RT^2\frac{d}{dT}(-\tfrac{3}{2}\ln p/p^{\ominus})$$

$$=-\tfrac{3}{2}RT^2\frac{d\ln p}{dT}$$

$$=-\tfrac{3}{2}RT^2\left(\frac{14.64\times10^3\,\text{K}}{T^2}-\frac{5.65}{T}\right)$$

$$=-\tfrac{3}{2}R(14.64\times10^3\,\text{K}-5.65T)$$

$$=\underline{-(2.196\times10^4\,\text{K}-8.48\,T)R}$$

$$\Delta C_p=\left(\frac{\partial\,\Delta H_f^{\ominus}}{\partial T}\right)_p=\underline{8.48R}$$

9.2 $CaCl_2\cdot NH_3(s) \rightleftharpoons CaCl_2(s)+NH_3(g) \quad K=p/p^{\ominus}$

$$\Delta G^{\ominus}=-RT\ln K=-RT\ln p/p^{\ominus}$$

$$=-8.314\,\text{J K}^{-1}\,\text{mol}^{-1}\times400\,\text{K}\times\ln\frac{12.8\,\text{Torr}}{750\,\text{Torr}}\,[p^{\ominus}=750.3\,\text{Torr}]$$

$$=+13.5\,\text{kJ mol}^{-1}\text{ at }400\,\text{K}$$

$$\frac{\Delta G^{\ominus}(T)}{T}-\frac{\Delta G^{\ominus}(T')}{T'}=\Delta H^{\ominus}\left(\frac{1}{T}-\frac{1}{T'}\right) \qquad [12]$$

Therefore, taking $T'=400$ K,

$$\Delta G^{\ominus}(T) = \frac{T}{400\text{ K}} \times 13.5\text{ kJ mol}^{-1} + 78\text{ kJ mol}^{-1} \times \left(1 - \frac{T}{400\text{ K}}\right)$$

$$= 78\text{ kJ mol}^{-1} + \frac{(13.5 - 78)}{400}\text{ kJ mol}^{-1} \times \frac{T}{\text{K}}$$

That is,

$$\Delta G^{\ominus}(T)/(\text{kJ mol}^{-1}) = \underline{78 - 0.161(T/\text{K})}$$

9.3 $CO(g) + H_2(g) \rightleftharpoons H_2CO(l) \qquad \Delta G^{\ominus} = +28.95\text{ kJ mol}^{-1}$

$H_2CO(l) \rightleftharpoons H_2CO(g) \qquad K = p/p^{\ominus}$

$$\Delta G^{\ominus}_{\text{vap}} = -RT\ln K = -RT\ln\frac{p}{p^{\ominus}}$$

$$= -8.314\text{ J K}^{-1}\text{ mol}^{-1} \times 298\text{ K} \times \ln\frac{1500\text{ Torr}}{750\text{ Torr}}$$

$$= -1.72\text{ kJ mol}^{-1}$$

Therefore, for the reaction

$$CO(g) + H_2(g) \rightleftharpoons H_2CO(g),$$

$$\Delta G^{\ominus} = +28.95 + (-1.72)\text{ kJ mol}^{-1} = +27.23\text{ kJ mol}^{-1}$$

Hence,

$$K = e^{-27.23\times 10^3\text{ J mol}^{-1}/8.314\text{ J K}^{-1}\text{ mol}^{-1}\times 298\text{ K}}$$

$$= e^{-10.99} = \underline{1.68 \times 10^{-5}}$$

9.4 The equilibrium we need to consider in $A_2(g) \rightleftharpoons 2A(g)$

	A	A_2	Total
Initially	0	n	n
At equilibrium	$2\alpha n$	$(1-\alpha)n$	$(1+\alpha)n$
Mole fraction	$\frac{2\alpha}{1+\alpha}$	$\frac{1-\alpha}{1+\alpha}$	1
Partial pressure	$\frac{2\alpha p}{1+\alpha}$	$\left(\frac{1-\alpha}{1+\alpha}\right)p$	p

The equilibrium constant for the dissociation is

$$K_p = \frac{(p_A/p^\ominus)^2}{p_{A_2}/p^\ominus} = \frac{p_A^2}{p_{A_2}p^\ominus} = \frac{4\alpha^2(p/p^\ominus)}{1-\alpha^2}$$

We also know that

$$pV = n_{\text{total}}RT = (1+\alpha)nRT, \text{ implying that } \alpha = \frac{pV}{nRT} - 1$$

and $n = \dfrac{m}{M}$

In the first experiment,

$$\alpha = \frac{pVM}{mRT} - 1 = \frac{764.3\ \text{Torr} \times 21.45 \times 10^{-3}\ \text{L} \times 120.1\ \text{g mol}^{-1}}{0.0519\ \text{g} \times 62.364\ \text{L Torr K}^{-1}\ \text{mol}^{-1} \times 437\ \text{K}} - 1$$

$$= \underline{0.392}$$

Hence, $K = \dfrac{4 \times 0.392^2 \times (764.3/750.1)}{1 - 0.392^2} = \underline{0.740}$

In the second experiment

$$\alpha = \frac{pVM}{mRT} - 1 = \frac{764.3\ \text{Torr} \times 21.45 \times 10^{-3}\ \text{L} \times 120.1\ \text{g mol}^{-1}}{0.038\ \text{g} \times 62.364\ \text{L Torr K}^{-1}\ \text{mol}^{-1} \times 471\ \text{K}} - 1$$

$$= \underline{0.764}$$

Hence,

$$K = \frac{4 \times 0.764^2 \times (764.3/750.1)}{1 - 0.764^2} = \underline{5.71}$$

The enthalpy of dissociation is

$$\Delta H^\ominus = \frac{R \ln K'/K}{\dfrac{1}{T} - \dfrac{1}{T'}}\ [12]$$

$$= \frac{R \ln(5.71/0.740)}{\dfrac{1}{437\ \text{K}} - \dfrac{1}{471\ \text{K}}} = +103\ \text{kJ mol}^{-1}$$

The enthalpy of dimerization is the negative of this value, or $\underline{-103\ \text{kJ mol}^{-1}}$ (i.e. per mole of dimer).

9.5 $\Delta H^{\ominus} = -R\dfrac{\mathrm{d}\ln K}{\mathrm{d}(1/T)}$

$\ln K = \ln s = 2.303\,\lg s$

$$\Delta H^{\ominus}(\mathrm{H_2}) = -2.303R\frac{\mathrm{d}}{\mathrm{d}(1/T)}\left(-5.39 - \frac{768\ \mathrm{K}}{T}\right) = 2.303R \times 768\ \mathrm{K}$$

$$= \underline{+14.7\ \mathrm{kJ\ mol^{-1}}}$$

$$\Delta H^{\ominus}(\mathrm{CO}) = -2.303R\frac{\mathrm{d}}{\mathrm{d}(1/T)}\left(-5.98 - \frac{980\ \mathrm{K}}{T}\right) = 2.303R \times 980\ \mathrm{K}$$

$$= \underline{+18.8\ \mathrm{kJ\ mol^{-1}}}$$

9.6 Draw up the following table using $H_2(g) + I_2(g) \rightleftharpoons 2HI(g)$

	H_2	I_2	HI	Total
Initial amounts/mol	0.300	0.400	0.200	0.900
Change/mol	$-x$	$-x$	$+2x$	
Equilibrium amounts/mol	$0.300 - x$	$0.400 - x$	$0.200 + 2x$	0.900
Mole fraction	$\dfrac{0.300 - x}{0.900}$	$\dfrac{0.400 - x}{0.900}$	$\dfrac{0.200 + 2x}{0.900}$	1

$$K_p = \frac{(p(\mathrm{HI})/p^{\ominus})^2}{(p(\mathrm{H_2})/p^{\ominus})(p(\mathrm{I_2})/p^{\ominus})} = \frac{x(\mathrm{HI})^2}{x(\mathrm{H_2})x(\mathrm{I_2})}\ [p(\mathrm{J}) = x_{\mathrm{J}}p]$$

$$= \frac{(0.200 + 2x)^2}{(0.300 - x)(0.400 - x)} = 870\ [\text{given}]$$

Therefore,

$$0.0400 + 0.800x + 4x^2 = 870 \times (0.120 - 0.700x + x^2)$$

$$\text{or } 866x^2 - 610x + 104 = 0$$

which solves to $x = 0.289$ [$x = 0.42$ is excluded because x cannot exceed 0.300]. The final composition is therefore $\underline{0.011\ \mathrm{mol\ H_2}}$, $\underline{0.111\ \mathrm{mol\ I_2}}$, and $\underline{0.779\ \mathrm{mol\ HI}}$.

9.7 Draw up the following table using the reaction stoichiometry

$$2A + B \rightarrow 3C + 2D$$

	A	B	C	D	Total
Initial amounts/mol	1.00	2.00	0	1.00	4.00
Stated change/mol			+0.90		
Implied change/mol	−0.60	−0.30	+0.90	+0.60	
Equilibrium amounts/mol	0.40	1.70	0.90	1.60	4.60
Mole fractions	0.087	0.370	0.196	0.348	$1.00\bar{1}$

$$K_p = \frac{(p_C/p^\ominus)^3(p_D/p^\ominus)^2}{(p_A/p^\ominus)^2(p_B/p^\ominus)} = \frac{x_C^3 x_D^2}{x_A^2 x_B} \cdot \left(\frac{p}{p^\ominus}\right)^2 = K_x\left(\frac{p}{p^\ominus}\right)^2$$

$$K_x = \frac{0.196^3 \times 0.348^2}{0.087^2 \times 0.370} = \underline{0.33}$$

9.8 The equilibrium constant K and its logarithm $\ln K$ are plotted against temperature in Fig. 9.2. At $\theta = 20\,°\mathrm{C}$ we find $K = 23\,300$. Therefore, at this

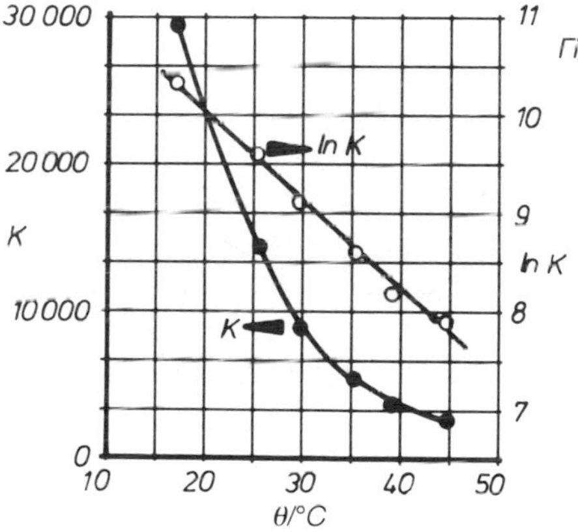

Fig 9.2

temperature,

$$\Delta G^\ominus = -RT \ln K = -8.314\ \mathrm{J\,K^{-1}\,mol^{-1}} \times 293.15\ \mathrm{K} \times \ln 23\,300$$
$$= \underline{-24.5\ \mathrm{kJ\,mol^{-1}}}$$

From the $\ln K$ graph, at 20 °C we find

$$\frac{\mathrm{d}\ln K}{\mathrm{d}T} = \frac{-0.0926}{\mathrm{K}}$$

Therefore

$$\Delta H^{\ominus} = RT^2 \frac{\mathrm{d}\ln K}{\mathrm{d}T} = 8.314\ \mathrm{J\,K^{-1}\,mol^{-1}} \times (293.15\ \mathrm{K})^2 \times (-0.0926\ \mathrm{K^{-1}})$$

$$= \underline{-66.1\ \mathrm{kJ\,mol^{-1}}}$$

$$\Delta S^{\ominus} = \frac{\Delta H^{\ominus} - \Delta G^{\ominus}}{T} = \frac{(-66.1 - (-24.5))\ \mathrm{kJ\,mol^{-1}}}{293.15\ \mathrm{K}} = \underline{-142\ \mathrm{J\,K^{-1}\,mol^{-1}}}$$

9.9 The equilibrium $I_2(g) \rightleftharpoons 2I(g)$ is described by the equilibrium constant

$$K = \frac{x(\mathrm{I})^2}{x(\mathrm{I_2})} \cdot \frac{p}{p^{\ominus}} = \frac{4\alpha^2(p/p^{\ominus})}{1-\alpha^2} \quad \text{[Problem 9.4]}$$

If $p^{\circ} = nRT/V$, then $p = (1+\alpha)p^{\circ}$, implying that

$$\alpha = \frac{p - p^{\circ}}{p^{\circ}}$$

We therefore draw up the following table:

	973 K	1073 K	1173 K
p/atm	0.06244	0.07500	0.09181
$10^4\, n_{\mathrm{I}}$	2.4709	2.4555	2.4366
p°/atm	0.05757	0.06309	0.06844 [$p^{\circ} = n_{\mathrm{I}}RT/V$]
α	0.08459	0.1888	0.3415
K_p	1.800×10^{-3}	1.109×10^{-2}	4.848×10^{-2}

$$\Delta H^{\ominus} = RT^2 \frac{\mathrm{d}\ln K}{\mathrm{d}T} = 8.314\ \mathrm{J\,K^{-1}\,mol^{-1}} \times (1073\ \mathrm{K})^2 \times \left(\frac{-3.027 - (-6.320)}{200\ \mathrm{K}}\right)$$

$$= +158\ \mathrm{kJ\,mol^{-1}}$$

9.10 $K_p = \dfrac{p(\mathrm{P})}{p(\mathrm{A})^3}$

$p(\mathrm{P}) = x_{\mathrm{P}} p_{\mathrm{P}}$ [p_{P} is vapor pressure of pure paraldehyde]

$p(\mathrm{A}) = x_{\mathrm{A}} p_{\mathrm{A}}$ [p_{A} is vapor pressure of pure acetaldehyde]

In each case, x is the mole fraction in the liquid.

$$p = p(\mathrm{A}) + p(\mathrm{P})$$

$$= x_{\mathrm{A}} p_{\mathrm{A}} + x_{\mathrm{P}} p_{\mathrm{P}} = x_{\mathrm{A}} p_{\mathrm{A}} + (1 - x_{\mathrm{A}}) p_{\mathrm{P}}$$

implying that

$$x_A = \frac{p - p_P}{p_A - p_P}, \; p(A) = \frac{(p - p_P)p_A}{p_A - p_P}$$

Similarly,

$$p(P) = \frac{(p - p_A)p_P}{p_P - p_A}$$

$$\text{Hence, } K_p = \frac{(p - p_A)p_P}{(p_P - p_A)} \cdot \frac{(p_A - p_P)^3}{(p - p_P)^3 p_A^3} = \frac{p_P(p_A - p)(p_A - p_P)^2}{p_A^3(p - p_P)^3}$$

For the vapor pressures use

$$\ln p/\text{kPa} = a - \frac{\Delta H_{vap}}{R(T/\text{K})} \text{ [given]}$$

Hence, for acetaldehyde

$$\ln p_A/\text{kPa} = 15.1 - \frac{25.6 \text{ kJ mol}^{-1}}{8.314 \text{ J K}^{-1} \text{ mol}^{-1} \times T/\text{K}} = 15.1 - \frac{307\bar{9} \text{ K}}{T}$$

$$\ln p_P/\text{kPa} = 17.2 - \frac{41.5 \text{ kJ mol}^{-1}}{8.314 \text{ J K}^{-1} \text{ mol}^{-1} \times T/\text{K}} = 17.2 - \frac{499\bar{2} \text{ K}}{T}$$

We can therefore draw up the following table:

θ/°C	20.0	22.0	26.0	28.0	30.0	32.0	34.0
T/K	293.2	295.2	299.2	301.2	303.2	305.2	207.2
p_A/kPa	98.9	106.2	122.1	130.8	139.9	149.5	159.7
p_P/kPa	1.20	1.34	1.69	1.88	2.10	2.34	2.60
p/kPa	23.9	27.3	36.5	42.6	49.9	56.9	65.1
$10^5 K_p$	7.59	5.55	2.73	1.82	1.20	0.865	0.610
$\ln K_p$	−9.49	−9.80	−10.51	−10.91	−11.33	−11.66	−12.01

θ/°C	36.0	38.0	40.0
T/K	309.2	311.2	313.2
p_A/kPa	170.4	181.6	193.5
p_P/kPa	2.89	3.21	3.55
p/kPa	74.3	85.0	96.2
$10^5 K_p$	0.433	0.301	0.216
$\ln K_p$	−12.35	−12.71	−13.05

$\ln K_p$ is plotted in Fig. 9.3. We then use

$$\Delta H^{\ominus} = RT^2 \frac{\mathrm{d} \ln K_p}{\mathrm{d}T}, \quad \mathrm{d} \ln K_p/\mathrm{d}T = -0.185\ \mathrm{K}^{-1} \text{ at } 298\ \mathrm{K}$$

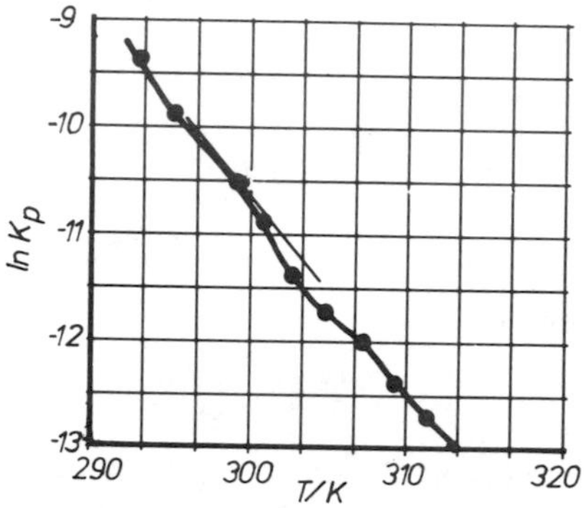

Fig 9.3

Therefore,

$$\Delta H^{\ominus} = 8.314\ \mathrm{J\ K^{-1}\ mol^{-1}} \times (298.15\ \mathrm{K})^2 \times (-0.185\ \mathrm{K^{-1}}) = \underline{-137\ \mathrm{kJ\ mol^{-1}}}$$

Since $\Delta G^{\ominus} = -RT \ln K = -8.314\ \mathrm{J\ K^{-1}\ mol^{-1}} \times 298.15\ \mathrm{K} \times (-10.3) =$ $\underline{+26\ \mathrm{kJ\ mol^{-1}}}$

It follows that

$$\Delta S^{\ominus} = \frac{\Delta H^{\ominus} - \Delta G^{\ominus}}{T} = \frac{(-137 - 26)\ \mathrm{kJ\ mol^{-1}}}{298.15\ \mathrm{K}} = \underline{-547\ \mathrm{J\ K^{-1}\ mol^{-1}}}$$

For the values in the liquid, we use

$$3\mathrm{A}(l) \rightarrow 3\mathrm{A}(g) \quad \Delta H^{\ominus}_{\mathrm{vap}} = 3 \times 25.6\ \mathrm{kJ\ mol^{-1}} = +76.8\ \mathrm{kJ\ mol^{-1}}$$

$$\Delta S^{\ominus}_{\mathrm{vap}} = \frac{3 \times 25.6\ \mathrm{kJ\ mol^{-1}}}{294\ \mathrm{K}} = +261\ \mathrm{J\ K^{-1}\ mol^{-1}}$$

$$\mathrm{A}_3(l) \rightarrow \mathrm{A}_3(g) \quad \Delta H^{\ominus}_{\mathrm{vap}} = 41.5\ \mathrm{kJ\ mol^{-1}}$$

$$\Delta S^{\ominus}_{\mathrm{vap}} = \frac{41.5\ \mathrm{kJ\ mol^{-1}}}{398\ \mathrm{K}} = +104\ \mathrm{J\ K^{-1}\ mol^{-1}}$$

Therefore, for $3\mathrm{A}(l) \rightarrow \mathrm{A}_3(l)$

$$\Delta H^{\ominus} = 76.8 - 137 - 41.5\ \mathrm{kJ\ mol^{-1}} = \underline{-102\ \mathrm{kJ\ mol^{-1}}}$$

$$\Delta S^{\ominus} = 261 - 547 - 104\ \mathrm{J\ K^{-1}\ mol^{-1}} = \underline{-390\ \mathrm{J\ K^{-1}\ mol^{-1}}}$$

9.11 $K = K_\gamma K_p$, but $\left(\frac{\partial K}{\partial p}\right)_T = 0$ [8]

Therefore

$$\left(\frac{\partial K}{\partial p}\right)_T = K_\gamma\left(\frac{\partial K_p}{\partial p}\right)_T + K_p\left(\frac{\partial K_\gamma}{\partial p}\right)_T = 0$$

which implies that

$$\left(\frac{\partial K_\gamma}{\partial p}\right)_T = -\left(\frac{\partial K_p}{\partial p}\right)_T \times \frac{K_\gamma}{K_p}$$

and therefore that if K_p increases with pressure, K_γ must decrease [because K_γ/K_p is positive].

9.12 We draw up the following table using the stoichiometry $A + 3B \rightarrow 2C$ and $\Delta n = \nu\xi$:

	A	B	C	Total
Initial amount/n	1	3	0	4
Change	$-\xi$	-3ξ	$+2\xi$	
Equilibrium amount/n	$1-\xi$	$3(1-\xi)$	2ξ	$2(2-\xi)$
Mole fraction	$\dfrac{1-\xi}{2(2-\xi)}$	$\dfrac{3(1-\xi)}{2(2-\xi)}$	$\dfrac{\xi}{2-\xi}$	1

$$K_p = \frac{(p_C/p^\ominus)^2}{(p_A/p^\ominus)(p_B/p^\ominus)^3} = \frac{x_C^2}{x_A x_B^3}\left(\frac{p^\ominus}{p}\right)^2$$

$$= \frac{\xi^2}{(2-\xi)^2} \cdot \frac{2(2-\xi)}{1-\xi} \cdot \frac{2^3(2-\xi)^3}{3^3(1-\xi)^3} \cdot \left(\frac{p^\ominus}{p}\right)^2$$

$$= \frac{16(2-\xi)^2\xi^2}{27(1-\xi)^4} \cdot \left(\frac{p^\ominus}{p}\right)^2$$

Since K_p is independent of the pressure

$$\frac{(2-\xi)^2\xi^2}{(1-\xi)^4} = a^2\left(\frac{p}{p^\ominus}\right)^2 \qquad a^2 = \frac{27}{16}K_p, \text{ a constant.}$$

Therefore

$$(2-\xi)\xi = a\left(\frac{p}{p^{\ominus}}\right)(1-\xi)^2$$

$$(1+ap/p^{\ominus})\xi^2 - 2(1+ap/p^{\ominus})\xi + ap/p^{\ominus} = 0$$

which solves to

$$\xi = 1 - \left(\frac{1}{1+ap/p^{\ominus}}\right)^{1/2}$$

We choose the root with the negative sign because ξ lies between 0 and 1.

The variation of ξ with p is shown in Fig. 9.4.

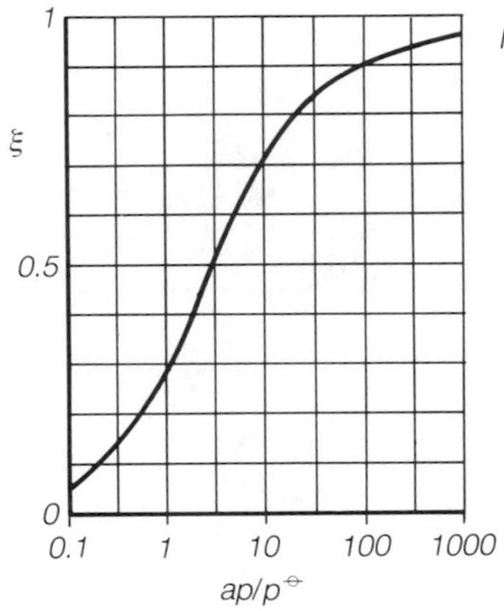

Fig 9.4

9.13 $K_p = \frac{p(NO_2)^2}{p(N_2O_4)p^{\ominus}}$ with $p(NO_2) + p(N_2O_4) = p$

Since $p(NO_2)^2 + p(NO_2)K_p - pK_p = 0 \qquad [p \equiv p/p^{\ominus}]$

$$p(NO_2) = \frac{(1+4p/K_p)^{1/2} - 1}{(2/K_p)}$$

We choose the root with the positive sign because p must be positive.

For equal absorptions,

$$l_1 p_1(NO_2) = l_2 p_2(NO_2), \text{ or } \rho p_1 = p_2 \qquad [\rho = l_1/l_2]$$

Therefore

$$\rho\{(1+4p_1/K_p)^{1/2}-1\}=(1+4p_2K_p)^{1/2}-1$$

$$\rho(1+4p_1/K_p)^{1/2}=\rho-1+(1+4p_2/K_p)^{1/2}$$

$$\rho^2(1+4p_1/K_p)=(\rho-1)^2+(1+4p_2/K_p)+2(\rho-1)(1+4p_2/K_p)^{1/2}$$

$$\rho-1+2(p_1\rho^2-p_2)/K_p=(\rho-1)(1+4p_2/K_p)^{1/2}$$

$$\{\rho-1+2(p_1\rho^2-p_2)/K_p\}^2=(\rho-1)^2(1+4p_2/K_p)$$

$$(p_1\rho^2-p_2)^2/K_p^2+\{(\rho-1)(p_1\rho^2-p_2)-(\rho-1)^2p_2\}/K_p=0$$

Hence $K_p=\dfrac{(p_1\rho^2-p_2)^2}{\rho(\rho-1)(p_2-p_1\rho)p^{\ominus}}$ [reinstating $p^{\ominus}$]

Since $\rho=\dfrac{395\text{ mm}}{75\text{ mm}}=5.2\overline{7}$

$$p^{\ominus}K_p=\frac{(27.8p_1-p_2)^2}{22.5(p_2-5.27p_1)}$$

We can therefore draw up the following table:

Absorbance	p_1/Torr	p_2/Torr	$p^{\ominus}K_p$/Torr
0.05	1.00	5.47	110.8
0.10	2.10	12.00	102.5
0.15	3.15	18.65	103.0

Mean: 105

Hence, since $p^{\ominus}=750$ Torr (1 bar), $K_p=\underline{0.140}$

9.14 $\Delta G=\Delta H-T\Delta S$

$$\Delta H'=\Delta H+\int_T^{T'}\Delta C_p\,\mathrm{d}T$$

$$\Delta S'=\Delta S+\int_T^{T'}\frac{\Delta C_p}{T}\,\mathrm{d}T$$

$$\Delta G'=\Delta G+\int_T^{T'}\Delta C_p\,\mathrm{d}T+(T-T')\,\Delta S-T'\int_T^{T'}\frac{\Delta C_p}{T}\,\mathrm{d}T$$

$$= \Delta G + (T - T')\,\Delta S + \int_T^{T'} \left(1 - \frac{T'}{T}\right) \Delta C_p \,\mathrm{d}T$$

$$\Delta C_p = \Delta a + T\,\Delta b + \frac{\Delta c}{T^2}$$

$$\left(1 - \frac{T'}{T}\right) \Delta C_p = \Delta a + T\Delta b + \frac{\Delta c}{T^2} - \frac{T'\Delta a}{T} - T'\Delta b - \frac{T'\Delta c}{T^3}$$

$$= \Delta a - T'\,\Delta b + T\Delta b - \frac{T'\Delta a}{T} + \frac{\Delta c}{T^2} - \frac{T'\Delta c}{T^3}$$

$$\int_T^{T'} \left(1 - \frac{T'}{T}\right) \Delta C_p \,\mathrm{d}T = (\Delta a - T'\,\Delta b)(T' - T) + \tfrac{1}{2}(T'^2 - T^2)\,\Delta b$$

$$- T'\,\Delta a \ln\frac{T'}{T} + \Delta c\left(\frac{1}{T} - \frac{1}{T'}\right)$$

$$- \tfrac{1}{2}T'\,\Delta c\left(\frac{1}{T^2} - \frac{1}{T'^2}\right)$$

Therefore, $\underline{\Delta G' = \Delta G + (T - T')\,\Delta S + \alpha\,\Delta a + \beta\,\Delta b + \gamma\,\Delta c}$

where $\alpha = T' - T - T' \ln\dfrac{T'}{T}$

$$\beta = \tfrac{1}{2}(T'^2 - T^2) - T'(T' - T)$$

$$\gamma = \frac{1}{T} - \frac{1}{T'} + \tfrac{1}{2}T'\left(\frac{1}{T'^2} - \frac{1}{T^2}\right)$$

For water,

$H_2(g) + \tfrac{1}{2}O_2(g) \rightarrow H_2O(l)$ $\qquad \Delta G_f^{\ominus}(\mathfrak{T}) = -237.13\ \mathrm{kJ\ mol^{-1}}$

$\Delta S^{\ominus}(\mathfrak{T}) = -163.34\ \mathrm{J\ K^{-1}\ mol^{-1}}$

$\Delta a = a(H_2O) - a(H_2) - \tfrac{1}{2}a(O_2)$

$= 75.48 - 27.28 - 14.98\ \mathrm{J\ K^{-1}\ mol^{-1}} = +33.22\ \mathrm{J\ K^{-1}\ mol^{-1}}$

$\Delta b = 0 - 3.26 \times 10^{-3} - 2.09 \times 10^{-3}\ \mathrm{J\ K^{-2}\ mol^{-1}} = -5.35 \times 10^{-3}\ \mathrm{J\ K^{-2}\ mol^{-1}}$

$\Delta c = 0 - 0.50 \times 10^5 + 0.83 \times 10^5\ \mathrm{J\ K\ mol^{-1}} = +0.33 \times 10^5\ \mathrm{J\ K\ mol^{-1}}$

$T = 298\ \mathrm{K}$, $T' = 372\ \mathrm{K}$, so

$\alpha = -8.5\ \mathrm{K}$, $\beta = -2738\ \mathrm{K^2}$, $\gamma = -8.288 \times 10^{-5}\ \mathrm{K^{-1}}$

and so

$$\Delta G_f^{\ominus}(372\text{ K}) = -237.13\text{ kJ mol}^{-1} + (-74\text{ K}) \times (-163.34\text{ J K}^{-1}\text{ mol}^{-1})$$
$$+ (-8.5\text{ K}) \times (33.22 \times 10^{-3}\text{ kJ K}^{-1}\text{ mol}^{-1})$$
$$+ (-2738\text{ K}^2) \times (-5.53 \times 10^{-6}\text{ kJ K}^{-2}\text{ mol}^{-1})$$
$$+ (-8.288 \times 10^{-5}\text{ K}^{-1}) \times (0.33 \times 10^2\text{ kJ K mol}^{-1})$$
$$= -237.13 + 12.09 - 0.28 + 0.015 - 0.003\text{ kJ mol}^{-1}$$
$$= \underline{-225.31\text{ kJ mol}^{-1}}$$

Note that the β and γ terms are not significant (for this reaction and temperature range).

10. Equilibrium electrochemistry

Exercises

10.1 $HgCl_2(s) \rightleftharpoons Hg^{2+}(aq) + 2Cl^-(aq) \quad K = [Hg^{2+}][Cl^-]^2$

$[Cl^-] = 2 \times [Hg^{2+}]$; therefore $K = 4[Hg^{2+}]^3$

and the solubility of the salt is

$$S = [Hg^{2+}] = (\tfrac{1}{4}K)^{1/3}\ \text{M}$$

From $\Delta G^\ominus = \Delta G_f^\ominus(Hg^{2+}) + 2\Delta G_f^\ominus(Cl^-) - \Delta G_f^\ominus(HgCl_2)$

$$= +164.40 + 2 \times (-131.23) - (-178.6)\ \text{kJ mol}^{-1} = +80.54\ \text{kJ mol}^{-1}$$

$$\ln K = \frac{-\Delta G^\ominus}{RT} = \frac{-80.54 \times 10^3\ \text{J mol}^{-1}}{8.314\ \text{J K}^{-1}\ \text{mol}^{-1} \times 298.15\ \text{K}} = -32.49$$

Hence $K = 7.75 \times 10^{-15}$

and $\quad S = \underline{1.25 \times 10^{-5}\ \text{M}}$

10.2

		$\Delta G^\ominus/(\text{kJ mol}^{-1})$ [Section 10.1]		
		Cl^-	F^-	
Dissociation of H_2	$\tfrac{1}{2}H_2 \rightarrow H$	+203	+203	
Ionization of H	$H \rightarrow H^+ + e^-$	+1318	+1318	
Hydration of H^+	$H^+(g) \rightarrow H^+(aq)$	x	x	
Dissociation of X_2	$\tfrac{1}{2}X_2 \rightarrow X$	+122	79	
Electron gain by X	$X + e^- \rightarrow X^-$	−348.7	−322	[Table 2.5]
Hydration of X^-	$X^-(g) \rightarrow X^-(aq)$	y	y'	
Overall		$\Delta G_f^\ominus(Cl^-)$	$\Delta G_f^\ominus(F^-)$	

Hence $\Delta G_f^\ominus(Cl^-) = x + y + 1294\ \text{kJ mol}^{-1}$

$$\Delta G_f^\ominus(F^-) = x + y' + 1278\ \text{kJ mol}^{-1}$$

and $\Delta G_f^\ominus(Cl^-) - \Delta G_f^\ominus(F^-) = y - y' + 16\ \text{kJ mol}^{-1}$

The ratio of hydration Gibbs functions is

$$\frac{\Delta G_H^\ominus(F^-)}{\Delta G_H^\ominus(Cl^-)} = \frac{r(Cl^-)}{r(F^-)}\ [1]$$

$$= \frac{181\ \text{pm}}{131\ \text{pm}}\ [\text{Example 10.3}] = 1.38$$

Therefore, since $\Delta G_{\mathrm{H}}^{\ominus}(\mathrm{Cl^-}) = -379\ \mathrm{kJ\ mol^{-1}}$ [Example 10.3],

$$\Delta G_{\mathrm{H}}^{\ominus}(\mathrm{F^-}) = 1.38 \times (-379\ \mathrm{kJ\ mol^{-1}}) = -523\ \mathrm{kJ\ mol^{-1}}$$

and $\Delta G_{\mathrm{f}}^{\ominus}(\mathrm{Cl^-}) - \Delta G_{\mathrm{f}}^{\ominus}(\mathrm{F^-}) = -379 - (-523) + 16\ \mathrm{kJ\ mol^{-1}} = +160\ \mathrm{kJ\ mol^{-1}}$

Hence,

$$\Delta G_{\mathrm{f}}^{\ominus}(\mathrm{F^-}) = -131.23 - 160\ \mathrm{kJ\ mol^{-1}} = \underline{-290\ \mathrm{kJ\ mol^{-1}}}$$

(The 'experimental' value, Table 2.10, is $-278.79\ \mathrm{kJ\ mol^{-1}}$.)

10.3 $I = \frac{1}{2}\sum_i m_i z_i^2$

and for an $\mathrm{M}_a\mathrm{X}_b$ salt, $m_+ = am$, $m_- = bm$, so

$I = \frac{1}{2}(az_+^2 + bz_-^2)m$

$I(\mathrm{KCl}) = \frac{1}{2}(1+1)m = m$

$I(\mathrm{MgCl_2}) = \frac{1}{2}(2^2 + 2\times 1)m = 3m$

$I(\mathrm{FeCl_3}) = \frac{1}{2}(3^2 + 3\times 1)m = 6m$

$I(\mathrm{Al_2(SO_4)_3}) = \frac{1}{2}(2\times 3^2 + 3\times 2^2)m = 15m$

$I(\mathrm{CuSO_4}) = \frac{1}{2}(2^2 + 2^2)m = 4m$

10.4 $I = I(\mathrm{KCl}) + I(\mathrm{CuSO_4}) = m(\mathrm{KCl}) + 4m(\mathrm{CuSO_4})$ [Exercise 10.3]

$= 0.10 + 4\times 0.20\ \mathrm{mol\ kg^{-1}} = \underline{0.90\ \mathrm{mol\ kg^{-1}}}$

10.5 $I = I(\mathrm{K_3[Fe(CN)_6]}) + I(\mathrm{KCl}) + I(\mathrm{NaBr})$

$= \frac{1}{2}(3 + 3^2)m(\mathrm{K_3[Fe(CN)_6]}) + m(\mathrm{KCl}) + m(\mathrm{NaBr})$

$= 6\times 0.040 + 0.030 + 0.050\ \mathrm{mol\ kg^{-1}} = \underline{0.320\ \mathrm{mol\ kg^{-1}}}$

10.6 $I = I(\mathrm{KNO_3}) = m(\mathrm{KNO_3}) = 0.150\ \mathrm{mol\ kg^{-1}}$

Therefore, the ionic strengths of the added salts must be $0.100\ \mathrm{mol\ kg^{-1}}$.

(a) $I(\mathrm{Ca(NO_3)_2}) = \frac{1}{2}(2^2 + 2)m = 3m$

Therefore, the solution should be made $\frac{1}{3}\times 0.100\ \mathrm{mol\ kg^{-1}} = 0.0333\ \mathrm{mol\ kg^{-1}}$ in $\mathrm{Ca(NO_3)_2}$. The mass that should be added to 500 g of the solution is therefore

$$0.500\ \mathrm{kg} \times 0.0333\ \mathrm{mol\ kg^{-1}} \times 164\ \mathrm{g\ mol^{-1}} = \underline{2.73\ \mathrm{g}}$$

[We are neglecting the fact that the mass of solution is slightly different from the mass of solvent.]

(b) $I(\mathrm{NaCl}) = m$; therefore, with $m = 0.100\ \mathrm{mol\ kg^{-1}}$,

$$0.500\ \mathrm{kg} \times 0.100\ \mathrm{mol\ kg^{-1}} \times 58.4\ \mathrm{g\ mol^{-1}} = \underline{2.92\ \mathrm{g}}$$

10.7 $I(\mathrm{KCl}) = m$, $I(\mathrm{CuSO_4}) = 4m$

For $I(\mathrm{KCl}) = I(\mathrm{CuSO_4})$, $m(\mathrm{KCl}) = 4m(\mathrm{CuSO_4})$.

Therefore, if $m(\mathrm{KCl}) = 1.00\ \mathrm{mol\ kg^{-1}}$, we require $m(\mathrm{CuSO_4}) = \underline{0.25\ \mathrm{mol\ kg^{-1}}}$

10.8 $\gamma_\pm = (\gamma_+^p \gamma_-^q)^{1/s} \quad s = p + q$ [4a]

with $p = 1$, $q = 2$, $s = 3$, $\underline{\gamma_\pm = (\gamma_+ \gamma_-^2)^{1/3}}$

10.9 $I(\mathrm{LaCl_3}) = \frac{1}{2}(3^2 + 3)m = 6m = 3.000\ \mathrm{mol\ kg^{-1}}$

From the limiting law,

$$\lg \gamma_\pm = -0.509|z_+ z_-|(I/\mathrm{mol\ kg^{-1}})^{1/2}$$
$$= -0.509 \times 3 \times (3.000)^{1/2} = -2.64\overline{5}$$

Hence

$\gamma_\pm = 2.3 \times 10^{-3}$

and the error is about $\underline{1 \times 10^4 \text{ per cent (!)}}$.

10.10 $\lg \gamma_\pm = \dfrac{-A|z_+ z_-|I^{1/2}}{1 + BI^{1/2}}$ [7]

$$B = -\left(\frac{1}{I^{1/2}} + \frac{A|z_+ z_-|}{\lg \gamma_\pm}\right)$$

For HBr, $I = m$ and $|z_+ z_-| = 1$; so

$$B = -\left(\frac{1}{m^{1/2}} + \frac{0.509}{\lg \gamma_\pm}\right) \quad [m \equiv m/m^\ominus]$$

Hence, draw up the following table:

$m/(\mathrm{mol\ kg^{-1}})$	5.0×10^{-3}	10.0×10^{-3}	20.0×10^{-3}
$\gamma_\pm$	0.930	0.907	0.879
B	−2.01	−2.01	−2.02

10.11 $\mathrm{CaF_2}(s) \rightleftharpoons \mathrm{Ca^{2+}}(aq) + 2\mathrm{F^-}(aq) \quad K_s = 3.9 \times 10^{-11}$

$$\Delta G^{\ominus} = -RT \ln K_s = -8.314\ \text{J K}^{-1}\ \text{mol}^{-1} \times 298.15\ \text{K} \times \ln 3.9 \times 10^{-11}$$

$$= +59.4\ \text{kJ mol}^{-1}$$

$$= \Delta G_f^{\ominus}(\text{CaF}_2, aq) - \Delta G_f^{\ominus}(\text{CaF}_2, s)$$

Hence,

$$\Delta G_f^{\ominus}(\text{CaF}_2, aq) = \Delta G^{\ominus} + \Delta G_f^{\ominus}(\text{CaF}_2, s)$$

$$= 59.4 - 1167.3\ \text{kJ mol}^{-1} = \underline{-1107.9\ \text{kJ mol}^{-1}}$$

10.12 $\Delta E = \dfrac{RT}{F} \ln \dfrac{a_1(\text{H}^+)}{a_2(\text{H}^+)}$ [Nernst equation]

$$= \frac{RT}{F} \ln \frac{\gamma_{\pm} m_1}{\gamma_{\pm} m_2} = 25.7\ \text{mV} \times \ln \frac{20.0 \times 0.879}{5.0 \times 0.930}$$

$$= \underline{34.2\ \text{mV}}$$

10.13 R: $\text{Cl}_2(g) + 2\text{e}^- \rightarrow 2\text{Cl}^-(aq)$ $E^{\ominus} = +1.36\ \text{V}$

L: $\text{Mn}^{2+}(aq) + 2\text{e}^- \rightarrow \text{Mn}(s)$ $E^{\ominus} = ?$

The call corresponding to these half-reactions is

$\text{Mn}|\text{MnCl}_2(aq)|\text{Cl}_2(g)|\text{Pt}$ $E^{\ominus} = 1.36\ \text{V} - E^{\ominus}(\text{Mn}, \text{Mn}^{2+})$

Hence, $E^{\ominus}(\text{Mn}, \text{Mn}^{2+}) = 1.36\ \text{V} - 2.54\ \text{V} = \underline{-1.18\ \text{V}}$

10.14 (a) R: $2\text{Ag}^+(aq) + 2\text{e}^- \rightarrow 2\text{Ag}(s)$ $+0.80\ \text{V}$

L: $\text{Zn}^+(aq) + 2\text{e}^- \rightarrow \text{Zn}(s)$ $-0.76\ \text{V}$

Overall (R − L): $2\text{Ag}^+(aq) + \text{Zn}(s) \rightarrow 2\text{Ag}(s) + \text{Zn}^{2+}(aq)$ $+1.56\ \text{V}$

(b) R: $2\text{H}^+(aq) + 2\text{e}^- \rightarrow \text{H}_2(g)$ 0

L: $\text{Cd}^{2+}(aq) + 2\text{e}^- \rightarrow \text{Cd}(s)$ $-0.40\ \text{V}$

R − L: $\text{Cd}(s) + 2\text{H}^+(aq) \rightarrow \text{Cd}^{2+}(aq) + \text{H}_2(g)$ $+0.40\ \text{V}$

(c) R: $\text{Cr}^{3+}(aq) + 3\text{e}^- \rightarrow \text{Cr}(s)$ -0.74

L: $3[\text{Fe(CN)}_6]^{3-}(aq) + 3\text{e}^- \rightarrow 3[\text{Fe(CN)}_6]^{4-}(aq)$ $+0.36\ \text{V}$

R − L: $\text{Cr}^{3+}(aq) + 3[\text{Fe(CN)}_6]^{4-}(aq) \rightarrow \text{Cr}(s)$

$+ 3[\text{Fe(CN)}_6]^{3-}(aq)$ $-1.10\ \text{V}$

(d) R: $\text{Ag}_2\text{CrO}_4(s) + 2\text{e}^- \rightarrow 2\text{Ag}(s) + \text{CrO}_4^{2-}(aq)$ $+0.45\ \text{V}$

L: $\text{Cl}_2(g) + 2\text{e}^- \rightarrow 2\text{Cl}^-(aq)$ $+1.36\ \text{V}$

R − L: $Ag_2CrO_4(s) + 2Cl^-(aq)$

$\rightarrow 2Ag(s) + CrO_4^{2-}(aq) + Cl_2(g)$ −0.91 V

(e) R: $Sn^{4+}(aq) + 2e^- \rightarrow Sn^{2+}(aq)$ +0.15 V

L: $2Fe^{3+}(aq) + 2e^- \rightarrow 2Fe^{2+}(aq)$ +0.77 V

R − L: $Sn^{4+}(aq) + 2Fe^{2+}(aq) \rightarrow Sn^{2+}(aq) + 2Fe^{3+}(aq)$ −0.62 V

(f) R: $MnO_2(s) + 4H^+(aq) + 2e^- \rightarrow Mn^{2+}(aq) + 2H_2O(l)$ +1.23 V

L: $Cu^{2+}(aq) + 2e^- \rightarrow Cu(s)$ +0.34 V

R − L: $Cu(s) + MnO_2(s) + 4H^+(aq)$

$\rightarrow Cu^{2+}(aq) + Mn^{2+}(aq) + 2H_2O(l)$ +0.89 V

10.15 We first identify the half-reactions, and then set up the corresponding cell:

(a) R: $Cu^{2+}(aq) + 2e^- \rightarrow Cu(s)$ +0.34 V

L: $Zn^{2+}(aq) + 2e^- \rightarrow Zn(s)$ −0.76 V

Hence the cell is

$Zn(s)|ZnSO_4(aq)\|CuSO_4(aq)|Cu(s)$ +1.10 V

(b) R: $AgCl(s) + e^- \rightarrow Ag(s) + Cl^-(aq)$ +0.22 V

L: $H^+(aq) + e^- \rightarrow \frac{1}{2}H_2(g)$ 0

and the cell is

$Pt|H_2(g)|H^+(aq)|AgCl(s)|Ag(s)$

or $Pt|H_2(g)|HCl(aq)|AgCl(s)|Ag(s)$ +0.22 V

(c) R: $O_2(g) + 4H^+(aq) + 4e^- \rightarrow 2H_2O(l)$ +1.23 V

L: $4H^+(aq) + 4e^- \rightarrow 2H_2(g)$ 0

and the cell is

$Pt|H_2(g)|H^+(aq), Cl^-(aq)|O_2(g)|Pt$ +1.23 V

(d) R: $2H_2O(l) + 2e^- \rightarrow 2OH^-(aq) + H_2(g)$ −0.83 V

L: $2Na^+(aq) + 2e^- \rightarrow 2Na(s)$ −2.71 V

and the cell is

$Na(s)|Na^+(aq), OH^-(aq)|H_2(g)|Pt$ +1.88 V

or more simply

$Na(s)|NaOH(aq)|H_2(g)|Pt$

(e) R: $I_2(s) + 2e^- \rightarrow 2I^-(aq)$ $\quad +0.54\ V$

L: $2H^+(aq) + 2e^- \rightarrow H_2(g)$ $\quad 0$

and the cell is

$Pt|H_2(g)|H^+(aq), I^-(aq)|I_2(s)|Pt$ $\quad +0.54\ V$

or more simply

$Pt|H_2(g)|HI(aq)|I_2(s)|Pt$

10.16 See the solutions above, where we have used $E^\ominus = E_R^\ominus - E_L^\ominus$

10.17 R: $2Tl^+(aq) + 2e^- \rightarrow 2Tl(s)$ $\quad -0.34\ V$

L: $Hg^{2+}(aq) + 2e^- \rightarrow Hg(l)$ $\quad 0.86\ V$

(a) $E^\ominus = -1.20\ V$

(b) Overall: $2Tl^+(aq) + Hg(l) \rightarrow 2Tl(s) + Hg^{2+}(aq)$

$$Q = \frac{a(Hg^{2+})}{a(Tl^+)^2}, \quad \nu = 2$$

$$E = E^\ominus - \frac{RT}{\nu F} \ln Q \ [11]$$

$$= -1.20\ V - \frac{25.693\ mV}{2} \times \ln \frac{0.150}{0.93^2}$$

$$= -1.20\ V + 0.023\ V = \underline{-1.18\ V}$$

10.18 (a) $2Na(s) + 2H_2O(l) \rightarrow 2NaOH(aq) + H_2(g)$ $\quad E^\ominus = +1.88\ V$ [Exercise 10.16d]

Therefore, $\Delta G^\ominus = -\nu F E^\ominus$

$$= -2 \times 96.485\ kC\ mol^{-1} \times 1.88\ V = \underline{-363\ kJ\ mol^{-1}}$$

(b) $2K(s) + 2H_2O(l) \rightarrow 2KOH(aq) + H_2(g)$

$$E^\ominus = E^\ominus(H_2O, OH^-, H_2) - E^\ominus(K, K^+) = -0.83\ V - (-2.93\ V)$$

$$= +2.10\ V \text{ with } \nu = 2$$

Therefore, $\Delta G^\ominus = -2 \times 96.485\ kC\ mol^{-1} \times 2.10\ V = \underline{-405\ kJ\ mol^{-1}}$

(c) R: $S_2O_8^{2-}(aq) + 2e^- \rightarrow 2SO_4^{2-}(aq)$ $+2.05$ V
L: $I_2(s) + 2e^- \rightarrow 2I^-(aq)$ $+0.54$ V } $+1.51$ V

$\Delta G^\ominus = -2 \times 96.485\ \text{kC mol}^{-1} \times 1.51\ \text{V} = \underline{-291\ \text{kJ mol}^{-1}}$

(d) $Zn^{2+}(aq) + 2e^- \rightarrow Zn(s)$ -0.76 V
$Pb^{2+}(aq) + 2e^- \rightarrow Pb(s)$ -0.13 V } $E^\ominus = -0.63$ V

$\Delta G^\ominus = -2 \times 96.485\ \text{kC mol}^{-1} \times (-0.63\ \text{V}) = \underline{+122\ \text{kJ mol}^{-1}}$

10.19 (a) $E^\ominus = \dfrac{-\Delta G^\ominus}{\nu F} = \dfrac{+62.5\ \text{kJ mol}^{-1}}{2 \times 96.485\ \text{kC mol}^{-1}} = \underline{+0.324\ \text{V}}$

(b) $E^\ominus = E^\ominus(Fe^{3+}, Fe^{2+}) - E^\ominus(Ag, Ag_2CrO_4, CrO_4^{2-})$

Therefore,

$$E^\ominus(Ag, Ag_2CrO_4, CrO_4^{2-}) = E^\ominus(Fe^{3+}, Fe^{2+}) - E^\ominus = +0.77 - 0.324\ \text{V} = \underline{+0.45\ \text{V}}$$

10.20 R: $Cd^{2+}(aq) + 2e^- \rightarrow Cd(s)$ -0.40 V
L: $2AgBr(s) + 2e^- \rightarrow 2Ag(s) + 2Br^-(aq)$ $+0.07$ V

Hence, overall (R − L):

$Cd^{2+}(aq) + 2Ag(s) + 2Br^-(aq) \rightarrow Cd(s) + 2AgBr(s)$ -0.47 V

$$Q = \frac{1}{a(Cd^{2+})a(Br^-)^2}$$

$$E = E^\ominus + \frac{RT}{2F} \ln a(Cd^{2+})a(Br^-)^2$$

$$= E^\ominus + \frac{RT}{2F} \ln m(Cd^{2+})m(Br^-)^2 + \frac{2.303RT}{2F} \lg \gamma_\pm(Cd^{2+})\gamma_\pm(Br^-)^2$$

$$\lg \gamma_\pm(Cd^{2+}) \approx -A|z_+z_-|I^{1/2},\ I = 3m = 0.030\ \text{mol kg}^{-1}$$
$$\approx -0.509 \times 2 \times (0.030)^{1/2} = -0.18$$

$$\lg \gamma_\pm(Br^-) \approx -A|z_+z_-|I^{1/2},\ I = m = 0.050\ \text{mol kg}^{-1}$$
$$\approx -0.509 \times 1 \times (0.050)^{1/2} = -0.11$$

Hence,

$$E = -0.47\ \text{V} + \frac{25.693\ \text{mV}}{2} \ln 0.010 \times 0.050^2$$
$$+ \frac{2.303 \times 25.693\ \text{mV}}{2}(-0.18 + 2 \times (-0.11)) = \underline{-0.62\ \text{V}}$$

10.21 $2Ag(s) + Fe^{2+}(aq) \rightarrow 2Ag^+(aq) + Fe(s)$

$E = E^{\ominus}(Fe^{2+}, Fe) - E^{\ominus}(Ag^+, Ag) = -0.44 - 0.80\ V = \underline{-1.24\ V}$

$$\Delta G^{\ominus} = 2\Delta G_f^{\ominus}(Ag^+, aq) - \Delta G_f^{\ominus}(Fe^{2+}, aq)$$
$$= 2 \times 77.1 - (-78.90)\ kJ\ mol^{-1} = \underline{+223.1\ kJ\ mol^{-1}}$$

$$\Delta H^{\ominus} = 2\Delta G^{\ominus}(Ag^+, aq) - \Delta G_f^{\ominus}(Fe^{2+}, aq)$$
$$= 2 \times 105.58 - (-89.1)\ kJ\ mol^{-1} = \underline{+300.3\ kJ\ mol^{-1}}$$

$$\left(\frac{\partial \Delta G^{\ominus}}{\partial T}\right)_p = -\Delta S^{\ominus} = \frac{\Delta G^{\ominus} - \Delta H^{\ominus}}{T} \quad [\Delta G = \Delta H - T\Delta S]$$

$$= \frac{(223.1 - 300.3)\ kJ\ mol^{-1}}{298.15\ K} = -0.259\ kJ\ mol^{-1}\ K^{-1}$$

Therefore, $\Delta G^{\ominus}(333\ K) \approx 223.1 + 5\ K \times (-0.259\ K^{-1})\ kJ\ mol^{-1}$

$$\approx \underline{+221.8\ kJ\ mol^{-1}}$$

10.22 $Cu_3(PO_4)_2(s) \rightleftharpoons 3Cu^{2+}(aq) + 2PO_4^{3-}(aq)$

$K_{sp} = a(Cu^{2+})^3 a(PO_4^{3-})^2 \approx m(Cu^{2+})^3 m(PO_4^{3-})^2$

(a) $S = m(Cu_3(PO_4)_2) = \frac{1}{3}m(Cu^{2+})$

However, $m(PO_4^{3-}) = \frac{2}{3}m(Cu^{2+})$

Therefore

$K_{sp} = \frac{4}{9}m(Cu^{2+})^5$, which implies that $S = \frac{1}{3} \times (\frac{9}{4}K_{sp})^{1/5}$

Hence,

$S = \frac{1}{3} \times (\frac{9}{4} \times 1.3 \times 10^{-37})^{1/5} = \underline{1.6 \times 10^{-8}\ [mol\ kg^{-1}]}$

(b) The cell reaction is

R:	$Cu^{2+}(aq) + 2e^- \rightarrow Cu(s)$	+0.34 V
L:	$2H^+(aq) + 2e^- \rightarrow H_2(g)$	0
Overall:	$Cu^{2+}(aq) + H_2(g) \rightarrow Cu(s) + 2H^+(aq)$	+0.34 V

From the Nernst equation,

$$E = E^{\ominus} - \frac{RT}{\nu F} \ln Q$$

$$= 0.34\ V - \frac{25.693 \times 10^{-3}\ V}{2} \ln \frac{a(H^+)^2}{a(Cu^+)}$$

$$= 0.34\ \text{V} - \frac{25.693 \times 10^{-3}\ \text{V}}{2} \ln \frac{1}{3 \times 1.6 \times 10^{-8}}\ [m(\text{Cu}^{2+}) = 3S]$$

$$= 0.34\ \text{V} - 0.22\ \text{V} = \underline{+0.12\ \text{V}}$$

10.23 (a) $\text{Sn}(s) + \text{Sn}^{4+}(aq) \rightleftharpoons 2\text{Sn}^{2+}(aq)$

$$\left.\begin{array}{lll} \text{R:} & \text{Sn}^{4+} + 2\text{e}^- \rightarrow \text{Sn}^{2+}(aq) & +0.15\ \text{V} \\ \text{L:} & \text{Sn}^{2+}(aq) + 2\text{e}^- \rightarrow \text{Sn}(s) & -0.14\ \text{V} \end{array}\right\} E^{\ominus} = +0.29\ \text{V}$$

$$\ln K = \frac{\nu F E^{\ominus}}{RT} = \frac{2 \times 0.29\ \text{V}}{25.693\ \text{mV}} = 22.\overline{6},\ K = \underline{6.5 \times 10^{9}}$$

(b) $\text{Sn}(s) + 2\text{AgCl}(s) \rightleftharpoons \text{SnCl}_2(aq) + 2\text{Ag}(s)$

$$\left.\begin{array}{lll} \text{R:} & 2\text{AgCl}(s) + 2\text{e}^- \rightarrow 2\text{Ag}(s) + 2\text{Cl}^-(aq) & +0.22\ \text{V} \\ \text{L:} & \text{Sn}^{2+}(aq) + 2\text{e}^- \rightarrow \text{Sn}(s) & -0.14\ \text{V} \end{array}\right\} +0.36\ \text{V}$$

$$\ln K = \frac{2 \times 0.36\ \text{V}}{25.693\ \text{mV}} = +28.\overline{0},\ K = \underline{1.5 \times 10^{12}}$$

(c) $2\text{Ag}(s) + \text{Cu(NO}_3)_2(aq) \rightleftharpoons \text{Cu}(s) + 2\text{AgNO}_3(aq)$

$$\left.\begin{array}{lll} \text{R:} & \text{Cu}^{2+}(aq) + 2\text{e}^- \rightarrow \text{Cu}(s) & +0.34\ \text{V} \\ \text{L:} & 2\text{Ag}^{+}(aq) + 2\text{e}^- \rightarrow 2\text{Ag}(s) & +0.80\ \text{V} \end{array}\right\} -0.46\ \text{V}$$

$$\ln K = \frac{2 \times (-0.46\ \text{V})}{25.693\ \text{mV}} = -35.\overline{8},\ K = \underline{2.8 \times 10^{-16}}$$

(d) $\text{Sn}(s) + \text{CuSO}_4(aq) \rightleftharpoons \text{Cu}(s) + \text{SnSO}_4(aq)$

$$\left.\begin{array}{lll} \text{R:} & \text{Cu}^{2+}(aq) + 2\text{e}^- \rightarrow \text{Cu}(s) & +0.34\ \text{V} \\ \text{L:} & \text{Sn}^{2+}(aq) + 2\text{e}^- \rightarrow \text{Sn}(s) & +0.14 \end{array}\right\} +0.48\ \text{V}$$

$$\ln K = \frac{2 \times 0.48\ \text{V}}{25.693\ \text{mV}} = +37.\overline{4},\ K = \underline{1.7 \times 10^{16}}$$

(e) $\text{Cu}^{2+}(aq) + \text{Cu}(s) \rightleftharpoons 2\text{Cu}^{+}(aq)$

$$\left.\begin{array}{lll} \text{R:} & \text{Cu}^{2+}(aq) + \text{e}^- \rightarrow \text{Cu}^{+}(aq) & +0.16\ \text{V} \\ \text{L:} & \text{Cu}^{+}(aq) + \text{e}^- \rightarrow \text{Cu}(s) & +0.52\ \text{V} \end{array}\right\} -0.36\ \text{V}$$

$$\ln K = \frac{-0.36\ \text{V}}{25.693\ \text{mV}} = -14.\overline{0},\ K = \underline{8.2 \times 10^{-7}}$$

10.24 $S(\text{AgCl}) = m(\text{Ag}^+)$

$\text{AgCl}(s) \rightleftharpoons \text{Ag}^+(aq) + \text{Cl}^-(aq) \qquad K_{sp} \approx m(\text{Ag}^+)m(\text{Cl}^-)/m^{\ominus 2}$

Since $m(\text{Ag}^+) = m(\text{Cl}^-)$

$$K_{sp} \approx m(\text{Ag}^+)^2/m^{\ominus 2} = S^2/m^{\ominus 2} = (1.34 \times 10^{-5})^2$$

$$\approx \underline{1.80 \times 10^{-10}}$$

$S(\text{BaSO}_4) = m(\text{Ba}^{2+})$

$\text{BaSO}_4(s) \rightleftharpoons \text{Ba}^{2+}(aq) + \text{SO}_4^{2-}(aq)$

As above, $K_{sp} \approx S^2/m^{\ominus 2} = (9.51 \times 10^{-4})^2 = \underline{9.04 \times 10^{-7}}$

We can estimate the activity coefficients using

$$\lg \gamma_\pm = -A|z_+z_-|I^{1/2}, \ A = 0.509$$

For AgCl, $I = S$, $|z_+z_-| = 1$, and so

$$\lg \gamma_\pm = -0.509 \times (1.34 \times 10^{-5})^{1/2} = -1.86 \times 10^{-3}, \ \gamma_\pm \approx 0.9957$$

Hence,

$$K_{sp} = \gamma_\pm^2 \times K_{sp}^\circ \ [K_{sp}^\circ \text{ calculated previously}] \approx \underline{0.991 K_{sp}^\circ}$$

For BaSO_4, $I = 4S$, $|z_+z_-| = 4$, and so

$$\lg \gamma_\pm = -0.509 \times 4 \times (4 \times 9.51 \times 10^{-4})^{1/2} = -0.126, \ \gamma_\pm \approx 0.75$$

Hence

$$K_{sp} \approx \gamma_\pm^2 K_{sp}^\circ \approx 0.75^2 K_{sp}^\circ = \underline{0.56 K_{sp}^\circ}$$

Thus, the neglect of activity coefficients is significant for BaSO_4.

10.25 The half-reaction is

$$\text{Cr}_2\text{O}_7^{2-}(aq) + 14\text{H}^+(aq) + 6\text{e}^- \rightarrow 2\text{Cr}^{3+}(aq) + 7\text{H}_2\text{O}(l)$$

The reaction quotient is

$$Q = \frac{a(\text{Cr}^{3+})^2}{a(\text{Cr}_2\text{O}_7^{2-})a(\text{H}^+)^{14}} \qquad \nu = 6$$

Hence,

$$E = E^\ominus - \frac{RT}{6F} \ln \frac{a(\text{Cr}^{3+})^2}{a(\text{Cr}_2\text{O}_7^{2-})a(\text{H}^+)^{14}}$$

10.26

$$\left.\begin{array}{lll} \text{R:} & 2\text{AgCl}(s) + 2\text{e}^- \rightarrow 2\text{Ag}(s) + 2\text{Cl}^-(aq) & +0.22\text{ V} \\ \text{L:} & 2\text{H}^+(aq) + 2\text{e}^- \rightarrow \text{H}_2(g) & 0 \end{array}\right\} 0.22\text{ V}$$

Overall: $2AgCl(s) + H_2(g) \rightarrow 2Ag(s) + 2H^+(aq) + 2Cl^-(aq)$

$$Q = a(H^+)^2 a(Cl^-)^2 \quad \nu = 2$$
$$= a(H^+)^4 \quad [a(H^+) = a(Cl^-)]$$

Therefore, from the Nernst equation,

$$E = E^\ominus - \frac{RT}{2F} \ln a(H^+)^4 = E^\ominus - \frac{2RT}{F} \ln a(H^+)$$

$$= E^\ominus + 2 \times 2.303 \frac{RT}{F} \text{pH}$$

Hence

$$\text{pH} = \frac{F}{2 \times 2.303RT} \times (E - E^\ominus) = \frac{E - 0.22\text{ V}}{0.1183\text{ V}}$$

$$= \frac{0.322\text{ V} - 0.22\text{ V}}{0.1183\text{ V}} = \underline{0.86}$$

10.27 R: $AgBr(s) + e^- \rightarrow Ag(s) + Br^-(aq)$

L: $Ag^+(aq) + e^- \rightarrow Ag(s)$

Overall: $AgBr(s) \rightarrow Ag^+(aq) + Br^-(aq)$

Therefore, since the cell reaction is the solubility equilibrium, for a saturated solution there is no further tendency to dissolve and so $\underline{E = 0}$.

10.28 R: $Ag^+(aq) + e^- \rightarrow Ag(s)$ $\quad +0.80\text{ V}$

L: $AgI(s) + e^- \rightarrow Ag(s) + I^-(aq)$ $\quad -0.15\text{ V}$

(together: $+0.95\overline{09}\text{ V}$)

Overall (R − L): $Ag^+(aq) + I^-(aq) \rightarrow AgI(s)$ $\quad \nu = 1$

$$\ln K = \frac{0.9509\text{ V}}{25.693\text{ V}} = 37.01\bar{0}, \quad K = 1.184 \times 10^{16}$$

However, $K_{sp} = K^{-1}$ since the solubility equilibrium is written as the reverse of the cell reaction. Therefore, $K_{sp} = \underline{8.45 \times 10^{-17}}$. The solubility is obtained from $m(Ag^+) \approx m(I^-)$ and $S = m(Ag^+)$, so $K_{sp} \approx m(Ag^+)^2$, implying that

$$S \approx (K_{sp})^{1/2} = (8.45 \times 10^{-17})^{1/2} = \underline{9.19 \times 10^{-9}\ [\text{mol kg}^{-1}]}$$

Problems

10.1 R: $Hg_2SO_4(s) + 2e^- \rightarrow 2Hg(l) + SO_4^{2-}(aq)$ $+0.62\ \text{V}$

L: $PbSO_4(s) + 2e^- \rightarrow Pb(s) + SO_4^{2-}(aq)$ $-0.36\ \text{V}$

R − L: $Pb(s) + Hg_2SO_4(s) \rightarrow PbSO_4(s) + 2Hg(l)$ $+0.98\ \text{V}$

Hence, a suitable cell would be

$$Pb(s)|PbSO_4(s)|H_2SO_4(aq)|Hg_2SO_4(s)|Hg(l)$$

or, alternatively,

$$Pb(s)|PbSO_4(s)|H_2SO_4(aq)\|H_2SO_4(aq)|Hg_2SO_4(s)|Hg(l)$$

For the cell

$$Pb(s)|PbSO_4(s)|PbSO_4(aq)\|Hg_2SO_4(aq)|Hg_2SO_4(s)|Hg(l)$$

The electrode potentials are

$$E_R = E_R^{\ominus} - \frac{RT}{2F}\ln a(SO_4^{2-}) = E_R^{\ominus} - \frac{RT}{2F}\ln\,(K_{sp}(Hg_2SO_4))^{1/2}$$

$$E_L = E_L^{\ominus} - \frac{RT}{2F}\ln a(SO_4^{2-}) = E_L^{\ominus} - \frac{RT}{2F}\ln(K_{sp}(PbSO_4))^{1/2}$$

because $K_{sp} = a_+a_- = (a_-)^2$

Therefore,

$$E = 0.98\ \text{V} - \frac{RT}{2F}\ln\frac{K_{sp}(Hg_2SO_4)^{1/2}}{K_{sp}(PbSO_4)^{1/2}}$$

$$= 0.98\ \text{V} - \frac{RT}{4F}\ln\frac{K_{sp}(Hg_2SO_4)}{K_{sp}(PbSO_4)}$$

$$= 0.98\ \text{V} - \frac{25.693\times10^{-3}\ \text{V}}{4}\ln\frac{6.6\times10^{-7}}{1.6\times10^{-8}}\quad \text{[Table 10.6]}$$

$$= 0.98\ \text{V} - 0.024\ \text{V} = \underline{0.96\ \text{V}}$$

10.2 (a) $H_2(g) + \tfrac{1}{2}O_2(g) \rightarrow H_2O(l)$

$\Delta G^{\ominus} = \Delta G_f^{\ominus}(H_2O, l) = -237.13\ \text{kJ mol}^{-1}$ [Table 2.10]

$$E^{\ominus} = -\frac{\Delta G^{\ominus}}{\nu F} = \frac{+237.13\ \text{kJ mol}^{-1}}{2\times96.485\ \text{kC mol}^{-1}} = \underline{+1.23\ \text{V}}$$

(b) $C_4H_{10}(g) + \frac{13}{2}O_2(g) \rightarrow 4CO_2(g) + 5H_2O(l)$

$$\Delta G^{\ominus} = 4\Delta G_f^{\ominus}(CO_2, g) + 5\Delta G_f^{\ominus}(H_2O, l) - \Delta G_f^{\ominus}(C_4H_{10}, g)$$

$$= 4 \times (-394.36) + 5 \times (-237.13) - (-17.03)\ \text{kJ mol}^{-1} \quad \text{[Tables 2.9, 2.10]}$$

$$= -2746.06\ \text{kJ mol}^{-1}$$

To find the number of electrons transferred, note that the cathode half-reaction is the reduction of oxygen to produce $5H_2O$:

$$\tfrac{5}{2}O_2(g) + 10e^- + 10H^+(aq) \rightarrow 5H_2O(l) \quad \nu = 10$$

Therefore,

$$E^{\ominus} = \frac{-\Delta G^{\ominus}}{\nu F} = \frac{+2746.06\ \text{kJ mol}^{-1}}{10 \times 96.485\ \text{kC mol}^{-1}} = \underline{+2.85\ \text{V}}$$

10.3 $Pt|H_2(g)|HCl(aq)|Hg_2Cl_2(s)|Hg(l)$

$$H_2(g) + Hg_2Cl_2(s) \rightarrow 2Hg(l) + 2HCl(aq) \quad \nu = 2$$

$$Q = \frac{a(H^+)^2 a(Cl^-)^2}{f(H_2)/p^{\ominus}} = \frac{\gamma_{\pm}^2 m^2}{f/p^{\ominus}}$$

$$E = E^{\ominus} - \frac{RT}{2F}\ln Q = E^{\ominus} - \frac{RT}{F}\ln \gamma_{\pm} m + \frac{RT}{2F}\ln\frac{f}{p^{\ominus}}$$

$$f = \gamma p \text{ with } \ln \gamma = \int_0^p \left(\frac{Z-1}{p}\right) dp \quad \text{[Chapter 5]}$$

Therefore,

$$\ln \gamma = \int_0^p (5.37 \times 10^{-4}\ \text{atm}^{-1} + 3.5 \times 10^{-8} p\ \text{atm}^{-2})\, dp$$

$$= 5.37 \times 10^{-4}(p/\text{atm}) + \tfrac{1}{2} \times 3.5 \times 10^{-8}(p/\text{atm})^2$$

Hence, at 500 atm,

$$\ln \gamma = 0.268\overline{5} + 0.0044 = 0.2729, \quad \gamma = 1.31\overline{4}$$

At 0.10 mol kg^{-1}, $\gamma_{\pm} = 0.798$ [Table 10.4], so

$$E = E^{\ominus} - \frac{RT}{F}\ln 0.798 \times 0.10 + \frac{RT}{2F}\ln\frac{500\ \text{atm} \times 1.31\overline{4}}{1\ \text{bar}}$$

$$= 0.27\ \text{V} - 25.693\ \text{mV} \ln 0.079\overline{8} + \frac{25.693\ \text{mV}}{2}\ln 1.31\overline{4} \times 500 \times 1.0133$$

$=0.27\text{ V}+0.065\bar{0}\text{ V}+0.083\bar{5}\text{ V}=\underline{+0.42\text{ V}}$

10.4 $H_2(g)|HCl(aq)|Cl_2(g)$ $H_2(g)+Cl_2(g)\rightarrow 2HCl(aq)$ $\nu=2$

$$E=E^{\ominus}-\frac{RT}{2F}\ln Q,\quad Q=\frac{a(H^+)^2a(Cl^-)^2}{f(Cl_2)/p^{\ominus}},\quad E^{\ominus}=+1.36\text{ V},\ f/p^{\ominus}=1$$

For $m=0.010\text{ mol kg}^{-1}$, $\gamma_\pm=0.905$ [Table 10.4], $a(H^+)a(Cl^-)=\gamma_\pm^2m^2$

$$E=1.36\text{ V}-25.693\text{ mV}\ln 0.905^2\times 0.010^2+25.693\text{ mV}\ln\left(\frac{f}{p^{\ominus}}\right)$$

$$=1.60\bar{2}\text{ V}+\tfrac{1}{2}\times 25.693\text{ mV}\ln\frac{f}{p^{\ominus}}$$

Therefore,

$$\ln\frac{f}{p^{\ominus}}=\frac{E-1.60\bar{2}\text{ V}}{0.01285\text{ V}}\quad\text{with } p^{\ominus}=1\text{ bar}$$

Hence, we can draw up the following table:

p/bar	1.000	50.00	100.0
E/V	1.5962	1.6419	1.6451
$f/p^{\ominus}$	0.637	22.3	28.6
γ	0.637†	0.446	0.286

† This seems abnormally low at this pressure.

10.5 $H_2(g)|HCl(aq)|Hg_2Cl_2(s)|Hg(l)$

$$E=E^{\ominus}-\frac{RT}{F}\ln a(H^+)a(Cl^-)$$

$$=E^{\ominus}-\frac{2RT}{F}\ln m-\frac{2RT}{F}\ln\gamma_\pm$$

$=E^{\ominus}-0.1183\text{ V}\lg m+0.1183\text{ V}\times A\times m^{1/2}$ [Debye-Hückel and $2\times 2.303RT/F=0.1183\text{ V}$]

$E+0.1183\text{ V}\lg m=E^{\ominus}+\text{constant}\times m^{1/2}$

Therefore, plot $E+0.1183\text{ V}\lg m$ against $m^{1/2}$, and the intercept at $m=0$ is $E^{\ominus}$/V. Draw up the following table:

$m/(\text{mmol kg}^{-1})$	1.6077	3.0769	5.0403	7.6938	10.9474
$(m/m^{\ominus})^{1/2}$	0.04010	0.05547	0.07100	0.08771	0.1046
$E/\text{V} + 0.1183 \lg m$	0.27029	0.27109	0.27186	0.27260	0.27337

The points are plotted in Fig. 10.1. The intercept is at 0.26835, so $E^{\ominus} = +0.26835$ V. The least-squares best fit (Appendix) gives $E^{\ominus} = \underline{+0.26838\text{ V}}$ and a coefficient of determination equal to 0.99895.

For the activity coefficients we form:

$$\ln \gamma_{\pm} = \frac{E^{\ominus} - E}{2RT/F} - \ln \frac{m}{m^{\ominus}}$$

$$= \frac{0.26838 - E/\text{V}}{0.05139} - \ln \frac{m}{m^{\ominus}}$$

and draw up the following table:

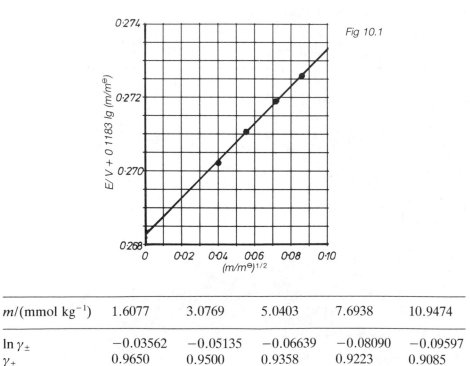

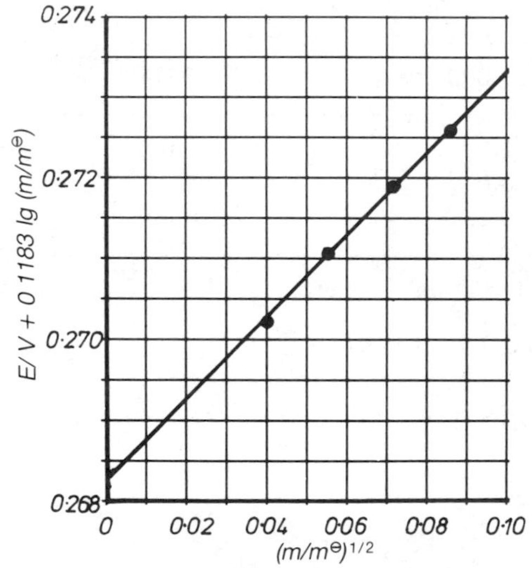

Fig 10.1

$m/(\text{mmol kg}^{-1})$	1.6077	3.0769	5.0403	7.6938	10.9474
$\ln \gamma_{\pm}$	−0.03562	−0.05135	−0.06639	−0.08090	−0.09597
$\gamma_{\pm}$	0.9650	0.9500	0.9358	0.9223	0.9085

10.6 $Pt|H_2(g)|NaOH(aq), NaCl(aq)|AgCl(s)|Ag(s)$

$H_2(g) + 2AgCl(s) \rightarrow 2Ag(s) + 2Cl^-(aq) + 2H^+(aq) \quad \nu = 2$

$$E = E^\ominus - \frac{RT}{2F}\ln Q, \; Q = a(H^+)^2 a(Cl^-)^2 \quad [f/p^\ominus = 1]$$

$$= E^\ominus - \frac{RT}{F}\ln a(H^+)a(Cl^-)$$

$$= E^\ominus - \frac{RT}{F}\ln \frac{K_w a(Cl^-)}{a(OH^-)}$$

$$= E^\ominus - \frac{RT}{F}\ln \frac{K_w \gamma_\pm m(Cl^-)}{\gamma_\pm m(OH^-)} = E^\ominus - \frac{RT}{F}\ln \frac{K_w m(Cl^-)}{m(OH^-)}$$

$$= E^\ominus - \frac{RT}{F}\ln K_w - \frac{RT}{F}\ln \frac{m(Cl^-)}{m(OH^-)}$$

$$= E^\ominus + 2.303\frac{RT}{F} \times pK_w - \frac{RT}{F}\ln \frac{m(Cl^-)}{m(OH^-)}$$

Hence,

$$pK_w = \frac{E - E^\ominus}{2.303RT/F} + \frac{\ln m(Cl^-)/m(OH^-)}{2.303}$$

$$= \frac{E - E^\ominus}{2.303RT/F} + 0.05114$$

We then draw up the following table with $E^\ominus = +0.2223$ V:

θ/°C	20.0	25.0	30.0
E/V	1.04774	1.04864	1.04942
$(2.303RT/F)$/V	0.05819	0.05918	0.06018
pK_w	14.23	14.01	13.79

$$\frac{d \ln K_w}{dT} = \frac{\Delta H^\ominus}{RT^2}$$

Hence,

$$\Delta H^\ominus = -2.303RT^2 \frac{d}{dT}(pK_w)$$

$$\approx 2.303 \times 8.314\ \mathrm{J\,K^{-1}\,mol^{-1}} \times (298.15\ \mathrm{K})^2 \times \frac{13.79 - 14.23}{10\ \mathrm{K}}$$

$$= \underline{+74.9\ \mathrm{kJ\,mol^{-1}}}$$

$$\Delta G^{\ominus} = -RT \ln K_w = 2.303RT \times \mathrm{p}K_w = \underline{+80.0\ \mathrm{kJ\,mol^{-1}}}$$

$$\Delta S^{\ominus} = \frac{\Delta H^{\ominus} - \Delta G^{\ominus}}{T} = \underline{-17.1\ \mathrm{J\,K^{-1}\,mol^{-1}}}$$

See the original reference for a careful analysis of the precise data.

10.7 $\mathrm{Ag}(s)|\mathrm{AgX}(s)|\mathrm{MX}(m_1)|\mathrm{M}_x\mathrm{Hg}(s)$

R: $\mathrm{M}^+(m_1) + \mathrm{e}^- \xrightarrow{\mathrm{Hg}} \mathrm{M}_x\mathrm{Hg}(s)$ [Reduction of M^+ and formation of amalgam]

L: $\mathrm{AgX}(s) + \mathrm{e}^- \rightarrow \mathrm{Ag}(s) + \mathrm{X}^-(m_1)$

R − L: $\mathrm{Ag}(s) + \mathrm{M}^+(m_1) + \mathrm{X}^-(m_1) \xrightarrow{\mathrm{Hg}} \mathrm{M}_x\mathrm{Hg}(s) + \mathrm{AgX}(s) \quad \nu = 1$

$$Q = \frac{a(\mathrm{M}_x\mathrm{Hg})}{a(\mathrm{M}^+)a(\mathrm{X}^-)}$$

$$E = E^{\ominus} - \frac{RT}{F} \ln Q$$

For a pair of such cells back to back,

$\mathrm{Ag}(s)|\mathrm{AgX}(s)|\mathrm{MX}(m_1)|\mathrm{M}_x\mathrm{Hg}(s)|\mathrm{MX}(m_2)|\mathrm{AgX}(s)|\mathrm{Ag}(s)$

$$E_{\mathrm{R}} = E^{\ominus} - \frac{RT}{F} \ln Q_{\mathrm{R}}$$

$$E_{\mathrm{L}} = E^{\ominus} - \frac{RT}{F} \ln Q_{\mathrm{L}}$$

$$E = -\frac{RT}{F} \ln \frac{Q_{\mathrm{L}}}{Q_{\mathrm{R}}} = \frac{RT}{F} \ln \frac{(a(\mathrm{M}^+)a(\mathrm{X}^-))_{\mathrm{L}}}{(a(\mathrm{M}^+)a(\mathrm{X}^-))_{\mathrm{R}}}$$

$$= \frac{2RT}{F} \ln \frac{m_1}{m_2} + \frac{2RT}{F} \ln \frac{\gamma_{\pm}(1)}{\gamma_{\pm}(2)}$$

Take $m_2 = 0.09141\ \mathrm{mol\,kg^{-1}}$ (the reference value), and write $m = m_1/m^{\ominus}$

$$E = \frac{2RT}{F}\left(\ln \frac{m}{0.09141} + \ln \frac{\gamma_{\pm}}{\gamma_{\pm}(\mathrm{ref.})}\right)$$

For $m = 0.09141$, the extended Debye–Hückel law gives

$$\lg \gamma_{\pm} = \frac{-1.461 \times (0.09141)^{1/2}}{1 + 1.70 \times (0.09141)^{1/2}} + 0.20 \times 0.09141 = -0.273\overline{5}$$

$$\gamma_{\pm} = 0.532\overline{8}$$

and

$$E = 0.05139\ \mathrm{V} \times \left(\ln \frac{m}{0.09141} + \ln \frac{\gamma_{\pm}}{0.5328}\right)$$

$$\ln \gamma_{\pm} = \frac{E}{0.05139\ \mathrm{V}} - \ln \frac{m}{0.09141 \times 0.05328}$$

We then draw up the following table:

$m/(\mathrm{mol\ kg^{-1}})$	0.0555	0.09141	0.1652	0.2171	1.040	1.350
E/V	−0.0220	0.0000	0.0263	0.0379	0.1156	0.1336
γ	0.572	0.533	0.492	0.469	0.444	0.486

A more precise procedure is described in the original references for the temperature dependence of $E^{\ominus}(\mathrm{Ag, AgCl, Cl^-})$, see Problem 10.10.

10.8 $\mathrm{H_2}(g)|\mathrm{HCl}(m)|\mathrm{AgCl}(s)|\mathrm{Ag}(s)$

$\frac{1}{2}\mathrm{H_2}(g) + \mathrm{AgCl}(s) \rightarrow \mathrm{HCl}(aq) + \mathrm{Ag}(s)$

$$E = E^{\ominus} - \frac{RT}{F} \ln a(\mathrm{H^+})a(\mathrm{Cl^-}) = E^{\ominus} - \frac{2RT}{F} \ln m - \frac{2RT}{F} \ln \gamma_{\pm}$$

$$= E^{\ominus} - \frac{2RT}{F} \ln m - 2 \times 2.303 \frac{RT}{F} \lg \gamma_{\pm}$$

$$= E^{\ominus} - \frac{2RT}{F} \ln m - 2 \times 2.303 \frac{RT}{F} \{-0.509(m/m^{\ominus})^{1/2} + k(m/m^{\ominus})\}$$

Therefore, with $2RT/F \times 2.303 = 0.1183\ \mathrm{V}$,

$$E/\mathrm{V} + 0.1183 \lg m - 0.0602 m^{1/2} = E^{\ominus}/\mathrm{V} - 0.1183 km \quad [m \equiv m/m^{\ominus}]$$

hence, with $y = E/\mathrm{V} + 0.1183 \lg m - 0.0602 m^{1/2}$,

$$\underline{y = E^{\ominus}/\mathrm{V} - 0.1183 km}$$

We now draw up the following table:

$m/(\text{mmol kg}^{-1})$	123.8	25.63	9.138	5.619	3.215
y	0.2135	0.2204	0.2216	0.2218	0.2221

(a) The last three points are plotted in Fig. 10.2, and extrapolate to 0.2223 V,

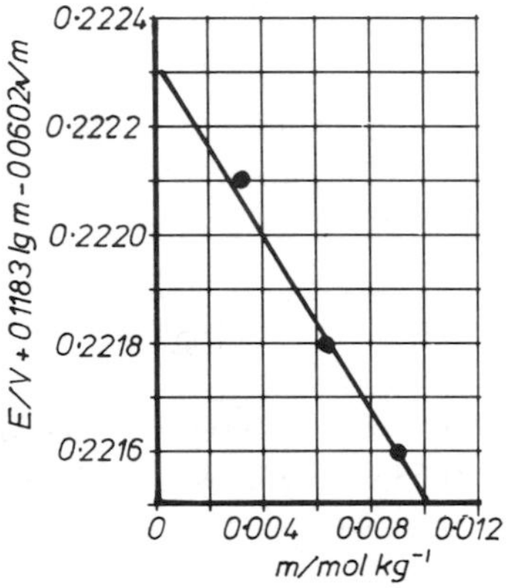

Fig 10.2

hence $E^{\ominus} = \underline{+0.2223 \text{ V}}$.

(b) $E = E^{\ominus} - \dfrac{2RT}{F} \ln m - \dfrac{2RT}{F} \ln \gamma_{\pm}$

and so

$$\ln \gamma_{\pm} = \frac{E^{\ominus} - E - 0.0514 \text{ V} \ln m}{0.0514 \text{ V}}$$

$$= \frac{0.2223 - 0.3524 - 0.0514 \ln 0.100}{0.0514}$$

$$= -0.228\bar{5}, \text{ implying that } \gamma_{\pm} = \underline{0.796}$$

Since $a(\text{H}^+) = \gamma_{\pm} m/m^{\ominus}$, $a(\text{H}^+) = 0.796 \times 0.100 = 0.0796$, and hence

$$\text{pH} = -\lg a(\text{H}^+) = -\lg 0.0796 = \underline{1.10}$$

10.9 According to the Debye–Hückel limiting law,

$$\lg \gamma_{\pm} = -0.509|z_+z_-|I^{1/2} = -0.509(m/m^{\ominus})^{1/2} \quad [5]$$

We draw up the following table:

$1000m/m^{\ominus}$	1.0	2.0	5.0	10.0	20.0
$(I/m^{\ominus})^{1/2}$	0.032	0.045	0.071	0.100	0.141
$\gamma_{\pm}$(calc)	0.964	0.949	0.920	0.889	0.847
$\gamma_{\pm}$(exp)	0.9649	0.9519	0.9275	0.9024	0.8712
$\lg \gamma_{\pm}$(calc)	−0.0161	−0.0228	−0.0360	−0.0509	−0.0720
$\lg \gamma_{\pm}$(exp)	−0.0155	−0.0214	−0.0327	−0.0446	−0.0599

The points are plotted against $I^{1/2}$ in Fig. 10.3. Note that the limiting slopes of

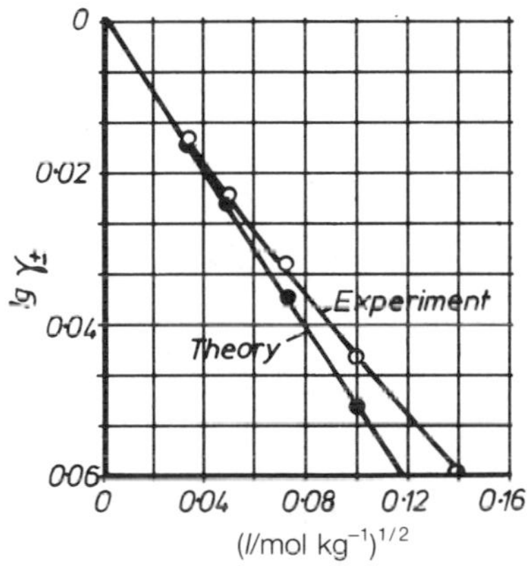

Fig 10.3

the calculated and experimental curves coincide.

10.10 $\Delta G^{\ominus} = -\nu F E^{\ominus}$

At 298.15 K (25.00 °C),

$$E^{\ominus}/\text{V} = 0.23659 - 4.8564 \times 10^{-4} \times 25.00 - 3.4205 \times 10^{-6} \times (25.00)^2$$
$$+ 5.869 \times 10^{-9} \times (25.00)^3 = +0.22240 \text{ V}$$

Therefore, $\Delta G^{\ominus} = -96.485 \text{ kC mol}^{-1} \times 0.22240 \text{ V} = -21.46 \text{ kJ mol}^{-1}$

$$\Delta S^{\ominus} = \left(\frac{\partial E^{\ominus}}{\partial T}\right)_p \times \nu F = \nu F \left(\frac{\partial E^{\ominus}}{\partial \theta}\right)_p \frac{°\text{C}}{\text{K}} \quad [\text{d}\theta/°\text{C} = \text{d}T/\text{K}]$$

$$\left(\frac{\partial E^{\ominus}}{\partial \theta}\right)_p \frac{1}{\big/} \text{V} = -4.8564 \times 10^{-4}/°\text{C} - 2 \times 3.4205 \times 10^{-6}\theta/(°\text{C})^2$$

$$+ 3 \times 5.869 \times 10^{-9}\theta^2/(°\text{C})^3$$

$$\left(\frac{\partial E^{\ominus}}{\partial \theta}\right)_p \Big/ (\text{V}/°\text{C}) = -4.8564 \times 10^{-4} - 6.8410 \times 10^{-6}(\theta/°\text{C})$$

$$+ 1.7607 \times 10^{-8}(\theta/°\text{C})^2$$

Therefore, at 25.00 °C,

$$\left(\frac{\partial E^{\ominus}}{\partial \theta}\right)_p = -6.4566 \times 10^{-4}\ \text{V}/°\text{C}$$

and $\left(\frac{\partial E^{\ominus}}{\partial T}\right)_p = -6.4566 \times 10^{-4}\ \text{V}/°\text{C} \times °\text{C}/\text{K} = -6.4566 \times 10^{-4}\ \text{V K}^{-1}$

Hence,

$$\Delta S^{\ominus} = -96.485\ \text{kC mol}^{-1} \times 6.4566 \times 10^{-4}\ \text{V K}^{-1} = -62.30\ \text{J K}^{-1}\ \text{mol}^{-1}$$

and $\Delta H^{\ominus} = \Delta G^{\ominus} + T\Delta S^{\ominus}$

$$= -21.46\ \text{kJ mol}^{-1} + 298.15\ \text{K} \times (-62.30\ \text{J K}^{-1}\ \text{mol}^{-1})$$

$$= -40.03\ \text{kJ mol}^{-1}$$

For the cell reaction

$$\tfrac{1}{2}\text{H}_2(g) + \text{AgCl}(s) \rightarrow \text{Ag}(s) + \text{HCl}(aq)$$

$$\Delta G^{\ominus} = \Delta G_f^{\ominus}(\text{H}^+) + \Delta G_f^{\ominus}(\text{Cl}^-) - \Delta G_f^{\ominus}(\text{AgCl})$$

$$= \Delta G_f^{\ominus}(\text{Cl}^-) - \Delta G_f^{\ominus}(\text{AgCl}) \quad [\Delta G_f^{\ominus}(\text{H}^+) = 0]$$

Hence

$$\Delta G_f^{\ominus}(\text{Cl}^-) = \Delta G^{\ominus} + \Delta G_f^{\ominus}(\text{AgCl}) = -21.46 - 109.79\ \text{kJ mol}^{-1}$$

$$= \underline{-131.25\ \text{kJ mol}^{-1}}$$

Similarly,

$$\Delta H_f^{\ominus}(\text{Cl}^-) = \Delta H^{\ominus} + \Delta H_f^{\ominus}(\text{AgCl}) = -40.03 - 127.07\ \text{kJ mol}^{-1}$$

$$= \underline{-167.10\ \text{kJ mol}^{-1}}$$

For the entropy of Cl^- in solution we use

$$\Delta S^{\ominus} = S^{\ominus}(\text{Ag}) + S^{\ominus}(\text{H}^+) + S^{\ominus}(\text{Cl}^-) - \tfrac{1}{2}S^{\ominus}(\text{H}_2) - S^{\ominus}(\text{AgCl})$$

with $S^{\ominus}(\text{H}^+) = 0$. Then,

$$S^\ominus(\text{Cl}^-) = \Delta S^\ominus - S^\ominus(\text{Ag}) + \tfrac{1}{2}S^\ominus(\text{H}_2) + S^\ominus(\text{AgCl})$$
$$= -62.30 - 42.55 + \tfrac{1}{2}\times 130.68 + 96.2 = \underline{+56.8\ \text{J K}^{-1}\ \text{mol}^{-1}}$$

10.11 Draw up the following table using $K_f(\text{H}_2\text{O}) = 1.86\ \text{K kg mol}^{-1}$ [Table 8.2]:

$m/(\text{mol kg}^{-1})$	0.01	0.02	0.03	0.04	0.05
$\Delta T/\text{K}$	0.0355	0.0697	0.0343	0.137	0.172
$\phi = \Delta T/2mK_f$	0.955	0.938	0.925	0.922	0.926
$(1-\phi)/(m/m^\ominus)$	4.500	3.100	2.500	1.950	1.480

$(1-\phi)/m$ is plotted against m in Fig. 10.4. The value of $(1-\phi)/m$ approaches

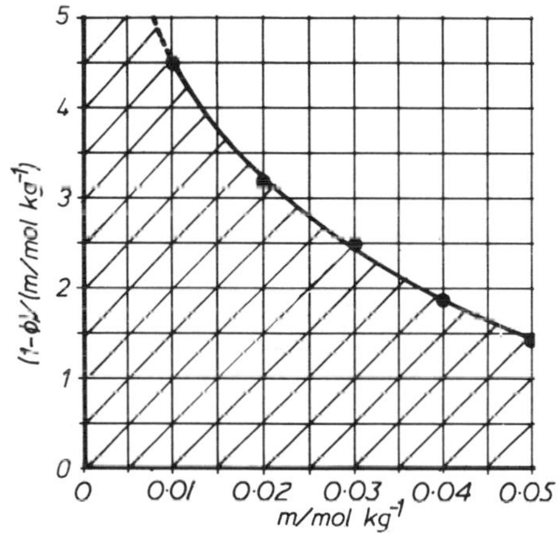

Fig 10.4

infinity as $m \to 0$, but we are confident about the validity of the Debye–Hückel limiting law in this region, and evaluate the integral analytically up to $m = 0.010m^\ominus$[See Problem 10.18 for details]:

$$\int_0^m \left(\frac{1-\phi}{m}\right) \mathrm{d}m = \tfrac{1}{3}A' \int_0^m \frac{\mathrm{d}m}{m^{1/2}} = \tfrac{2}{3}A'm^{1/2},\ A' = 2.303A$$

Therefore, up to $m = 0.010m^\ominus$ the value of the integral is 0.0781. Above that molality, evaluate the integral numerically. In the range from $0.010m^\ominus$ to $0.050m^\ominus$ its value is 0.106. Therefore,

$$\ln\gamma_\pm = 0.926 - 1 - (0.106 + 0.0781) = -0.258$$

Hence $\gamma_{\pm}=\underline{0.77}$.

10.12 $K_a=\dfrac{a(H^+)a(A^-)}{a(HA)}=\dfrac{\gamma_{\pm}^2 m(H^+)m(A^-)}{m(HA)}=\gamma_{\pm}^2 K_a'$

$$K_a'=\frac{m(H^+)m(A^-)}{m(HA)}=\frac{\alpha^2 m}{1-\alpha}$$

Hence,

$$\lg K_a'=\lg K_a-2\lg\gamma_{\pm}=\lg K_a+2A(I/m^{\ominus})^{1/2}$$
$$=\lg K_a+2A(\alpha m)^{1/2}\quad [I=\alpha m]$$

We therefore construct the following table:

$1000m/m^{\ominus}$	0.0280	0.114	0.2184	1.0283	2.414	5.9115
$1000(\alpha m/m^{\ominus})^{1/2}$	3.89	6.04	7.36	11.3	14.1	17.9
$10^5\times K_a'$	1.768	1.779	1.781	1.799	1.809	1.822
$\lg K_a'$	−4.753	−4.750	−4.749	−4.745	−4.743	−4.739

$\lg K_a'$ is plotted against $(\alpha m/m^{\ominus})^{1/2}$ in Fig. 10.5, and we see that a good

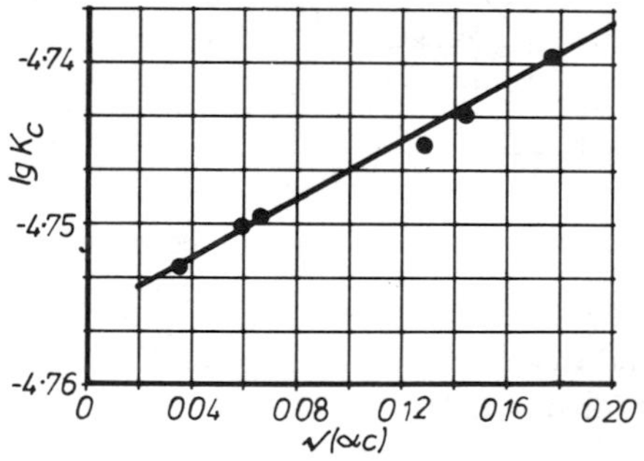

Fig 10.5

straight line is obtained.

10.13 The reduction reaction is

$$Sb_2O_3(s)+3H_2O(l)+6e^-\rightarrow 2Sb(s)+6OH^-(aq)$$

$Q=a(OH^-)^6\quad \nu=6$

Therefore,

$$\text{(a)}\ E = E^{\ominus} - \frac{RT}{6F}\ln a(\mathrm{OH^-})^6 = E^{\ominus} - \frac{RT}{F}\ln a(\mathrm{OH^-})$$

$$= \underline{E^{\ominus} + \frac{2.303RT}{F}\mathrm{pOH}}$$

(b) Since $\mathrm{pOH} + \mathrm{pH} = \mathrm{p}K_w$,

$$\underline{E = E^{\ominus} + \frac{2.303RT}{F}(\mathrm{p}K_w - \mathrm{pH})}$$

(c) The change in potential is

$$\Delta E = \frac{2.303RT}{F}(\mathrm{pOH_f} - \mathrm{pOH_i})$$

$$\mathrm{pOH_f} = -\lg(0.050\gamma_\pm) = -\lg 0.050 - \lg\gamma_\pm$$
$$= -\lg 0.050 + A\surd(0.050) = 1.41\bar{5}$$
$$\mathrm{pOH_i} = -\lg(0.010\gamma_\pm) = -\lg 0.010 - \lg\gamma_\pm$$
$$= -\lg 0.010 + A\surd(0.010) = 2.05\bar{1}$$

Hence, $\Delta E = 59.17\ \mathrm{mV} \times (1.41\bar{5} - 2.05\bar{1}) = \underline{-37.6\ \mathrm{mV}}$

10.14 $\frac{1}{2}H_2(g) + Uup^+(aq) \rightarrow Uup(s) + H^+(aq)$

We draw up the following thermodynamic cycle:

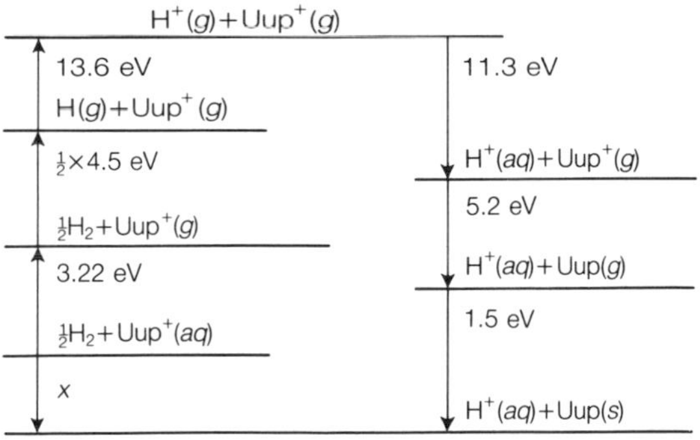

Since the distance up on the left = distance up on the right,

$$13.6 + \tfrac{1}{2} \times 4.5 + 3.22 + x = 11.3 + 5.2 + 1.5$$

which solves to $x = -1.0\bar{7}$ eV. Therefore:

$$\tfrac{1}{2}H_2(g) + Uup^+(aq) \rightarrow Uup(s) + H^+(aq) \quad \Delta H^\ominus = +1.0\bar{7}\text{ eV}$$

$$\Delta S^\ominus = S^\ominus(Uup, s) + S^\ominus(H^+, aq) - \tfrac{1}{2}S^\ominus(H_2, g) - S^\ominus(Uup^+, aq)$$

$$= 0.69 + 0 - \tfrac{1}{2} \times 1.354 - 1.34\text{ meV K}^{-1} = -1.33\text{ meV K}^{-1}$$

$$\Delta G^\ominus = \Delta H^\ominus - T\,\Delta S^\ominus = 1.0\bar{7}\text{ eV} + 298.15\text{ K} \times 1.33\text{ meV K}^{-1}$$

$$= +1.4\bar{7}\text{ eV, which corresponds to } \underline{+14\bar{2}\text{ kJ mol}^{-1}}$$

The electrode potential is therefore $-\Delta G^\ominus/\nu F$, with $\nu = 1$, or $\underline{-1.47\text{ V}}$

10.15 $K_s = a(M^+)a(X^-) = m(M^+)m(X^-)\gamma_\pm^2$

$m(M^+) = m(X^-) = S$

$\ln \gamma_\pm = 2.303 \lg \gamma_\pm = -2.303 \times 0.509 \times S^{1/2} = -1.172S^{1/2}$

$\gamma_\pm = e^{-1.172S^{1/2}}$,

Hence, $K_s/\gamma_\pm^2 = S^2$

implying that

$$S = K_s^{1/2}/\gamma_1 = \underline{K_s\, e^{1.172S^{1/2}}}$$

10.16 $MX(s) \rightleftharpoons M^+(aq) + X^-(aq)$, $K_s \approx m(M^+)m(X^-)$ $[m \equiv m/m^\ominus]$

$m(M^+) = S$, $m(X^-) = S + C$

$K_s = S(S + C)$, or $S^2 + CS - K_s = 0$

which solves to

$$\underline{S = \tfrac{1}{2}(C^2 + 4K_s)^{1/2} - \tfrac{1}{2}C}$$

If $4K_s \ll C^2$,

$$S = \tfrac{1}{2}C\left(1 + \frac{4K_s}{C^2}\right)^{1/2} - \tfrac{1}{2}C$$

$$\approx \tfrac{1}{2}C\left(1 + \frac{2K_s}{C^2}\right) - \tfrac{1}{2}C \quad [(1+x)^{1/2} \approx 1 + \tfrac{1}{2}x + \cdots]$$

$$\approx \underline{K_s/C}$$

10.17 $K_s = a(M^+)a(X^-) = m(M^+)m(X^-)\gamma_\pm^2$

$$= S(S + C) \times e^{-4.606AS^{1/2}} \quad [\lg \gamma_\pm = -AS^{1/2}]$$

We solve

$$S^2+SC-K_s/\gamma_\pm^2=0$$

to give

$$S=\tfrac{1}{2}(C^2+4K_s/\gamma_\pm^2)^{1/2}-\tfrac{1}{2}C\approx K_s/C\gamma_\pm^2 \quad \text{[as in Problem 10.16]}$$

Therefore, since

$$\gamma_\pm^2=\mathrm{e}^{-4.606AC^{1/2}}$$

$$S\approx\frac{K_s\,\mathrm{e}^{+4.606AC^{1/2}}}{C}$$

10.18 $\ln a_A=\dfrac{-\Delta G_{fus}}{RT}$

$$\frac{\mathrm{d}\ln a_A}{\mathrm{d}T}=-\frac{1}{R}\frac{\mathrm{d}}{\mathrm{d}T}\left(\frac{\Delta G_{fus}}{T}\right)=\frac{\Delta H_{fus}}{RT^2} \quad \text{[Gibbs–Helmholtz]}$$

For $\Delta T=T_f^*-T$, $\mathrm{d}\,\Delta T=-\mathrm{d}T$

and $\dfrac{\mathrm{d}\ln a_A}{\mathrm{d}\,\Delta T}=\dfrac{-\Delta H_{fus}}{RT^2}\approx\dfrac{-\Delta H_{fus}}{RT_f^2}$

But $K_f=\dfrac{RT_f^{*2}M_A}{\Delta H_{fus}}$

Therefore

$$\frac{\mathrm{d}\ln a_A}{\mathrm{d}\,\Delta T}=\frac{-M_A}{K_f} \text{ and } \mathrm{d}\ln a_A=\frac{-M_A\,\mathrm{d}\,\Delta T}{K_f}$$

According to the Gibbs–Duhem equation [Chapter 7]

$$n_A\,\mathrm{d}\mu_A+n_B\,\mathrm{d}\mu_B=0$$

which implies that

$$n_A\,\mathrm{d}\ln a_A+n_B\,\mathrm{d}\ln a_B=0 \quad [\mu=\mu^\ominus+RT\ln a]$$

and hence that

$$\mathrm{d}\ln a_A=-\frac{n_B}{n_A}\,\mathrm{d}\ln a_B$$

Hence

$$\frac{\mathrm{d}\ln a_B}{\mathrm{d}\,\Delta T}=\frac{n_AM_A}{n_BK_f}=\frac{1}{m_BK_f} \quad [\text{for } n_AM_A=1\text{ kg}]$$

We know from the Gibbs–Duhem equation that

$$x_A \,d\ln a_A + x_B \,d\ln a_B = 0$$

and hence that

$$\int d\ln a_A = -\int \frac{x_B}{x_A} d\ln a_B$$

Therefore

$$\ln a_A = -\int \frac{x_B}{x_A} d\ln a_B$$

The osmotic coefficient was defined in Problem 7.19 as

$$\phi = -\frac{1}{r}\ln a_A = -\frac{x_A}{x_B}\ln a_A$$

Therefore,

$$\phi = \frac{x_A}{x_B}\int \frac{x_B}{x_A} d\ln a_B = \frac{1}{m}\int_0^m m\,d\ln a_B = \frac{1}{m}\int_0^m d\ln \gamma m$$

$$= \frac{1}{m}\int_0^m m\,d\ln m + \frac{1}{m}\int_0^m m\,d\ln\gamma = 1 + \frac{1}{m}\int_0^m m\,d\ln\gamma$$

From the Debye–Hückel limiting law,

$$\ln\gamma = -A'm^{1/2} \quad [A' = 2.303A]$$

Hence $\quad d\ln\gamma = -\tfrac{1}{2}A'm^{-1/2}\,dm$

and so

$$\phi = 1 + \frac{1}{m}(-\tfrac{1}{2}A')\int_0^m m^{1/2}\,dm = 1 - \tfrac{1}{2}\left(\frac{A'}{m}\right)\tfrac{2}{3}m^{3/2}$$

$$= \underline{1 - \tfrac{1}{3}A'm^{1/2}}$$

For the depression of freezing point in a 1,1-electrolyte

$$\ln a_A = \frac{-\Delta G_{fus}}{RT} + \frac{\Delta G_{fus}}{RT^*}$$

and hence

$$-r\phi = \frac{-\Delta H_{\text{fus}}}{R}\left(\frac{1}{T} - \frac{1}{T^*}\right)$$

Therefore,

$$\phi = \frac{\Delta H_{\text{fus}} x_{\text{A}}}{R x_{\text{B}}}\left(\frac{1}{T} - \frac{1}{T^*}\right) = \frac{\Delta H_{\text{fus}} x_{\text{A}}}{R x_{\text{B}}}\left(\frac{T^* - T}{TT^*}\right)$$

$$\approx \frac{\Delta H_{\text{fus}} x_{\text{A}}\, \Delta T}{R x_{\text{B}} T^{*2}} \approx \frac{\Delta H_{\text{fus}}\, \Delta T}{\nu R M_{\text{B}} T^{*2} M_{\text{A}}}$$

where $\nu = 2$. Therefore, since $K_{\text{f}} = MRT^{*2}/\Delta H_{\text{fus}}$

$$\underline{\phi = \frac{\Delta T}{2 m_{\text{B}} K_{\text{f}}}}$$

PART 2: STRUCTURE

11. Quantum theory: introduction and principles

Exercises

11.1 $M=\sigma T^4$ [9b]

$P=\sigma T^4\times A=5.67\times10^{-8}\,\mathrm{W\,m^{-2}\,K^{-4}}\times(1500\,\mathrm{K})^4\times6.0\,\mathrm{m}^2$

$=\underline{1.7\,\mathrm{MW}}$

11.2 $E=P\times t,\ E=Nh\nu$

$$\nu=\frac{Pt}{Nh}=\frac{0.72\times10^{-6}\,\mathrm{W}\times3.8\times10^{-3}\,\mathrm{s}}{8.0\times10^{7}\times6.626\times10^{-34}\,\mathrm{J\,Hz^{-1}}}=\underline{5.2\times10^{16}\,\mathrm{Hz}}$$

11.3 $p=mv$ and $p=\dfrac{h}{\lambda}$ [176]

Therefore,

$$v=\frac{h}{m\lambda}=\frac{6.626\times10^{-34}\,\mathrm{J\,s}}{9.109\times10^{-31}\,\mathrm{kg}\times0.45\times10^{-9}\,\mathrm{m}}=\underline{1.6\times10^{6}\,\mathrm{m\,s^{-1}}}$$

11.4 $p=\dfrac{h}{\lambda}$ [17b]

(a) $p=\dfrac{6.626\times10^{-34}\,\mathrm{J\,s}}{750\times10^{-9}\,\mathrm{m}}=\underline{8.83\times10^{-28}\,\mathrm{kg\,m\,s^{-1}}}$

(b) $p=\dfrac{6.626\times10^{-34}\,\mathrm{J\,s}}{70\times10^{-12}\,\mathrm{m}}=\underline{9.5\times10^{-24}\,\mathrm{kg\,m\,s^{-1}}}$

(c) $p=\dfrac{6.626\times10^{-34}\,\mathrm{J\,s}}{19\,\mathrm{m}}=\underline{3.5\times10^{-35}\,\mathrm{kg\,m\,s^{-1}}}$

11.5 $\tfrac{1}{2}mv^2=h\nu-I=\dfrac{hc}{\lambda}-I$

Hence, $\lambda = \dfrac{hc}{I + \frac{1}{2}mv^2} = \dfrac{6.626 \times 10^{-34}\ \text{J s} \times 2.998 \times 10^8\ \text{m s}^{-1}}{3.44 \times 10^{-18}\ \text{J} + \frac{1}{2} \times 9.109 \times 10^{-31}\ \text{kg} \times (1.03 \times 10^6\ \text{m s}^{-1})}$

$= 5.06 \times 10^{-8}\ \text{m} = \underline{50.6\ \text{nm}}$

11.6 $\delta\lambda = \dfrac{h}{m_e c}(1 - \cos\theta)$ [16, 18], $\lambda_c = \dfrac{h}{m_e c} = 2.43\ \text{pm}$

$= 2.43\ \text{pm} \times (1 - \cos 70) = 1.60\ \text{pm}$

Therefore, $\lambda_f = 70.78 + 1.60\ \text{pm} = \underline{72.38\ \text{pm}}$

11.7 $\Delta p \approx 0.0100$ per cent of p_0, $p_0 = m_p v$

$= p_0 \times 1.00 \times 10^{-4}$

$\Delta q \approx \dfrac{\hbar}{2\Delta p}$ [33]

$\approx \dfrac{1.055 \times 10^{-34}\ \text{J s}}{2 \times 1.673 \times 10^{-27}\ \text{kg} \times 4.5 \times 10^5\ \text{m s}^{-1} \times 1.00 \times 10^{-4}}$

$\approx 7.0\bar{1} \times 10^{-10}\ \text{m}$, or $\underline{70\ \text{nm}}$

11.8 $E = \dfrac{n^2h^2}{8mL^2}$ [given]

Hence $L = \left(\dfrac{n^2h^2}{8mE}\right)^{1/2} = \dfrac{nh}{(8mE)^{1/2}}$

$= \dfrac{3 \times 6.626 \times 10^{-34}\ \text{J s}}{(8 \times 6.65 \times 10^{-27}\ \text{kg} \times 2.00 \times 10^{-24}\ \text{J})^{1/2}}$

$= 6.09 \times 10^{-9}\ \text{m}$, or $\underline{6.09\ \text{nm}}$

11.9 $\psi = \left(\dfrac{2}{L}\right)^{1/2} \sin\left(\dfrac{n\pi x}{L}\right)$ [given]

$= \left(\dfrac{2}{L}\right)^{1/2} \sin\dfrac{\pi x}{L}$ $[n = 1]$

The wavefunction has its greatest value when

$$\frac{\pi x}{L}=\frac{\pi}{2}, \text{ or } x=\tfrac{1}{2}L$$

and at that location

$$\psi^2=\frac{2}{L} \quad [\text{probability} \propto \psi^2]$$

The value of x at which ψ^2 has 25 per cent of this value is the solution of

$$\frac{2}{L}\sin^2\frac{\pi x}{L}=\frac{1}{4}\times\frac{2}{L}$$

$$\text{or } \sin^2\frac{\pi x}{L}=\frac{1}{4}$$

That is, $x=\pm\frac{L}{\pi}\arcsin\frac{1}{2}=\pm 0.17L$ [arcsin in radians]

and the location is at $0.17L$ from the left or the right walls

$$x=\underline{0.17L} \text{ or } \underline{0.83L}$$

11.10 $\Delta E=(5^2-4^2)\frac{h^2}{8mL^2}=\frac{9h^2}{8mL^2}$

$$=\frac{9\times(6.626\times10^{-34}\text{ J s})^2}{8\times(2.0141\times1.6605\times10^{-27}\text{ kg})\times(5.0\times10^{-9}\text{ m})^2}=\underline{5.9\times10^{-24}\text{ J}}$$

11.11 $E=h\nu=\frac{hc}{\lambda}$

$$hc=6.62608\times10^{-34}\text{ J s}\times2.99792\times10^{8}\text{ m s}^{-1}=1.986\times10^{-25}\text{ J m}$$

$$N_{\text{A}}hc=6.02214\times10^{23}\text{ mol}^{-1}\times1.986\times10^{-25}\text{ J m}=0.1196\text{ J m mol}^{-1}$$

We can therefore draw up the following table:

λ/nm	E/J	E/(kJ mol^{-1})	p/(kg m s^{-1})
(a) 600	3.31×10^{-19}	199	1.10×10^{-27}
(b) 550	3.61×10^{-19}	218	1.20×10^{-27}
(c) 400	4.97×10^{-19}	299	1.66×10^{-27}
(d) 200	9.93×10^{-19}	598	3.31×10^{-27}
(e) 150 pm	1.32×10^{-15}	7.98×10^{5}	4.42×10^{-24}
(f) 1.00 cm	1.99×10^{-23}	0.012	6.63×10^{-32}

11.12 $p=\dfrac{h}{\lambda}=\dfrac{6.626\times10^{-34}\text{ J s}}{\lambda}$; the entries are in the table above.

11.13 If a photon is absorbed, the atom acquires its momentum p. It therefore reaches a speed v such that $p=mv$. We use

$$m_{\mathrm{H}}=1.008\text{ u}=1.008\times1.6605\times10^{-27}\text{ kg}=1.674\times10^{-27}\text{ kg}$$

and draw up the following table using the information in the table above:

λ/nm	v/(m s^{-1})
600	0.66
550	0.72
400	0.99
200	1.98
150 pm	2640
1.00 cm	3.96×10^{-5}

11.14 The energy of a photon of 650 nm light is $E=hc/\lambda$ with $\lambda=650$ nm. The total number of photons emitted in an interval τ is

$$N=\frac{P\tau}{E}=\frac{P\tau\lambda}{hc}$$

with $P=0.10$ W and $\tau=10$ y. The total momentum emitted is

$$p=\frac{Nh}{\lambda}=\frac{P\tau\lambda}{hc}\times\frac{h}{\lambda}=\frac{P\tau}{c}$$

The momentum is acquired by the source, and since its mass is m, and $p = mv$, its final speed is

$$v = \frac{P\tau}{cm} = \frac{0.10\ \mathrm{J\ s^{-1}} \times 3.16 \times 10^{8}\ \mathrm{s}}{2.998 \times 10^{8}\ \mathrm{m\ s^{-1}} \times 5.0 \times 10^{-3}\ \mathrm{kg}}$$

$$= \underline{21\ \mathrm{m\ s^{-1}}}$$

Note that the answer is independent of the wavelength of the radiation emitted: the greater the wavelength ther smaller the photon momentum, but the greater the number of photons emitted.

11.15 $N = \dfrac{P}{h\nu}$ $[P = \text{power in J s}^{-1}] = \dfrac{P\lambda}{hc}$

$$= \frac{P\lambda}{6.626 \times 10^{-34}\ \mathrm{J\ Hz^{-1}} \times 2.998 \times 10^{8}\ \mathrm{m\ s^{-1}}}$$

$$= \frac{(P/\mathrm{W}) \times (\lambda/\mathrm{nm})\ \mathrm{s^{-1}}}{1.99 \times 10^{-16}} = 5.03 \times 10^{15} (P/\mathrm{W}) \times (\lambda/\mathrm{nm})\ \mathrm{s^{-1}}$$

(a) $N = 5.03 \times 10^{15} \times 1.0 \times 550\ \mathrm{s^{-1}} = \underline{2.8 \times 10^{18}\ \mathrm{s^{-1}}}$

(b) $N = 5.03 \times 10^{15} \times 100 \times 550\ \mathrm{s^{-1}} = \underline{2.8 \times 10^{20}\ \mathrm{s^{-1}}}$

11.16 From Wien's law,

$T\lambda_{\max} = \frac{1}{5}c_2 = 1.44\ \mathrm{cm\ K}$ [8]

Therefore,

$$T = \frac{1.44\ \mathrm{cm\ K}}{5 \times 480 \times 10^{-7}\ \mathrm{cm}} = \underline{6000\ \mathrm{K}}$$

11.17 $\frac{1}{2}mv^2 = h\nu - \Phi = \dfrac{hc}{\lambda} - \Phi$

$\Phi = 2.14\ \mathrm{eV} \triangleq 2.14 \times 1.602 \times 10^{-19}\ \mathrm{J} = 3.43 \times 10^{-19}\ \mathrm{J}$

(a) $hc/\lambda = \dfrac{6.626 \times 10^{-34}\ \mathrm{J\ s} \times 2.998 \times 10^{8}\ \mathrm{m\ s^{-1}}}{700 \times 10^{-9}\ \mathrm{m}}$

$= 2.84 \times 10^{-19}\ \mathrm{J} < \Phi$, so no ejection occurs

(b) $hc/\lambda = 6.62 \times 10^{-19}\ \mathrm{J}$

Hence $\frac{1}{2}mv^2 = (6.62 - 3.43) \times 10^{-19}\ \mathrm{J} = \underline{3.19 \times 10^{-19}\ \mathrm{J}}$

$$v=\left(\frac{2\times 3.19\times 10^{-19}\,\text{J}}{9.109\times 10^{-31}\,\text{kg}}\right)^{1/2}=\underline{837\,\text{km s}^{-1}}$$

11.18 $\delta\lambda=\lambda_c(1-\cos\theta)$ [16] $=\lambda_c$ when $\theta=90°$

(a) $\lambda_c=2.43$ pm [16], so $\delta\lambda=\underline{2.43\text{ pm}}$

(b) $\lambda_c=\dfrac{h}{m_p c}$ [18, $m_e\to m_p$]

$$=\frac{6.626\times 10^{-34}\,\text{J s}}{1.673\times 10^{-27}\,\text{kg}\times 2.998\times 10^{8}\,\text{m s}^{-1}}=1.32\times 10^{-15}\,\text{m}$$

Therefore, $\delta\lambda=\underline{1.32\text{ fm}}$

11.19 $\Delta E=h\nu=\dfrac{h}{T}$ [T = period]

(a) $\Delta E=\dfrac{6.626\times 10^{-34}\,\text{J s}}{10^{-15}\,\text{s}}=\underline{7\times 10^{-19}\,\text{J}}$

corresponding to $N_A\times 7\times 10^{-19}\,\text{J}=\underline{400\text{ kJ mol}^{-1}}$

(b) $\Delta E=\dfrac{6.626\times 10^{-34}\,\text{J s}}{10^{-14}\,\text{s}}=\underline{7\times 10^{-20}\,\text{J}}$, $\underline{40\text{ kJ mol}^{-1}}$

(c) $\Delta E=\dfrac{6.626\times 10^{-34}\,\text{J s}}{1\,\text{s}}=\underline{7\times 10^{-34}\,\text{J}}$, $\underline{4\times 10^{-13}\text{ kJ mol}^{-1}}$

11.20 $\lambda=\dfrac{h}{p}=\dfrac{h}{mv}$

(a) $\lambda=\dfrac{6.626\times 10^{-34}\,\text{J s}}{1.0\times 10^{-3}\,\text{kg}\times 1.0\times 10^{-2}\,\text{m s}^{-1}}=\underline{6.6\times 10^{-29}\,\text{m}}$

(b) $\lambda=\dfrac{6.626\times 10^{-34}\,\text{J s}}{1.0\times 10^{-3}\,\text{kg}\times 1.00\times 10^{5}\,\text{m s}^{-1}}=\underline{6.6\times 10^{-36}\,\text{m}}$

(c) $\lambda=\dfrac{6.626\times 10^{-34}\,\text{J s}}{4.003\times 1.6605\times 10^{-27}\,\text{kg}\times 1000\,\text{m s}^{-1}}=\underline{99.7\text{ pm}}$

11.21 $\frac{1}{2}mv^2=e\,\Delta\phi$, implying that $v=\left(\dfrac{2e\,\Delta\phi}{m}\right)^{1/2}$ and that $p = mv = (2me\Delta\phi)^{1/2}$. Therefore,

$$\lambda = \frac{h}{p} = \frac{h}{(2me\Delta\phi)^{1/2}}$$

$$= \frac{6.626 \times 10^{-34}\ \mathrm{J\ s}}{(2 \times 9.109 \times 10^{-31}\ \mathrm{kg} \times 1.602 \times 10^{-19}\ \mathrm{C} \times \Delta\phi)^{1/2}}$$

$$= \frac{1.226\ \mathrm{nm}}{(\Delta\phi/\mathrm{V})^{1/2}} \quad [1\ \mathrm{J} = 1\ \mathrm{C\ V}]$$

(a) $\Delta\phi = 100\ \mathrm{V},\ \lambda = \dfrac{1.226\ \mathrm{nm}}{10.0} = \underline{123\ \mathrm{pm}}$

(b) $\Delta\phi = 1.0\ \mathrm{kV},\ \lambda = \dfrac{1.226\ \mathrm{nm}}{31.6} = \underline{39\ \mathrm{pm}}$

(c) $\Delta\phi = 100\ \mathrm{kV},\ \lambda = \dfrac{1.226\ \mathrm{nm}}{316.2} = \underline{3.88\ \mathrm{pm}}$

11.22 $\Delta p\, \Delta q \geqslant \frac{1}{2}\hbar,\ \Delta p = m\, \Delta v$

$$\Delta v_{\min} = \frac{\hbar}{2m\, \Delta q} = \frac{1.055 \times 10^{-34}\ \mathrm{J\ s}}{2 \times 0.500\ \mathrm{kg} \times 1.0 \times 10^{-6}\ \mathrm{m}} = \underline{1.1 \times 10^{-28}\ \mathrm{m\ s^{-1}}}$$

$$\Delta q_{\min} = \frac{\hbar}{2m\, \Delta v} = \frac{1.055 \times 10^{-34}\ \mathrm{J\ s}}{2 \times 5.0 \times 10^{-3}\ \mathrm{kg} \times 1 \times 10^{-5}\ \mathrm{m\ s^{-1}}} = \underline{1 \times 10^{-27}\ \mathrm{m}}$$

11.23 $\Delta p_{\min} = \dfrac{\hbar}{2\Delta q} = \dfrac{1.055 \times 10^{-34}\ \mathrm{J\ s}}{2 \times 100 \times 10^{-12}\ \mathrm{m}} = \underline{5 \times 10^{-25}\ \mathrm{kg\ m\ s^{-1}}}$

$$\Delta v_{\min} = \frac{\Delta p_{\min}}{m_e} = \frac{5 \times 10^{-25}\ \mathrm{kg\ m\ s^{-1}}}{9.109 \times 10^{-31}\ \mathrm{kg}} = \underline{5 \times 10^{5}\ \mathrm{m\ s^{-1}}}$$

11.24 $\frac{1}{2}mv^2 = h\nu - I,\ \nu = \dfrac{c}{\lambda}$

$$I = \frac{hc}{\lambda} - \tfrac{1}{2}mv^2 = \frac{6.626 \times 10^{-34}\ \mathrm{J\ s} \times 2.998 \times 10^{8}\ \mathrm{m\ s^{-1}}}{150 \times 10^{-12}\ \mathrm{m}}$$

$$- \tfrac{1}{2} \times 9.109 \times 10^{-31}\ \mathrm{kg} \times (2.14 \times 10^{7}\ \mathrm{m\ s^{-1}})^2 = \underline{1.12 \times 10^{-15}\ \mathrm{J}}$$

Problems

11.1 $\rho = \frac{8\pi hc}{\lambda^5}\left(\frac{1}{e^{hc/\lambda kT}-1}\right)$ [12], $\Delta\mathcal{U} = \rho\,\Delta\lambda$, $\lambda \approx 652.5$ nm

$$\frac{hc}{\lambda k} = \frac{1.439 \times 10^{-2}\ \text{m K}}{\lambda} = 2.205 \times 10^4\ \text{K}$$

$$\frac{8\pi hc}{\lambda^5} = \frac{8\pi \times 6.626 \times 10^{-34}\ \text{J s} \times 2.998 \times 10^8\ \text{m s}^{-1}}{(652.5 \times 10^{-9}\ \text{m})^5} = 4.221 \times 10^7\ \text{J m}^{-4}$$

$$\Delta\mathcal{U} = 4.221 \times 10^7\ \text{J m}^{-4} \times \left(\frac{1}{e^{2.205 \times 10^4\ \text{K}/T}-1}\right) \times 5 \times 10^{-9}\ \text{m}$$

(a) $T = 298$ K, $\Delta\mathcal{U} = \frac{0.211\ \text{J m}^{-3}}{e^{2.205 \times 10^4/298}-1} = \underline{1.6 \times 10^{-33}\ \text{J m}^{-3}}$

(b) $T = 3273$ K, $\Delta\mathcal{U} = \frac{0.211\ \text{J m}^{-3}}{e^{2.205 \times 10^4/3273}-1} = \underline{2.5 \times 10^{-4}\ \text{J m}^{-3}}$

11.2 $\lambda_{\max}T = hc/5k$ [8, and $c_2 = hc/k$]. Therefore

$$\lambda_{\max} = \frac{hc}{5k} \times \frac{1}{T}$$

and if we plot $\lambda_{\max}$ against $1/T$ we can obtain h from the slope. We draw up the following table:

$\theta/°\text{C}$	1000	1500	2000	2500	3000	3500
T/K	1273	1773	2273	2773	3273	3773
$10^4/(T/\text{K})$	7.86	5.64	4.40	3.61	3.06	2.65
$\lambda_{\max}/\text{nm}$	2181	1600	1240	1035	878	763

The points are plotted in Fig. 11.1. From the graph, the slope is 2.83×10^6, so

$$\frac{hc}{5k} = 2.83 \times 10^6 \frac{\text{nm}}{1/\text{K}} = 2.83 \times 10^{-3}\ \text{m K}$$

and

$$h = \frac{5 \times 1.38066 \times 10^{-23}\ \text{J K}^{-1} \times 2.83 \times 10^{-3}\ \text{m K}}{2.99792 \times 10^8\ \text{m s}^{-1}} = \underline{6.52 \times 10^{-34}\ \text{J s}}$$

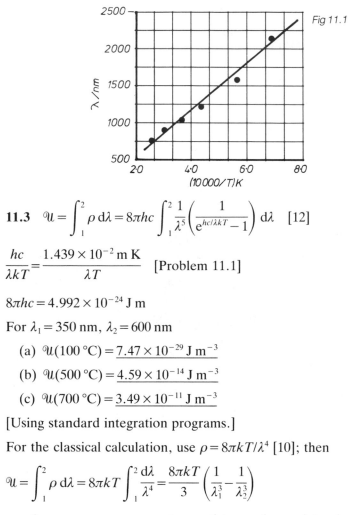

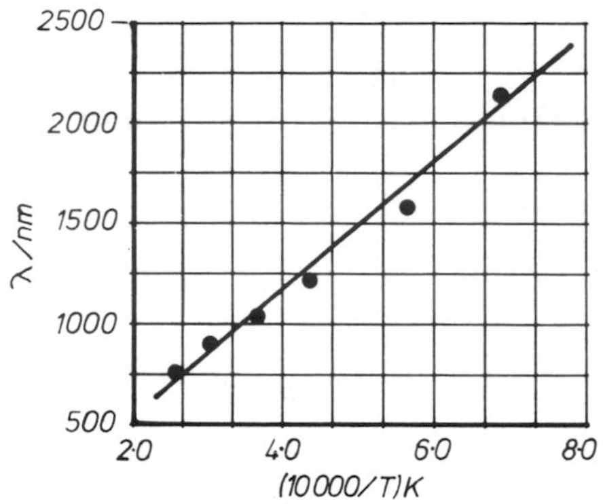

Fig 11.1

11.3 $\mathcal{U}=\int_1^2 \rho\,d\lambda = 8\pi hc\int_1^2 \frac{1}{\lambda^5}\left(\frac{1}{e^{hc/\lambda kT}-1}\right)d\lambda$ [12]

$\frac{hc}{\lambda kT}=\frac{1.439\times10^{-2}\text{ m K}}{\lambda T}$ [Problem 11.1]

$8\pi hc = 4.992\times10^{-24}\text{ J m}$

For $\lambda_1=350$ nm, $\lambda_2=600$ nm

(a) $\mathcal{U}(100\,°\text{C})=\underline{7.47\times10^{-29}\text{ J m}^{-3}}$

(b) $\mathcal{U}(500\,°\text{C})=\underline{4.59\times10^{-14}\text{ J m}^{-3}}$

(c) $\mathcal{U}(700\,°\text{C})=\underline{3.49\times10^{-11}\text{ J m}^{-3}}$

[Using standard integration programs.]

For the classical calculation, use $\rho=8\pi kT/\lambda^4$ [10]; then

$$\mathcal{U}=\int_1^2 \rho\,d\lambda = 8\pi kT\int_1^2 \frac{d\lambda}{\lambda^4}=\frac{8\pi kT}{3}\left(\frac{1}{\lambda_1^3}-\frac{1}{\lambda_2^3}\right)$$

$$=\frac{8\pi}{3}\times1.381\times10^{-23}\text{ J}\times(T/\text{K})\times\left\{\left(\frac{1}{3.50\times10^{-7}\text{m}}\right)^3-\left(\frac{1}{6.00\times10^{-7}\text{m}}\right)^3\right\}$$

$$=2.16\times10^{-3}\text{ J m}^{-3}\times(T/\text{K})$$

Then,

(a) $\mathcal{U}(100\,°\text{C})=0.807\text{ J m}^{-3}$

(b) $\mathcal{U}(500\,°\text{C})=1.67\text{ J m}^{-3}$

(c) $\mathcal{U}(700\,°\text{C})=2.10\text{ J m}^{-3}$

All three classical values are very much larger than the quantum values.

11.4 $\theta_E = \frac{h\nu}{k}$, $[\theta_E] = \frac{\text{J s} \times \text{s}^{-1}}{\text{J K}^{-1}} = \text{K}$

The Einstein formula [14] reverts to the classical expression when $kT \gg h\nu$, or $T \gg h\nu/k = \theta_E$. The criterion for classical behavior is therefore that $\underline{T \gg \theta_E}$

$$\theta_E = \frac{h\nu}{k} = \frac{6.626 \times 10^{-34}\ \text{J Hz}^{-1} \times \nu}{1.381 \times 10^{-23}\ \text{J K}^{-1}} = 4.798 \times 10^{-11}(\nu/\text{Hz})\ \text{K}$$

(a) For $\nu = 4.65 \times 10^{13}$ Hz, $\theta_E = 4.798 \times 10^{-11} \times 4.65 \times 10^{13}\ \text{K} = \underline{223\bar{1}\ \text{K}}$

(b) For $\nu = 7.15 \times 10^{12}$ Hz, $\theta_E = 4.798 \times 10^{-11} \times 7.15 \times 10^{12}\ \text{K} = \underline{343\ \text{K}}$

$$C_V = 3R\left(\frac{\theta_E}{T}\right)^2 \left\{\frac{e^{\theta_E/2T}}{e^{\theta_E/T} - 1}\right\}^2 \quad [14], \text{ classical value} = 3R$$

(a) $C_V/3R = \left(\frac{2231\ \text{K}}{298\ \text{K}}\right)^2 \times \left\{\frac{e^{2231/2\times 298}}{e^{2231/298} - 1}\right\}^2 = \underline{0.031}$

(b) $C_V/3R = \left(\frac{343\ \text{K}}{298\ \text{K}}\right)^2 \times \left\{\frac{e^{343/2\times 298}}{e^{343/298} - 1}\right\}^2 = \underline{0.897}$

11.5 $\psi^2 = \frac{2}{L}\sin^2\frac{\pi x}{L}$

The probability that the particle will be found between a and b is

$$P(a, b) = \int_a^b \psi^2\, dx = \frac{2}{L}\int_a^b \sin^2\frac{\pi x}{L}\, dx$$

$$= \left(\frac{x}{L} - \frac{1}{2\pi}\sin\frac{2\pi x}{L}\right)\Bigg|_a^b$$

$$= \frac{b-a}{L} - \frac{1}{2\pi}\left(\sin\frac{2\pi b}{L} - \sin\frac{2\pi a}{L}\right)$$

$L = 10.0$ nm

(a) $P(4.95, 5.05) = \frac{0.10}{10.0} - \frac{1}{2\pi}\left(\sin\frac{2\pi \times 5.05}{10.0} - \sin\frac{2\pi \times 4.95}{10.0}\right)$

$= 0.010 + 0.010 = \underline{0.020}$

(b) $P(1.95, 2.05) = \dfrac{0.10}{10.0} - \dfrac{1}{2\pi}\left(\sin\dfrac{2\pi\times 2.05}{10.0} - \sin\dfrac{2\pi\times 1.95}{10.0}\right)$

$= 0.010 - 0.0031 = \underline{0.007}$

(c) $P(9.90, 10.0) = \dfrac{0.10}{10.0} - \dfrac{1}{2\pi}\left(\sin\dfrac{2\pi\times 10.0}{10.0} - \sin\dfrac{2\pi\times 9.90}{10.0}\right)$

$= 0.010 - 0.009993 = \underline{6\times 10^{-6}}$

(d) $P(5.0, 10.0) = \underline{0.5}$ [by symmetry]

(e) $P(\tfrac{1}{3}L, \tfrac{2}{3}L) = \dfrac{1}{3} - \dfrac{1}{2\pi}\left(\sin\dfrac{4\pi}{3} - \sin\dfrac{2\pi}{3}\right) = \underline{0.61}$

11.6 $\psi^2 = \dfrac{1}{\pi a_0^3}\mathrm{e}^{-2r/a_0}$, $\delta\tau = \tfrac{4}{3}\pi r_0^3$, $r_0 = 1.0\,\mathrm{pm}$

If we assume that the volume δt is so small that ψ does not vary within it, the probability is given by

$$\psi^2\,\delta\tau = \frac{4}{3}\frac{r_0^3}{a_0^3}\mathrm{e}^{-2r/a_0} = \frac{4}{3}\times\left(\frac{1.0}{53}\right)^3 \mathrm{e}^{-2r/a_0}$$

(a) $r = 0$:

$$\psi^2\,\delta\tau = \frac{4}{3}\left(\frac{1.0}{53}\right)^3 = \underline{9.0\times 10^{-6}}$$

(b) $r = a_0$

$$\psi^2\,\delta\tau = \frac{4}{3}\left(\frac{1.0}{53}\right)^3 \mathrm{e}^{-2} = \underline{1.2\times 10^{-6}}$$

11.7 We look for the value of λ at which ρ is a maximum, using (as appropriate) the short wavelength (high frequency) approximation,

$$\rho = \frac{8\pi hc}{\lambda^5}\left(\frac{1}{\mathrm{e}^{hc/\lambda kT} - 1}\right)$$

$$\frac{\mathrm{d}\rho}{\mathrm{d}\lambda} = -\frac{5}{\lambda}\rho + \frac{hc}{\lambda^2 kT}\left(\frac{\mathrm{e}^{hc/\lambda kT}}{\mathrm{e}^{hc/\lambda kT} - 1}\right)\rho = 0 \quad \text{at } \lambda = \lambda_{\max}$$

$$-5 + \frac{hc}{\lambda kT}\frac{\mathrm{e}^{hc/\lambda kT}}{\mathrm{e}^{hc/\lambda kT} - 1} = 0$$

Hence

$$5-5\,e^{hc/\lambda kT}+\frac{hc}{\lambda kT}e^{hc/\lambda kT}=0$$

and if $hc/\lambda kT \gg 1$, we neglect the initial 5, cancel the two exponentials, and obtain

$$hc=5\lambda kT \text{ for } \lambda=\lambda_{\max} \text{ and } hc/\lambda kT \gg 1$$

or

$$\lambda_{\max}T=\frac{hc}{5k}=2.88\text{ mm K, in accord with observation.}$$

11.8 Refer to Fig. 11.2.

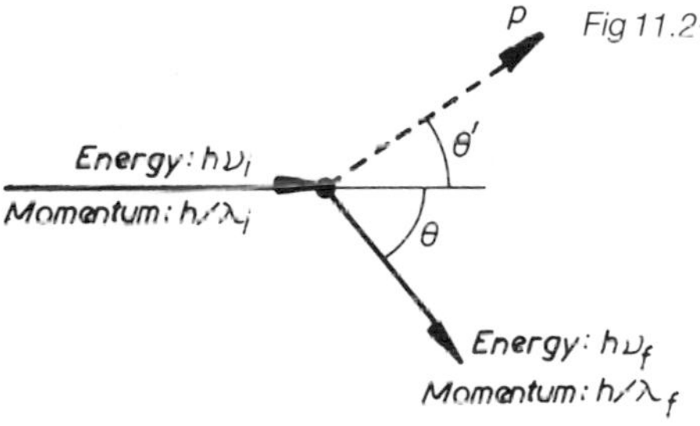

Fig 11.2

(1) Energy conservation:

$$h\nu_i+m_ec^2=h\nu_f+(p^2c^2+m_e^2c^4)^{1/2}$$

(2) Momentum conservation:

Parallel: $\dfrac{h\nu_i}{c}=\dfrac{h\nu_f}{c}\cos\theta+p\cos\theta'$

Perpendicular: $0=\dfrac{h\nu_f}{c}\sin\theta-p\sin\theta'$

From condition (2):

$$p^2\cos^2\theta' + p^2\sin^2\theta' = \left(\frac{h\nu_i}{c} - \frac{h\nu_f}{c}\cos\theta\right)^2 + \left(\frac{h\nu_f}{c}\sin\theta\right)^2$$

Hence $p^2 = \dfrac{h^2}{c^2}(\nu_i^2 + \nu_f^2\cos^2\theta - 2\nu_i\nu_f\cos\theta + \nu_f^2\sin^2\theta)$

$$= \frac{h^2}{c^2}(\nu_i^2 + \nu_f^2 - 2\nu_i\nu_f\cos\theta)$$

But from condition (1):

$$p^2c^2 = (h\nu_i + m_ec^2 - h\nu_f)^2 - m_ec^4$$

which implies that

$$\nu_i^2 + \nu_f^2 - 2\nu_i\nu_f\cos\theta = \nu_i^2 + \nu_f^2 + 2\left(\frac{m_ec^2}{h}\right)(\nu_i - \nu_f) - 2\nu_i\nu_f$$

or $\quad 2\nu_i\nu_f(1-\cos\theta) = \left(\dfrac{2m_ec^2}{h}\right)(\nu_i - \nu_f)$

and that $\quad \dfrac{\nu_i - \nu_f}{\nu_i\nu_f} = \dfrac{h}{m_ec^2}(1-\cos\theta)$

But $\quad \dfrac{\nu_i - \nu_f}{\nu_i\nu_f} = \dfrac{1}{\nu_f} - \dfrac{1}{\nu_i} = \dfrac{\lambda_f - \lambda_i}{c} = \dfrac{\delta\lambda}{c}$

Therefore,

$$\underline{\delta\lambda = \frac{h}{m_ec}(1-\cos\theta)}$$

11.9 We require $\int \psi^*\psi\,d\tau = 1$, and so write $\psi = Nf$ and find N for the given f.

(a) $N^2\displaystyle\int_0^L \sin^2\frac{n\pi x}{L}\,dx = \tfrac{1}{2}N^2\int_0^L \left(1-\cos\frac{2n\pi x}{L}\right)dx$

$$= \tfrac{1}{2}N^2\left(x - \frac{L}{2n\pi}\sin\frac{2n\pi x}{L}\right)\Bigg|_0^L$$

$$= \frac{L}{2}N^2 = 1 \text{ if } \underline{N = \left(\frac{2}{L}\right)^{1/2}}$$

(b) $N^2\displaystyle\int_{-L}^{L} c^2\,dx = 2N^2c^2L = 1$ if $\underline{N = \dfrac{1}{c(2L)^{1/2}}}$

(c) $N^2\int_0^\infty e^{-2r/a}r^2\,dr\int_0^\pi \sin\theta\,d\theta\int_0^{2\pi} d\phi \quad [d\tau = r^2\sin\theta\,dr\,d\theta\,d\phi]$

$$=N^2\left(\frac{a^3}{4}\right)\times 2\times 2\pi = 1 \text{ if } \underline{N=\frac{1}{(\pi a^3)^{1/2}}}$$

(d) $N^2\int_0^\infty r^2\times r^2 e^{-r/a}\,dr\int_0^\pi \sin^3\theta\,d\theta\int_0^{2\pi}\cos^2\phi\,d\phi \quad [x=r\cos\phi\sin\theta]$

$$=N^2 4!a^5\times\frac{4}{3}\times\pi = 32\pi a^5N^2 = 1 \text{ if } \underline{N=\frac{1}{(32\pi a^5)^{1/2}}}$$

where we have used

$$\int_0^\pi \cos^n\theta\sin\theta\,d\theta = -\int_1^{-1}\cos^n\theta\,d\cos\theta = \int_{-1}^1 x^n\,dx$$

and $\int_0^{2\pi}\cos^2\phi\,d\phi = \int_0^{2\pi}\sin^2\phi\,d\phi$ by symmetry

with $\int_0^{2\pi}(\cos^2\phi+\sin^2\phi)\,d\phi = \int_0^{2\pi} d\phi = 2\pi$

11.10 (a) $\psi = N\left(2-\frac{r}{a_0}\right)e^{-r/2a_0}$

$$\psi^2 = N^2\left(2-\frac{r}{a_0}\right)^2 e^{-r/a_0}$$

$$\int\psi^2\,d\tau = N^2\int_0^\infty\left(4r^2-\frac{4r^3}{a_0}+\frac{r^4}{a_0^2}\right)e^{-r/a_0}\,dr\int_0^\pi\sin\theta\,d\theta\int_0^{2\pi}d\phi$$

$$=N^2\left(4\times 2a_0^3 - 4\times\frac{6a_0^4}{a_0}+\frac{24a_0^5}{a_0^2}\right)\times 2\times 2\pi$$

$$=32\pi a_0^3N^2, \text{ hence } \underline{N=\left(\frac{1}{32\pi a_0^3}\right)^{1/2}}$$

(b) $\psi = Nr\sin\theta\cos\phi\,e^{-r/2a_0}$

$$\int\psi^2\,d\tau = N^2\int_0^\infty r^4 e^{-r/2a_0}\,dr\int_0^\pi\sin^2\theta\sin\theta d\theta\int_0^{2\pi}\cos^2\phi\,d\phi$$

$$= N^2 4! a_0^5 \int_{-1}^{1} (1-\cos^2\theta)\,\mathrm{d}\cos\theta \times \pi$$

$$= N^2 4! a_0^5 \left(2 - \frac{2}{3}\right)\pi = 32\pi a_0^5 N_0^2; \text{ hence } \underline{N = \left(\frac{1}{32\pi a_0^5}\right)^{1/2}}$$

11.11 (a) $\frac{\mathrm{d}}{\mathrm{d}x}\mathrm{e}^{\mathrm{i}kx} = \mathrm{i}k\,\mathrm{e}^{ihx}$; yes; eigenvalue $= \mathrm{i}k$.

(b) $\frac{\mathrm{d}}{\mathrm{d}x}\cos kx = -k\sin kx$; no.

(c) $\frac{\mathrm{d}}{\mathrm{d}x}k = 0$; yes; eigenvalue $= 0$.

(d) $\frac{\mathrm{d}}{\mathrm{d}x}kx = k = \frac{1}{x}kx$; no [$1/x$ is not a constant].

(e) $\frac{\mathrm{d}}{\mathrm{d}x}\mathrm{e}^{-\alpha x^2} = -2\alpha x\,\mathrm{e}^{-\alpha x^2}$; no [$-2\alpha x$ is not a constant].

11.12 (a) $\frac{\mathrm{d}^2}{\mathrm{d}x^2}\mathrm{e}^{\mathrm{i}kx} = -k^2\,\mathrm{e}^{\mathrm{i}kx}$; yes; eigenvalue $= -k^2$

(b) $\frac{\mathrm{d}^2}{\mathrm{d}x^2}\cos kx = -k^2\cos kx$; yes; eigenvalue $= -k^2$

(c) $\frac{\mathrm{d}^2}{\mathrm{d}x^2}k = 0$; yes; eigenvalue $= 0$.

(d) $\frac{\mathrm{d}^2}{\mathrm{d}x^2}kx = 0$; yes; eigenvalue $= 0$.

(e) $\frac{\mathrm{d}^2}{\mathrm{d}x^2}\mathrm{e}^{-\alpha x^2} = (-2\alpha + 4\alpha^2x^2)\,\mathrm{e}^{-\alpha x^2}$; no.

Hence, (a, b, c, d) are eigenfunctions of $\mathrm{d}^2/\mathrm{d}x^2$; (b, d) are eigenfunctions of $\mathrm{d}^2/\mathrm{d}x^2$ but not of $\mathrm{d}/\mathrm{d}x$.

11.13 $\psi = \mathrm{e}^{\mathrm{i}kx}\cos\chi + \mathrm{e}^{-\mathrm{i}kx}\sin\chi$

(a) $P=\underline{\cos^2\chi}$ [since e^{ikx} is an eigenfunction of the linear momentum with eigenvalue $+k\hbar$]

(b) $P=\underline{\sin^2\chi}$ [since e^{-ikx} corresponds to the eigenvalue $-k\hbar$]

(c) $\cos^2\chi=0.90$, so $\cos\chi=0.95$; $\sin^2\chi=0.10$, so $\sin\chi=\pm0.32$; hence

$$\psi=\underline{0.95\,e^{ikx}\pm0.32\,e^{-ikx}}$$

11.14 $\langle T\rangle = N^2\int\psi^*\left(\frac{\hat{p}^2}{2m}\right)\psi\,d\tau$

$$=\frac{\int\psi^*\left(\frac{\hat{p}^2}{2m}\right)\psi\,d\tau}{\int\psi^*\psi\,d\tau}$$

$$=\frac{\frac{-\hbar^2}{2m}\int\psi^*\frac{d^2}{dx^2}(e^{ikx}\cos\chi+e^{-ikx}\sin\chi)\,d\tau}{\int\psi^*\psi\,d\tau}$$

$$=\frac{\frac{-\hbar^2}{2m}\int\psi^*(-k^2)(e^{ikx}\cos\chi+e^{-ikx}\sin\chi)\,d\tau}{\int\psi^*\psi\,d\tau}$$

$$=\frac{\hbar^2k^2}{2m}\frac{\int\psi^*\psi\,d\tau}{\int\psi^*\psi\,d\tau}=\underline{\frac{\hbar^2k^2}{2m}}$$

11.15 $\langle p_x\rangle=\dfrac{\int\psi^*\hat{p}_x\psi\,dx}{\int\psi^*\psi\,dx}=\dfrac{\hbar}{i}\int\psi^*\left(\dfrac{d\psi}{dx}\right)dx\Big/\int\psi^*\psi\,dx$

(a) $\psi=e^{ikx}$, $\dfrac{d\psi}{dx}=ik\psi$.

Hence

$$\langle p_x\rangle = \frac{\hbar}{\mathrm{i}} \times \mathrm{i}k \int \psi^*\psi\,\mathrm{d}x \bigg/ \int \psi^*\psi\,\mathrm{d}x = \underline{k\hbar}$$

(b) $\psi = \cos kx,\ \dfrac{\mathrm{d}\psi}{\mathrm{d}x} = -k\sin kx$

$$\int_{-\infty}^{\infty} \psi^* \frac{\mathrm{d}\psi}{\mathrm{d}x}\,\mathrm{d}x = -k\int_{-\infty}^{\infty} \cos kx \sin kx\,\mathrm{d}x = 0$$

Therefore, $\langle p_x\rangle = \underline{0}$

(c) $\psi = \mathrm{e}^{-\alpha x^2},\ \dfrac{\mathrm{d}\psi}{\mathrm{d}x} = -2\alpha x\,\mathrm{e}^{-\alpha x^2}$

$$\int_{-\infty}^{\infty} \psi^* \frac{\mathrm{d}\psi}{\mathrm{d}x}\,\mathrm{d}x = -2\alpha\int_{-\infty}^{\infty} x\,\mathrm{e}^{-2\alpha x^2}\,\mathrm{d}x = 0 \quad \text{[by symmetry]}$$

Therefore, $\langle p_x\rangle = \underline{0}$

11.16 $\langle r\rangle = N^2\displaystyle\int \psi^* r\psi\,\mathrm{d}\tau,\ \langle r^2\rangle = N^2\int \psi^* r^2\psi\,\mathrm{d}\tau$

(a) $\psi = \left(2-\dfrac{r}{a_0}\right)\mathrm{e}^{-r/2a_0},\ N = \left(\dfrac{1}{32\pi a_0^3}\right)^{1/2}$ [Problem 11.10]

$$\langle r\rangle = \frac{1}{32\pi a_0^3}\int_0^{\infty} r\left(2-\frac{r}{a_0}\right)^2 r^2\,\mathrm{e}^{-r/a_0}\,\mathrm{d}r \times 4\pi$$

$$= \frac{1}{8a_0^3}\int_0^{\infty}\left(4r^3 - \frac{4r^4}{a_0} + \frac{r^5}{a_0^2}\right)\mathrm{e}^{-r/a_0}\,\mathrm{d}r$$

$$= \frac{1}{8a_0^3}(4\times 3!a_0^4 - 4\times 4!a_0^5 + 5!a_0^5) = \underline{6a_0}$$

$$\langle r^2\rangle = \frac{1}{8a_0^3}\int_0^{\infty}\left(4r^4 - \frac{4r^5}{a_0} + \frac{r^6}{a_0^2}\right)\mathrm{e}^{-r/a_0}\,\mathrm{d}r$$

$$= \frac{1}{8a_0^3}(4\times 4! - 4\times 5! + 6!)a_0^5 = \underline{42a_0^2}$$

(b) $\psi = Nr\sin\theta\cos\phi\,\mathrm{e}^{-r/2a_0},\ N = \left(\dfrac{1}{32\pi a_0^5}\right)^{1/2}$ [Problem 11.10]

$$\langle r \rangle = \frac{1}{32\pi a_0^5}\int_0^\infty r^5\,\mathrm{e}^{-r/a_0}\,\mathrm{d}r \times \frac{4\pi}{3}$$

$$= \frac{1}{24a_0^5} \times 5!a_0^6 = \underline{5a_0}$$

$$\langle r^2 \rangle = \frac{1}{24a_0^5}\int_0^\infty r^6\,\mathrm{e}^{-r/a_0}\,\mathrm{d}r = \frac{1}{24a_0^5} \times 6!a_0^7 = \underline{30a_0^2}$$

11.17 $\psi = \left(\frac{1}{\pi a_0^3}\right)^{1/2} \mathrm{e}^{-r/a_0}$ [Example 11.8]

$$\langle V \rangle = \int \psi^* \left(\frac{-e^2}{4\pi\varepsilon_0} \cdot \frac{1}{r}\right) \psi\,\mathrm{d}\tau$$

$$= \frac{1}{\pi a_0^3}\left(\frac{-e^2}{4\pi\varepsilon_0}\right)\int_0^\infty r\,\mathrm{e}^{-2r/a_0}\,\mathrm{d}r \times 4\pi$$

$$= \frac{1}{\pi a_0^3}\left(\frac{-e^2}{4\pi\varepsilon_0}\right)\left(\frac{a_0}{2}\right)^2 = \underline{\frac{-e^2}{4\pi\varepsilon_0 a_0}}$$

12. Quantum theory: techniques and applications

Exercises

12.1 $E=\dfrac{n^2h^2}{8m_eL^2}$

$$\frac{h^2}{8m_eL^2}=\frac{(6.626\times10^{-34}\ \mathrm{J\ s})^2}{8\times9.109\times10^{-31}\ \mathrm{kg}\times(1.0\times10^{-9}\ \mathrm{m})^2}=6.02\times10^{-20}\ \mathrm{J}$$

(a) $E_2-E_1=(4-1)\dfrac{h^2}{8m_eL^2}=3\times6.02\times10^{-20}\ \mathrm{J}$

$$=18.06\times10^{-20}\ \mathrm{J}=\underline{1.81\times10^{-19}\ \mathrm{J}},\ \underline{110\ \mathrm{kJ\ mol^{-1}}},\ \underline{1.1\ \mathrm{eV}},\ \underline{9\overline{100}\ \mathrm{cm^{-1}}}$$

(b) $E_6-E_5=(36-25)\dfrac{h^2}{8m_eL^2}=\dfrac{11h^2}{8m_eL^2}=11\times6.02\times10^{-20}\ \mathrm{J}$

$$=\underline{6.6\times10^{-19}\ \mathrm{J}},\ \underline{40\bar{0}\ \mathrm{kJ\ mol^{-1}}},\ \underline{4.1\ \mathrm{eV}},\ \underline{33\ \overline{000}\ \mathrm{cm^{-1}}}$$

12.2 $E=(n_1^2+n_2^2+n_3^2)\dfrac{h^2}{8mL^2}$

$$E_{111}=\frac{3h^2}{8mL^2},\quad 3E_{111}=\frac{9h^2}{8mL^2}$$

Hence, we require the values of n_1, n_2, and n_3 that make

$$n_1^2+n_2^2+n_3^2=9$$

Therefore, $(n_1, n_2, n_3)=\underline{(1, 2, 2)}$, $\underline{(2, 1, 2)}$, and $\underline{(2, 2, 1)}$ and the degeneracy is $\underline{3}$.

12.3 $E=(n_1^2+n_2^2+n_3^2)\dfrac{h^2}{8mL^2}=\dfrac{K}{L^2},\quad K=(n_1^2+n_2^2+n_3^2)\dfrac{h^2}{8m}$

$$\frac{\Delta E}{E}=\frac{\dfrac{K}{(0.9L)^2}-\dfrac{K}{L^2}}{K/L^2}=\frac{1}{0.81}-1=\underline{0.23},\ \text{or}\ \underline{23\ \text{per cent}}$$

12.4 $E=(v+\frac{1}{2})\hbar\omega,\ \omega=\left(\dfrac{k}{m}\right)^{1/2}$

$$E_0=\tfrac{1}{2}\hbar\omega=\tfrac{1}{2}\hbar\left(\frac{k}{m}\right)^{1/2}$$

$$=\tfrac{1}{2}\times 1.055\times 10^{-34}\,\mathrm{J\,s}\times\left(\frac{155\,\mathrm{N\,m^{-1}}}{2.33\times 10^{-26}\,\mathrm{kg}}\right)^{1/2}=\underline{4.30\times 10^{-21}\,\mathrm{J}}$$

12.5 $\Delta E=\hbar\omega\quad [E_{v+1}-E_v=\hbar\omega]=\hbar\left(\dfrac{k}{m}\right)^{1/2}$

Hence $k=m\left(\dfrac{\Delta E}{\hbar}\right)^2=1.33\times 10^{-25}\,\mathrm{kg}\times\left(\dfrac{4.82\times 10^{-21}\,\mathrm{J}}{1.055\times 10^{-34}\,\mathrm{J\,s}}\right)^2$

$$=\underline{278\,\mathrm{N\,m^{-1}}}\quad [1\,\mathrm{J}=1\,\mathrm{N\,m}]$$

12.6 $\Delta E=h\nu=\dfrac{hc}{\lambda}$ and $\Delta E=\hbar\omega$

Therefore, $\dfrac{hc}{\lambda}=\dfrac{h\omega}{2\pi}=\dfrac{h}{2\pi}\left(\dfrac{k}{m}\right)^{1/2}$

$$\lambda=2\pi c\left(\frac{m}{k}\right)^{1/2}=2\pi\times 2.998\times 10^8\,\mathrm{m\,s^{-1}}\times\left(\frac{1.673\times 10^{-27}\,\mathrm{kg}}{855\,\mathrm{N\,m^{-1}}}\right)$$

$$=2.63\times 10^{-6}\,\mathrm{m}=2.63\,\mu\mathrm{m}$$

12.7 (a) $\omega=\left(\dfrac{l}{g}\right)^{1/2}$ [elementary physics]

$\Delta E=\hbar\omega$ [harmonic oscillator level separations]

$$=1.055\times 10^{-34}\,\mathrm{J\,s}\times\left(\frac{1\,\mathrm{m}}{9.81\,\mathrm{m\,s^{-2}}}\right)^{1/2}=\underline{3.4\times 10^{-35}\,\mathrm{J}}$$

(b) $\Delta E=h\nu=6.626\times 10^{-34}\,\mathrm{J\,Hz^{-1}}\times 5\,\mathrm{Hz}=\underline{3.3\times 10^{-33}\,\mathrm{J}}$

(c) $\Delta E=h\nu=6.626\times 10^{-34}\,\mathrm{J\,Hz^{-1}}\times 33\times 10^3\,\mathrm{Hz}=\underline{2.2\times 10^{-29}\,\mathrm{J}}$

(d) $\Delta E=\hbar\omega=\hbar\left(\dfrac{k}{\mu}\right)^{1/2}\ \dfrac{1}{\mu}=\dfrac{1}{m_1}+\dfrac{1}{m_2}$ with $m_1=m_2$

$$\Delta E=\hbar\left(\frac{2k}{m}\right)^{1/2}=1.055\times 10^{-34}\,\mathrm{J\,s}\times\left(\frac{2\times 1177\,\mathrm{N\,m^{-1}}}{16.00\times 1.6605\times 10^{-27}\,\mathrm{kg}}\right)^{1/2}$$

$$=\underline{3.14\times 10^{-20}\,\mathrm{J}}$$

12.8 Since $\lambda \propto m^{1/2}$, $\lambda_{\text{new}} = 2^{1/2}\lambda_{\text{old}} = 2^{1/2} \times 2.63\,\mu\text{m} = \underline{3.72\,\mu\text{m}}$

The change in wavelength is $\lambda_{\text{new}} - \lambda_{\text{old}} = \underline{0.09\,\mu\text{m}}$

12.9 For rotation in a plane,

$$E = \frac{l^2\hbar^2}{2mr^2} \quad [15,\ I = mr^2]$$

$$r = \frac{l\hbar}{(2mE)^{1/2}} = \frac{2 \times 1.055 \times 10^{-34}\ \text{J s}}{(2 \times 39.95 \times 1.6605 \times 10^{-27}\ \text{kg} \times 2.47 \times 10^{-23}\ \text{J})^{1/2}}$$

$$= 1.17 \times 10^{-10}\ \text{m} = \underline{117\ \text{pm}}$$

12.10 $J = \{l(l+1)\}^{1/2}\hbar$ [21a], $\quad J_z = m_l\hbar$ [21b]

$$= 2^{1/2} \times \hbar = \underline{1.49 \times 10^{-34}\ \text{J s}}$$

$J_z = 0, \pm\hbar = \underline{0, \pm 1.06 \times 10^{-34}\ \text{J s}}$

12.11 $P = \dfrac{1}{1+G}$, $G = \dfrac{(e^{L/D} - e^{-L/D})^2}{4\varepsilon(1-\varepsilon)}$ [7]

with $D = \left\{\dfrac{\hbar^2}{2m(V-E)}\right\}^{1/2}$ and $\varepsilon = \dfrac{E}{V}$

Therefore, with $E = 0.90$ eV, $V = 2.00$ eV, $L = 0.25$ nm, and $m = m_e$,

$$D = \frac{1.055 \times 10^{-34}\ \text{J s}}{(2 \times 9.109 \times 10^{-31}\ \text{kg} \times 1.10 \times 1.60219 \times 10^{-19}\ \text{J})^{1/2}} = 1.86 \times 10^{-10}\ \text{m}$$

$$\varepsilon = \frac{0.90}{2.00} = 0.45$$

$$\frac{L}{D} = \frac{250\ \text{pm}}{186\ \text{pm}} = 1.34\bar{4}$$

Hence, $G = \dfrac{(e^{1.34\bar{4}} - e^{-1.34\bar{4}})^2}{4 \times 0.45 \times 0.55} = 12.90$

and $P = \dfrac{1}{1 + 12.90} = \underline{0.072}$

12.12 The diagrams are drawn by forming a vector of length $\{j(j+1)\}^{1/2}$ with a projection m_j on the z axis (see Fig. 12.1). Each vector represents the edge of

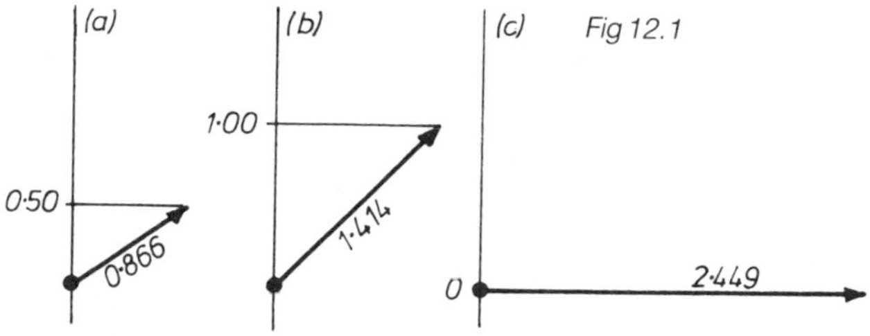

Fig 12.1

a cone around the z axis (that for $m_j = 0$ represents the side view of a disk perpendicular to z).

12.13 The cones are constructed as described in Exercise 12.12; their edges are of length $\{6(6+1)\}^{1/2} = 6.48$ and their projections are $m_j = +6, +5, \ldots, -6$. See Fig. 12.2.

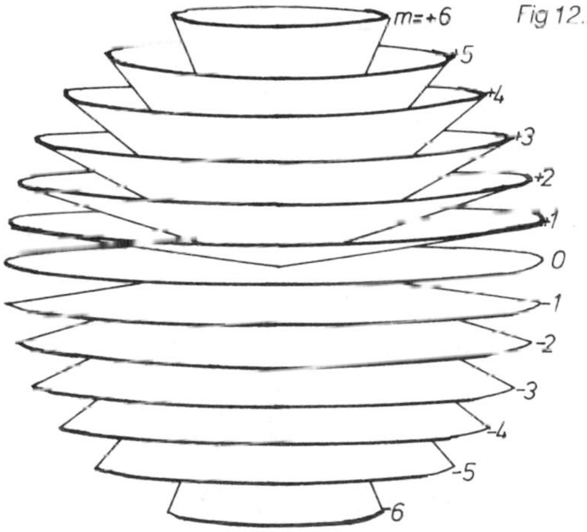

Fig 12.2

Problems

12.1 $E = \dfrac{n^2h^2}{8mL^2}$, $E_2 - E_1 = \dfrac{3h^2}{8mL^2}$

We take $m(O_2) = 32.00 \times 1.6605 \times 10^{-27}$ kg, and find

$$E_2 - E_1 = \frac{3 \times (6.626 \times 10^{-34}\ \text{J s})^2}{8 \times 32.00 \times 1.6605 \times 10^{-27}\ \text{kg} \times (5.0 \times 10^{-2}\ \text{m})^2} = \underline{1.24 \times 10^{-39}\ \text{J}}$$

Since $\dfrac{h^2}{8mL^2} = 4.13 \times 10^{-40}\ \text{J}$

for $n^2 \times 4.13 \times 10^{-40}\ \text{J} = \frac{1}{2} \times 1.381 \times 10^{-23}\ \text{J K}^{-1} \times 300\ \text{K}$

$$= 2.07 \times 10^{-21}\ \text{J}$$

we require $\qquad n = \left(\dfrac{2.07 \times 10^{-21}\ \text{J}}{4.13 \times 10^{-40}\ \text{J}}\right)^{1/2} = \underline{2.2 \times 10^9}$

At this level,

$$E_n - E_{n-1} = \{n^2 - (n-1)^2\}\frac{h^2}{8mL^2} = (2n-1)\frac{h^2}{8mL^2}$$

$$\approx 2n \times \frac{h^2}{8mL^2} = 4.4 \times 10^9 \times 4.13 \times 10^{-40}\ \text{J}$$

$$\approx \underline{1.8 \times 10^{-30}\ \text{J}}\ (\text{or } 1.1\ \mu\text{J mol}^{-1})$$

12.2 $\omega = \left(\dfrac{k}{\mu}\right)^{1/2}, \ \omega = 2\pi\nu = \dfrac{2\pi c}{\lambda} = 2\pi c\tilde{\nu}$

Therefore $k = \omega^2\mu = 4\pi^2c^2\tilde{\nu}^2\mu = \dfrac{4\pi^2c^2\tilde{\nu}^2 m_1 m_2}{m_1 + m_2}$

We draw up the following table using the information inside the back cover:

	$^1H^{35}Cl$	$^1H^{80}Br$	$^1H^{127}I$	$^{12}C^{16}O$	$^{14}N^{16}O$
$\tilde{\nu}/\text{m}^{-1}$	299000	265000	231000	217000	190400
$10^{27}\ m_1/\text{kg}$	1.6735	1.6735	1.6735	19.926	23.2521
$10^{27}\ m_2/\text{kg}$	58.066	134.36	210.72	26.568	26.568
$k/(\text{N m}^{-1})$	516	412	314	1900	1600

Therefore, the order of stiffness is CO > NO > HCl > HBr > HI

12.3 $E = \dfrac{l^2\hbar^2}{2mr^2}\quad [15,\ I = mr^2]$

$E_0 = 0 \quad [l = 0]$

$$E_1 = \frac{\hbar^2}{2mr^2} = \frac{(1.055 \times 10^{-34}\ \text{J s})^2}{2 \times 1.008 \times 1.6605 \times 10^{-27}\ \text{kg} \times (16.0 \times 10^{-12}\ \text{m})^2}$$

$$= \underline{1.30 \times 10^{-22}\ \text{J}} \quad (1.96 \times 10^{11}\ \text{Hz})$$

The minimum angular momentum is $\underline{\pm\hbar}$.

12.4 $E = \dfrac{J(J+1)\hbar^2}{2\mu r^2} \quad [20, I = \mu r^2]$

$$= \frac{J(J+1) \times (1.055 \times 10^{-34}\ \text{J s})^2}{2 \times 1.6605 \times 10^{-27}\ \text{kg} \times (160 \times 10^{-12}\ \text{m})^2}\left(\frac{1}{1.008} + \frac{1}{126.90}\right)$$

$$\left[\frac{1}{\mu} = \frac{1}{m_1} + \frac{1}{m_2}\right]$$

$$= J(J+1) \times 1.31 \times 10^{-22}\ \text{J} \quad (\text{equivalent to } J(J+1) \times 198\ \text{GHz})$$

Hence the energies (and equivalent frequencies, from $E = h\nu$) are:

$J =$	0	1	2	3
$10^{22}\,E/\text{J}$	0	2.62	7.86	15.72
ν/GHz	0	396	1188	2376

12.5 $-\dfrac{\hbar^2}{2m}\left(\dfrac{\partial^2}{\partial x^2} + \dfrac{\partial^2}{\partial y^2} + \dfrac{\partial^2}{\partial z^2}\right)\psi = E\psi$

We try the solution $\psi = X(x)Y(y)Z(z)$:

$$-\frac{\hbar^2}{2m}(X''YZ + XY''Z + XYZ'') = EXYZ$$

$$-\frac{\hbar^2}{2m}\left(\frac{X''}{X} + \frac{Y''}{Y} + \frac{Z''}{Z}\right) = E$$

X''/X depends only on x; therefore, when x changes only this term changes, but the sum of the three terms is constant. Therefore, X''/X must also be constant. We write

$$-\frac{\hbar^2}{2m}\frac{X''}{X} = E^X, \text{ with analogous terms for } y, z$$

Hence we solve

$$\left.\begin{aligned} -\frac{\hbar^2}{2m}X'' &= E^X X \\ -\frac{\hbar^2}{2m}Y'' &= E^Y Y \\ -\frac{\hbar^2}{2m}Z'' &= E^Z Z \end{aligned}\right\} E = E^X + E^Y + E^Z,\ \psi = XYZ$$

The three-dimensional equation has therefore separated into three one-dimensional equations, and we can write

$$E = \frac{h^2}{8m}\left(\frac{n_1^2}{L_1^2} + \frac{n_2^2}{L_2^2} + \frac{n_3^2}{L_3^2}\right) \qquad n_1, n_2, n_3 = 1, 2, 3, \ldots$$

$$\psi = \left(\frac{8}{L_1 L_2 L_3}\right)^{1/2} \sin\left(\frac{n_1 \pi x}{L_1}\right) \sin\left(\frac{n_2 \pi y}{L_2}\right) \sin\left(\frac{n_3 \pi z}{L_3}\right)$$

For a cubic box

$$\underline{E = (n_1^2 + n_2^2 + n_3^2)\frac{h^2}{8mL^2}}$$

12.6 (a) $P = \int_{\text{Barrier}} \psi^2\, d\tau = \int_0^\infty N^2\, e^{-2\kappa x}\, dx = \underline{\frac{N^2}{2\kappa}}$

(b) $\langle x \rangle = \int_0^\infty x\psi^2\, dx = N^2 \int_0^\infty x\, e^{-2\kappa x}\, dx$

$$= \frac{N^2 2!}{(2\kappa)^2} = \frac{N^2}{2\kappa^2} = \underline{\frac{P}{\kappa}}$$

12.7 Proceed as in the example, matching the amplitudes and slopes of the wavefunctions at the interfaces of the zones.

Zone A: $\psi_A = A\, e^{ikx} + A'\, e^{-ikx} \qquad k = \left(\frac{2mE}{\hbar^2}\right)^{1/2}$

Zone B: $\psi_B = B\, e^{\kappa x} + B'\, e^{-\kappa x} \qquad \kappa = \left\{\frac{2m(V - E)}{\hbar^2}\right\}^{1/2}$

Zone C: $\psi_C = C\, e^{ik'x} + C'\, e^{-ik'x} \qquad k' = \left\{\frac{2m(E - V')}{\hbar^2}\right\}^{1/2}$

The boundary conditions are

$C'=0$ [No particles from right]

$\psi_A(0)=\psi_B(0)$, implying that $A+A'=B+B'$

$\psi'_A(0)=\psi'_B(0)$, implying that $ikA-ikA'=\kappa B-\kappa B'$

$\psi_B(L)=\psi_C(L)$, implying that $B\,e^{\kappa L}+B'\,e^{-\kappa L}=C\,e^{ik'L}$

$\psi'_B(L)=\psi'_C(L)$, implying that $\kappa B\,e^{\kappa L}-\kappa B'\,e^{-\kappa L}=ik'C\,e^{ik'L}$

The first pair of conditions solve to

$$A=\frac{1}{2}\left(1+\frac{\kappa}{ik}\right)B+\frac{1}{2}\left(1-\frac{\kappa}{ik}\right)B'$$

and the final pair solve to

$$B=\frac{1}{2}\left(1+\frac{ik'}{\kappa}\right)C\,e^{ik'L-\kappa L}$$

$$B'=\frac{1}{2}\left(1-\frac{ik'}{\kappa}\right)C\,e^{ik'L+\kappa L}$$

Hence

$$A=\frac{1}{4}\left(1+\frac{\kappa}{ik}\right)\left(1+\frac{ik'}{\kappa}\right)C\,e^{ik'L-\kappa L}$$

$$+\frac{1}{4}\left(1-\frac{\kappa}{ik}\right)\left(1-\frac{ik'}{\kappa}\right)C\,e^{ik'L+\kappa L}$$

$$=\tfrac{1}{2}C\,e^{ik'L}\left\{(1+\lambda)\cosh\kappa L-i\left(\frac{k'}{\kappa}-\frac{\kappa}{k}\right)\sinh\kappa L\right\}$$

with $\lambda=k'/k$

Hence, $$\left|\frac{A}{C}\right|^2=\frac{1}{4}\left\{(1+\lambda)^2\cosh^2\kappa L+\left(\frac{k'}{\kappa}-\frac{\kappa}{k}\right)^2\sinh^2\kappa L\right\}$$

$$=\frac{1}{4}\left\{2\lambda+(1+\lambda^2)\cosh^2\kappa L+\left(\frac{\lambda^2k^2}{\kappa^2}+\frac{\kappa^2}{k^2}\right)\sinh^2\kappa L\right\}$$

Hence,

$$P=\left|\frac{C}{A}\right|^2=\frac{4}{2\lambda+(1+\lambda^2)\cosh^2\kappa L+\left\{\lambda^2\left(\frac{k}{\kappa}\right)^2+\left(\frac{\kappa}{k}\right)^2\right\}\sinh^2\kappa L}$$

$$=\frac{4}{(1+\lambda)^2+\left\{1+\lambda^2+\lambda^2\left(\frac{k}{\kappa}\right)^2+\left(\frac{\kappa}{k}\right)^2\right\}\sinh^2\kappa L}$$

$$=\frac{1}{\left(\frac{1+\lambda}{2}\right)^2+G}$$

where

$$G=\frac{1}{4}\left\{1+\left(\frac{\kappa}{k}\right)^2+\lambda^2\left[1+\left(\frac{k}{\kappa}\right)^2\right]\right\}\sinh^2\kappa L$$

$$=\frac{1}{16}\left\{1+\left(\frac{\kappa}{k}\right)^2+\lambda^2\left[1+\left(\frac{k}{\kappa}\right)^2\right]\right\}(e^{\kappa L}-e^{-\kappa L})^2$$

Note that

$$\left(\frac{k}{\kappa}\right)^2=\frac{E}{E-V}=\frac{\varepsilon}{1-\varepsilon}$$

and so

$$G=\frac{1}{16}\left\{\frac{1}{\varepsilon}+\frac{\lambda^2}{1-\varepsilon}\right\}(e^{\kappa L}-e^{-\kappa L})^2$$

$$=\underline{\frac{1+(\lambda^2-1)\varepsilon}{16\varepsilon(1-\varepsilon)}(e^{\kappa L}-e^{-\kappa L})^2}$$

This result reduces to eqn 7 in the text when $\lambda=1$.

12.8 As in Problem 12.7, we write

Zone A: $\psi_A=A\,e^{ikx}+A'\,e^{-ikx}\quad k=(2mE/\hbar^2)^{1/2}$

Zone B: $\psi_B=B\,e^{ik'x}+B'\,e^{-ik'x}\quad k'=\{2m(E-V)/\hbar^2\}^{1/2}$

Zone C: $\psi_C=C\,e^{ikx}+C'\,e^{-ikx}\quad k=(2mE/\hbar^2)^{1/2}$

Note that ψ is oscillatory in zone B now that $E > V$ and k' is real. We now write $C' = 0$ [no particles incident from right] and impose the boundary conditions

$\psi_A(0) = \psi_B(0)$, implying that $A + A' = B + B'$

$\psi'_A(0) = \psi'_B(0)$, implying that $kA - kA' = k'B - k'B'$

$\psi_B(L) = \psi_C(L)$, implying that $B\,e^{ik'L} + B'\,e^{-ik'L} = C\,e^{ikL}$

$\psi'_B(L) = \psi'_C(L)$, implying that $k'B\,e^{ik'L} - B'k'\,e^{-ik'L} = kCe^{ikL}$

These equations solve to

$$A = \frac{1}{2}\left\{\left(1 + \frac{k'}{k}\right)B + \left(1 - \frac{k'}{k}\right)B'\right\}$$

$$B = \frac{1}{2}\left(1 + \frac{k}{k'}\right)C\,e^{i(k-k')L}$$

$$B' = \frac{1}{2}\left(1 + \frac{k}{k'}\right)C\,e^{i(k+k')L}$$

which give A in terms of C. Then straightforward algebra leads to

$$\frac{|A|^2}{|C|^2} = 1 + \frac{\lambda^2 \sin^2 k'L}{4(1-\lambda)}, \text{ with } \lambda = \frac{V}{E}$$

Therefore,

$$P = \frac{|C|^2}{|A|^2} = \frac{1}{1+G}, \text{ with } G = \frac{\lambda^2 \sin^2 k'L}{4(1-\lambda)}$$

Note that when $V \to 0$ ($\lambda \to 0$), $G \to 0$ and $P \to 1$.

12.9 We can use the calculation in Problem 12.8 with $V \to -V$ and

$$P(\text{reflection}) = 1 - P(\text{transmission})$$
$$= 1 - \frac{1}{1+G} = \frac{G}{1+G}$$

where

$$G = \frac{(V/E)^2 \sin^2\{2m(E+V)/\hbar^2\}^{1/2}L}{4(1+V/E)}$$

We write $\gamma = E/V$, so

$$G = \frac{\sin^2\{[(2mV/\hbar^2)(1+\gamma)]^{1/2}L\}}{4\gamma(1+\gamma)}$$

and take $V = 5.0\,\text{eV}$, $L = 100\,\text{pm}$,

$$\left(\frac{2mV}{\hbar^2}\right)^{1/2} L = 49.09(\text{proton}),\ 69.42(\text{deuteron})$$

Note that $P = 0$ when $G = 0$, which occurs when

$$(2mV/\hbar^2)^{1/2} L(1+\gamma)^{1/2} = n\pi,\ n \text{ an integer}$$

or at

$$\gamma = \left(\frac{\hbar}{2mV}\right)\left(\frac{n\pi}{L}\right)^2 - 1$$

We find these values first (to simplify the plotting), and then calculate P for $0 \leq \gamma \leq 2$. The results are drawn in Fig. 12.3.

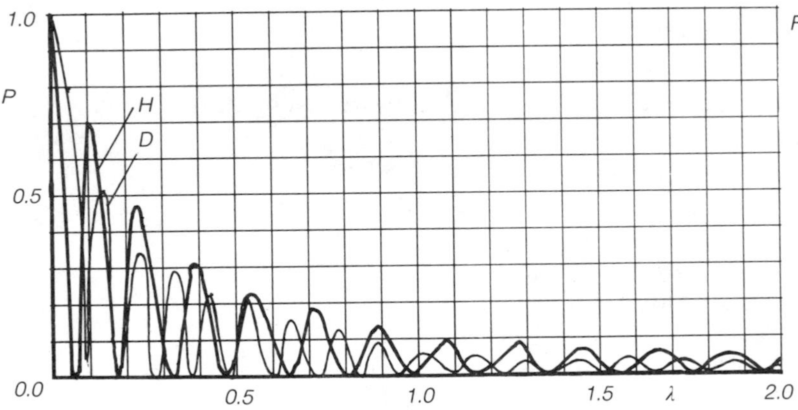

Fig 12.3

12.10 The Schrödinger equation is $-\dfrac{\hbar^2}{2m}\dfrac{d^2\psi}{dx^2} + \tfrac{1}{2}kx^2\psi = E\psi$

and we write $\psi = e^{-gx^2}$, so $d\psi/dx = -2gx\,e^{-gx^2}$

$$\frac{d^2\psi}{dx^2} = -2g\,e^{-gx^2} + 4g^2x^2\,e^{-gx^2} = -2g\psi + 4g^2x^2\psi$$

$$\left(\frac{\hbar^2 g}{m}\right)\psi - \left(\frac{2\hbar^2 g^2}{m}\right)x^2\psi + \tfrac{1}{2}kx^2\psi = E\psi$$

$$\left\{\left(\frac{\hbar^2 g}{m}\right) - E\right\}\psi + \left(\tfrac{1}{2}k - \frac{2\hbar^2 g^2}{m}\right)x^2\psi = 0$$

This equation is satisfied if

$$E = \frac{\hbar^2 g}{m} \text{ and } 2\hbar^2 g^2 = \tfrac{1}{2}mk, \text{ or } \underline{g = \frac{1}{2}\left(\frac{mk}{\hbar^2}\right)^{1/2}}$$

Therefore,

$$E = \tfrac{1}{2}\hbar\left(\frac{k}{m}\right)^{1/2} = \tfrac{1}{2}\hbar\omega \text{ if } \omega = \left(\frac{k}{m}\right)^{1/2}$$

12.11 $\langle T\rangle = \int \psi^* \hat{T}\psi \, dx$ with $\hat{T} = \dfrac{\hat{p}^2}{2m}$ and $\hat{p} = \dfrac{\hbar}{i}\dfrac{d}{dx}$

$$\hat{T} = -\frac{\hbar^2}{2m}\frac{d^2}{dx^2} = -\frac{\hbar^2}{2m\alpha^2}\frac{d^2}{dy^2} = -\tfrac{1}{2}\hbar\omega\frac{d^2}{dy^2}, \ [x = \alpha y, \ \alpha^2 = \hbar/m\omega]$$

which implies that

$$\hat{T}\psi = -\tfrac{1}{2}\hbar\omega\left(\frac{d^2\psi}{dy^2}\right)$$

We then use $\psi = NHe^{-y^2/2}$, and obtain

$$\frac{d^2\psi}{dy^2} = N\frac{d^2}{dy^2}(He^{-y^2/2}) - N\{H'' - 2yH' - H + y^2H\}e^{-y^2/2}$$

From Table 12.1

$$H_v'' - 2yH_v' = -2vH_v$$

$$\begin{aligned} y^2H_v &= y(\tfrac{1}{2}H_{v+1} + vH_{v-1}) \\ &= \tfrac{1}{2}\{\tfrac{1}{2}H_{v+2} + (v+1)H_v\} + v\{\tfrac{1}{2}H_v + (v-1)H_{v-2}\} \\ &= \tfrac{1}{4}H_{v+2} + v(v-1)H_{v-2} + (v+\tfrac{1}{2})H_v \end{aligned}$$

Hence, $\dfrac{d^2\psi}{dy^2} = N\{\tfrac{1}{4}H_{v+2} + v(v-1)H_{v-2} - (v+\tfrac{1}{2})H_v\}e^{-y^2/2}$

Therefore,

$\langle T \rangle =$

$$N^2(-\tfrac{1}{2}\hbar\omega)\int H_v\{\tfrac{1}{4}H_{v+2}+v(v-1)H_{v-2}-(v+\tfrac{1}{2})H_v\}\,e^{-y^2/2}\,dx \quad [dx=\alpha\,dy]$$

$$=\alpha N^2(-\tfrac{1}{2}\hbar\omega)\{0+0-(v+\tfrac{1}{2})\pi^{1/2}2^v v!\}$$

$$=\underline{\tfrac{1}{2}(v+\tfrac{1}{2})\hbar\omega} \quad \left[N_v^2=\frac{1}{\alpha\pi^{1/2}2^v v!},\ \text{Table 12.1}\right]$$

12.12 $\langle x^n\rangle=\alpha^n\langle y^n\rangle$ [Box 12.1]

$$=\alpha^n\int \psi y^n\psi\,dx=\alpha^{n+1}\int \psi^2 y^n\,dy \quad [x=\alpha y]$$

(a) $\langle x^3\rangle \propto \int \psi^2 y^3\,dy=\underline{0}$ by symmetry

(b) $\langle x^4\rangle=\alpha^5\int \psi y^4\psi\,dy$

$$y^4\psi=y^4NH_v\,e^{-y^2/2}$$

$$\begin{aligned}
y^4H_v&=y^3\{\tfrac{1}{2}H_{v+1}+vH_{v-1}\}\\
&=y^2\{\tfrac{1}{2}[\tfrac{1}{2}H_{v+2}+(v+1)H_v]+v[\tfrac{1}{2}H_v+(v-1)H_{v-2}]\}\\
&=y^2\{\tfrac{1}{4}H_{v+2}+(v+\tfrac{1}{2})H_v+v(v-1)H_{v-2}\}\\
&=y\{\tfrac{1}{4}[\tfrac{1}{2}H_{v+3}+(v+2)H_{v+1}]+(v+\tfrac{1}{2})[\tfrac{1}{2}H_{v+1}+vH_{v-1}]\\
&\qquad +v(v-1)[\tfrac{1}{2}H_{v-1}+(v-2)H_{v-3}]\}\\
&=y\{\tfrac{1}{8}H_{v+3}+\tfrac{3}{4}(v+1)H_{v+1}+\tfrac{3}{2}V^2H_{v-1}+v(v-1)(v-2)H_{v-3}\}
\end{aligned}$$

Only yH_{v+1} and yH_{v-1} lead to H_v and contribute to the expectation value (since H_v is orthogonal to all except H_v); hence

$$\begin{aligned}
y^4H_v&=\tfrac{3}{4}y\{(v+1)H_{v+1}+2v^2H_{v-1}\}+\cdots\\
&=\tfrac{3}{4}\{(v+1)[\tfrac{1}{2}H_{v+2}+(v+1)H_v]+2v^2[\tfrac{1}{2}H_v+(v-1)H_{v-2}]\}+\cdots\\
&=\tfrac{3}{4}\{(v+1)^2H_v+v^2H_v\}+\cdots\\
&=\tfrac{3}{4}(2v^2+2v+1)H_v+\cdots
\end{aligned}$$

Therefore,

$$\int \psi y^4\psi\,dy=\tfrac{3}{4}(2v^2+2v+1)N^2\int H_v^2\,e^{-y^2}\,dy=\frac{3}{4\alpha}(2v^2+2v+1)$$

and so

$$\langle x^4\rangle = \alpha^5 \times \frac{3}{4\alpha}(2v^2+2v+1) = \underline{\tfrac{3}{4}(2v^2+2v+1)\alpha^4}$$

12.13 $$\mu = \int \psi_{v'} x \psi_v \, dx = \alpha^2 \int \psi_{v'} y \psi_v \, dy \quad [x = \alpha y]$$

$y\psi_v = N_v(\tfrac{1}{2}H_{v+1} + vH_{v-1})\,e^{-y^2/2}$ [Table 12.1]

Hence,

$$\mu = \alpha^2 N_v N_{v'} \int (\tfrac{1}{2}H_{v'}H_{v+1} + vH_{v'}H_{v-1})\,e^{-y^2/2}\,dy$$

$= 0$ unless $v' = v \pm 1$

(a) $v' = v + 1$

$$\mu = \tfrac{1}{2}\alpha^2 N_v N_{v+1} \int H_{v+1}^2 \, e^{-y^2}\,dy = \tfrac{1}{2}\alpha^2 N_v N_{v+1} \pi^{1/2} 2^{v+1}(v+1)!$$

$$= \underline{\alpha\left(\frac{v+1}{2}\right)^{1/2}}$$

(b) $v' = v - 1$

$$\mu = v\alpha^2 N_v N_{v-1} \int H_{v-1}^2 \, e^{-y^2} dy = v\alpha^2 N_v N_{v-1} \pi^{1/2} 2^{v-1}(v-1)!$$

$$= \underline{\alpha\left(\frac{v}{2}\right)^{1/2}}$$

12.14 $$V = -\frac{e^2}{4\pi\varepsilon_0} \cdot \frac{1}{r} = ax^b \text{ with } b = -1 \quad [x \to r]$$

Since $2\langle T\rangle = b\langle V\rangle$ [the virial theorem, Chapter 11]

$2\langle T\rangle = -\langle V\rangle$

Therefore, $\underline{\langle T\rangle = -\tfrac{1}{2}\langle V\rangle}$

12.15 (a) $\hat{l}_z\, e^{i\phi} = \dfrac{\hbar}{i}\dfrac{d}{d\phi}\, e^{i\phi} = \hbar\, e^{i\phi}$, hence $\underline{J_z = +\hbar}$

(b) $\hat{l}_z \mathrm{e}^{-2\mathrm{i}\phi} = \frac{\hbar}{\mathrm{i}}\frac{\mathrm{d}}{\mathrm{d}\phi}\mathrm{e}^{-2\mathrm{i}\phi} = -2\hbar\,\mathrm{e}^{-2\mathrm{i}\phi}$, hence $J_z = \underline{-2\hbar}$

(c) $\langle l_z \rangle \propto \int_0^{2\pi} \cos\phi\left(\frac{\hbar}{\mathrm{i}}\frac{\mathrm{d}}{\mathrm{d}\phi}\cos\phi\right)\mathrm{d}\phi \propto -\frac{\hbar}{\mathrm{i}}\int_0^{2\pi}\cos\phi\sin\phi\,\mathrm{d}\phi = \underline{0}$

(d) $$\langle l_z \rangle = N^2\int_0^{2\pi}(\cos\chi\,\mathrm{e}^{\mathrm{i}\phi}+\sin\chi\,\mathrm{e}^{-\mathrm{i}\phi})^*\left(\frac{\hbar}{\mathrm{i}}\frac{\mathrm{d}}{\mathrm{d}\phi}\right)(\cos\chi\,\mathrm{e}^{\mathrm{i}\phi}+\sin\chi\,\mathrm{e}^{-\mathrm{i}\phi})\,\mathrm{d}\phi$$

$$=\frac{\hbar}{\mathrm{i}}N^2\int_0^{2\pi}(\cos\chi\,\mathrm{e}^{-\mathrm{i}\phi}+\sin\chi\,\mathrm{e}^{\mathrm{i}\phi})(\mathrm{i}\cos\chi\,\mathrm{e}^{\mathrm{i}\phi}-\mathrm{i}\sin\chi\,\mathrm{e}^{-\mathrm{i}\phi})\,\mathrm{d}\phi$$

$$=\hbar N^2\int_0^{2\pi}(\cos^2\chi-\sin^2\chi+\cos\chi\sin\chi[\mathrm{e}^{2\mathrm{i}\phi}-\mathrm{e}^{-2\mathrm{i}\phi}])\,\mathrm{d}\phi$$

$$=\hbar N^2(\cos^2\chi-\sin^2\chi)\times 2\pi = 2\pi\hbar N^2\cos 2\chi$$

$$N^2\int_0^{2\pi}(\cos\chi\,\mathrm{e}^{\mathrm{i}\phi}+\sin\chi\,\mathrm{e}^{-\mathrm{i}\phi})^*(\cos\chi\,\mathrm{e}^{\mathrm{i}\phi}+\sin\chi\,\mathrm{e}^{-\mathrm{i}\phi})\,\mathrm{d}\phi$$

$$=N^2\int_0^{2\pi}(\cos^2\chi+\sin^2\chi+\cos\chi\sin\chi[\mathrm{e}^{2\mathrm{i}\phi}+\mathrm{e}^{-2\mathrm{i}\phi}])\,\mathrm{d}\phi$$

$$=2\pi N^2(\cos^2\chi+\sin^2\chi)=2\pi N^2=1 \text{ if } N^2=\frac{1}{2\pi}$$

Therefore,

$$\langle l_z\rangle = \underline{\hbar\cos 2\chi}$$

For the kinetic energy, use $\hat{T}=\frac{1}{2I}\hat{l}_z^2=-\frac{\hbar^2}{2I}\frac{\mathrm{d}^2}{\mathrm{d}\phi^2}$

(a) $\hat{T}\mathrm{e}^{\mathrm{i}\phi}=-\frac{\hbar^2}{2I}(\mathrm{i}^2\,\mathrm{e}^{\mathrm{i}\phi})=\frac{\hbar^2}{2I}\mathrm{e}^{\mathrm{i}\phi}$, and hence $\langle T\rangle=\underline{\frac{\hbar^2}{2I}}$

(b) $\hat{T}\mathrm{e}^{-2\mathrm{i}\phi}=-\frac{\hbar^2}{2I}(2\mathrm{i})^2\,\mathrm{e}^{-2\mathrm{i}\phi}=\frac{4\hbar^2}{2I}\mathrm{e}^{-2\mathrm{i}\phi}$, and hence $\langle T\rangle=\underline{\frac{2\hbar^2}{I}}$

(c) $\hat{T}\cos\phi=-\frac{\hbar^2}{2I}(-\cos\phi)=\frac{\hbar^2}{2I}\cos\phi$, and hence $\langle T\rangle=\underline{\frac{\hbar^2}{2I}}$

(d) $\hat{T}(\cos\chi\,\mathrm{e}^{\mathrm{i}\phi}+\sin\chi\,\mathrm{e}^{-\mathrm{i}\phi})=-\frac{\hbar^2}{2I}(-\cos\chi\,\mathrm{e}^{\mathrm{i}\phi}-\sin\chi\,\mathrm{e}^{-\mathrm{i}\phi})$

$=\frac{\hbar^2}{2I}(\cos\chi\,\mathrm{e}^{\mathrm{i}\phi}+\sin\chi\,\mathrm{e}^{-\mathrm{i}\phi})$, and hence $\langle T\rangle=\underline{\frac{\hbar^2}{2I}}$

12.16 $\psi = N(a\,\mathrm{e}^{\mathrm{i}\phi} + b\,\mathrm{e}^{2\mathrm{i}\phi} + c\,\mathrm{e}^{3\mathrm{i}\phi})$

First, normalize the wavefunction:

$$N^2 \int_0^{2\pi} (a\,\mathrm{e}^{-\mathrm{i}\phi} + b\,\mathrm{e}^{-2\mathrm{i}\phi} + c\,\mathrm{e}^{-3\mathrm{i}\phi})(a\,\mathrm{e}^{\mathrm{i}\phi} + b\,\mathrm{e}^{2\mathrm{i}\phi} + c\,\mathrm{e}^{3\mathrm{i}\phi})\,\mathrm{d}\phi$$

$$= N^2 \int_0^{2\pi} (a^2 + b^2 + c^2 + \cdots)\,\mathrm{d}\phi \quad [\ldots \text{ integrate to zero}]$$

$$= 2\pi N^2(a^2 + b^2 + c^2) = 1 \text{ if } N = \left\{\frac{1}{2\pi(a^2 + b^2 + c^2)}\right\}^{1/2}$$

Now evaluate the expectation value:

$$\text{(a) } \langle l_z \rangle = N^2\left(\frac{\hbar}{\mathrm{i}}\right) \int_0^{2\pi} (a\,\mathrm{e}^{-\mathrm{i}\phi} + b\,\mathrm{e}^{-2\mathrm{i}\phi} + c\,\mathrm{e}^{-3\mathrm{i}\phi})\frac{\mathrm{d}}{\mathrm{d}\phi}(a\,\mathrm{e}^{\mathrm{i}\phi} + b\,\mathrm{e}^{2\mathrm{i}\phi} + c\,\mathrm{e}^{3\mathrm{i}\phi})\,\mathrm{d}\phi$$

$$= \hbar N^2 \int_0^{2\pi} (a\,\mathrm{e}^{-\mathrm{i}\phi} + b\,\mathrm{e}^{-2\mathrm{i}\phi} + c\,\mathrm{e}^{-3\mathrm{i}\phi})(a\,\mathrm{e}^{\mathrm{i}\phi} + 2b\,\mathrm{e}^{2\mathrm{i}\phi} + 3c\,\mathrm{e}^{3\mathrm{i}\phi})\,\mathrm{d}\phi$$

$$= \hbar N^2 2\pi(a^2 + 2b^2 + 3c^2)$$

$$= \underline{\left(\frac{a^2 + 2b^2 + 3c^2}{a^2 + b^2 + c^2}\right)\hbar}$$

$$\text{(b) } \langle T \rangle = \frac{\langle l_z^2 \rangle}{2I}$$

$$\langle l_z^2 \rangle = -\hbar^2 N^2 \int_0^{2\pi} (a\,\mathrm{e}^{-\mathrm{i}\phi} + b\,\mathrm{e}^{-2\mathrm{i}\phi} + c\,\mathrm{e}^{-3\mathrm{i}\phi})\frac{\mathrm{d}^2}{\mathrm{d}\phi^2}(a\,\mathrm{e}^{\mathrm{i}\phi} + b\,\mathrm{e}^{2\mathrm{i}\phi} + c\,\mathrm{e}^{3\mathrm{i}\phi})\,\mathrm{d}\phi$$

$$= \hbar^2 N^2 \int_0^{2\pi} (a\,\mathrm{e}^{-\mathrm{i}\phi} + b\,\mathrm{e}^{-2\mathrm{i}\phi} + c\,\mathrm{e}^{-3\mathrm{i}\phi})(a\,\mathrm{e}^{\mathrm{i}\phi} + 4b\,\mathrm{e}^{2\mathrm{i}\phi} + 9c\,\mathrm{e}^{3\mathrm{i}\phi})\,\mathrm{d}\phi$$

$$= 2\pi\hbar^2 N^2(a^2 + 4b^2 + 9c^2)$$

$$= \left(\frac{a^2 + 4b^2 + 9c^2}{a^2 + b^2 + c^2}\right)\hbar^2$$

and so

$$\langle T\rangle = \left(\frac{a^2+4b^2+9c^2}{a^2+b^2+c^2}\right)\times\frac{\hbar^2}{2I}$$

(c) $$\frac{\langle l_z^2\rangle - \langle l_z\rangle^2}{\hbar^2} = \frac{a^2+4b^2+9c^2}{a^2+b^2+c^2} - \left(\frac{a^2+2b^2+3c^2}{a^2+b^2+c^2}\right)^2$$

$$= \frac{a^2b^2+4a^2c^2+b^2c^2}{(a^2+b^2+c^2)^2}$$

Hence,

$$\delta l_z = (\langle l_z^2\rangle - \langle l_z\rangle^2)^{1/2} = \frac{(a^2b^2+4a^2c^2+b^2c^2)^{1/2}\hbar}{a^2+b^2+c^2}$$

12.17 The Schrödinger equation is

$$-\frac{\hbar^2}{2m}\nabla^2\psi = E\psi \quad [18, \text{ with } V=0]$$

and hence

$$\Lambda^2\psi = -\frac{2IE}{\hbar^2}\psi \quad [19]$$

Then, from eqn 22

(a) $\Lambda^2 Y_{0,0} = \underline{0}$ [$l=0$, $m_l=0$], implying that $E=0$ and angular momentum $=\underline{0}$ [from $\{l(l+1)\}^{1/2}\hbar$].

(b) $\Lambda^2 Y_{2,-1} = -2(2+1)Y_{2,-1}$ [$l=2$], and hence

$$-2(2+1)Y_{2,-1} = -\frac{2IE}{\hbar^2}Y_{2,-1}, \text{ implying that } \underline{E = \frac{3\hbar^2}{I}}$$

and the angular momentum is $\{2(2+1)\}^{1/2}\hbar = \underline{6^{1/2}\hbar}$

(c) $\Lambda^2 Y_{3,3} = -3(3+1)Y_{3,3}$ [$l=3$], and hence

$$-3(3+1)Y_{3,3} = -\frac{2IE}{\hbar^2}Y_{3,3}, \text{ implying that } E = \underline{\frac{6\hbar^2}{I}}$$

and the angular momentum is $\{3(3+1)\}^{1/2}\hbar = \underline{2\sqrt{3}\hbar}$

12.18 $\displaystyle\int_0^\pi\int_0^{2\pi} Y^*_{3,3}Y_{3,3}\sin\theta\,d\theta\,d\phi$

$$= \int_0^\pi \left(\frac{1}{64}\right)\left(\frac{35}{\pi}\right)\sin^6\theta\sin\theta\,d\theta\int_0^{2\pi} d\phi \quad \text{[Table 12.3]}$$

$$= \left(\frac{1}{64}\right)\left(\frac{35}{\pi}\right)(2\pi)\int_{-1}^{1}(1-\cos^2\theta)^3\,d\cos\theta \quad [\sin\theta\,d\theta = d\cos\theta,$$
$\sin^2\theta = 1-\cos^2\theta$]

$$= \frac{35}{32}\int_{-1}^{1}(1-3x^2+3x^4-x^6)\,dx \quad [x=\cos\theta]$$

$$= \frac{35}{32}\left(x - x^3 + \frac{3}{5}x^5 - \frac{1}{7}x^7\right)\Bigg|_{-1}^{1} = \frac{35}{32}\times\frac{32}{35} = \underline{1}$$

22.19 From the diagram in Fig. 12.4, $\cos\theta = \dfrac{m_l}{\{l(l+1)\}^{1/2}}$

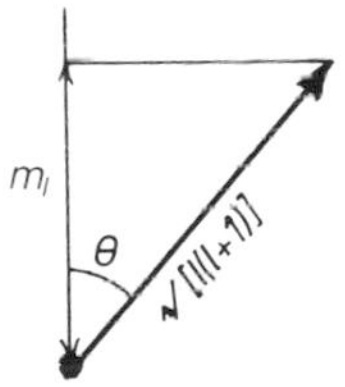

Fig 12.4

and hence $\theta = \underline{\arccos\dfrac{m_l}{\{l(l+1)\}^{1/2}}}$

For an α electron, $m_s = +\frac{1}{2}$, $s=\frac{1}{2}$ and [with $m_l \to m_s$, $l \to s$]

$$\theta = \arccos\frac{1/2}{(3/4)^{1/2}} = \arccos\frac{1}{\sqrt{3}} = \underline{54°44'}$$

The minimum angle occurs for $m_l = l$:

$$\lim_{l\to 0}\theta_{\min} = \lim_{l\to\infty}\arccos\left(\frac{l}{\{l(l+1)\}^{1/2}}\right) = \lim_{l\to\infty}\arccos\frac{l}{l} = \arccos 1 = \underline{0}$$

13. Atomic structure and atomic spectra

Exercises

13.1 $\dfrac{1}{\lambda}=\mathcal{R}_{\rm H}\left(\dfrac{1}{4}-\dfrac{1}{n^2}\right)$ $[1, \tilde{\nu}=1/\lambda]$

and hence

$$\lambda=\mathcal{R}_{\rm H}^{-1}\left(\frac{1}{4}-\frac{1}{n^2}\right)^{-1}=(1.09677\times10^7\ \text{m}^{-1})^{-1}\left(\frac{1}{4}-\frac{1}{16}\right)^{-1}$$

$$=\underline{486.3\ \text{nm}}$$

13.2 $\dfrac{1}{\lambda}=\mathcal{R}_{\rm H}\left(\dfrac{1}{9}-\dfrac{1}{n^2}\right)$

and hence

$$n=\left(\frac{1}{9}-\frac{1}{\lambda\mathcal{R}_{\rm H}}\right)^{-1/2}=\left(\frac{1}{9}-\frac{\nu}{c\mathcal{R}_{\rm H}}\right)^{-1/2}$$

$$=\left(\frac{1}{9}-\frac{2.7415\times10^{14}\ \text{s}^{-1}}{2.9979\times10^{8}\ \text{m s}^{-1}\times1.0968\times10^{7}\ \text{m}^{-1}}\right)^{-1/2}=6.005$$

That is, $\underline{n=6}$

13.3 $\dfrac{1}{\lambda}=\dfrac{1}{486.1\times10^{-7}\ \text{cm}}=20\,572\ \text{cm}^{-1}$

Hence, the term lies at

$$T=27\,414\ \text{cm}^{-1}-20\,572\ \text{cm}^{-1}=\underline{6842\ \text{cm}^{-1}}$$

13.4 $h\nu=\frac{1}{2}m_{\rm e}v^2+I$

$$I=h\nu-\tfrac{1}{2}m_{\rm e}v^2=6.626\times10^{-34}\ \text{J Hz}^{-1}\times\frac{2.998\times10^{8}\ \text{m s}^{-1}}{58.4\times10^{-9}\ \text{m}}$$

$$-\tfrac{1}{2}\times9.109\times10^{-31}\ \text{kg}\times(1.59\times10^{6}\ \text{m s}^{-1})^2$$

$=2.25\times10^{-18}$ J, corresponding to $\underline{14.0\ \text{eV}}$

13.5 $\psi \propto (2-\rho)\,e^{-\rho/2}$ with $\rho = r/a_0$ [Table 13.1]

$$\frac{d\psi}{dr} = \frac{1}{a_0}\frac{d\psi}{d\rho} = \frac{1}{a_0}(-1-1+\tfrac{1}{2}\rho)\,e^{-\rho/2} = 0 \text{ when } \rho = 4$$

Hence, the wavefunction has an extremum at $r = 4a_0$. Since $2-\rho<0$, $\psi<0$ and the extremum is a minimum (more formally: $d^2\psi/dr^2>0$ at $\rho=4$).

13.6 Since $\psi_{3,0} \propto 6-6\rho+\rho^2$ [Table 13.1], the radial nodes occur at

$6-6\rho+\rho^2 = 0$, or $\rho = 3 \pm \surd 3 = 1.27$ and 4.73

Since $\rho = 3\rho a_0/2$, the radial nodes occur at 101 pm and 376 pm.

13.7 Identify l and use angular momentum $= \{l(l+1)\}^{1/2}\hbar$.

(a) $l=0$, so ang. mom. $=0$

(b) $l=0$, so ang. mom. $=0$

(c) $l=2$, so ang. mom. $=\surd 6\hbar$

(d) $l=1$, so ang. mom. $=\surd 2\hbar$

(e) $l=1$, so ang. mom. $=\surd 2\hbar$

The total number of nodes is equal to $n-1$ and the number of angular nodes is equal to l; hence the number of radial nodes is equal to $n-l-1$. We can draw up the following table:

	1*s*	3*s*	3*d*	2*p*	3*p*	
n, l	1, 0	3, 0	3, 2	2, 1	3, 1	
Angular nodes	0	0	2	1	1	[l]
Radial nodes	0	2	0	0	1	[$n-l-1$]

13.8 We use the Clebsch–Gordan series [13] in the form

$j = l+s, l+s-1, \ldots |l-s|$

(a) $l=2$, $s=\frac{1}{2}$; so $j=\frac{5}{2}, \frac{3}{2}$

(b) $l=3$, $s=\frac{1}{2}$; so $j=\frac{7}{2}, \frac{5}{2}$

13.9 The Clebsch–Gordan series in Exercise 13.8 with $j=\frac{3}{2}, \frac{5}{2}$, requires $l=2$

13.10 Use the Clebsch–Gordan series in the form

$J = j_1+j_2, j_1+j_2-1, \ldots |j_1-j_2|$

Then, with $j_1 = 5$ and $j_2 = 3$

$$J = \underline{8, 7, 6, 5, 4, 3, 2}$$

13.11 The energies are $E = -\dfrac{hc\mathcal{R}_H}{n^2}$, and the orbital degeneracy g of an energy level of principal quantum number n is $g = n^2$ [Section 13.2].

(a) $E = -hc\mathcal{R}_H$ implies that $n = 1$, so $\underline{g = 1}$ (the 1s orbital).

(b) $E = -\dfrac{hc\mathcal{R}_H}{9}$ implies that $n = 3$, so $\underline{g = 9}$ (the 3s orbital, the three 3p orbitals, and the five 3d orbitals).

(c) $E = -\dfrac{hc\mathcal{R}_H}{25}$ implies that $n = 5$, so $\underline{g = 25}$ (the 5s orbital, the three 5p orbitals, the five 5d orbitals, the seven 5f orbitals, the nine 5g orbitals).

13.12 The letter D indicates that $L = 2$, the superscript 1 is the value of $2S + 1$, so $S = 0$, and the subscript 2 is the value of J. Hence,

$$\underline{L = 2,\ S = 0,\ J = 2}$$

13.13 The probability density varies as

$$\psi^2 = \frac{1}{\pi a_0^3}\,\mathrm{e}^{-2r/a_0}$$

Therefore, the maximum value is at $r = 0$ and ψ^2 is 50 per cent of the maximum when

$\mathrm{e}^{-2r/a_0} = 0.50$, implying that $r = -\tfrac{1}{2}a_0 \ln 0.50$ which is at $r = \underline{0.35a_0}$ (18 pm).

13.14 The radial distribution function varies as

$$P = 4\pi r^2\psi^2 = \frac{4}{a_0^3}r^2\,\mathrm{e}^{-2r/a_0}$$

The maximum value of P occurs at $r = a_0$ since

$$\frac{\mathrm{d}P}{\mathrm{d}r} \propto \left(2r - \frac{2r^2}{a_0}\right)\mathrm{e}^{-2r/a_0} = 0 \text{ at } r = a_0 \text{ and } P_{\max} = \frac{4}{a_0}\mathrm{e}^{-2}$$

P falls to a fraction f of its maximum when

$$f=\frac{4r^2}{a_0^3}\,e^{-2r/a_0}\Big/\frac{4}{a_0}\,e^{-2}=\frac{r^2}{a_0^2}\,e^2\,e^{-2r/a_0}$$

and hence we must solve

$$\frac{f^{1/2}}{e}=\frac{r}{a_0}\,e^{-r/a_0}$$

(a) $f=0.50$

$$0.260=\frac{r}{a_0}\,e^{-r/a_0}\text{ solves to }r=2.08a_0=\underline{110\text{ pm}}$$

(b) $f=0.75$:

$$0.319=\frac{r}{a_0}\,e^{-r/a_0}\text{ solves to }r=1.63a_0=\underline{86\text{ pm}}$$

In each case the equation is solved numerically (or graphically).

13.15 The selection rules to apply are $\Delta n=$ any integer; $\Delta l=\pm 1$.

(a) $2s\to 1s$; $\Delta l=0$, forbidden

(b) $2p\to 1s$; $\Delta l=-1$, allowed

(c) $3d\to 2p$; $\Delta l=-1$, allowed

(d) $5d\to 2s$; $\Delta l=-2$, forbidden

(e) $5p\to 3s$; $\Delta l=-1$, allowed

13.16 For a given l there are $2l+1$ values of m_l and hence $2l+1$ orbitals. Each orbital may be occupied by two electrons. Hence the maximum occupancy is $2(2l+1)$. Draw up the following table:

	l	$2(2l+1)$
(a) 1*s*	0	2
(b) 3*p*	1	6
(c) 3*d*	2	10
(d) 6*g*	4	18

13.17 We use the building-up principle with the orbitals occupied in the order 1*s*, 2*s*, 2*p*, 3*s*, 3*p*:

H							He
$1s^1$							$1s^2$
Li	Be	B	C	N	O	F	Ne
$K2s^1$	$K2s^2$	$K2s^22p^1$	$K2s^22p^2$	$K2s^22p^3$	$K2s^22p^4$	$K2s^22p^5$	$K2s^22p^6$
Na	Mg	Al	Si	P	S	Cl	Ar
$KL3s^1$	$KL3s^2$	$KL3s^23p^1$	$KL3s^23p^2$	$KL3s^23p^3$	$KL3s^23p^4$	$KL3s^23p^5$	$KL3s^23p^6$

where $K = 1s^2$, $L = 2s^22p^6$.

13.18 Use the Clebsch–Gordan series in the form

$$S' = s_1 + s_2,\ s_1 + s_2 - 1, \ldots |s_1 - s_2|$$

and

$$S = S' + s_1,\ S' + s_1 - 1, \ldots |S' - s_1|$$

in succession. The multiplicity is $2S + 1$

(a) $S = \frac{1}{2} + \frac{1}{2}, \frac{1}{2} - \frac{1}{2} = \underline{1, 0}$ with multiplicities $\underline{3, 1}$ respectively

(b) $S' = 1, 0$; then $S = \underline{\frac{3}{2}, \frac{1}{2} \text{ and } \frac{1}{2}}$ with multiplicities $\underline{4, 2, 2}$

(c) $S' = 1, 0$; then $S'' = \frac{3}{2}, \frac{1}{2}, \frac{1}{2}$;

then $S''' = 2, 1$ [from $\frac{3}{2}$], $1, 0$ [from $\frac{1}{2}$], $1, 0$ [from $\frac{1}{2}$]

and $S = \underline{\frac{5}{2}, \frac{3}{2}; \frac{3}{2}, \frac{1}{2}; \frac{3}{2}, \frac{1}{2}; \frac{1}{2}; \frac{3}{2}, \frac{1}{2}; \frac{1}{2}}$ with multiplicities $\underline{6}$ (for $S = \frac{5}{2}$), $\underline{4}$ (for $S = \frac{3}{2}$) and $\underline{2}$ (for $S = \frac{1}{2}$)

3.19 Use the Clebsch–Gordan series in the form

$$J = L + S,\ L + S - 1, \ldots |L - S|$$

The number of states (M_J values) is $2J + 1$ in each case.

(a) $L = 0$, $S = 0$; hence $\underline{J = 0}$ and there is only $\underline{1}$ state ($M_J = 0$)

(b) $L = 1$, $S = \frac{1}{2}$; hence $J = \underline{\frac{3}{2}, \frac{1}{2}}$ ($^2P_{3/2}$, $^2P_{1/2}$) with 4, 2 states respectively.

(c) $L = 2$, $S = 1$; hence $J = \underline{3, 2, 1}$ ($^3D_3$, $^3D_2$, $^3D_1$) with 7, 5, 3 states respectively.

(d) $L = 2$, $S = \frac{3}{2}$; hence $J = \underline{\frac{7}{2}, \frac{5}{2}, \frac{3}{2}, \frac{1}{2}}$ ($^4D_{7/2}$, $^4D_{5/2}$, $^4D_{3/2}$, $^4D_{1/2}$) with 8, 6, 4, 2 states respectively.

13.20 (a) Li [He]$2s^1$: $S = \frac{1}{2}$, $L = 0$; $J = \frac{1}{2}$, so the only term is $\underline{^2S_{1/2}}$

(b) Na [He]$3p^1$: $S=\frac{1}{2}$, $L=1$; $J=\frac{3}{2}, \frac{1}{2}$, so the terms are $^2P_{3/2}$ and $^2P_{1/2}$

(c) Sc [Ar]$3d^14s^2$: $S=\frac{1}{2}$, $L=2$; $J=\frac{5}{2}, \frac{3}{2}$, so the terms are $^2D_{5/2}$ and $^2D_{3/2}$

(d) Br [Ar]$3d^{10}4s^24p^5$. We treat the missing electron in the $4p$ subshell as equivalent to a single 'electron' with $l=1$, $s=\frac{1}{2}$. Hence $L=1$, $S=\frac{1}{2}$, and $J=\frac{3}{2}$, $\frac{1}{2}$; so the terms are $^2P_{3/2}$ and $^2P_{1/2}$.

13.21 $E=\mu_B B m_l$ [16b] with $\mu_B=9.273\times10^{-24}\ \text{J T}^{-1}$

Hence,

$$m_l=\frac{E}{\mu_B B}=\frac{2.23\times10^{-22}\ \text{J}}{12.0\ \text{T}\times9.273\times10^{-24}\ \text{J T}^{-1}}=2.00$$

Hence, $m_l=+2$.

13.22 $E=\mu_B B m_l$ [16b], implying that

$E_{m_l+1}-E_{m_l}=\mu_B B$ and therefore that

$hc\tilde{\nu}=\mu_B B$

Therefore,

$$B=\frac{hc\tilde{\nu}}{\mu_B}=\frac{6.626\times10^{-34}\ \text{J s}\times2.998\times10^{10}\ \text{cm s}^{-1}\times1.0\ \text{cm}^{-1}}{9.273\times10^{-24}\ \text{J T}^{-1}}$$

$$=2.1\ \text{T}.$$

Problems

13.1 $\dfrac{1}{\lambda}=\mathcal{R}_H\left(\dfrac{1}{n_1^2}-\dfrac{1}{n_2^2}\right)$ $\quad \mathcal{R}_H=109\,677\ \text{cm}^{-1}$

Find n_1 from the value of λ_{max}, which arises from the transition $n_1+1\to n_1$:

$$\frac{1}{\lambda_{max}\mathcal{R}_H}=\frac{1}{n_1^2}-\frac{1}{(n_1+1)^2}=\frac{2n_1+1}{n_1^2(n_1+1)^2}$$

$$\lambda_{max}\mathcal{R}_H=\frac{n_1^2(n_1+1)^2}{2n_1+1}$$

$$=12\,368\times10^{-9}\ \text{m}\times109\,677\times10^2\ \text{m}^{-1}=135.65$$

Since $n_1=1, 2, 3$, and 4 have already been accounted for, try $n_1=5, 6, \ldots$. With $n_1=6$ we get $n_1^2(n_1+1)^2/(2n_1+1)=136$. Hence, the Humphreys series is $n_2\to6$ and the transitions are given by

$$\frac{1}{\lambda}=109\,677\ \mathrm{cm^{-1}}\times\left(\frac{1}{36}-\frac{1}{n_2^2}\right),\ n_2=7,8,\ldots$$

and occur at 12 370 nm, 7503 nm, 5908 nm, 5129 nm, . . . 3908 nm (at $n_2=15$), converging to 3282 nm as $n_2\to\infty$.

13.2 $$\lambda_{\max}\mathcal{R}_{\mathrm{H}}=\frac{n_1^2(n_1+1)^2}{2n_1+1}\quad\text{[Problem 13.1]}$$

$$=656.46\times10^{-9}\ \mathrm{m}\times109\,677\times10^2\ \mathrm{m^{-1}}=7.20$$

and hence $n_1=2$. Therefore, the transitions are given by

$$\frac{1}{\lambda}=109\,677\ \mathrm{cm^{-1}}\times\left(\frac{1}{4}-\frac{1}{n_2^2}\right),\ n_2=3,4,5,6$$

The next line has $n_2=7$, and occurs at

$$\frac{1}{\lambda}=109\,677\ \mathrm{cm^{-1}}\times\left(\frac{1}{4}-\frac{1}{49}\right)=\underline{397.13\ \mathrm{nm}}$$

The energy required to ionize the atom is obtained by letting $n_2\to\infty$.

Then

$$\frac{1}{\lambda_\infty}=109\,677\ \mathrm{cm^{-1}}\times\left(\frac{1}{4}-0\right)=27\,419\ \mathrm{cm^{-1}},\ \text{or}\ \underline{3.40\ \mathrm{eV}}$$

(The answer, 3.40 eV, is the ionization energy of an H atom that is already in an excited state, with $n=2$.)

13.3 $$\frac{1}{\lambda}=K\left(1-\frac{1}{n^2}\right),\ n=2,3,\ldots$$

Therefore, if the formula is appropriate, we expect to find that

$\lambda^{-1}(1-1/n^2)^{-1}$ is a constant (K). We therefore draw up the following table

n	2	3	4
$\lambda^{-1}/\mathrm{cm^{-1}}$	740 747	877 924	925 933
$\lambda^{-1}(1-1/n^2)^{-1}/\mathrm{cm^{-1}}$	987 663	987 665	987 662

Hence, the formula does describe the transitions, and $\underline{K = 987\,663\ \mathrm{cm}^{-1}}$. The Balmer transitions lie at

$$\frac{1}{\lambda} = K\left(\frac{1}{4} - \frac{1}{n^2}\right) \quad n = 3, 4, \ldots$$

$$= 987\,663\ \mathrm{cm}^{-1}\left(\frac{1}{4} - \frac{1}{n^2}\right) = \underline{137\,175\ \mathrm{cm}^{-1}},\ \underline{185\,187\ \mathrm{cm}^{-1}}, \ldots$$

The ionization energy of the ground state ion is given by

$$\frac{1}{\lambda} = K\left(1 - \frac{1}{n^2}\right),\ n \to \infty$$

and hence corresponds to

$$\frac{1}{\lambda} = 987\,663\ \mathrm{cm}^{-1},\ \text{or}\ \underline{122.5\ \mathrm{eV}}$$

13.4 Refer to Fig. 13.1, which shows an interpretation of the data in terms of

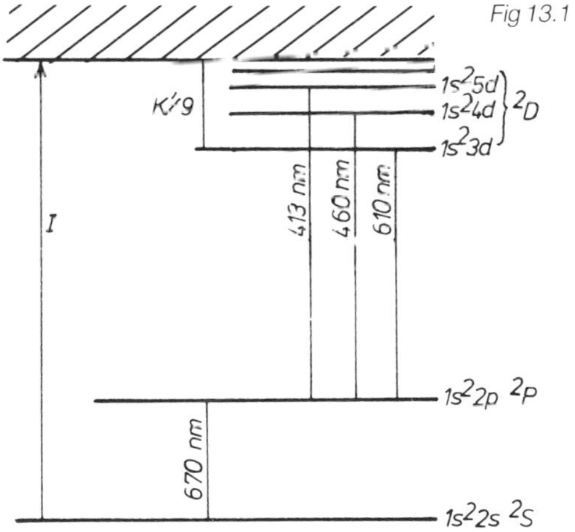

the energy levels of the atoms. Since

$$E(1s^2nd^1, {}^2\mathrm{D}) = -\frac{K'}{n^2} \quad \text{[energies are hydrogen-like]}$$

for the ${}^2\mathrm{D} \to {}^2\mathrm{P}$ transition

$$\frac{1}{\lambda}=\frac{|E(1s^22p^1,\,^2\mathrm{P})|}{hc}-\frac{K'}{n^2}\qquad\left[\Delta E=h\nu=\frac{hc}{\lambda}\right]$$

from which we can write

$$|E(1s^22p^1,\,^2\mathrm{P})|/hc=\frac{1}{\lambda}+\frac{K'}{n^2}$$

$$=\begin{cases}\dfrac{1}{610.36\times10^{-7}\,\mathrm{cm}}+\dfrac{K'}{9} & \text{(a)}\\[2ex] \dfrac{1}{460.29\times10^{-7}\,\mathrm{cm}}+\dfrac{K'}{16} & \text{(b)}\\[2ex] \dfrac{1}{413.23\times10^{-7}\,\mathrm{cm}}+\dfrac{K'}{25} & \text{(c)}\end{cases}$$

Then (b)–(a) solves to $K'=109\,886\ \mathrm{cm}^{-1}$
(a)–(c) solves to $K'=109\,910\ \mathrm{cm}^{-1}$ } Mean $=109\,920\ \mathrm{cm}^{-1}$
(b)–(c) solves to $K'=109\,963\ \mathrm{cm}^{-1}$

The binding energies are therefore

$$E(1s^23d^1,\,^2\mathrm{D})=-\frac{K'}{9}=-12\,213\ \mathrm{cm}^{-1}$$

$$E(1s^22p,\,^2\mathrm{P})=-\frac{1}{610.36\times10^{-7}\,\mathrm{cm}}-12\,213\ \mathrm{cm}^{-1}=-28\,597\ \mathrm{cm}^{-1}$$

$$E(1s^22s^1,\,^2\mathrm{S})=-\frac{1}{670.78\times10^{-7}\,\mathrm{cm}}-28\,597\ \mathrm{cm}^{-1}=-43\,505\ \mathrm{cm}^{-1}$$

Therefore, the ionization energy is

$$I(1s^22s^1,\,^2\mathrm{S})=43\,505\ \mathrm{cm}^{-1},\ \text{or}\ \underline{5.39\ \mathrm{eV}}.$$

13.5 The ground term is $[\mathrm{Ar}]4s^1\,^2\mathrm{S}_{1/2}$ and the excited term is $[\mathrm{Ar}]4p^1\,^2\mathrm{P}$. The latter has two levels with $J=1+\frac{1}{2}=\frac{3}{2}$ and $J=1-\frac{1}{2}=\frac{1}{2}$ which are split by spin-orbit coupling [Section 13.7]. Therefore, ascribe the transitions to $\underline{^2\mathrm{P}_{3/2}\rightarrow\,^2\mathrm{S}_{1/2}}$ and $\underline{^2\mathrm{P}_{1/2}\rightarrow\,^2\mathrm{S}_{1/2}}$ (since both are allowed). The splitting is equal to $\frac{3}{2}A$ [Example 13.9]. Hence, since

$$(766.70\times10^{-7}\,\mathrm{cm})^{-1}-(770.11\times10^{-7}\,\mathrm{cm})^{-1}=57.75\ \mathrm{cm}^{-1}$$

we can conclude that $A = \underline{38.50\ \text{cm}^{-1}}$.

13.6 The Rydberg constants for ^{1}H and ^{2}H are related to $\mathcal{R}_\infty$ (in which the mass of the electron occurs alone) by

$$\mathcal{R}_\text{H} = \frac{\mathcal{R}_\infty}{1 + m_\text{e}/m_\text{p}} \quad \mathcal{R}_\text{D} = \frac{\mathcal{R}_\infty}{1 + m_\text{e}/m_\text{d}} \quad [8]$$

where m_p is the mass of the proton and m_d the mass of the deuteron. The two lines in question lie at

$$\frac{1}{\lambda_\text{H}} = \mathcal{R}_\text{H}\left(1 - \frac{1}{4}\right) = \tfrac{3}{4}\mathcal{R}_\text{H} \quad \frac{1}{\lambda_\text{D}} = \mathcal{R}_\text{D}\left(1 - \frac{1}{4}\right) = \tfrac{3}{4}\mathcal{R}_\text{D}$$

and hence

$$\frac{\mathcal{R}_\text{H}}{\mathcal{R}_\text{D}} = \frac{\lambda_\text{D}}{\lambda_\text{H}} = \frac{\tilde{\nu}_\text{H}}{\tilde{\nu}_\text{D}}$$

Then, since

$$\frac{\mathcal{R}_\text{H}}{\mathcal{R}_\text{D}} = \frac{1 + m_\text{e}/m_\text{d}}{1 + m_\text{e}/m_\text{p}}$$

which rearranges to

$$m_\text{d} = \frac{m_\text{e}}{\left(1 + \dfrac{m_\text{e}}{m_\text{p}}\right)\dfrac{\mathcal{R}_\text{H}}{\mathcal{R}_\text{D}} - 1}$$

we can calculate m_d from

$$m_\text{d} = \frac{m_\text{e}}{\left(1 + \dfrac{m_\text{e}}{m_\text{p}}\right)\dfrac{\lambda_\text{D}}{\lambda_\text{H}} - 1} = \frac{m_\text{e}}{\left(1 + \dfrac{m_\text{e}}{m_\text{p}}\right)\dfrac{\tilde{\nu}_\text{H}}{\tilde{\nu}_\text{D}} - 1}$$

$$= \frac{9.109\,39 \times 10^{-31}\ \text{kg}}{\left(1 + \dfrac{9.109\,39 \times 10^{-31}\ \text{kg}}{1.672\,62 \times 10^{-27}\ \text{kg}}\right)\left(\dfrac{82\,259.098\ \text{cm}^{-1}}{82\,281.476\ \text{cm}^{-1}}\right) - 1}$$

$$= \underline{3.3429 \times 10^{-27}\ \text{kg}}$$

$$\frac{I_\text{D}}{I_\text{H}} = \frac{\mathcal{R}_\text{D}}{\mathcal{R}_\text{H}} = \frac{\tilde{\nu}_\text{D}}{\tilde{\nu}_\text{H}} = \frac{82\,281.476\ \text{cm}^{-1}}{82\,259.098\ \text{cm}^{-1}}$$

$$= \underline{1.000\,272}$$

13.7 The Rydberg constant for positronium ($\mathcal{R}_{Ps}$) is given by

$$\mathcal{R}_{Ps}=\frac{\mathcal{R}_\infty}{1+1}=\tfrac{1}{2}\mathcal{R}_\infty \quad [8;\text{ also Problem 13.6}]$$

$$=54\,869\text{ cm}^{-1} \quad [\mathcal{R}_\infty=109\,737\text{ cm}^{-1}]$$

Hence

$$\frac{1}{\lambda}=54\,869\text{ cm}^{-1}\times\left(\frac{1}{4}-\frac{1}{n^2}\right),\ n=3,4,\ldots$$

$$=\underline{7621\text{ cm}^{-1}},\ \underline{10\,288\text{ cm}^{-1}},\ \underline{11\,522\text{ cm}^{-1}},\ \ldots$$

The binding energy of Ps is

$E=-hc\mathcal{R}_{Ps}$, corresponding to $(-)54\,869\text{ cm}^{-1}$

The ionization energy is therefore $54\,869\text{ cm}^{-1}$, or $\underline{6.80\text{ eV}}$.

13.8 $r^*=\dfrac{a_0}{Z}$ [Example 13.5]

Therefore, $r^*=\dfrac{52.92\text{ pm}}{126}=\underline{0.420\text{ pm}}$

13.9 $\langle r\rangle_{2p}=\displaystyle\int_0^\infty R_{21}rR_{21}r^2\,\mathrm{d}r \quad [\rho=2Zr/na_0=Zr/a_0]$

$$=\left(\frac{Z}{a_0}\right)^3\left(\frac{1}{2\sqrt{6}}\right)^3\int_0^\infty r^3\rho^2\,\mathrm{e}^{-\rho}\,\mathrm{d}r \quad [\text{Table 13.1}]$$

$$=\left(\frac{Z}{a_0}\right)^3\times\frac{1}{24}\times\left(\frac{a_0}{Z}\right)^4\int_0^\infty \rho^5\,\mathrm{e}^{-\rho}\,\mathrm{d}\rho=\frac{1}{24}\times\frac{a_0}{Z}\times 5!$$

$$=\frac{5a_0}{Z}$$

$$\langle r\rangle_{2s}=\int_0^\infty R_{20}rR_{20}r^2\,\mathrm{d}r$$

$$=\left(\frac{Z}{a_0}\right)^3\times\frac{1}{8}\times\left(\frac{a_0}{Z}\right)^4\int_0^\infty \rho^3(2-\rho)^2\,\mathrm{e}^{-\rho}\,\mathrm{d}\rho$$

$$=\frac{a_0}{8Z}\int_0^\infty(4\rho^3-4\rho^4+\rho^5)\,\mathrm{e}^{-\rho}\,\mathrm{d}\rho=\frac{a_0}{8Z}(4\times 3!-4\times 4!+5!)$$

$$=\frac{6a_0}{Z}$$

Therefore, $\langle r\rangle_{2p} < \langle r\rangle_{2s}$, and the $2p$ electron is, on average, closer to the nucleus.

13.10 The most probable point lies along the z-axis, and is where the radial function has its maximum value (for ψ^2 is also a maximum at that point). From Table 13.1 we know that

$$R_{21} \propto \rho\, \mathrm{e}^{-\rho/2}$$

and so $\dfrac{\mathrm{d}R}{\mathrm{d}\rho} = (1 - \tfrac{1}{2}\rho)\, \mathrm{e}^{-\rho/2} = 0$ when $\rho = 2$.

Therefore, $r^* = 2a_0/Z$, and the point of maximum probability lies at $z = \pm 2a_0/Z = \underline{\pm 106\ \mathrm{pm}}$

13.11 The attractive Coulomb force $= \dfrac{Ze^2}{4\pi\varepsilon_0} \cdot \dfrac{1}{r^2}$

The repulsive centrifugal force $= \dfrac{(\text{angular momentum})^2}{m_e r^3}$

$$= \frac{(n\hbar)^2}{m_e r^3} \quad \text{[postulated]}$$

The two forces balance when

$$\frac{Ze^2}{4\pi\varepsilon_0} \times \frac{1}{r^2} = \frac{n^2\hbar^2}{m_e r^3}, \text{ implying that } r = \frac{4\pi n^2\hbar^2\varepsilon_0}{Ze^2 m_e}$$

The total energy is

$$E = E_K + V$$

$$= \frac{(\text{angular momentum})^2}{2I} - \frac{Ze^2}{4\pi\varepsilon_0} \times \frac{1}{r}$$

$$= \frac{n^2\hbar^2}{2m_e r^2} - \frac{Ze^2}{4\pi\varepsilon_0 r}$$

$$= \frac{n^2\hbar^2}{2m_e}\left(\frac{Ze^2 m_e}{4\pi n^2\hbar^2\varepsilon_0}\right)^2 - \frac{Ze^2}{4\pi\varepsilon_0}\left(\frac{Ze^2 m_e}{4\pi n^2\hbar^2\varepsilon_0}\right)$$

$$= \underline{-\frac{Z^2 e^4 m_e}{32\pi^2\varepsilon_0^2\hbar^2} \times \frac{1}{n^2}}$$

13.12 (a) The trajectory is defined, which is not allowed according to quantum mechanics. (b) The angular momentum of a three-dimensional system is given by $\{l(l+1)\}^{1/2}\hbar$, not by $n\hbar$. In the Bohr model, the ground state possesses orbital angular momentum ($n\hbar$, with $n=1$), but the actual ground state has no angular momentum ($l=0$). Moreover, the distribution of the electron is quite different in the two cases.

The two models can be distinguished experimentally by (a) showing that there is zero orbital angular momentum in the ground state (by examining its magnetic properties) and (b) examining the electron distribution (such as by showing that the electron and the nucleus do come into contact, Chapter 18).

14. Molecular structure

Examples

14.1 Refer to Fig. 14.12 of the text for the molecular orbital energy level diagram:

(a) Li_2 (6 electrons): $1s\sigma_g^2 1s\sigma_u^2 2s\sigma_g^2$, B. O. = 1

(b) Be_2 (8 electrons): $1s\sigma_g^2 1s\sigma_u^2 2s\sigma_g^2 2s\sigma_u^2$; B. O. = 0

(c) C_2 (12 electrons): $1s\sigma_g^2 1s\sigma_u^2 2s\sigma_g^2 2s\sigma_u^2 2p\pi_g^4$; B. O. = 2

14.2 Use Fig. 14.5 of the text for H_2^-, Fig. 14.12 for N_2 and Fig. 14.10 for O_2:

(a) H_2^- (3 electrons): $1s\sigma_g^2 1s\sigma_u^1$, B. O. = 0.5

(b) N_2 (14 electrons): $1s\sigma_g^2 1s\sigma_u^2 2s\sigma_g^2 2s\sigma_u^2 2p\pi_u^4 2p\sigma_g^2$, B. O. = 3

(c) O_2 (16 electrons): $1s\sigma_g^2 1s\sigma_u^2 2s\sigma_g^2 2s\sigma_u^2 2p\sigma_g^2 2p\pi_u^4 2p_x\pi_g^1 2p_y\pi_g^1$, B. O. = 2

14.3 Note that CO and CN^- are isoelectronic with N_2 and that NO is isoelectronic with N_2^-; hence use Fig. 14.12 of the text, but without the parity labels.

(a) CO (14 electrons): $1s\sigma^2 1s\sigma^{*2} 2s\sigma^2 2s\sigma^{*2} 2p\pi^4 2p\sigma^2$, B. O. = 3

(b) NO (15 electrons): $1s\sigma^2 1s\sigma^{*2} 2s\sigma^2 2s\sigma^{*2} 2p\pi^4 2p\sigma^2 2p\pi^{*1}$, B. O. = 2.5

(c) CN^- (14 electrons): $1s\sigma^2 1s\sigma^{*2} 2s\sigma^2 2s\sigma^{*2} 2p\pi^4 2p\sigma^2$, B. O. = 3

14.4 The bond orders of B_2 and C_2 are respectively 1 and 2; so $\underline{C_2}$ should have the greater bond dissociation enthalpy. The experimental values are approximately 4 eV and 6 eV respectively.

14.5 Decide whether the electron added or removed increases or decreases the bond order. The simplest procedure is to decide whether the electron occupies or is removed from a bonding or antibonding orbital. We can draw up the following table, which denotes the orbital involved:

	N_2	NO	O_2	C_2	F_2	CN
(a) AB^-	$2p\pi^*$	$2p\pi^*$	$2p\pi^*$	$2p\sigma$	$2p\sigma^*$	$2p\sigma$
Change in bond order	$-\frac{1}{2}$	$-\frac{1}{2}$	$-\frac{1}{2}$	$+\frac{1}{2}$	$-\frac{1}{2}$	$+\frac{1}{2}$
(b) AB^+	$2p\sigma$	$2p\pi^*$	$2p\pi^*$	$2p\pi$	$2p\pi^*$	$2p\sigma$
Change in bond order	$-\frac{1}{2}$	$+\frac{1}{2}$	$+\frac{1}{2}$	$-\frac{1}{2}$	$+\frac{1}{2}$	$-\frac{1}{2}$

Therefore, C_2 and CN are stabilized (have lower energy) by anion formation, whereas NO, O_2, and F_2 are stabilized by cation formation.

14.6 We can use a version of Figs. 14.10 and 14.12 of the text, but with the energy levels of O lower than those of C, and the energy levels of F lower than those of Xe, Fig. 14.1. For CO we accommodate 14 electrons, and for

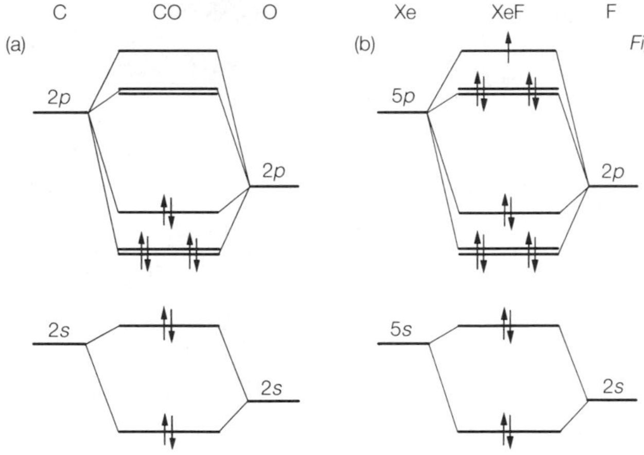

Fig 14.1

XeF we insert 15 valence electrons (the core orbitals and the electrons they supply may be neglected at this level of discussion). Since the bond order is increased when XeF^+ is formed from XeF (because an electron is removed from an antibonding orbital), XeF^+ will have a shorter bond length than XeF.

14.7 Refer to Fig. 14.17 of the text.

(a) π^* is gerade, g

(b) g, u is inapplicable to a heteronuclear molecule, for it has no center of inversion.

(c) A δ orbital (Fig. 14.2a) is gerade, g.

(d) A δ^* orbital (Fig. 14.2b) is ungerade, u.

Fig 14.2

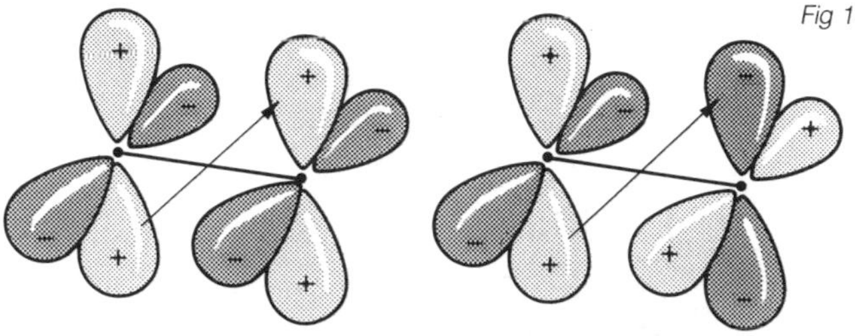

(a) g (g) u

14.8 Refer to Fig. 14.35 of the text. The plan view of the π orbitals should be interpreted with the shapes of the p orbitals in mind, and their nodal planes that lie in the plane of the molecule. The a_2 orbitals are therefore g, the e_1 orbitals are g, the e_2 orbitals are u, and the b_2 orbitals are g.

14.9 The left superscript is the value of $2S+1$, so $2S+1=2$ implies that $S=\frac{1}{2}$. The symbol Σ indicates that the total orbital angular momentum around the molecular axis is zero. The latter implies that the unpaired electron must be in a σ orbital. From Fig. 14.12 of the text, we predict the configuration of the ion to be $1s\sigma_g^2 1s\sigma_u^2 2s\sigma_g^2 2s\sigma_u^2 2p\pi_u^4 2p\sigma_g^1$, which is in accord with the ${}^2\Sigma_g$ term symbol.

14.10 According to Hund's rule, we expect one $2p\pi_u$ electron and one $2p\pi_g$ electron to be unpaired. Hence $S=1$ and the multiplicity of the spectroscopic term is 3. The overall parity is $u \times g = u$ since (apart from the complete core), one electron occupies a u orbital and another occupies a g orbital.

14.11 The bond orders of NO and N_2 are 2.5 and 3 respectively (Examples 14.2 and 14.3); hence N_2 should have the shorter bond length. The experimental values are 115 pm and 110 pm respectively.

14.12 Since the molecule has one unit of orbital angular momentum around the axis, and since one electron is in a σ orbital, the other electron must be in a π orbital. This suggests that the configuration is $1s\sigma_g^1 2p\pi_u^1$, which is consistent with the designation $^3\Pi_u$.

14.13 $$\int \psi^2\,d\tau = \tfrac{1}{3}\int (s+\sqrt{2}p)^2\,d\tau$$

$$= \tfrac{1}{3}\int (s^2+2p^2+2\sqrt{2}sp)\,d\tau$$

$$= \tfrac{1}{3}(1+2+0) = 1$$

as $\int s^2\,d\tau = 1$, $\int p^2\,d\tau = 1$, and $\int sp\,d\tau = 0$ [orthogonality]

14.14 $$\int \psi^2\,d\tau = N^2\int (\psi_A+\lambda\psi_B)^2\,d\tau$$

$$= N^2\int (\psi_A^2+\lambda^2\psi_B^2+2\lambda\psi_A\psi_B)\,d\tau$$

$$= N^2(1+\lambda^2-2\lambda S) \quad \left[\int \psi_A\psi_B\,d\tau = S\right]$$

Hence, we require

$$N = \left(\frac{1}{1+2\lambda S+\lambda^2}\right)^{1/2}$$

14.15 $$\int \psi(1s\sigma)\psi(1s\sigma^*)\,d\tau = \int (\psi_A+\psi_B)(\psi_A-\psi_B)\,d\tau$$

$$= \int (\psi_A^2-\psi_B^2)\,d\tau = 1-1 = \underline{0}$$

14.16 $$a^2 = \frac{\cos\Phi}{\cos\Phi - 1} \quad [19] \quad = \frac{\cos 92.2°}{\cos 92.2° - 1} = 0.0370$$

Hence, there is 3.7 per cent s character in the orbital.

14.17 (a) CO_2 is linear, either by VSEPR theory (two atoms attached to the central atom, no lone pairs on C), or by regarding the molecule as having a σ framework and π bonds between the C and O atoms.

(b) NO_2 is <u>non-linear</u>, since it is isoelectronic with CO_2^-. The extra electron is a 'half lone pair' and a bending agent. Alternatively, the extra electron is accommodated by the molecule bending so as to give the lone pair some *s* orbital character.

(c) NO_2^+ is <u>linear</u>, since it is isoelectronic with CO_2.

(d) NO_2^- is <u>non-linear</u>, since it has one more electron than NO_2 and a correspondingly stronger bonding influence.

(e) SO_2 is <u>non-linear</u>, since it is isoelectronic with NO_2^- (if the core electrons are disregarded).

(f) H_2O is <u>non-linear</u>, as explained in Fig. 14.25 of the text in connection with the Walsh diagram of an AH_2 molecule.

(g) H_2O^{2+} is <u>linear</u> since the electron pair responsible for the bending (see Fig. 14.25 of the text) is now absent.

14.18 The molecular orbital of the fragments and the molecular orbitals that they form are shown in Fig. 14.3.

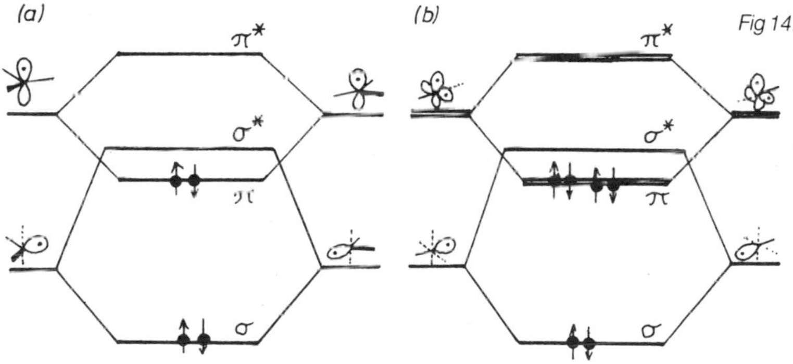

Fig 14.3

14.19 The atomic orbital basis is $1s_A$, $1s_B$, $1s_C$ in each case; in linear H_3 we ignore A, C overlap; in triangular H_3 we include it.

$$\text{(a)} \quad \begin{vmatrix} \alpha-E & \beta & 0 \\ \beta & \alpha-E & \beta \\ 0 & \beta & \alpha-E \end{vmatrix} = 0$$

$$\text{(b)} \quad \begin{vmatrix} \alpha-E & \beta & \beta \\ \beta & \alpha-E & \beta \\ \beta & \beta & \alpha-E \end{vmatrix} = 0$$

The symmetry-adapted combinations for (a) are $A+\lambda B+C$, $A-C$, and $A-\lambda B+C$, which factorizes the determinant; for (b) they are $A+B+C$ and the doubly degenerate pair $A-C$ and $A-2B+C$.]

14.20 From the molecular orbital energy level diagram in Fig. 14.35 of the text we can write

(a) C_6H_6 (6 electrons): $a_{2u}^2 e_{1g}^4$

$E = 2(\alpha+2\beta)+4(\alpha+\beta) = \underline{6\alpha+8\beta}$

(b) $C_6H_6^+$ (5 electrons): $a_{2u}^2 e_{1g}^3$

$E = 2(\alpha+2\beta)+3(\alpha+\beta) = \underline{5\alpha+7\beta}$

Problems

14.1 $\psi_A = \cos kx$ measured from A, $\psi_B = \cos k'(x-R)$ measuring x from A. Then

$$\psi = \cos kx + \cos k'(x-R)$$
$$= \cos kx + \cos k'R \cos k'x + \sin k'R \sin k'x$$

$$[\cos(a-b) = \cos a \cos b + \sin a \sin b]$$

(a) $k = k' = \pi/2R$; $\cos\dfrac{\pi}{2} = 0$, $\sin\dfrac{k'R}{2} = \sin\dfrac{\pi}{2} = 1$

$$\psi = \cos\frac{\pi x}{2R} + \sin\frac{\pi x}{2R}$$

For the mid point, $x = \frac{1}{2}R$, so $\psi(\frac{1}{2}R) = \cos\frac{1}{4}\pi + \sin\frac{1}{4}\pi = \sqrt{2}$

and there is constructive interference.

(b) $k = \pi/2R$, $k' = 3\pi/2R$; $\cos k'R = \cos\dfrac{3\pi}{2} = 0$, $\sin k'R = -1$.

$$\psi = \cos\frac{\pi x}{2R} - \sin\frac{\pi x}{2R}$$

For the mid point, $x=\frac{1}{2}R$, so $\psi(\frac{1}{2}R)=\cos\frac{1}{4}\pi-\sin\frac{1}{4}\pi=0$ and there is destructive interference.

14.2 Draw up the following table:

R/a_0	0	1	2	3	4	5	6	7	8	9	10
S	1.000	0.858	0.586	0.349	0.189	0.097	0.047	0.022	0.010	0.005	0.002

The points are plotted in Fig. 14.4.

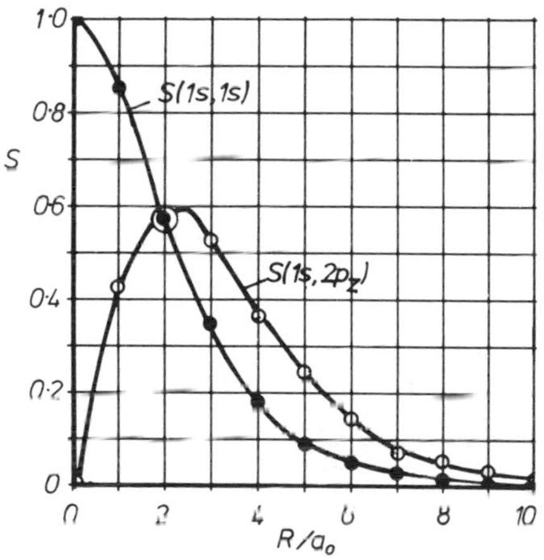

Fig 14.4

14.3 The *s* orbital begins to spread into the region of negative amplitude of the *p* orbital. When their centers coincide, the region of positive overlap cancels the negative region. Draw up the following table:

R/a_0	0	1	2	3	4	5	6	7	8	9	10
S	0	0.429	0.588	0.523	0.379	0.241	0.141	0.078	0.041	0.021	0.01

The points are plotted in Fig. 14.4. The maximum overlap occurs at $R=2.1a_0$.

14.4 $\psi_{\pm}=\psi_{1s}(A)\pm\psi_{1s}(B)$ [not normalized] with $\psi\propto e^{-r/a_0}$, with r measured from the parent nucleus. Hence

$$\psi_{\pm} \propto e^{-|z|/a_0} \pm e^{-|z-R|/a_0}$$

with z measured from A along the axis toward B. We draw up the following table with $R = 106$ pm and $a_0 = 52.9$ pm.

z/pm	−100	−80	−60	−40	−20	0	20	40
ψ_+	0.17	0.25	0.37	0.53	0.78	1.13	0.88	0.76
ψ_-	0.13	0.19	0.28	0.41	0.59	0.87	0.49	0.18

z/pm	60	80	100	120	140	160	180	200
ψ_+	0.74	0.83	1.04	0.87	0.60	0.41	0.28	0.19
ψ_-	−0.10	−0.39	−0.74	−0.66	−0.45	−0.31	−0.21	−0.15

The points are plotted in Fig. 14.5. Note that neither wavefunction is normalized.

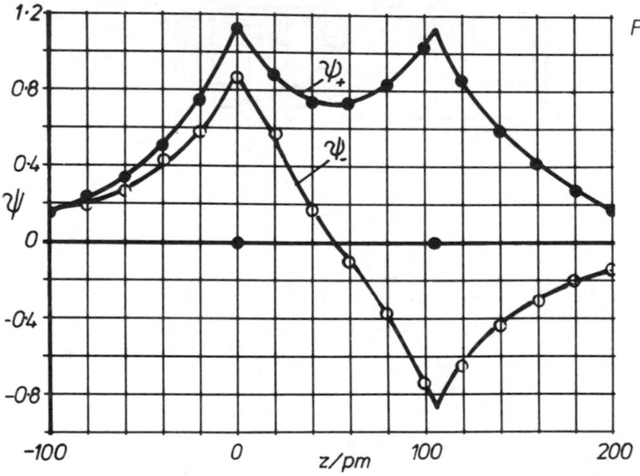

Fig 14.5

14.5 The electron densities are

$$\rho_+ = N_+^2\psi_+^2 = \frac{\psi_+^2}{(1218\ \text{pm})^3} \quad \rho_- = N_-^2\psi_-^2 = \frac{\psi_-^2}{(622\ \text{pm})^3}$$

with ψ_+ and ψ_- given in Problem 14.4. The 'atomic density' is

$$\rho = \frac{\psi_{1s}(A)^2 + \psi_{1s}(B)^2}{9.35 \times 10^5 \text{ pm}^3}, \quad \delta\rho_\pm = \rho_\pm - \rho$$

with $\psi^2 = e^{-2z/a_0}$. Draw up the following table using the information in Problem 14.4:

z/pm	−100	−80	−60	−40	−20	0	20	40
$\rho_+ \times 10^7/\text{pm}^{-3}$	0.19	0.42	0.92	1.89	4.19	8.61	5.22	3.89
$\rho_- \times 10^7/\text{pm}^{-3}$	0.44	0.93	2.03	4.34	9.00	19.6	6.21	0.84
$\rho \times 10^7/\text{pm}^{-3}$	0.25	0.53	1.13	2.40	5.11	10.9	5.44	3.26
$\delta\rho_+ \times 10^7/\text{pm}^{-3}$	−0.06	−0.09	−0.11	−0.51	−1.01	−2.3	−0.22	0.6
$\delta\rho_- \times 10^7/\text{pm}^{-3}$	0.19	0.40	0.90	1.94	3.89	8.7	0.77	−2.4

z/pm	60	80	100	120	140	160	180	200
$\rho_+ \times 10^7/\text{pm}^{-3}$	3.69	4.64	7.29	5.10	2.43	1.13	0.53	0.24
$\rho_- \times 10^7/\text{pm}^{-3}$	0.26	3.93	14.2	11.3	5.23	2.48	1.14	0.58
$\rho \times 10^7/\text{pm}^{-3}$	2.99	4.52	8.77	6.41	3.01	1.41	0.66	0.31
$\delta\rho_+ \times 10^7/\text{pm}^{-3}$	0.70	0.12	−1.48	−1.31	−0.58	−0.28	−0.13	−0.07
$\delta\rho_- \times 10^7/\text{pm}^{-3}$	−2.73	−0.59	5.4	4.9	2.22	1.07	0.48	0.27

The densities are plotted in Fig. 14.6 and the difference densities are plotted in Fig. 14.7.

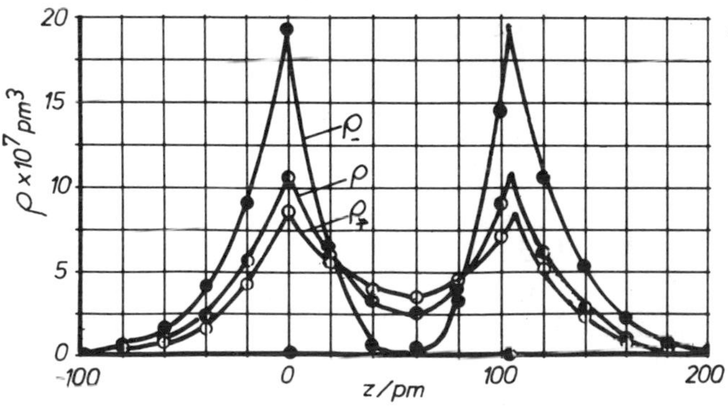

Fig 14.6

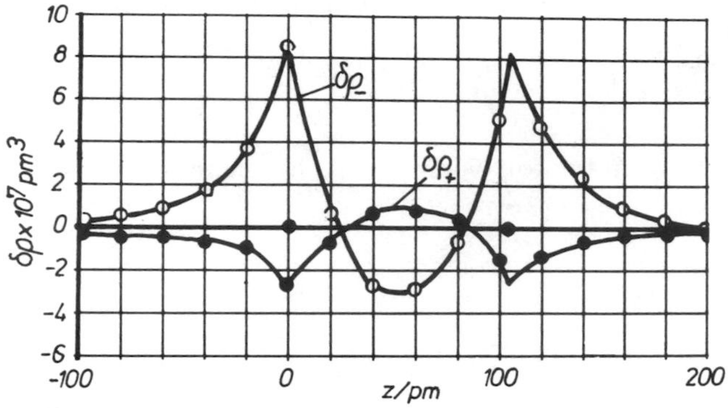

Fig 14.7

14.6 $P=|\psi|^2\,d\tau\approx|\psi|^2\,\delta\tau,\ \delta\tau=1.00\ pm^3$

(a) From Problem 14.5,

$$\psi_+^2(z=0)=\rho_+(z=0)=8.6\times10^{-7}\ pm^{-3}$$

Therefore, the probability of finding the electron in the volume $\delta\tau$ at nucleus A is

$$P=8.6\times10^{-7}\ pm^{-3}\times1.00\ pm^3=\underline{8.6\times10^{-7}}$$

(b) By symmetry (or by taking $z=106$ pm)

$$P=\underline{8.6\times10^{-7}}$$

(c) From Fig. 14.6,

$$\psi_+^2(\tfrac{1}{2}R)=3.7\times10^{-7}\ pm^{-3},\ \text{so}\ P=\underline{3.7\times10^{-7}}$$

(d) From Fig. 14.8, the point referred to lies at 22.4 pm from A and 86.6 pm

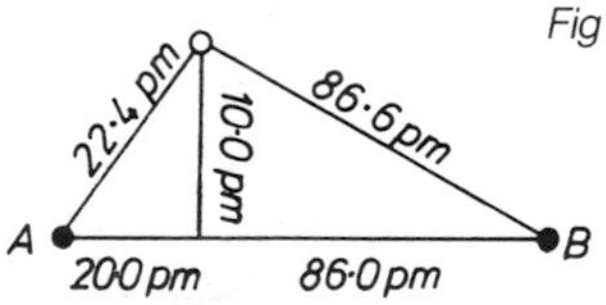

Fig 14.8

from B. Therefore,

$$\psi=\frac{e^{-22.4/52.9}+e^{-86.6/52.9}}{1218\ pm^{3/2}}=\frac{0.65+0.19}{1218\ pm^{3/2}}$$

$$=6.97\times10^{-4}\ pm^{-3/2}$$

$$\psi^2=4.9\times10^{-7}\ pm^{-3},\ \text{so}\ P=\underline{4.9\times10^{-7}}$$

For the antibonding orbital, we proceed similarly:

(a) $\psi_-^2(z=0)=19.6\times10^{-7}\,\text{pm}^{-3}$ [Problem 14.5], so $P=\underline{2.0\times10^{-6}}$

(b) By symmetry, $P=\underline{2.0\times10^{-6}}$

(c) $\psi_-^2(\tfrac{1}{2}R)=0$, so $P=\underline{0}$.

(d) We evaluate ψ_- at the point specified in Fig. 14.8:

$$\psi_-=\frac{0.65-0.19}{622\,\text{pm}^{3/2}}=7.40\times10^{-4}\,\text{pm}^{-3/2}$$

$\psi_-^2=5.47\times10^{-7}\,\text{pm}^{-3}$, so $P=\underline{5.5\times10^{-7}}$

14.7 Draw up the following table using the data in the question and using

$$\frac{e^2}{4\pi\varepsilon_0R}=\frac{e^2}{4\pi\varepsilon_0a_0}\times\frac{a_0}{R}=\frac{e^2}{4\pi\varepsilon_0\times(4\pi\varepsilon_0\hbar^2/m_ee^2)}\times\frac{a_0}{R}$$

$$=\frac{m_ee^4}{16\pi^2\varepsilon_0^2\hbar^2}\times\frac{a_0}{R}=\overline{R}_H\times\frac{a_0}{R}$$

so that

$$\frac{e^2}{4\pi\varepsilon_0R}\Big/\overline{R}_H=\frac{a_0}{R}$$

R/a_0	0	1	2	3	4	∞
$\dfrac{e^2}{4\pi\varepsilon_0R}\Big/\overline{R}_H$	∞	1	0.500	0.333	0.250	0
$(V_1+V_2)/\overline{R}_H$	2.000	1.465	0.879	0.529	0.342	0
$(E-E_H)/\overline{R}_H$	∞	0.212	−0.054	−0.059	−0.038	0

The points are plotted in Fig. 14.9. The minimum occurs at $R=2.5a_0$, so $R=130\,\text{pm}$. At that bond length

$$E-E_H=-0.07\overline{R}_H=-1.91\,\text{eV}$$

Hence, the dissociation energy is predicted to be about $\underline{1.9\,\text{eV}}$ and the equilibrium bond length about $\underline{130\,\text{pm}}$.

14.8 We proceed as in Problem 14.7, and draw up the following table:

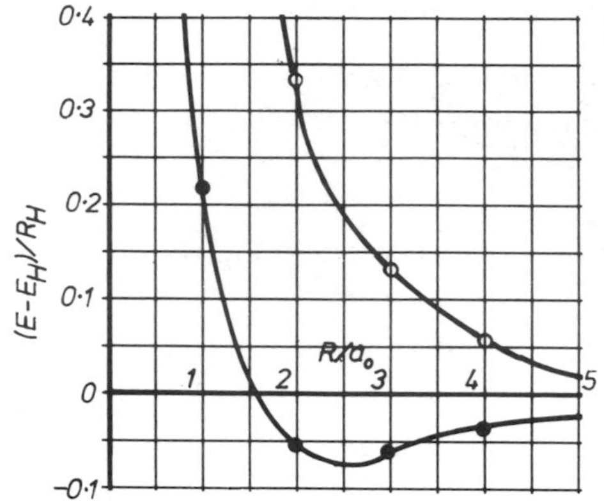

Fig 14.9

R/a_0	0	1	2	3	4	∞
$\dfrac{e^2}{4\pi\varepsilon_0 R}\Big/\bar{R}_H$	∞	1	0.500	0.333	0.250	0
$(V_1-V_2)/\bar{R}_H$	0	−0.007	0.067	0.131	0.158	0
$(E-E_H)/\bar{R}_H$	∞	1.049	0.338	0.132	0.055	0

The points are also plotted in Fig. 14.9. The contribution V_2 decreases rapidly because it depends on the overlap of the two orbitals.

14.9 $E_n = \dfrac{n^2h^2}{8mL^2}$, $n = 1, 2, \ldots$ and $\psi_n = \left(\dfrac{2}{L}\right)^{1/2} \sin\left(\dfrac{n\pi x}{L}\right)$

Two electrons occupy each level (by the Pauli principle), and so butadiene (in which there are four π electrons) has two electrons in ψ_1 and two electrons in ψ_2:

$$\psi_1 = \left(\frac{2}{L}\right)^{1/2} \sin\left(\frac{\pi x}{L}\right) \qquad \psi_2 = \left(\frac{2}{L}\right)^{1/2} \sin\left(\frac{2\pi x}{L}\right)$$

These orbitals are sketched in Fig. 14.10a. The minimum excitation energy is

$$\Delta E = E_3 - E_2 = 5\left(\frac{h^2}{8m_eL^2}\right)$$

Fig 14.10

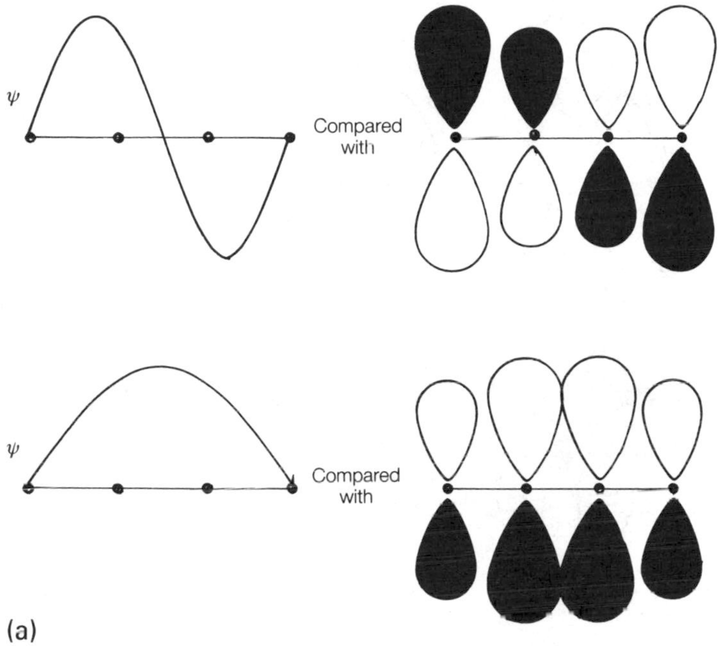

$CH_2{=}CH{-}CH{=}CH{-}CH{=}CH{-}CH{=}CH_2$ there are eight π electrons to accommodate, so the HOMO will be ψ_4 and the LUMO ψ_5. From the particle-in-a-box solutions (Chapter 12),

$$\Delta E = E_5 - E_4 = (25-16)\frac{h^2}{8m_eL^2} = \frac{9h^2}{8m_eL^2}$$

$$= \frac{9\times(6.626\times10^{-34}\ \mathrm{J\ s})^2}{8\times9.109\times10^{-31}\ \mathrm{kg}\times(1.12\times10^{-9}\ \mathrm{m})^2} = 4.3\times10^{-19}\ \mathrm{J}$$

which corresponds to 2.7 eV. It follows that

$$\lambda = \frac{hc}{\Delta E} = \frac{6.626\times10^{-34}\ \mathrm{J\ s}\times2.998\times10^{8}\ \mathrm{m\ s^{-1}}}{4.3\times10^{-19}\ \mathrm{J}}$$

$$= 4.6\times10^{-7}\ \mathrm{m,\ or\ 460\ nm}$$

The wavelength 460 nm corresponds to blue light; so the molecule is likely to appear orange in white light [since blue is subtracted]. The HOMO and LUMO are

$\psi_n = \left(\frac{2}{L}\right)^{1/2} \sin\left(\frac{n\pi x}{L}\right)$ with $n = 4, 5$ respectively and the two wavefunctions are sketched in Fig. 14.10b.

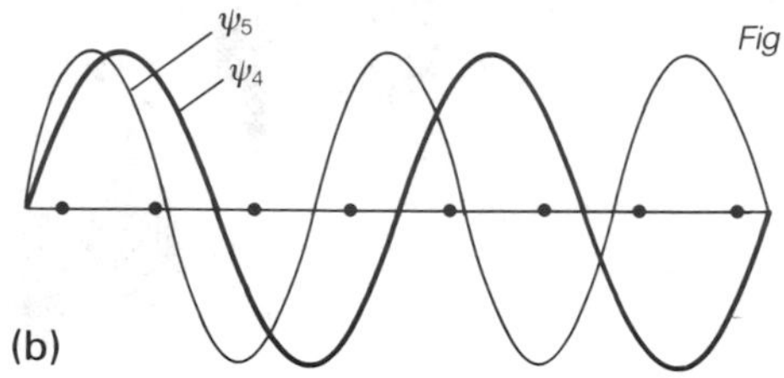

Fig 14.10

14.10 Since $\psi_{2s} = R_{20}Y_{00} = \frac{1}{2\sqrt{2}}\left(\frac{Z}{a_0}\right)^{3/2}(2-\rho)\,e^{-\rho/2} \times \left(\frac{1}{4\pi}\right)^{1/2}$ [Table 13.1]

$$= \frac{1}{4}\left(\frac{1}{2\pi}\right)^{1/2}\left(\frac{Z}{a_0}\right)^{3/2}(2-\rho)\,e^{-\rho/2}$$

$$\psi_{2p_z} = R_{21}Y_{10} = \frac{1}{2\sqrt{6}}\left(\frac{Z}{a_0}\right)^{3/2}\rho\,e^{-\rho/2} \times \left(\frac{3}{4\pi}\right)^{1/2}\cos\theta \quad \text{[Table 13.1]}$$

$$= \frac{1}{4}\left(\frac{1}{2\pi}\right)^{1/2}\left(\frac{Z}{a_0}\right)^{3/2}\rho e^{-\rho/2}\cos\theta$$

$$\psi_{2p_x} = \tfrac{1}{2}R_{21}(Y_{1,1} - Y_{1,-1})$$

$$= \frac{1}{2\sqrt{6}}\left(\frac{Z}{a_0}\right)^{3/2}\rho\,e^{-\rho/2}\left(\frac{3}{8\pi}\right)^{1/2}\sin\theta(e^{i\phi} + e^{-i\phi})$$

$$= \frac{1}{\sqrt{6}}\left(\frac{Z}{a_0}\right)^{3/2}\rho\,e^{-\rho/2}\left(\frac{3}{8\pi}\right)^{1/2}\sin\theta\cos\phi$$

$$= \frac{1}{4}\left(\frac{1}{\pi}\right)^{1/2}\left(\frac{Z}{a_0}\right)^{3/2}\rho\,e^{-\rho/2}\sin\theta\cos\phi$$

$$\psi_{2p_y} = \frac{1}{2i}R_{21}(Y_{1,1} + Y_{1,-1})$$

$$= \frac{1}{4}\left(\frac{1}{\pi}\right)^{1/2}\left(\frac{Z}{a_0}\right)^{3/2}\rho\,e^{-\rho/2}\sin\theta\sin\phi$$

Therefore,

$$\psi = \frac{1}{\sqrt{3}} \times \frac{1}{4} \times \left(\frac{1}{\pi}\right)^{1/2} \left(\frac{Z}{a_0}\right)^{3/2} \left\{ \frac{1}{\sqrt{2}}(2-\rho) - \frac{1}{\sqrt{2}}\rho \sin\theta \cos\phi + \frac{\sqrt{3}}{\sqrt{2}}\rho \sin\theta \sin\phi \right\} e^{-\rho/2}$$

$$= \frac{1}{4}\left(\frac{1}{6\pi}\right)^{1/2}\left(\frac{Z}{a_0}\right)^{3/2} \{2 - \rho - \rho\sin\theta\cos\phi + \sqrt{3}\rho\sin\theta\sin\phi\}\, e^{-\rho/2}$$

$$= \frac{1}{4}\left(\frac{1}{6\pi}\right)^{1/2}\left(\frac{Z}{a_0}\right)^{3/2} \{2 - \rho(1 + \sin\theta\cos\phi - \sqrt{3}\sin\theta\sin\phi)\}\, e^{-\rho/2}$$

$$= \frac{1}{4}\left(\frac{1}{6\pi}\right)^{1/2}\left(\frac{Z}{a_0}\right)^{3/2} \{2 - \rho(1 + [\cos\phi - \sqrt{3}\sin\phi]\sin\theta)\}\, e^{-\rho/2}$$

The maximum value of ψ occurs when $\sin\theta$ has its maximum value (+1) and the term multiplying ρ has its maximum negative value, which is −1 when $\phi = 120°$.

14.11 $$E_- + E_+ = -\frac{V_1 - V_2}{1 - S} + \frac{e^2}{4\pi\varepsilon_0 R} - \frac{V_1 + V_2}{1 + S} + \frac{e^2}{4\pi\varepsilon_0 R} + 2E_H$$

$$= -\frac{\{(V_1 - V_2)(1 + S) + (1 - S)(V_1 + V_2)\}}{(1 - S)(1 + S)} + \frac{2e^2}{4\pi\varepsilon_0 R} + 2E_H$$

$$= \frac{2(SV_2 - V_1)}{1 - S^2} + \frac{2e^2}{4\pi\varepsilon_0 R} + 2E_H$$

The nuclear repulsion term is always positive, and always tends to raise the mean energy of the orbitals above E_H. The contribution of the first term is difficult to assess. Where $S \approx 0$, $SV_2 \approx 0$ and $V_1 \approx 0$, and its contribution is dominated by the nuclear repulsion term. Where $S \approx 1$, $SV_2 \approx V_1$ and once again the nuclear repulsion term is dominant. At intermediate values of S, the first term is negative, but of smaller magnitude than the nuclear repulsion term.

14.12 $\int \psi^2\, d\tau = 1$, $\psi = N(A + B)$ in a simplified notation.

$$N^2 \int (A + B)^2\, d\tau = N^2 \int (A^2 + B^2 + 2AB)\, d\tau = N^2(1 + 1 + 2S)$$

Therefore, $N^2 = \dfrac{1}{2(1+S)}$

$$H = -\frac{\hbar^2}{2m}\nabla^2 - \frac{e^2}{4\pi\varepsilon_0}\cdot\frac{1}{r_A} - \frac{e^2}{4\pi\varepsilon_0}\cdot\frac{1}{r_B} + \frac{e^2}{4\pi\varepsilon_0}\cdot\frac{1}{R}$$

$H\psi = E\psi$ implies that

$$-\frac{\hbar^2}{2m}\nabla^2\psi - \frac{e^2}{4\pi\varepsilon_0}\cdot\frac{1}{r_A}\psi - \frac{e^2}{4\pi\varepsilon_0}\cdot\frac{1}{r_B}\psi + \frac{e^2}{4\pi\varepsilon_0}\frac{1}{R}\psi = E\psi$$

Multiply through by $\psi^*(=\psi)$ and integrate using

$$-\frac{\hbar^2}{2m}\nabla^2\psi_A - \frac{e^2}{4\pi\varepsilon_0}\cdot\frac{1}{r_A}\psi_A = E_H\psi_A$$

$$-\frac{\hbar^2}{2m}\nabla^2\psi_B - \frac{e^2}{4\pi\varepsilon_0}\cdot\frac{1}{r_B}\psi_B = E_H\psi_B$$

Then:

$$N\int \psi\left\{E_H\psi_A + E_H\psi_B - \frac{e^2}{4\pi\varepsilon_0}\cdot\frac{1}{r_A}\psi_B - \frac{e^2}{4\pi\varepsilon_0}\cdot\frac{1}{r_B}\psi_A + \frac{e^2}{4\pi\varepsilon_0}\cdot\frac{1}{R}(\psi_A + \psi_B)\right\}\mathrm{d}\tau = E$$

Whence

$$E_H\int \psi^2\,\mathrm{d}\tau + \frac{e^2}{4\pi\varepsilon_0}\cdot\frac{1}{R}\int \psi^2\,\mathrm{d}\tau - \frac{e^2}{4\pi\varepsilon_0}N\int \psi\left(\frac{\psi_A}{r_A} + \frac{\psi_B}{r_B}\right)\mathrm{d}\tau = E$$

and so

$$E_H + \frac{\mathrm{e}^2}{4\pi\varepsilon_0}\cdot\frac{1}{R} - \frac{e^2}{4\pi\varepsilon_0}N^2\int\left(\psi_A\frac{1}{r_A}\psi_B + \psi_B\frac{1}{r_A}\psi_B + \psi_A\frac{1}{r_B}\psi_A + \psi_B\frac{1}{r_A}\psi_A\right)\mathrm{d}\tau = E$$

Then use

$$\int \psi_A\frac{1}{r_A}\psi_B\,\mathrm{d}\tau = \int \psi_B\frac{1}{r_B}\psi_A\,\mathrm{d}\tau \quad \text{[by symmetry]} = V_2/(e^2/4\pi\varepsilon_0)$$

$$\int \psi_A\frac{1}{r_B}\psi_A\,\mathrm{d}\tau = \int \psi_B\frac{1}{r_A}\psi_B\,\mathrm{d}\tau \quad \text{[by symmetry]} = V_1/(e^2/4\pi\varepsilon_0)$$

which gives

$$E_H = \frac{\mathrm{e}^2}{4\pi\varepsilon_0}\cdot\frac{1}{R} - \left(\frac{1}{1+S}\right)(V_1 + V_2) = E$$

$$\text{or } E = E_H - \frac{V_1 + V_2}{1 + S} + \frac{e^2}{4\pi\varepsilon_0} \cdot \frac{1}{R}$$

14.13 The Walsh diagram is shown in Fig. 14.11. The steep rise in energy of

Fig 14.11

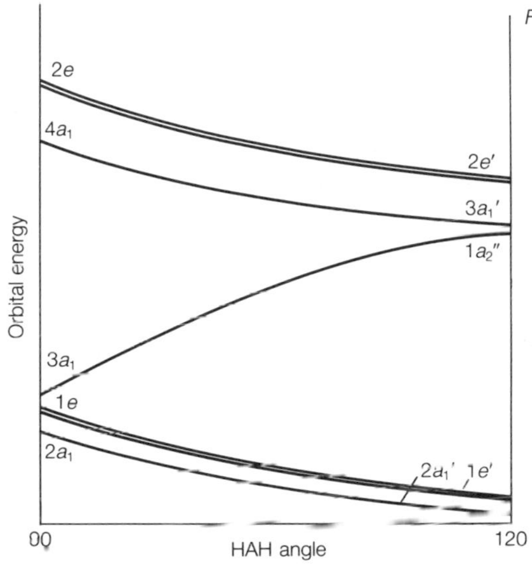

the $3a_1/1a_1''$ orbital arises from its loss of s character as the molecule becomes planar (120°). (a) In NH_3 there are $5+3=8$ valence electrons to accommodate. This demands occupancy of the $3a_1/1a_2''$ orbital, and the lowest energy is obtained when the molecule in nonplanar with the configuration $2a_1^2 1e^4 3a_1^2$. (b) CH_3^+ has only $4+3-1=6$ electrons. The $3a_1/1a_2''$ orbital is not occupied, and the lowest energy is attained with a planar molecule with configuration $2a_1'^2\, 1e'^4$.

14.14 (a) $\psi = e^{-kr}$, $H = -\dfrac{\hbar^2}{2\mu}\nabla^2 - \dfrac{e^2}{4\pi\varepsilon_0 r}$

$$\int \psi^2\, d\tau = \int_0^\infty r^2 e^{-2kr}\, dr \int_0^\pi \sin\theta\, d\theta \int_0^{2\pi} d\phi = \frac{\pi}{k^3}$$

$$\int \psi \frac{1}{r} \psi \, d\tau = \int_0^\infty r\, e^{-2kr} \, dr \int_0^\pi \sin\theta \, d\theta \int_0^{2\pi} d\phi = \frac{\pi}{k^2}$$

$$\int \psi \nabla^2 \psi \, d\tau = \int \psi \frac{1}{r} \frac{d^2}{dr^2} (r\, e^{-kr}) \, d\tau = \int \psi \left(k^2 - \frac{2k}{r}\right) \psi \, d\tau$$

$$= \frac{\pi}{k} - \frac{2\pi}{k} = -\frac{\pi}{k}$$

Therefore,

$$\int \psi H \psi \, d\tau = \frac{\hbar^2}{2\mu} \times \frac{\pi}{k} - \frac{e^2}{4\pi\varepsilon_0} \times \frac{\pi}{k^2}$$

and

$$E = \frac{\dfrac{\hbar^2 \pi}{2\mu k} - \dfrac{e^2 \pi}{4\pi\varepsilon_0 k^2}}{\pi / k^3} = \frac{\hbar^2 k^2}{2\mu} - \frac{e^2 k}{4\pi\varepsilon_0}$$

$$\frac{dE}{dk} = 2\left(\frac{\hbar^2}{2\mu}\right) k - \frac{e^2}{4\pi\varepsilon_0} = 0 \text{ when } k = \frac{e^2 \mu}{4\pi\varepsilon_0 \hbar^2}$$

The optimum energy is therefore

$$E = -\frac{e^4 \mu}{32\pi^2 \varepsilon_0^2 \hbar^2} = \underline{-hc\mathcal{R}_{\mathrm{H}}}, \text{ the exact value.}$$

(b) $\psi = e^{-kr^2}$, H as before.

$$\int \psi^2 \, d\tau = \int_0^\infty e^{-2kr^2} r^2 \, dr \int_0^\pi \sin\theta \sin d\theta \int_0^{2\pi} d\phi = \frac{\pi}{2} \left(\frac{\pi}{2k^3}\right)^{1/2}$$

$$\int \psi \frac{1}{r} \psi \, d\tau = \int_0^\infty r\, e^{-2kr^2} \, dr \int_0^\pi \sin\theta \, d\theta \int_0^{2\pi} d\phi = \frac{\pi}{k}$$

$$\int \psi \nabla^2 \psi \, d\tau = -2 \int \psi (3k - 2k^2 r^2) \psi \, d\tau$$

$$= -2 \int_0^\infty (3kr^2 - 2k^2 r^4) \, e^{-2kr^2} \, dr \int_0^\pi \sin\theta \, d\theta \int_0^{2\pi} d\phi$$

$$= -8\pi \left\{ \left(\frac{3k}{8}\right) \left(\frac{\pi}{2k^3}\right)^{1/2} - \frac{3k^2}{16} \left(\frac{\pi}{2k^5}\right)^{1/2} \right\}$$

Therefore,

$$E=\frac{3\hbar^2 k}{2\mu}-\frac{e^2 k^{1/2}}{\varepsilon_0(2\pi)^{1/2}}$$

$$\frac{\mathrm{d}E}{\mathrm{d}k}=0 \text{ when } k=\frac{e^4\mu^2}{18\pi^3\varepsilon_0^2\hbar^4}$$

and the optimum energy is therefore

$$E=-\frac{e^4\mu}{12\pi^3\varepsilon_0^2\hbar^2}=\underline{-\frac{8}{3\pi}\times hc\mathcal{R}_{\mathrm{H}}}$$

Since $8/3\pi<1$, the energy in (a) is lower than in (b), and so the exponential wavefunction is better than the gaussian.

15. Symmetry: its determination and consequences

Examples

15.1 Since the number of symmetry species of irreducible representations is equal to the number of classes [end of Section 15.6], there are four classes of operation in the group.

15.2 The elements, other than the identity E, are a C_3 axis and three vertical mirror planes σ_v. The symmetry axis passes through the C—Cl nuclei. The mirror planes are defined by the three ClCH planes.

15.3 A D group and a cubic group cannot possess an electric dipole moment [Section 15.3], so of the molecules listed only (a) pyridine, (b) nitroethane, and (c) chloromethane may be polar.

15.4 We use the procedure illustrated in Example 15.8, and draw up the following table of characters and their products:

	E	$2C_4$	C_2	$2\sigma_v$	$2\sigma_d$
$f_3 = p_z$	1	1	1	1	1
$f_2 = z$	1	1	1	1	1
$f_1 = p_x$	2	0	−2	0	0
$f_1 f_2 f_3$	2	0	−2	0	0

The number of times that A_1 appears is 0 [since 2 0 −2 0 0 are the characters of E itself], and so the integral is necessarily zero.

15.5 We proceed as in Example 15.8, considering all three components of the electric dipole moment operator:

Component:	x			y			z		
A_1	1	1	1	1	1	1	1	1	1
$\Gamma(\mu)$	2	−1	0	2	−1	0	1	1	1
A_2	1	1	−1	1	1	−1	1	1	−1
$A_1\Gamma(\mu)A_2$	2	−1	0	2	−1	0	1	1	−1
	E			E			A_2		

Since A_1 is not present in any product, the transition dipole moment must be zero.

15.6 We can determine the irreducible representations that contribute to the characters using the technique adopted in Example 15.8 and expressed formally in footnote 3 on p. 448 of the text. Thus, in this group of order 8, the numbers of appearances of each irreducible representation is

A_1: $\frac{1}{8}(5+2+1+6+2)=2$

A_2: $\frac{1}{8}(5+2+1-6-2)=0$

B_1: $\frac{1}{8}(5-2+1-6+2)=1$

B_2: $\frac{1}{8}(5-2+1-6+2)=0$

E: $\frac{1}{8}(10+0-2+0+0)=1$

That is, the orbitals span $2A_1+B_1+E$. One selection of atomic orbitals is therefore

$p_z(A_1)$, $d_{z^2}(A_1)$, $d_{x^2-y^2}(B_1)$, d_{xz} and $d_{yz}(E)$

and the composition of the hybrids is $\underline{p^1d^4}$.

15.7 Under each operation the function transforms as follows:

	E	C_2	C_4	σ_v	σ_d
x	x	$-x$	y	x	$-y$
y	y	$-y$	$-x$	$-y$	$-x$
xy	xy	xy	$-xy$	$-xy$	xy
χ	1	1	-1	-1	1

From the C_{4v} character table, we see that this set of characters belongs to $\underline{B_2}$.

15.8 In each case we must identify an improper rotation axis, perhaps in a disguised form ($S_1=\sigma$, $S_2=i$) [Section 15.3]. Thus, D_{2h} contains i, C_{3h} contains σ_h, T_h contains i, T_d contains S_4 [Refer to more extensive sets of character tables than those provided in the text: see *Further reading*.]

15.9 By inspection of the outcome of successive operations we can construct the following table:

First operation:		E	C_2	C_2'	C_2''
Second operation	E	E	C_2	C_2'	C_2''
	C_2	C_2	E	C_2''	C_2'
	C_2'	C_2'	C_2''	E	C_2
	C_2''	C_2''	C_2'	C_2	E

15.10 List the symmetry elements of the objects (the principal ones, not necessarily all the implied ones), then use the remarks in Section 15.2, and Fig. 15.1

(a) Sphere: an infinite number of symmetry axes; therefore $\underline{R_3}$.

(b) Isosceles triangle: E, C_2, σ_v, and σ_v'; therefore $\underline{C_{2v}}$

(c) Equilateral triangle: $\underbrace{\underbrace{E,\ C_3,\ C_2}_{D_3},\ \sigma_h}_{\underline{D_{3h}}}$

(d) Cylinder: E, C_∞, C_2, σ_h; therefore $\underline{D_{\infty h}}$

(e) Sharpened pencil: E, C_∞, σ_v; therefore $\underline{C_{\infty v}}$.

(f) Propellor: E, C_3, $3C_2$; therefore $\underline{D_3}$.

(g) Table: E, C_4, σ_v; therefore $\underline{C_{4v}}$.

(h) Person: E, σ_v (approximately); therefore $\underline{C_s}$.

15.11 (a) NO_2: E, C_2, σ_v, σ_v'; $\underline{C_{2v}}$

(b) N_2O: E, C_∞, C_2, σ_v; $\underline{C_{\infty v}}$

(c) $CHCl_3$: E, C_3, $3\sigma_v$; $\underline{C_{3v}}$

(d) $CH_2{=}CH_2$: E, C_2, $2C_2'$, σ_h; $\underline{D_{2h}}$

(e) *cis*-CHCl=CHCl; E, C_2, σ_v, σ_v'; $\underline{C_{2v}}$

(f) *trans*-CHCl=CHCl; E, C_2, σ_h, i; $\underline{C_{2h}}$

15.12 (a) Naphthalene: E, C_2, C', σ_h; $\underline{D_{2h}}$

(b) Anthracene: E, C_2, C_2', σ_h; $\underline{D_{2h}}$

(c) Dichlorobenzenes:

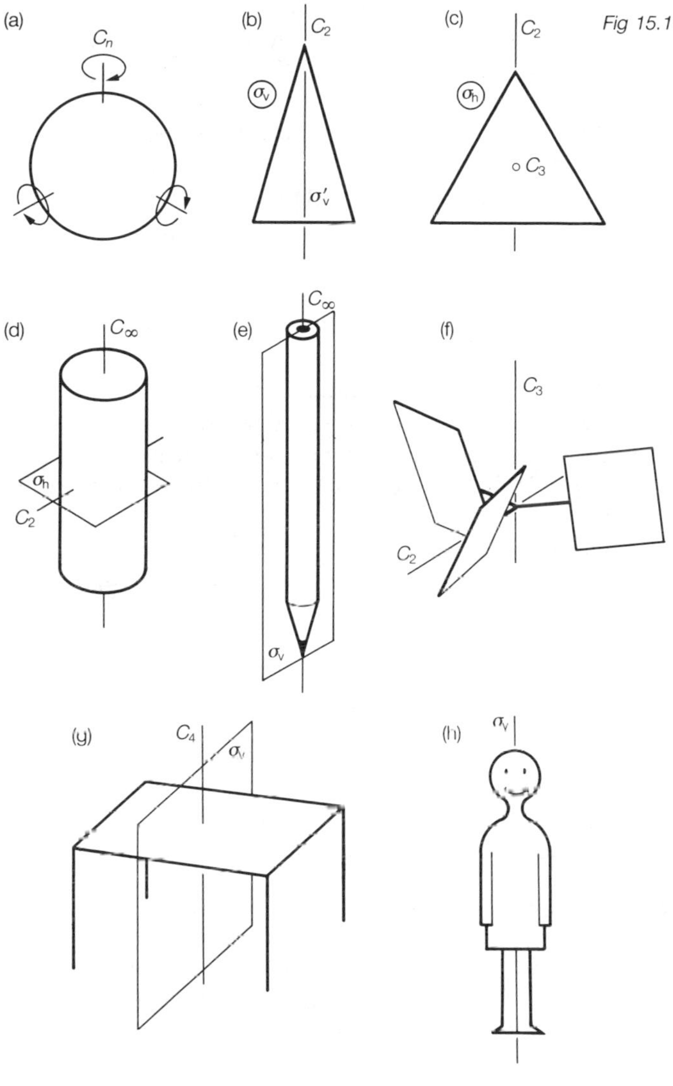

Fig 15.1

(i) 1,2-dichlorobenzene: E, C_2, σ_v, σ_v'; $\underline{C_{2v}}$

(ii) 1,3-dichlorobenzene: E, C_2, σ_v, σ_v'; $\underline{C_{2v}}$

(iii) 1,4-dichlorobenzene: E, C_2, C_2', σ_h; $\underline{D_{2h}}$

15.13 (a) No D or cubic point group molecule may be polar; so the only polar molecules are NO_2, N_2O, $CHCl_3$, 1,2-dichlorobenzene, and 1,3-

dichlorobenzene. The *trans*-dichloroethene molecule is also ruled out by its σ_h plane and its inversion center. (b) All the molecules have at least one mirror plane ($\sigma = S_1$) and so none is chiral.

15.14 Refer to the C_{2v} character table. The *s* orbital spans A_1 and the *p* orbitals of the central N atom span $A_1(p_z)$, $B_1(p_i)$, and $B_2(p_y)$. Therefore, no orbitals span A_2, and hence $p_x(A) - p_x(B)$ is a nonbonding combination. If *d* orbitals are available, we could form a molecular orbital with d_{xy}, which is a basis for A_2.

15.15 The electric dipole moment operator transforms as $x(B_1)$, $y(B_2)$, and $z(A_1)$ [C_{2v} character table]. Transitions are allowed if $\int \psi_f^* \mu \psi_i \, d\tau$ is non-zero [Example 15.10], and hence are forbidden unless $\Gamma_f \times \Gamma(\mu) \times \Gamma_i$ contains A_1. Since $\Gamma_i = A_1$, this requires $\Gamma_f \times \Gamma(\mu) = A_1$. Since $B_1 \times B_1 = A_1$ and $B_2 \times B_2 = A_1$, and $A_1 \times A_1 = A_1$, *x*-polarized light may cause a transition to a B_1 term, *y*-polarized light to a B_2 term, and *z*-polarized light to an A_1 term.

15.16 The product $\Gamma_f \times \Gamma(\mu) \times \Gamma_i$ must contain A_1 [Example 15.10]. Then, since $\Gamma_i = B_1$, $\Gamma(\mu) = \Gamma(y) = B_2$ [C_{2v} character table], we can draw up the following table of characters:

	E	C_2	σ_v	σ'_v	
B_2	1	−1	−1	1	
B_1	1	−1	1	−1	
B_1B_2	1	1	−1	−1	$= A_2$

Hence, the upper state is $\underline{A_2}$, because $A_2 \times A_2 = A_1$.

15.17 (a) The point group of benzene is D_{6h}, but we can draw conclusions by considering the smaller group C_{6v} because all the elements of C_{6v} are present in D_{6h}. In this group the components of μ transform as $E_1(x, y)$ and $A_1(z)$. The ground term is A_1. We note that $E_1 \times A_1 = E_1$ and $A_1 \times A_1 = A_1$. Therefore, the upper term must be E_1 (since $E_1 \times E_1$ contains A_1) or A_1 (since $A_1 \times A_1 = A_1$). In D_{6h} itself, μ spans $E_{1u}(x, y)$ and $A_{2u}(z)$, and the ground term is A_{1g}. Then, using $A_{2u} \times A_{ig} = A_{2u}$, $E_{1u} \times A_{1g} = E_{1u}$, $A_{2u} \times A_{2u} = A_{1g}$, and $E_{1u} \times E_{1u} = A_{1g} + A_{2g} + E_{2g}$, we conclude that the upper term is either E_{1u} or A_{2u}. (b) Naphthalene belongs to D_{2h}, but we can consider the simpler subgroup C_{2v}. The ground term is A_1 so we can use the conclusions in Exercise 15.15 for the same group. The upper terms are B_1 (*x*-polarized), B_2 (*y*-polarized) and A_1 (*z*-polarized). In D_{2h} itself, the components span $B_{3u}(x)$, $B_{2u}(y)$, and $B_{1u}(z)$

and the ground term is A_g. Hence, since $A_g \times \Gamma = \Gamma$ in this group, the upper terms are B_{3u} (x-polarized), B_{2u} (y-polarized), and B_{1u} (z-polarized).

15.18 We examine how the operations of the C_{3v} group affect $l_z = xp_y - yp_x$ when applied to it. The transformation of x, y, and z, and by analogy p_x, p_y, and p_z, are set out in Section 15.7:

$$El_z = xp_y - yp_x = l_z$$

$$\sigma_v l_z = -xp_y + yp_x = -l_z \quad [(x, y, z) \rightarrow (-x, y, z)]$$

$$C_3^+ l_z = (-\tfrac{1}{2}x + \tfrac{1}{2}\surd 3y)(-\tfrac{1}{2}\surd 3p_x - \tfrac{1}{2}p_y) - (-\tfrac{1}{2}\surd 3x - \tfrac{1}{2}y)(-\tfrac{1}{2}p_x + \tfrac{1}{2}\surd 3p_y)$$

$$[(x, y, z) \rightarrow (-\tfrac{1}{2}x + \tfrac{1}{2}\surd 3y,\ -\tfrac{1}{2}\surd 3x - \tfrac{1}{2}y, z)]$$

$$= \tfrac{1}{4}(\surd 3xp_x + xp_y - 3yp_x - \surd 3yp_y - \surd 3xp_x + 3xp_y - yp_x + \surd 3yp_y)$$

$$= xp_y - yp_x = l_z$$

The representatives of E, σ_v, and C_3^+ are therefore all one-dimensional matrices with characters $1, -1, 1$ respectively. It follows that l_z is a basis for A_2 [see the C_{3v} character table].

15.19 We consider the integral

$$I = \int_{-a}^{a} f_1 f_2 \, d\theta = \int_{-a}^{a} \sin\theta \cos\theta \, d\theta$$

and hence draw up the following table for the effect of operations in the group C_s:

	E	σ_h
$f_1 = \sin\theta$	$\sin\theta$	$-\sin\theta$
$f_2 = \cos\theta$	$\cos\theta$	$\cos\theta$

In terms of characters:

	E	σ_h	
f_1	1	-1	A″
f_2	1	1	A′
$f_1 f_2$	1	-1	A″

Since $f_1 f_2$ does not span A′, the integral must vanish. If the range of integration is not symmetrical, the reflection σ_h is not a symmetry element and the group becomes C_1, in which f_1 and f_2 both span A, and $A \times A = A$; so the integral does not necessarily vanish.

Problems

15.1 (a) Staggered CH_3CH_3: $E, C_3, C_2, 3\sigma_d$; D_{3d} [see Fig. 15.4 of the text]

(b) Chair C_6H_{12}: $E, C_3, C_2, 3\sigma_d$; D_{3d}

Boat C_6H_{12}: $E, C_2, \sigma_v, \sigma_v'$; C_{2v}

(c) B_2H_6: $E, C_2, 2C_2', \sigma_h$; D_{2h}

(d) $[Co(en)_3]^{3+}$: $E, 2C_3, 3C_2$; D_3

(e) Crown S_8: $E, C_4, C_2, 4C_2', 4\sigma_d, 2S_8$; D_{4d}

Only boat C_6H_{12} may be polar, since all the others are *D* point groups. Only $[Co(en)_3]^{3+}$ belongs to a group without an improper rotation axis ($S_1 \times \sigma$), and hence is chiral.

15.2 The operations are illustrated in Fig. 15.2. Note that $R^2 = E$ for all the

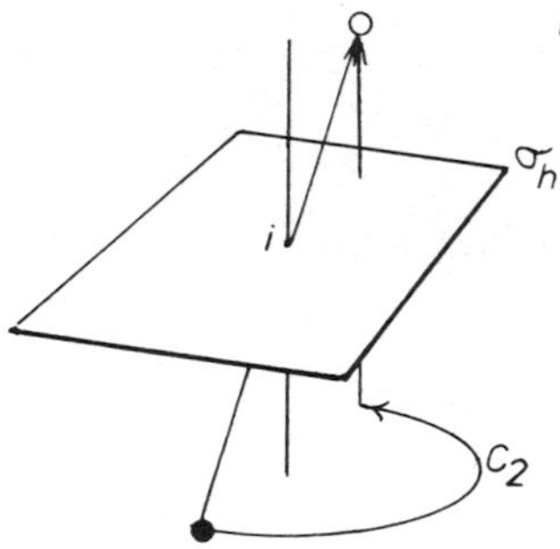

Fig 15.2

operations of the group, that $ER = RE = R$ always, and that $RR' = R'R$ for this group. Since $C_2\sigma_h = i$, $\sigma_h i = C_2$, and $iC_2 = \sigma_h$ we can draw up the following group multiplication table:

	E	C_2	σ_h	i
E	E	C_2	σ_h	i
C_2	C_2	E	i	σ_h
σ_h	σ_h	i	E	C_2
i	i	σ_h	C_2	E

The *trans*-CHCl=CHCl molecule belongs to the group C_{2h}.

15.3 Consider Fig. 15.3. The effect of σ_h on a point P is to generate $\sigma_h P$, and

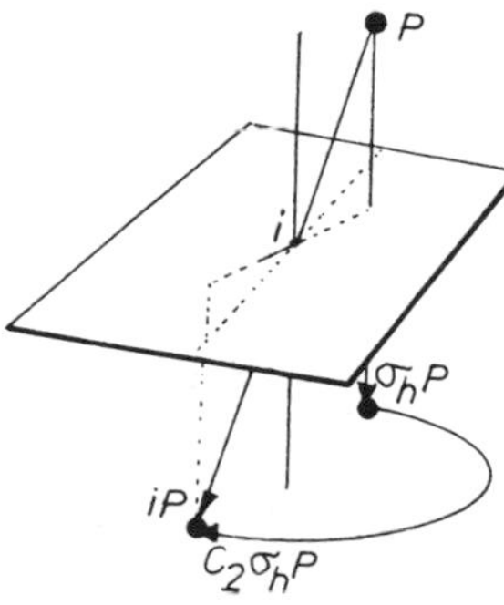

Fig 15.3

the effect of C_2 on $\sigma_h P$ is to generate the point $C_2\sigma_h P$. The same point is generated from P by the inversion i, so $C_2\sigma_h P = iP$ for all points P. Hence, $C_2\sigma_h = i$, and i must be a member of the group.

15.4 Refer to Fig. 15.3 of the text. Place orbitals h_1 and h_2 on the H atoms and s, p_x, p_y, and p_z on the O atom. The z-axis is the C_2 axis; x lies perpendicular to σ_v', y lies perpendicular to σ_v. Then draw up the following table of the effect of the operations on the basis:

	E	C_2	σ_v	σ_v'
h_1	h_1	h_2	h_2	h_1
h_2	h_2	h_1	h_1	h_2
s	s	s	s	s
p_x	p_x	$-p_x$	p_x	$-p_x$
p_y	p_y	$-p_y$	$-p_y$	p_y
p_z	p_z	p_z	p_z	p_z

Express the columns headed by each operation R in the form

$$(\text{new}) = (\text{original})D(R)$$

where $D(R)$ is the 6×6 representative of the operation R. We use the rules of matrix multiplication set out in the *Further information* section of Chapter 15.

(i) E: $(h_1, h_2, s, p_x, p_y, p_z) \leftarrow (h_1, h_2, s, p_x, p_y, p_z)$

is reproduced by the 6×6 unit matrix.

(ii) C_2: $(h_2, h_1, s, -p_x, -p_y, p_z)\leftarrow(h_1, h_2, s, p_x, p_y, p_z)$
is reproduced by

$$\boldsymbol{D}(C_2)=\begin{bmatrix} 0 & 1 & 0 & 0 & 0 & 0\\ 1 & 0 & 0 & 0 & 0 & 0\\ 0 & 0 & 1 & 0 & 0 & 0\\ 0 & 0 & 0 & -1 & 0 & 0\\ 0 & 0 & 0 & 0 & -1 & 0\\ 0 & 0 & 0 & 0 & 0 & 1 \end{bmatrix}$$

(iii) σ_v: $(h_2, h_1, s, p_x, -p_y, p_z)\leftarrow(h_1, h_2, s, p_x, p_y, p_z)$ is reproduced by

$$\boldsymbol{D}(\sigma_v)=\begin{bmatrix} 0 & 1 & 0 & 0 & 0 & 0\\ 1 & 0 & 0 & 0 & 0 & 0\\ 0 & 0 & 1 & 0 & 0 & 0\\ 0 & 0 & 0 & 1 & 0 & 0\\ 0 & 0 & 0 & 0 & -1 & 0\\ 0 & 0 & 0 & 0 & 0 & 1 \end{bmatrix}$$

(iv) σ_v': $(h_1, h_2, s, -p_x, p_y, p_z)\leftarrow(h_1, h_2, s, p_x, p_y, p_z)$ is reproduced by

$$\boldsymbol{D}(\sigma_v')=\begin{bmatrix} 1 & 0 & 0 & 0 & 0 & 0\\ 0 & 1 & 0 & 0 & 0 & 0\\ 0 & 0 & 1 & 0 & 0 & 0\\ 0 & 0 & 0 & -1 & 0 & 0\\ 0 & 0 & 0 & 0 & 1 & 0\\ 0 & 0 & 0 & 0 & 0 & 1 \end{bmatrix}$$

(a) To confirm the correct representation of $C_2\sigma_v=\sigma_v'$ we write

$$\boldsymbol{D}(C_2)\boldsymbol{D}(\sigma_v)=$$

$$\begin{bmatrix} 0 & 1 & 0 & 0 & 0 & 0\\ 1 & 0 & 0 & 0 & 0 & 0\\ 0 & 0 & 1 & 0 & 0 & 0\\ 0 & 0 & 0 & -1 & 0 & 0\\ 0 & 0 & 0 & 0 & -1 & 0\\ 0 & 0 & 0 & 0 & 0 & 1 \end{bmatrix}\begin{bmatrix} 0 & 1 & 0 & 0 & 0 & 0\\ 1 & 0 & 0 & 0 & 0 & 0\\ 0 & 0 & 1 & 0 & 0 & 0\\ 0 & 0 & 0 & 1 & 0 & 0\\ 0 & 0 & 0 & 0 & -1 & 0\\ 0 & 0 & 0 & 0 & 0 & 1 \end{bmatrix}$$

$$=\begin{bmatrix} 1 & 0 & 0 & 0 & 0 & 0\\ 0 & 1 & 0 & 0 & 0 & 0\\ 0 & 0 & 1 & 0 & 0 & 0\\ 0 & 0 & 0 & -1 & 0 & 0\\ 0 & 0 & 0 & 0 & 1 & 0\\ 0 & 0 & 0 & 0 & 0 & 1 \end{bmatrix}=\boldsymbol{D}(\sigma_v')$$

(b) Similarly, to confirm the correct representation of $\sigma_v\sigma'_v = C_2$, we write

$$\begin{bmatrix} 0 & 1 & 0 & 0 & 0 & 0 \\ 1 & 0 & 0 & 0 & 0 & 0 \\ 0 & 0 & 1 & 0 & 0 & 0 \\ 0 & 0 & 0 & 1 & 0 & 0 \\ 0 & 0 & 0 & 0 & -1 & 0 \\ 0 & 0 & 0 & 0 & 0 & 1 \end{bmatrix} \begin{bmatrix} 1 & 0 & 0 & 0 & 0 & 0 \\ 0 & 1 & 0 & 0 & 0 & 0 \\ 0 & 0 & 1 & 0 & 0 & 0 \\ 0 & 0 & 0 & -1 & 0 & 0 \\ 0 & 0 & 0 & 0 & 1 & 0 \\ 0 & 0 & 0 & 0 & 0 & 1 \end{bmatrix}$$

$$= \begin{bmatrix} 0 & 1 & 0 & 0 & 0 & 0 \\ 1 & 0 & 0 & 0 & 0 & 0 \\ 0 & 0 & 1 & 0 & 0 & 0 \\ 0 & 0 & 0 & -1 & 0 & 0 \\ 0 & 0 & 0 & 0 & -1 & 0 \\ 0 & 0 & 0 & 0 & 0 & 1 \end{bmatrix} = \boldsymbol{D}(C_2)$$

The characters of the representatives are the sums of their diagonal elements:

E	C_2	σ_v	σ'_v
6	0	2	4

(a) The characters are not those of any one irreducible representation, so the representation is reducible. (b) The sum of the characters of the specified sum is

	E	C_2	σ_v	σ'_v
$3A_1$	3	3	3	3
B_1	1	−1	1	−1
$2B_2$	2	−2	−2	2
$3A_1 + B_1 + 2B_2$	6	0	2	4

which is the same as the original. Therefore the representation is $3A_1 + B_1 + 2B_2$.

15.5 Representation 1:

$$\boldsymbol{D}(C_3)\boldsymbol{D}(C_2) = 1 \times 1 = 1 = \boldsymbol{D}(C_6)$$

and from the character table is either A_1 or A_2. Hence, either $\boldsymbol{D}(\sigma_v) = \boldsymbol{D}(\sigma_d) = +1$ or -1 respectively.

Representation 2:

$$D(C_3)D(C_2)=1\times(-1)=-1=D(C_6)$$

and from the character table is either B_1 or B_2. Hence, either $D(\sigma_v)=-D(\sigma_d)=1$ or $D(\sigma_v)=-D(\sigma_d)=-1$ respectively.

15.6 Use the technique specified in the Comment of Example 15.4.

E: All four orbitals are left unchanged, hence $\chi=4$

C_3: One orbital is left unchanged, hence $\chi=1$

C_2: No orbitals are left unchanged, hence $\chi=0$

S_4: No orbitals are left unchanged, hence $\chi=0$

σ_d: Two orbitals are left unchanged, hence $\chi=2$

The character set 4, 1, 0, 0, 2 spans A_1+T_2. Inspection of the character table of the group T_d shows that s spans A_1 and that the three p orbitals on the C atom span T_2. Hence, the s and p orbitals of the C atom may form molecular orbitals with the four H1s orbitals. In T_d, the d orbitals of the central atom span $E+T_2$ [Character table, final column], and so only the T_2 set (d_{xy}, d_{yz}, d_{zx}) may contribute to molecular orbital formation with the H orbitals.

15.7 (a) In C_{3v} symmetry the H1s orbitals span the same irreducible representations as in NH_3, which is A_1+A_1+E. There is an additional A_1 orbital because a fourth H atom lies on the C_3 axis. In C_{3v}, the d orbitals span A_1+E+E [see the final column of the C_{3v} character table]. Therefore, all five d orbitals may contribute to the bonding. (b) In C_{2v} symmetry the H1s orbitals span the same irreducible representations as in H_2O, but one 'H_2O' fragment is rotated by 90° with respect to the other. Therefore, whereas in H_2O the H1s orbitals span A_1+B_2 $[H_1+H_2, H_1-H_2]$, in the distorted CH_4 molecule they span $A_1+B_2+A_1+B_1$ $[H_1+H_2, H_1-H_2, H_3+H_4, H_3-H_4]$. In C_{2v} the d orbitals span $2A_1+B_1+B_2+A_2$ [C_{2v} character table]; therefore, all except $A_2(d_{xy})$ may participate in bonding.

15.8 (a) C_{2v}. The functions x^2, y^2, and z^2 are invariant under all operations of the group, and so $z(5z^2-3r^2)$ transforms as $z(A_1)$, $y(5y^2-3r^2)$ as $y(B_2)$, $x(5x^2-3r^2)$ as $x(B_1)$, and likewise for $z(x^2-y^2)$, $y(x^2-z^2)$, and $x(z^2-y^2)$. The function xyz transfers is $B_1\times B_2\times A_1=A_2$.

Therefore, in the group C_{2v}, $f\rightarrow 2A_1+A_2+2B_1+2B_2$.

(b) C_{3v}. In C_{3v}, z transforms as A_1, and hence so does z^3. From the C_{3v} character table, (x^2-y^2, xy) is a basis for E, and so $(xyz, z(x^2-y^2))$ is a basis for $A_1 \times E = E$. The linear combinations $y(5y^2 - 3r^2) + 5y(x^2 - z^2) \propto y$ and $x(5x^2 - 3r^2) + 5x(z^2 - y^2) \propto x$ are a basis for E. Likewise, the two linear combinations orthogonal to these are another basis for E. Hence, in the group C_{3v}, $f \rightarrow \underline{A_1 + 3E}$.

(c) T_d. Make the inspired guess that the f orbitals are a basis of dimension $3+3+1$, suggesting the decomposition T+T+A. Is the A representation A_1 or A_2? We see from the character table that the effect of S_4 discriminates between A_1 and A_2. Under S_4, $x \rightarrow y$, $y \rightarrow -x$, $z \rightarrow -z$, and so $xyz \rightarrow xyz$. The character is $\chi = 1$, and so xyz spans A_1. Likewise, $(x^3, y^3, z^3) \rightarrow (y^3, -x^3, -z^3)$ and $\chi = 0 + 0 - 1 = -1$. Hence, this trio spans T_1. Finally,

$$\{x(z^2 - y^2), y(z^2 - x^2), z(x^2 - y^2)\} \rightarrow \{y(z^2 - x^2), -x(z^2 - y^2), -z(y^2 - z^2)\}.$$

resulting in $\chi = 1$, indicating T_2. Therefore, in T_d, $f \rightarrow \underline{A_1 + T_1 + T_2}$.

(d) O_h. Anticipate an A+T+T decomposition as in the other cubic group. Since x, y, and z all have odd parity, all the irreducible representatives will be u. Under S_4, $xyz \rightarrow xyz$ (as in (c)), and so the representation is A_{2u} [see the character table]. Under S_4, $(x^3, y^3, z^3) \rightarrow (y^3, -x^3, -z^3)$, as before, and $\chi = -1$, indicating T_{1u}. In the same way, the remaining three functions span T_{2u}. Hence, in O_h, $f \rightarrow \underline{A_{2u} + T_{1u} + T_{2u}}$.
[The shapes of the orbitals are shown in *Inorganic chemistry*, D. F. Shriver, P. W. Atkins, and C. H. Langford, Oxford University Press and W. H. Freeman & Co (1990).]

The f orbitals will cluster into sets according to their irreducible representations. Thus (a) $f \rightarrow A_1 + T_1 + T_2$ in T_d symmetry, and there is one nondegenerate orbital and two sets of triply degenerate orbitals. (b) $f \rightarrow A_{2u} + T_{1u} + T_{2u}$, and the pattern of splitting (but not the order of energies) is the same.

15.9 (a) In T_d, the dipole moment transforms as T_2 [see the character table], and we require $\Gamma_f \times T_2 \times \Gamma_i$ to contain A_1 if the transition is to be allowed.

(i) $\Gamma(d_{z^2}) = E$, $\Gamma(d_{xy}) = T_2$, $\Gamma_f \times T_2 \times \Gamma_i = T_2 \times T_2 \times E$

Then, since $T_2 \times E = (6, 0, -2, 0, 0)$, it follows that

$$T_2 \times T_2 \times E = (18, 0, 2, 0, 0)$$

The number of times that A_1 appears in this set is determined using the recipe in Example 15.8 (and footnote 3 on p. 448 of the text), and is 1. Therefore the transition $d_{xy} \rightarrow d_{z^2}$ is not forbidden. However, closer analysis (dealing with the representations rather than the characters) shows that the transition is not in fact allowed.

(ii) For the transition $d_{xy} \rightarrow f_{xyz}$ we use

$\Gamma_i = T_2$, $T_f = A_1$ [Problem 15.8]

$\Gamma_f \times T_2 \times \Gamma_i = A_1 \times T_2 \times T_2 = T_2 \times T_2 = A_1 + E + T_1 + T_2$

Since the product contains A_1, the transition is allowed.

(b) In O_h the electric dipole moment operator transforms as T_{1u}

(i) $\Gamma(d_{z^2}) = E_g$, $\Gamma(d_{xy}) = T_{2g}$

But $g \times u \times g = u$; therefore the product $\Gamma_i \times \Gamma_{1u} \times \Gamma_f$ cannot contain A_{1g} and so the transition is forbidden.

(ii) $\Gamma_i(d_{xy}) = T_{2g}$, $\Gamma_f(f_{xyz}) = A_{2u}$ [Problem 15.8]

$$\begin{aligned}\Gamma_f \times T_{1u} \times \Gamma_i &= A_{2u} \times T_{1u} \times T_{2g} \\ &= A_{2u} \times (A_{2u} + E_u + T_{1u} + T_{2u}) \\ &= A_{1g} + E_g + T_{2g} + T_{1g}\end{aligned}$$

The product contains A_{1g}, so the transition is allowed.

15.10 (a) xyz changes sign under the inversion operation (one of the symmetry elements of a cube); hence it does not span A_{1g} and its integral must be zero.

(b) xyz spans A_1 in T_d [Problem 15.8] and so its integral need not be zero.

(c) $xyz \to -xyz$ under $z \to -z$ (the σ_h operation in D_{6h}), and so its integral must be zero.

15.11 Refer to Fig. 15.4, and draw up the following table:

	π_1	π_2	π_3	π_4	π_5	π_6	π_7	π_8	π_9	π_{10}	χ
E	π_1	π_2	π_3	π_4	π_5	π_6	π_7	π_8	π_9	π_{10}	10
C_2	π_5	π_6	π_7	π_8	π_1	π_2	π_3	π_4	π_{10}	π_9	0
σ_v	π_4	π_3	π_2	π_1	π_8	π_7	π_6	π_5	π_{10}	π_9	0
σ_v'	π_8	π_7	π_6	π_5	π_4	π_3	π_2	π_1	π_9	π_{10}	2

[χ is obtained from the number of unchanged orbitals.] The character set

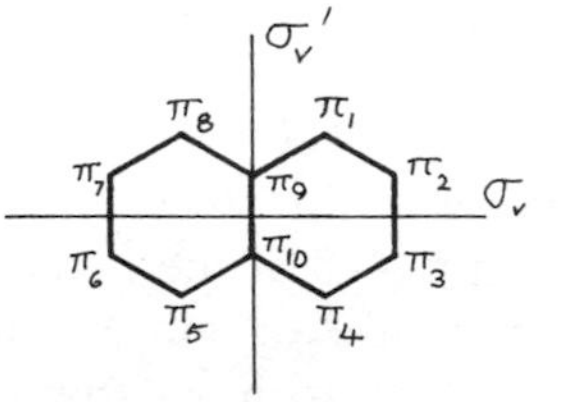

Fig 15.4

(10, 0, 0, 2) decomposes into $3A_1 + 2A_2 + 2B_1 + 3B_2$. Now form symmetry adapted linear combinations as explained in Section 15.9:

$\pi(A_1) = \pi_1 + \pi_4 + \pi_5 + \pi_8$ [from column 1]

$\pi(A_1) = \pi_2 + \pi_3 + \pi_6 + \pi_7$ [column 2]

$\pi(A_1) = \pi_9 + \pi_{10}$ [column 9]

$\pi(A_2) = \pi_1 + \pi_5 - \pi_4 - \pi_8$ [column 1]

$\pi(A_2) = \pi_2 + \pi_6 - \pi_3 - \pi_7$ [column 2]

$\pi(B_1) = \pi_1 - \pi_5 + \pi_4 - \pi_8$ [column 1]

$\pi(B_1) = \pi_2 - \pi_6 + \pi_3 - \pi_7$ [column 2]

$\pi(B_2) = \pi_1 - \pi_5 - \pi_4 + \pi_8$ [column 1]

$\pi(B_2) = \pi_2 - \pi_6 - \pi_3 + \pi_7$ [column 2]

$\pi(B_2) = \pi_9 - \pi_{10}$ [column 9]

[The other columns yield the same orbitals.]

15.12 We proceed as in Problem 15.11, and begin by drawing up the following table:

	N2s	N2p_x	N2p_y	N2p_z	O2p_x	O2p_y	O2p_z	O′2p_x	O′2p_y	O′2p_z	χ
E	N2s	N2p_x	N2p_y	N2p_z	O2p_x	O2p_y	O2p_z	O′2p_x	O′2p_y	O′2p_z	10
C_2	N2s	−N2p_x	−N2p_y	N2p_z	−O′2p_x	−O′2p_y	O′2p_z	−O2p_x	−O2p_y	O2p_z	0
σ_v	N2s	N2p_x	−N2p_y	N2p_z	O′2p_x	−O′2p_y	O′2p_z	O2p_x	−O2p_y	O2p_z	2
$\sigma_{v'}$	N2s	−N2p_x	N2p_y	N2p_z	−O2p_x	O2p_y	O2p_z	−O′2p_x	O′2p_y	O′2p_z	4

The character set (10, 0, 2, 4) decomposes into $4A_1 + 2B_1 + 3B_2 + A_2$. We then form symmetry adapted linear combinations as described in Section 15.9:

$\psi(A_1) = \text{N}2s$ [column 1]

$\psi(A_1) = \text{N}2p_z$ [column 4]

$\psi(A_1) = \text{O}2p_z + \text{O}'2p_z$ [column 7]

$\psi(A_1) = \text{O}2p_y - \text{O}'2p_y$ [column 9]

$\psi(B_1) = \text{N}2p_x$ [column 2]

$\psi(B_1) = \text{O}2p_x + \text{O}'2p_y$ [column 5]

$\psi(B_2) = \text{N}2p_y$ [column 3]

$\psi(B_2) = \text{O}2p_y + \text{O}'2p_y$ [column 6]

$\psi(B_2) = O2p_z - O'2p_z$ [column 7]
$\psi(A_2) = O2p_x - O'2p_x$ [column 5]
[The other columns yield the same combinations.]

15.13 We shall adapt the simpler subgroup C_{6v} of the full D_{6h} point group. The six π-orbitals span $A_1 + B_1 + E_1 + E_2$, and are

$$a_1 = \frac{1}{\sqrt{6}}(\pi_1 + \pi_2 + \pi_3 + \pi_4 + \pi_5 + \pi_6)$$

$$b_1 = \frac{1}{\sqrt{6}}(\pi_1 - \pi_2 + \pi_3 - \pi_4 + \pi_5 - \pi_6)$$

$$e_1 = \begin{cases} \dfrac{1}{\sqrt{12}}(2\pi_1 - \pi_2 - \pi_3 + 2\pi_4 - \pi_5 - \pi_6) \\ \dfrac{1}{\sqrt{2}}(\pi_2 - \pi_3 + \pi_5 - \pi_6) \end{cases}$$

$$e_2 = \begin{cases} \dfrac{1}{\sqrt{12}}(2\pi_1 + \pi_2 - \pi_3 - 2\pi_4 - \pi_5 + \pi_6) \\ \dfrac{1}{\sqrt{2}}(\pi_2 + \pi_3 - \pi_5 - \pi_6) \end{cases}$$

The hamiltonian transforms as A_1; therefore all integrals of the form $\int \psi' H \psi \, d\tau$ vanish unless ψ' and ψ belong to the same symmetry species. It follows that the secular determinant factorizes into four determinants:

$$A_1\text{: } H_{a_1a_1} = \frac{1}{6}\int (\pi_1 + \cdots + \pi_6) H (\pi_1 + \cdots + \pi_6)\, d\tau = \alpha + 2\beta$$

$$B_1\text{: } H_{b_1b_1} = \frac{1}{6}\int (\pi_1 - \pi_2 + \cdots) H (\pi_1 - \pi_2 + \cdots)\, d\tau = \alpha - 2\beta$$

E_1: $H_{e_1(a)e_1(a)} = \alpha - \beta$, $H_{e_1(b)e_1(b)} = \alpha - \beta$, $H_{e_1(a)e_1(b)} = 0$,

$$\text{Hence: } \begin{vmatrix} \alpha - \beta - \varepsilon & 0 \\ 0 & \alpha - \beta - \varepsilon \end{vmatrix} = 0 \quad \text{solves to } \varepsilon = \alpha - \beta \text{ (twice)}$$

E_2: $H_{e_2(a)e_2(a)} = \alpha + \beta$, $H_{e_2(b)e_2(b)} = \alpha + \beta$, $H_{e_2(a)e_2(b)} = 0$

$$\text{Hence: } \begin{vmatrix} \alpha + \beta - \varepsilon & 0 \\ 0 & \alpha + \beta - \varepsilon \end{vmatrix} = 0 \quad \text{solves to } \varepsilon = \alpha + \beta \text{ (twice)}$$

16. Rotational and vibrational spectra

Exercises

16.1 $\dfrac{1}{\mu}=\dfrac{1}{m_1}+\dfrac{1}{m_2}$ [Section 16.7]

We work in atomic mass units (u) and convert at the end of the calculation. Nuclide masses are given inside the back cover of the text.

(a) $\dfrac{1}{\mu/\text{u}}=\dfrac{1}{1.0078}+\dfrac{1}{34.9688}$, giving $\mu=0.9796\ \text{u}=\underline{1.6266\times10^{-27}\ \text{kg}}$

(b) $\dfrac{1}{\mu/\text{u}}=\dfrac{1}{2.0141}+\dfrac{1}{34.9688}$, giving $\mu=1.9044\ \text{u}=\underline{3.1624\times10^{-27}\ \text{kg}}$

(c) $\dfrac{1}{\mu/\text{u}}=\dfrac{1}{1.0078}+\dfrac{1}{36.9651}$, giving $\mu=0.9811\ \text{u}=\underline{1.6291\times10^{-27}\ \text{kg}}$

In each case, the reduced mass is dominated by the lighter atom.

16.2 $I=\mu R^2$ [Table 16.1]

$$=\frac{m_1m_2}{m_1+m_2}\times R^2=\frac{78.9183\times80.9163\ \text{u}}{78.9183+80.9163}\times R^2$$

$$=39.9524\ \text{u}\times R^2$$

$$=39.9524\times1.6605\times10^{-27}\ \text{kg}\times(2.28\times10^{-10}\ \text{m})^2$$

$$=\underline{3.45\times10^{-45}\ \text{kg m}^2}$$

16.3 $B=\dfrac{\hbar}{4\pi cI}$ [14], implying that $I=\dfrac{\hbar}{4\pi cB}$

Then, with $I=\mu R^2$,

$$R=\left(\frac{\hbar}{4\pi cB}\right)^{1/2}$$

We use

$$\mu=\frac{m_1m_2}{m_1+m_2}=\frac{126.904\times34.9688}{126.904+34.9688}\ \text{u}=27.4146\ \text{u}$$

and hence obtain

$$R = \left(\frac{1.054\,57\times10^{-34}\,\text{J s}}{4\pi\times27.4146\times1.660\,54\times10^{-27}\,\text{kg}\times2.997\,92\times10^{10}\,\text{cm s}^{-1}\times0.1142\,\text{cm}^{-1}}\right)^{1/2}$$

$$= \underline{232.1\,\text{pm}}$$

16.4 The wavenumber of the $J = 2 \leftarrow 0$ transition is

$$\tilde{\nu} = B(J+2)(J+3) - BJ(J+1);\ \text{with}\ J=0,\ \tilde{\nu} = 6B$$

Since $B = 1.9987\,\text{cm}^{-1}$ [Table 16.2], the Stokes line appears at

$$\tilde{\nu} = 20\,487 - 6\times1.9987\,\text{cm}^{-1} = \underline{20\,475\,\text{cm}^{-1}}$$

16.5 In the transition, $v = 1 \leftarrow 0$ and $J = 3 \leftarrow 2$; hence its wavenumber is

$$\tilde{\nu} = \tilde{\nu}_0 + 6B \quad [2B(J+1) = 6B]$$

$$= 2648.98 + 6\times8.465\,\text{cm}^{-1} \quad [\text{Table 16.2}] = \underline{2699.77\,\text{cm}^{-1}}$$

16.6 $\omega = \left(\dfrac{k}{\mu}\right)^{1/2}$ [Section 16.7]

$$\frac{\omega' - \omega}{\omega} = \left(\frac{\mu}{\mu'}\right)^{1/2} - 1$$

$$= \left\{\frac{m(^{23}\text{Na})m(^{35}\text{Cl})\{m(^{23}\text{Na}) + m(^{37}\text{Cl})\}}{\{m(^{23}\text{Na}) + m(^{35}\text{Cl})\}m(^{23}\text{Na})m(^{37}\text{Cl})}\right\}^{1/2} - 1$$

$$= \left\{\frac{m(^{35}\text{Cl})}{m(^{37}\text{Cl})}\cdot\frac{m(^{23}\text{Na}) + m(^{37}\text{Cl})}{m(^{23}\text{Na}) + m(^{35}\text{Cl})}\right\}^{1/2} - 1$$

$$= \left\{\frac{34.9688}{36.9651}\cdot\frac{22.9898 + 36.9651}{22.9898 + 34.9688}\right\}^{1/2} - 1$$

$$= -0.0108$$

Hence, the difference is $\underline{\text{1.08 per cent}}$.

16.7 $\omega = \left(\dfrac{k}{\mu}\right)^{1/2}$ and $\omega = 2\pi\nu = 2\pi c\tilde{\nu}$

Therefore,

$$k=\mu\omega^2=4\pi^2\mu c^2\tilde{\nu}^2,\ \mu=\tfrac{1}{2}m(^{35}\text{Cl})$$

$$=4\pi^2\times\frac{34.9688}{2}\times 1.660\,54\times 10^{-27}\,\text{kg}$$

$$\times(2.997\,924\times 10^{10}\,\text{cm s}^{-1}\times 564.9\,\text{cm}^{-1})^2$$

$$=\underline{328.7\,\text{N m}^{-1}}$$

16.8 $\Delta G_{v+1/2}=\tilde{\nu}-2(v+1)x_e\tilde{\nu}+\cdots$ [25b]

The transitions are therefore

$$\Delta G_{1/2}=\tilde{\nu}-2x_e\tilde{\nu}$$

$$\Delta G_{3/2}=\tilde{\nu}-4x_e\tilde{\nu}$$

$$\Delta G_{5/2}=\tilde{\nu}-6x_e\tilde{\nu}$$

and so on. Clearly, the fundamental transition with the highest wavenumber is

$$\Delta G_{1/2}=\tilde{\nu}-2x_e\tilde{\nu}=384.3-3.0\,\text{cm}^{-1}=\underline{381.3\,\text{cm}^{-1}}$$

and the next highest is

$$\Delta G_{3/2}=\tilde{\nu}-4x_e\tilde{\nu}-384.3-6.0\,\text{cm}^{-1}=\underline{378.3\,\text{cm}^{-1}}$$

16.9 The zero-point energy is

$$G(0)=\tfrac{1}{2}\tilde{\nu}-\tfrac{1}{4}x_0\tilde{\nu}\quad [24c]$$

$$=\tfrac{1}{2}(384.3-0.75)\,\text{cm}^{-1}=\underline{191.8\,\text{cm}^{-1}}$$

and

$$D_e=D_0+\tfrac{1}{2}\hbar\omega=D_0+G(0)$$

$$=2.153\times 8065.5\,\text{cm}^{-1}+191.8\,\text{cm}^{-1}=1.756\times 10^4\,\text{cm}^{-1},\ \underline{2.177\,\text{eV}}.$$

16.10 Use the character table for the group C_{2v} [and see Example 16.10]. The rotations span $A_2+B_1+B_2$. The translations span $A_1+B_1+B_2$. Hence the normal modes of vibration span $\underline{4A_1+A_2+2B_1+2B_2}$. ($A_1$, B_1, and B_2 are infrared active; all modes are Raman active.)

16.11 Select the polar molecules. They are (b) HCl, (d) $CHCl_3$, (e) CH_2Cl_2, (f) H_2O, (g) H_2O_2, (h) NH_3.

16.12 Select those in which a vibration gives rise to a change in dipole moment. They are (b) HCl, (c) CO_2, (d) H_2O, (e) CH_3CH_3, (f) CH_4, (g) CH_3Cl.

16.13 Select those with an anisotropic polarizability. They are (a) H_2, (b) HCl, (d) CH_3Cl, (e) CH_2Cl_2, (f) CH_3CH_3.

16.14 $\lambda_{obs}=\left(1+\dfrac{v}{c}\right)\lambda$ [Section 16.3, $\nu \propto 1/\lambda$]. When using this formula, take $v>0$ for recession and $v<0$ for approach. Since 50 m.p.h. corresponds to $22.\bar{4}\ \mathrm{m\,s^{-1}}$,

$$\lambda_{obs}=\left(1-\frac{22.\bar{4}\ \mathrm{m\,s^{-1}}}{2.998\times10^{8}\ \mathrm{m\,s^{-1}}}\right)\times 660\ \mathrm{nm}=\underline{0.999\,999\,925\times 660\ \mathrm{nm}}$$

$$v=\left(\frac{\lambda_{obs}}{\lambda}-1\right)c=2.998\times10^{8}\ \mathrm{m\,s^{-1}}\times\left(\frac{520\ \mathrm{nm}}{660\ \mathrm{nm}}-1\right)$$

$$=\underline{-6.36\times10^{7}\ \mathrm{m\,s^{-1}}},\ \text{or about } 1.4\times10^{8}\ \text{m.p.h.}$$

[Since $v\approx c$, the relativistic expression

$$\nu_{obs}=\left(\frac{1-\dfrac{v}{c}}{1+\dfrac{v}{c}}\right)^{1/2}\nu$$

should really be used. It gives $v=-7.02\times10^{7}\ \mathrm{m\,s^{-1}}$.]

16.15 $v=\left(\dfrac{\lambda_{obs}}{\lambda}-1\right)c$ [Section 16.3, Exercise 16.14]

$$=\left(\frac{706.5\ \mathrm{nm}}{654.2\ \mathrm{nm}}-1\right)\times2.998\times10^{8}\ \mathrm{m\,s^{-1}}=\underline{2.4\times10^{4}\ \mathrm{km\,s^{-1}}}$$

$\delta\lambda=\dfrac{2\lambda}{c}\left(\dfrac{2kT}{m}\ln 2\right)^{1/2}$ [11b], which implies that

$$T=\frac{m}{2k\ln 2}\left(\frac{c\delta\lambda}{2\lambda}\right)^{2}$$

$$=\frac{48\times1.6605\times10^{-27}\ \mathrm{kg}}{2\times1.381\times10^{-23}\ \mathrm{J\,K^{-1}}\times\ln 2}\left(\frac{2.998\times10^{8}\ \mathrm{m\,s^{-1}}\times61.8\times10^{-12}\ \mathrm{m}}{2\times654.2\times10^{-9}\ \mathrm{m}}\right)^{2}$$

$$=\underline{8.4\times10^{5}\ \mathrm{K}}$$

16.16 $\delta\tilde{\nu} \approx \dfrac{5.3\ \text{cm}^{-1}}{\tau/\text{ps}}$ [12b], implying that $\tau \approx \dfrac{5.3\ \text{ps}}{\delta\tilde{\nu}/\text{cm}^{-1}}$

(a) $\tau \approx \dfrac{5.3\ \text{ps}}{0.1} = \underline{5\bar{3}\ \text{ps}}$

(b) $\tau \approx \dfrac{5.3\ \text{ps}}{1} = \underline{5\ \text{ps}}$

(c) $\tau = \dfrac{5.3\ \text{ps} \times 2.998 \times 10^{10}\ \text{cm s}^{-1}}{100 \times 10^{6}\ \text{s}^{-1}\ \text{cm}} = \underline{2\ \text{ns}}$

16.17 $\delta\tilde{\nu} \approx \dfrac{5.31\ \text{cm}^{-1}}{\tau/\text{ps}}$ [12b]

(a) $\tau \approx 1 \times 10^{-13}\ \text{s} = 0.1\ \text{ps}$, implying that $\delta\tilde{\nu} \approx \underline{50\ \text{cm}^{-1}}$

(b) $\tau \approx 100 \times (1 \times 10^{-13}\ \text{s}) = 10\ \text{ps}$, implying that $\delta\tilde{\nu} \approx \underline{0.5\ \text{cm}^{-1}}$

16.18 $\dfrac{N(\text{upper})}{N(\text{lower})} = e^{-\Delta E/kT}$ [Boltzmann distribution; Example 16.2]

$= e^{-hc\tilde{\nu}/kT}$

$\dfrac{hc\tilde{\nu}}{k} = 1.4388\ \text{cm K} \times 559.7\ \text{cm}^{-1}$ [inside front cover]

$= 805.3\ \text{K}$

$\dfrac{N(\text{upper})}{N(\text{lower})} = e^{-805.3\ \text{K}/T}$

(*a*) $\dfrac{N(\text{upper})}{N(\text{lower})} = e^{-805.3/298} = \underline{0.067}$ (1 : 15)

(b) $\dfrac{N(\text{upper})}{N(\text{lower})} = e^{-805.3/500} = \underline{0.20}$ (1 : 5)

16.19 $2B = 13.10\ \text{cm}^{-1}$ [19], $B = \dfrac{\hbar}{4\pi cI}$ [14], $I = \mu R^2$ [Table 16.1]

$$\mu=\frac{1.0078\times126.9045}{1.0078+126.9045}\,\mathrm{u}=0.9999\,\mathrm{u}$$

$$R=\left(\frac{I}{\mu}\right)^{1/2}=\left(\frac{\hbar}{4\pi c\mu B}\right)^{1/2}$$

$$=\left(\frac{1.054\,57\times10^{-34}\,\mathrm{J\,s}}{4\pi\times2.9979\times10^{10}\,\mathrm{cm\,s^{-1}}\times0.9999\times1.660\,54\times10^{-27}\,\mathrm{kg}\times\frac{1}{2}\times13.10\,\mathrm{cm^{-1}}}\right)^{1/2}$$

$$=1.604\bar{4}\times10^{-10}\,\mathrm{m}=\underline{160.4\,\mathrm{pm}}$$

16.20 $\omega=\left(\frac{k}{\mu}\right)^{1/2}$, so $k=\mu\omega^2=4\pi^2\mu c^2\tilde{\nu}^2$

$$\mu(\mathrm{HF})=\frac{1.0078\times18.9908}{1.0078+18.9908}\,\mathrm{u}=0.9570\,\mathrm{u}$$

$$\mu(\mathrm{H^{35}Cl})=\frac{1.0078\times34.9688}{1.0078+34.9688}\,\mathrm{u}=0.9796\,\mathrm{u}$$

$$\mu(\mathrm{H^{81}Br})=\frac{1.0078\times80.9163}{1.0078+80.9163}\,\mathrm{u}=0.9954\,\mathrm{u}$$

$$\mu(\mathrm{H^{127}I})=\frac{1.0078\times126.9045}{1.0078+126.9045}\,\mathrm{u}=0.9999\,\mathrm{u}$$

We then draw up the following table:

	HF	HCl	HBr	HI
$\tilde{\nu}/\mathrm{cm^{-1}}$	4141.3	2988.9	2649.7	2309.5
μ/u	0.9570	0.9796	0.9954	0.9999
$k/(\mathrm{N\,m^{-1}})$	967.1	515.6	411.8	314.2

Note the order of stiffness HF > HCl > HBr > HI.

16.21 Form $\tilde{\nu}=\frac{\omega}{2\pi c}=\frac{1}{2\pi c}\left(\frac{k}{\mu}\right)^{1/2}$ with the values of k calculated in Exercise 16.20 and the following reduced masses:

$$\mu(^2\mathrm{HF})=\frac{2.0141\times18.9908}{2.0141+18.9908}\,\mathrm{u}=1.8210\,\mathrm{u}$$

and similarly for the other halides. Then we draw up the following table:

	^{2}HF	^{2}HCl	^{2}HBr	^{2}HI
$k/(\mathrm{N\,m^{-1}})$	967.1	515.6	411.8	314.2
μ/u	1.8210	1.9044	1.9652	1.9826
$\tilde{\nu}/\mathrm{cm^{-1}}$	3002.3	2143.7	1885.9	1640.1

An alternative procedure is to use

$$\frac{\tilde{\nu}(^2\mathrm{HX})}{\tilde{\nu}(^1\mathrm{HX})}=\left(\frac{\mu(^1\mathrm{HX})}{\mu(^2\mathrm{HX})}\right)^{1/2}$$

16.22 $\Delta G_{v+1/2}=\tilde{\nu}-2(v+1)x_e\tilde{\nu}$ [25b]

where $\Delta G_{v+1/2}=G(v+1)-G(v)$

Therefore, since

$$\Delta G_{v+1/2}=(1-2x_e)\tilde{\nu}-2vx_e\tilde{\nu}$$

a plot of $\Delta G_{v+1/2}$ against v should give a straight line which gives $(1-2x_e)\tilde{\nu}$ from the intercept at $v=0$ and $-2x_e\tilde{\nu}$ from the slope. We draw up the following table:

v	0	1	2	3	4
$G(v)/\mathrm{cm^{-1}}$	1481.86	4367.50	7149.04	9826.48	12 399.8
$\Delta G_{v+1/2}/\mathrm{cm^{-1}}$	2885.64	2781.54	2677.44	2573.34	

The points are plotted in Fig. 16.1. The intercept lies at 2885.6 and the

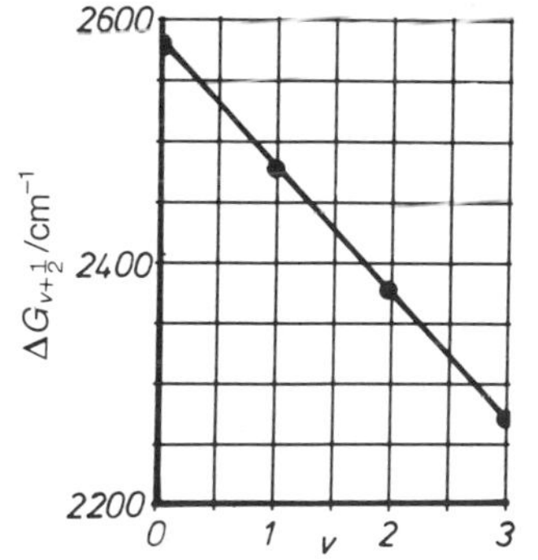

Fig 16.1

slope is $-312.3/3=-104.1$; hence $x_e\tilde{\nu}=52.1\,\mathrm{cm^{-1}}$. Since $\tilde{\nu}-2x_e\tilde{\nu}=2885.6\ \mathrm{cm^{-1}}$, it follows that $\tilde{\nu}=2989.8\ \mathrm{cm^{-1}}$

The dissociation energy may be obtained by assuming that the molecule is described by a Morse potential, for then

$$D_e/hc = \frac{\tilde{\nu}^2}{4x_e\tilde{\nu}} \quad \text{[combine eqns 23b and 24c]}$$

$$= \frac{(2989.8\ \text{cm}^{-1})^2}{4 \times 52.1\ \text{cm}^{-1}} = 42.9 \times 10^3\ \text{cm}^{-1},\ \underline{5.32\ \text{eV}}$$

16.23 The separation of lines is $4B$ [Section 16.6], so $B = 0.2438\ \text{cm}^{-1}$. Then we use

$$R = \left(\frac{\hbar}{4\pi\mu c B}\right)^{1/2} \quad \text{[Exercise 16.19]}$$

with $\mu = \frac{1}{2}m(^{35}\text{Cl}) = \frac{1}{2} \times 34.9688\ \text{u} = 17.4844\ \text{u}$

Therefore:

$$R = \left(\frac{1.054\,57 \times 10^{-34}\ \text{J s}}{4\pi \times 17.4844 \times 1.6605 \times 10^{-27}\ \text{kg} \times 2.9979 \times 10^{10}\ \text{cm s}^{-1} \times 0.2438\ \text{cm}^{-1}}\right)^{1/2}$$

$$= 1.989 \times 10^{-10}\ \text{m} = \underline{198.9\ \text{pm}}$$

16.24 Decide which modes correspond to (i) a changing electric dipole moment, (ii) a changing polarizability, and take note of the exclusion rule [Section 16.13].

(a) Nonlinear: all modes both infrared and Raman active.

(b) Linear: The symmetric stretch is infrared inactive but Raman active.

The antisymmetric stretch is infrared active and (by the exclusion rule) Raman inactive. The two bending modes are infrared active and therefore Raman inactive.

16.25 The molecule is centrosymmetric, and so the exclusion rule applies [Section 16.13]. The mode is infrared inactive (symmetric breathing leaves the molecular dipole moment unchanged at zero), and therefore the mode may be Raman active (and is). In group theoretical terms, the breathing mode has symmetry A_{1g}, and the quadratic forms $x^2 + y^2$ and z^2 have this symmetry (and hence the mode is Raman active).

Problems

16.1 $\dfrac{\delta\lambda}{\lambda}=\dfrac{2}{c}\left(\dfrac{2kT\ln 2}{m}\right)^{1/2}$ [11b]

$$=\frac{2}{2.998\times 10^{8}\,\text{m s}^{-1}}\times\left(\frac{2\times 1.381\times 10^{-23}\,\text{J K}^{-1}\times 298\,\text{K}\times\ln 2}{(m/\text{u})\times 1.6605\times 10^{-27}\,\text{kg}}\right)^{1/2}$$

$$=\frac{1.237\times 10^{-5}}{(m/\text{u})^{1/2}}$$

(a) For HCl, $m\approx 1+35\,\text{u}=36\,\text{u}$, so $\dfrac{\delta\lambda}{\lambda}\approx\underline{2.1\times 10^{-6}}$

(b) For ICl, $m\approx 127+35\,\text{u}=162\,\text{u}$, so $\dfrac{\delta\lambda}{\lambda}\approx\underline{9.7\times 10^{-7}}$

For the second part of the problem, we also need

$$\frac{\delta\tilde{\nu}}{\tilde{\nu}}=\frac{\delta\nu}{\nu}=\frac{2}{c}\left(\frac{2kT\ln 2}{m}\right)^{1/2}\quad[11a]=\frac{\delta\lambda}{\lambda}$$

(a) For HCl, $\nu(\text{rotation})\approx 2Bc\approx 2\times 10.6\,\text{cm}^{-1}\times 2.998\times 10^{10}\,\text{cm s}^{-1}$

$\approx 6.4\times 10^{11}\,\text{s}^{-1}$ or 6.4×10^{11} Hz

Therefore, $\delta\nu(\text{rotation})\approx 2.1\times 10^{-6}\times 6.4\times 10^{11}\,\text{Hz}=\underline{1.3\,\text{MHz}}$

$\tilde{\nu}(\text{vibration})\approx 2991\,\text{cm}^{-1}$ [Table 16.2]; therefore

$\delta\tilde{\nu}(\text{vibration})\approx 2.1\times 10^{-6}\times 2991\,\text{cm}^{-1}=\underline{0.0063\,\text{cm}^{-1}}$

(b) For ICl, $\nu(\text{rotation})\approx 2\times 0.1142\,\text{cm}^{-1}\times 2.998\times 10^{10}\,\text{cm s}^{-1}$

$\approx 6.8\times 10^{9}$ Hz

$\delta\nu(\text{rotation})\approx 9.7\times 10^{-7}\times 6.8\times 10^{9}\,\text{Hz}=\underline{6.6\,\text{kHz}}$

$\tilde{\nu}(\text{vibration})\approx 384\,\text{cm}^{-1}$

$\delta\tilde{\nu}(\text{vibration})\approx 9.7\times 10^{-7}\times 384\,\text{cm}^{-1}\approx\underline{0.0004\,\text{cm}^{-1}}$

16.2 $\tau=\dfrac{1}{z}=\underline{\dfrac{kT}{4\sigma p}\left(\dfrac{\pi m}{kT}\right)^{1/2}}$

For HCl, with $m \approx 36\,\text{u}$,

$$\tau \approx \frac{1.381\times10^{-23}\,\text{J K}^{-1}\times298\,\text{K}}{4\times0.30\times10^{-18}\,\text{m}^2\times1.013\times10^5\,\text{Pa}}$$

$$\times\left(\frac{\pi\times36\times1.661\times10^{-27}\,\text{kg}}{1.381\times10^{-23}\,\text{J K}^{-1}\times298\,\text{K}}\right)^{1/2}$$

$$\approx 2.3\times10^{-10}\,\text{s}$$

The width of the collision broadened line is therefore approximately

$$\delta\nu \approx \frac{1}{2\pi\tau} = \frac{1}{2\pi\times2.3\times10^{-10}\,\text{s}} \approx \underline{700\,\text{MHz}}$$

The Doppler width is approximately 1.3 MHz [Problem 16.1]. Since the collision width is proportional to p [$\delta\nu \propto 1/\tau$ and $\tau \propto 1/p$], the pressure must be reduced by a factor of about $1.3/700 = 0.002$ before Doppler broadening begins to dominate collision broadening. Hence, the pressure must be reduced to below $0.002\times760\,\text{Torr} = \underline{1\,\text{Torr}}$.

16.3 Rotational line separations are $2B$ (in wavenumber units) and $2Bc$ (in frequency units). Hence, the transitions are separated by $\underline{596\,\text{GHz}}$ or $\underline{19.9\,\text{cm}^{-1}}$. We know that

$$B = \frac{\hbar}{4\pi c I_\perp} \quad [15\text{b}]$$

and from Table 16.1,

$$I_\perp = m_A R^2(1-\cos\theta) + \left(\frac{m_A m_B}{m}\right)R^2(1+2\cos\theta)$$

$m_A = 1.6735\times10^{-27}\,\text{kg}$, $m_B = 2.3252\times10^{-26}\,\text{kg}$, and $m = 2.8273\times10^{-26}\,\text{kg}$ with $R = 101.4\,\text{pm}$ and $\theta = 106°47'$, which give

$$I_\perp = 1.6735\times10^{-27}\,\text{kg}\times(101.4\times10^{-12}\,\text{m})^2\times(1-\cos 106°47')$$

$$+\frac{1.6735\times10^{-27}\times2.3252\times10^{-26}\,\text{kg}^2}{2.8273\times10^{-26}\,\text{kg}}\times(101.4\times10^{-12}\,\text{m})^2$$

$$\times(1+2\cos 106°47')$$

$$= 2.815\overline{8}\times10^{-47}\,\text{kg m}^2$$

Therefore,

$$B = \frac{1.054\,57\times10^{-34}\,\text{J s}}{4\pi\times2.9979\times10^8\,\text{m s}^{-1}\times2.815\overline{8}\times10^{-47}\,\text{kg m}^2}$$

$$= 994.1\,\text{m}^{-1} = \underline{9.941\,\text{cm}^{-1}}$$

which is in accord with the data.

16.4 $\Delta G_{v+1/2}=\tilde{\nu}-2(v+1)x_e\tilde{\nu}$ and $D_e=\dfrac{\tilde{\nu}^2}{4x_e\tilde{\nu}}$ [25b and Exercise 16.22]

A plot of $\Delta G_{v+1/2}$ against $v+1$ should give a straight line with intercept $\tilde{\nu}$ at $v+1=0$ and slope $-2x_e\tilde{\nu}$. Draw up the following table:

$v+1$	1	2	3
$\Delta G_{v+1/2}/\text{cm}^{-1}$	284.50	283.00	281.50

The points are plotted in Fig. 16.2. The intercept is at 286.0, so $\tilde{\nu}=286\ \text{cm}^{-1}$.

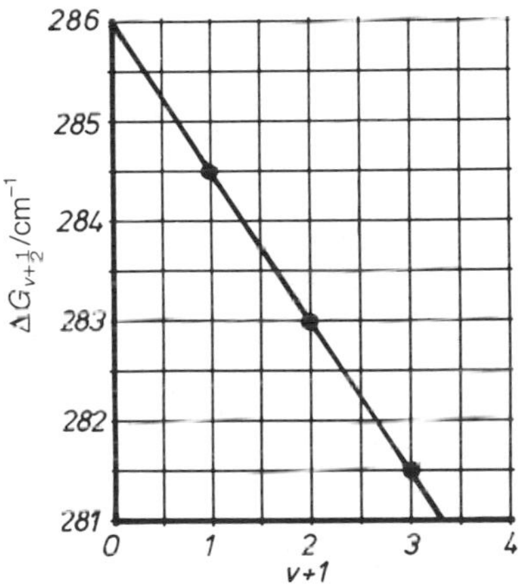

Fig 16.2

The slope is -1.50, so $x_e\tilde{\nu}=0.750\ \text{cm}^{-1}$. It follows that

$$D_e=\frac{(286\ \text{cm}^{-1})^2}{4\times 0.750\ \text{cm}^{-1}}=27\,300\ \text{cm}^{-1},\ \text{or}\ 3.38\ \text{eV}.$$

The zero-point level lies at $\underline{142.81\ \text{cm}^{-1}}$, and so $D_0=\underline{3.36\ \text{eV}}$.

Since $\mu=\dfrac{22.99\times 126.90}{22.99+126.90}\ \text{u}=19.46\bar{4}\ \text{u}$

the force constant of the molecule is

$$k = 4\pi^2\mu c^2\tilde{\nu}^2$$
$$= 4\pi^2 \times 19.46\overline{4} \times 1.6605 \times 10^{-27}\,\text{kg} \times (2.998 \times 10^{10}\,\text{cm s}^{-1} \times 286\,\text{cm}^{-1})^2$$
$$= \underline{93.8\,\text{N m}^{-1}}$$

16.5 $I = \mu R^2$

$$\mu(^{12}\text{C}^{16}\text{O}) = \frac{12.000 \times 15.9949}{12.000 + 15.9949}\,\text{u} = 6.8562\,\text{u}$$

$$\mu(^{13}\text{C}^{16}\text{O}) = \frac{13.0034 \times 15.9949}{13.0034 + 15.9949}\,\text{u} = 7.1724\,\text{u}$$

$$cB(^{12}\text{C}^{16}\text{O}) = \frac{\hbar}{4\pi I} = \frac{1.054\,57 \times 10^{-34}\,\text{J s}}{4\pi \times 6.8562 \times 1.660\,54 \times 10^{-27}\,\text{kg} \times (112.82 \times 10^{-12}\,\text{m})^2}$$

$$= 5.7911 \times 10^{10}\,\text{Hz} = 57.911\,\text{GHz}.$$

The first four transitions lies at 115.82 GHz, 231.64 GHz, 347.47 GHz, and 463.29 GHz [separation $2Bc$].

Since the ratio of reduced masses is 1.0461, the $1 \leftarrow 0$ transition of $^{13}\text{C}^{16}\text{O}$ will lie at

$$\frac{115.82\,\text{GHz}}{1.0461} = 110.71\,\text{GHz}$$

This differs from the $^{12}\text{C}^{16}\text{O}$ transition by 5.11 GHz. Hence, the equipment must be able to resolve lines separated by <u>5 GHz</u>.

16.6 The separations between neighboring lines are:

20.81, 20.60, 20.64, 20.52, 20.34, 20.37, 20.26 mean: 20.51 cm^{-1}

Hence $B = \frac{1}{2} \times 20.51\,\text{cm}^{-1} = 10.26\,\text{cm}^{-1}$ and

$$I = \frac{\hbar}{4\pi cB} = \frac{1.054\,57 \times 10^{-34}\,\text{J s}}{4\pi \times 2.997\,93 \times 10^{10}\,\text{cm s}^{-1} \times 10.26\,\text{cm}^{-1}} = \underline{2.728 \times 10^{-47}\,\text{kg m}^2}$$

$$R = \left(\frac{I}{\mu}\right)^{1/2} \quad \text{[Table 16.1] with } \mu = 1.6266 \times 10^{-27}\,\text{kg} \quad \text{[Exercise 16.1]}$$

$$= \left(\frac{2.728 \times 10^{-47}\,\text{kg m}^2}{1.6266 \times 10^{-27}\,\text{kg}}\right)^{1/2} = \underline{129.5\,\text{pm}}$$

[A more accurate value would be obtained by ascribing the variation of the separations to centrifugal distortion, and not taking a simple average.]

Since $B \propto 1/I$ and $I \propto \mu$, $B \propto 1/\mu$. Hence, the corresponding lines in $^2H^{35}Cl$ will lie at a factor

$$\frac{\mu(^1H^{35}Cl)}{\mu(^2H^{35}Cl)} = \frac{1.6266}{3.1624} = 0.5144$$

to low frequency of the $^1H^{35}Cl$ lines. Hence, we expect lines at 10.56, 21.11, 31.67, . . . cm^{-1}.

16.7 It is sensible to do Problem 16.14 first, and then to use the result that

$F_J = (\Delta E^R_{J-1} - \Delta E^P_{J+1})/hc = 2B_0(2J+1)$

We draw up the following table:

^{1}HCl $J=$	1	2	3	4	5	6
$\Delta\tilde{\nu}^R_{J-1}/cm^{-1}$	2906.25	2925.92	2944.99	2963.35	2981.05	2998.05
$\Delta\tilde{\nu}^P_{J+1}/cm^{-1}$	2843.63	2821.59	2799.00	2775.77	2752.01	
F_J/cm^{-1}	62.62	104.33	145.90	187.58	229.04	
$2B_0/cm^{-1}$	20.87	20.87	20.86	20.84	20.82	

Hence, the mean B_0 is 10.43 cm^{-1}.

^{2}HCl $J=$	1	2	3	4	5	6
$\Delta\tilde{\nu}^R_{J-1}/cm^{-1}$	2101.60	2111.94	2122.05	2131.91	2141.53	2150.93
$\Delta\tilde{\nu}^P_{J+1}/cm^{-1}$	2069.24	2058.02	2046.58	2034.95	2023.12	
F_J/cm^{-1}	32.36	53.92	75.47	93.96	118.41	
$2B_0/cm^{-1}$	10.79	10.78	10.78	10.77	10.76	

Hence, the mean B_0 is 5.39 cm^{-1}.

Since $\mu(^1H^{35}Cl) = 1.6266 \times 10^{-27}$ kg and $\mu(^2H^{35}Cl) = 3.1624 \times 10^{-27}$ kg [Exercise 16.1], we conclude that

$$R = \left(\frac{\hbar}{4\pi\mu c B}\right)^{1/2} = 128.5 \text{ pm } (^1H^{35}Cl) \text{ and } 128.\bar{2} \text{ pm}$$

and hence the bond lengths are essentially equal.

[In the original reference, the effects of centrifugal distortion are taken into account.]

16.8 $R = \left(\dfrac{\hbar}{4\pi\mu c B}\right)^{1/2}$ and $\Delta\nu = 2cB(J+1)$

We use

$$\mu(\text{CuBr}) \approx \frac{63.55 \times 79.91}{63.55 + 79.91}\,\text{u} = 35.40\,\text{u}$$

and draw up the following table:

J	13	14	15	
$\Delta\nu/\text{MHz}$	84 421.34	90 449.25	96 476.72	
B/cm^{-1}	0.100 57	0.100 57	0.100 57	$[B = \Delta\nu/2c(J+1)]$

Hence,

$$R = \left(\frac{1.054\,57 \times 10^{-34}\,\text{J s}}{4\pi \times 35.40 \times 1.6605 \times 10^{-27}\,\text{kg} \times 2.9979 \times 10^{10}\,\text{cm s}^{-1} \times 0.100\,57\,\text{cm}^{-1}}\right)^{1/2}$$

$$= \underline{218\,\text{pm}}$$

16.9 From Table 16.1

$$I(^{16}\text{O}^{12}\text{C}^{32}\text{S}) = \frac{m(^{16}\text{O})m(^{32}\text{S})}{m(^{16}\text{O}^{12}\text{C}^{32}\text{S})}(R+R')^2 + \frac{m(^{12}\text{C})\{m(^{16}\text{O})R^2 + m(^{32}\text{S})R'^2\}}{m(^{16}\text{O}^{12}\text{C}^{32}\text{S})}$$

$$I(^{16}\text{O}^{12}\text{C}^{34}\text{S}) = \frac{m(^{16}\text{O})m(^{34}\text{S})}{m(^{16}\text{O}^{12}\text{C}^{34}\text{S})}(R+R')^2 + \frac{m(^{12}\text{C})\{m(^{16}\text{O})R^2 + m(^{34}\text{S})R'^2\}}{m(^{16}\text{O}^{12}\text{C}^{34}\text{S})}$$

$m(^{16}\text{O}) = 15.9949\,\text{u}$, $m(^{12}\text{C}) = 12.0000\,\text{u}$, $m(^{32}\text{S}) = 31.9721\,\text{u}$, and $m(^{34}\text{S}) = 33.9679\,\text{u}$. Hence,

$$I(^{16}\text{O}^{12}\text{C}^{32}\text{S})/\text{u} = 8.5279(R+R')^2 + 0.20011(15.9949R^2 + 31.9721R'^2)$$

$$I(^{16}\text{O}^{12}\text{C}^{34}\text{S})/\text{u} = 8.7684(R+R')^2 + 0.19366(15.9949R^2 + 33.9679R'^2)$$

The moments of inertia may also be obtained from the spectral data, since the lines occur at $2cB(J+1)$. The mean values are

$$I(^{16}\text{O}^{12}\text{C}^{32}\text{S}) = 1.379\,98 \times 10^{-45}\,\text{kg m}^2$$

$I(^{16}O^{12}C^{34}S) = 1.414\,60 \times 10^{-45}\ \text{kg m}^2$

Therefore, after conversion of the atomic mass units to kg, the equations we must solve are

$$1.379\,98 \times 10^{-45}\ \text{m}^2 = 1.4161 \times 10^{-26} \times (R \times R')^2 + 5.3150 \times 10^{-27} R^2 + 1.0624 \times 10^{-26} R'^2$$

$$1.414\,60 \times 10^{-45}\ \text{m}^2 = 1.4560 \times 10^{-26} \times (R + R')^2 + 5.1437 \times 10^{-27} R^2 + 1.0923 \times 10^{-26} R'^2$$

These two equations may be solved for R and R'. They are tedious to solve, but straightforward. The outcome is $\underline{R = 116.28\ \text{pm}}$ and $\underline{R' = 155.97\ \text{pm}}$.

16.10 $D_0 = D_e - \tilde{\nu}'$ with $\tilde{\nu}' = \frac{1}{2}\tilde{\nu} - \frac{1}{4}x_e\tilde{\nu}$ [24c]

(a) ^{1}HCl: $\tilde{\nu}' = 1344.8 - \frac{1}{4} \times 52.05\ \text{cm}^{-1} = 1481.8\ \text{cm}^{-1}$, or 0.184 eV

Hence, $D_0 = 5.33 - 0.18 = \underline{5.15\ \text{eV}}$

(b) ^{2}HCl: $\dfrac{2\mu\omega x_e}{\hbar} = a^2$ [24c], so $\tilde{\nu}x_e \propto 1/\mu$ as a is a constant. We also have

$D_e = \tilde{\nu}^2/4x_e\tilde{\nu}$ [Exercise 16.22]; so $\tilde{\nu}^2 \propto 1/\mu$, implying $\tilde{\nu} \propto 1/\mu^{1/2}$. Reduced masses were calculated in Exercise 16.1, and we can write

$$\tilde{\nu}(^2\text{HCl}) = \left(\frac{\mu(^1\text{HCl})}{\mu(^2\text{HCl})}\right)^{1/2} \times \tilde{\nu}(^1\text{HCl}) = 0.7172 \times 2989.7\ \text{cm}^{-1}$$

$$= 2144.2\ \text{cm}^{-1}$$

$$x_e\tilde{\nu}(^2\text{HCl}) = \frac{\mu(^1\text{HCl})}{\mu(^2\text{HCl})} \times x_e\tilde{\nu}(^1\text{HCl}) = 0.5144 \times 52.05\ \text{cm}^{-1}$$

$$= 26.77\ \text{cm}^{-1}$$

$$\tilde{\nu}_0 = \tfrac{1}{2} \times 2144.2 - \tfrac{1}{4} \times 26.77\ \text{cm}^{-1} = 1065.4\ \text{cm}^{-1},\ 0.132\ \text{eV}$$

Hencc,

$$D_0 = 5.33 - 0.132\ \text{eV} = \underline{5.20\ \text{eV}}$$

16.11 $V(R) = D_e\{1 - e^{-a(R-R_e)}\}^2$ [23]

$$\tilde{\nu} = \frac{\omega}{2\pi c} = 936.8\ \text{cm}^{-1},\ x_e\tilde{\nu} = 14.15\ \text{cm}^{-1}$$

$$a = \omega\left(\frac{\mu}{2D_e}\right)^{1/2},\ x = \frac{\hbar a^2}{2\mu\omega},\ D_e = \frac{\hbar\omega}{4x} = \frac{hc\tilde{\nu}}{4x}$$

$$\mu(\text{RbH}) \approx \frac{1.008 \times 85.47}{1.008 + 85.47}\,\text{u} = 1.654 \times 10^{-27}\,\text{kg}$$

$$D_e/hc = \frac{\tilde{\nu}^2}{4x_e\tilde{\nu}} = \frac{(936.8\,\text{cm}^{-1})^2}{4 \times 14.15\,\text{cm}^{-1}} = 15\,50\overline{5}\,\text{cm}^{-1}\ (1.92\,\text{eV})$$

$$a = 2\pi c\tilde{\nu}\left(\frac{\mu}{2D_e}\right)^{1/2} = 2\pi c\tilde{\nu}\left\{\frac{\mu}{2(D_e/hc)hc}\right\}^{1/2}$$

$$= 2\pi \times 2.998 \times 10^{10}\,\text{cm s}^{-1} \times 936.8\,\text{cm}^{-1}$$

$$\times \left\{\frac{1.654 \times 10^{-27}\,\text{kg}}{2 \times 15\,505\,\text{cm}^{-1} \times 6.626 \times 10^{-34}\,\text{J s} \times 2.998 \times 10^{10}\,\text{cm s}^{-1}}\right\}^{1/2}$$

$$= 9.144 \times 10^{9}\,\text{m}^{-1} = 9.144\,\text{nm}^{-1} = 1/(0.1094\,\text{nm})$$

Therefore,

$$\frac{V(R)}{D_e} = \{1 - e^{-(R-R_e)/(0.1094\,\text{nm})}\}^2$$

with $R_e = 236.7$ pm. We draw up the following table:

R/pm	50	100	200	300	400	500	600	700	800
V/D_e	20.4	6.20	0.159	0.193	0.601	0.828	0.929	0.971	0.988

These points are plotted in Fig. 16.3 as the line labeled $J = 0$.

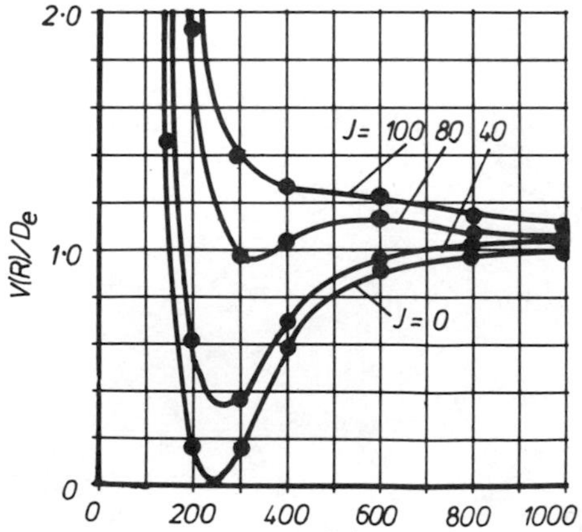

Fig 16.3

For the second part, we note that $B \propto 1/R^2$ and write

$$V_J^* = V + hcB_e J(J+1) \times \frac{R_e^2}{R^2}$$

with B_e the equilibrium rotational constant, $B_e = 3.020\ \text{cm}^{-1}$. We then draw up the following table using the values of V calculated above:

R/pm	50	100	200	300	400	600	800	1000
R_e/R	4.73	2.37	1.18	0.79	0.59	0.39	0.30	0.24
V/D_e	20.4	6.20	0.159	0.193	0.601	0.929	0.988	1.000
V_{40}^*/D_e	27.5	7.99	0.606	0.392	0.713	0.979	1.016	1.016
V_{80}^*/D_e	48.7	13.3	1.93	0.979	1.043	1.13	1.099	1.069
V_{100}^*/D_e	64.5	17.2	2.91	1.42	1.29	1.24	1.16	1.11

These points are also plotted in Fig. 16.3.

16.12 The center of mass of a diatomic molecule lies at a distance x from atom A and is such that

$$m_A x = m_B(R - x)$$

and hence is at

$$x = \frac{m_B}{m} R, \quad m = m_A + m_B$$

The moment of inertia of the molecule is

$$I = m_A x^2 + m_B(R-x)^2$$

$$= \frac{m_A m_B^2 R^2}{m^2} + \frac{m_B m_A^2 R^2}{m^2} = \frac{m_A m_B}{m} R^2$$

$$= \underline{\mu R^2} \text{ since } \mu = \frac{m_A m_B}{m_A + m_B}$$

16.13 $N_J \propto (2J+1)\,e^{-hcBJ(J+1)/kT}$ [Boltzmann distribution]

The maximum population occurs when

$$\frac{d}{dJ} N_J \propto \left\{2 - (2J+1)^2 \frac{hcB}{kT}\right\} e^{-hcBJ(J+1)/kT} = 0$$

which occurs at

$$(2J+1)^2\frac{hcB}{kT}=2$$

or when

$$J_{\max}=\left(\frac{kT}{2hcB}\right)^{1/2}-\frac{1}{2}$$

For ICl, with $kT/hc = 207.22\ \mathrm{cm}^{-1}$ (inside front cover).

$$J_{\max}=\left(\frac{207.22\ \mathrm{cm}^{-1}}{0.2284\ \mathrm{cm}^{-1}}\right)^{1/2}-\frac{1}{2}=\underline{30}$$

For a spherical rotor,

$N_J \propto (2J+1)^2\,\mathrm{e}^{-hcBJ(J+1)/kT}$

and the greatest population occurs when

$$\frac{\mathrm{d}N_J}{\mathrm{d}J}\propto\left\{8J+4-\frac{hcB(2J+1)^3}{kT}\right\}\mathrm{e}^{-hcBJ(J+1)/kT}=\underline{0}$$

which occurs when

$$4(2J+1)=\frac{kcB(2J+1)^3}{kT}$$

or at

$$\underline{J_{\max}=\left(\frac{kT}{hcB}\right)^{1/2}-\frac{1}{2}}$$

For CH_4,

$$J_{\max}=\left(\frac{207.22\ \mathrm{cm}^{-1}}{5.24\ \mathrm{cm}^{-1}}\right)^{1/2}-\frac{1}{2}=\underline{6}$$

16.14 $S(v,J)=G(v)+F(J)$ [Section 16.9]

$$=(v+\tfrac{1}{2})\tilde{\nu}+B_vJ(J+1)$$

$S(v+1,J')-S(v,J)=\tilde{\nu}+B_{v+1}J'(J'+1)-B_vJ(J+1)$

For the P-branch ($J'=J-1$):

$$\Delta S_J^{\mathrm{P}}=\tilde{\nu}+B_{v+1}(J-1)J-B_vJ(J+1)$$

$$=\underline{\tilde{\nu}-(B_{v+1}+B_v)J+(B_{v+1}-B_v)J^2}$$

For the Q-branch ($J'=J$):

$$\Delta S_J^{\mathrm{Q}}=\tilde{\nu}+B_{v+1}J(J+1)-B_vJ(J+1)$$
$$=\tilde{\nu}+(B_{v+1}-B_v)J(J+1)$$

For the R-branch ($J'=J+1$):

$$\Delta S_J^{\mathrm{R}}=\tilde{\nu}+B_{v+1}(J+1)(J+2)-B_vJ(J+1)$$
$$=\underline{\tilde{\nu}+2B_{v+1}+(3B_{v+1}-B_v)J+(B_{v+1}-B_v)J^2}$$

Note that

$$\Delta S_J^{\mathrm{R}}-\Delta S_J^{\mathrm{P}}=2B_{v+1}+(3B_{v+1}-B_v)J+(B_{v+1}+B_v)J$$
$$=2B_{v+1}+4B_{v+1}J$$
$$=2B_{v+1}(2J+1)$$
$$\Delta S_{J-1}^{\mathrm{R}}-\Delta S_{J+1}^{\mathrm{P}}=2B_{v+1}+(3B_{v+1}-B_v)(J-1)+(B_{v+1}-B_v)(J-1)^2$$
$$-\{-(B_{v+1}+B_v)(J+1)+(B_{v+1}-B_v)(J+1)^2\}$$
$$=2B_v(2J+1)$$

Hence,

$$B_{v+1}=\frac{\Delta S_J^{\mathrm{R}}-\Delta S_J^{\mathrm{P}}}{2(2J+1)},\quad B_v=\frac{\Delta S_{J-1}^{\mathrm{R}}-\Delta S_{J+1}^{\mathrm{P}}}{2(2J+1)}$$

We then draw up the following table:

J:	0	1	2	3
$\Delta S_J^{\mathrm{R}}/\mathrm{cm}^{-1}$	2906.2	2925.9	2945.0	2963.3
$\Delta S_J^{\mathrm{P}}/\mathrm{cm}^{-1}$		2865.1	2843.6	2821.6
$(\Delta S_J^{\mathrm{R}}-\Delta S_J^{\mathrm{P}})/\mathrm{cm}^{-1}$		60.80	101.4	141.7
$(\Delta S_{J-1}^{\mathrm{R}}-\Delta S_{J-1}^{\mathrm{P}})/\mathrm{cm}^{-1}$		62.60	104.3	
B_{v+1}/cm^{-1}		10.13	10.14	10.12
B_v/cm^{-1}		10.43	10.43	

Hence, $B_0=10.43\ \mathrm{cm}^{-1}$ and $B_1=10.13\ \mathrm{cm}^{-1}$. We then use

$$R_v=\left(\frac{\hbar}{4\pi\mu cB_v}\right)^{1/2}\quad \text{with } \mu=1.6266\times10^{-27}\ \mathrm{kg}\quad \text{[Exercise 16.1]}$$

and obtain

$R_0=\underline{128\ \mathrm{pm}}$, $R_1=\underline{130\ \mathrm{pm}}$

For the force constant use

$$\Delta S_0^{\mathrm{R}} = \tilde{\nu} + 2B_{v+1} \text{ with } v = 0$$

$$\tilde{\nu} = 2906.2 - 2 \times 10.13\ \mathrm{cm}^{-1} = 2885.9\ \mathrm{cm}^{-1}$$

$$k = 4\pi^2 \mu c^2 \tilde{\nu}^2 = \underline{480.7\ \mathrm{N\ m}^{-1}}$$

16.15 For substitution of an atom that lies on the figure axis, the problem is solved if we can treat the case of a linear molecule. Let an atom of mass m lie at z from the center of mass of the molecule and another m' lie at z' (the latter 'atom' may represent the remainder of the molecule). Then $mz = m'z'$ and $I = mz^2 + m'z'^2$. If the separation of the two atoms is R, we also have $z + z' = R$. Now let m be changed to $m + \delta m$ but remain at the same position. The center of mass is now determined by $(m + \delta m)\bar{z} = m'\bar{z}'$ but still $\bar{z} + \bar{z}' = R$. The new moment of inertia is

$$I' = (m + \delta m)\bar{z}^2 + m'\bar{z}^2$$

We now construct an expression for $I' - I$. First, note that

$$z' = \frac{m}{m'} \times z \text{ and } z' = R - z$$

Then also

$$\bar{z}' = \frac{m + \delta m}{m'} \times \bar{z} \text{ and } \bar{z} = R - \bar{z}'$$

It follows that

$$\bar{z} = \frac{m'R}{m + m' + \delta m} = \frac{m'R}{M + \delta m} \quad [M = m + m']$$

$$= \frac{m'}{M + \delta m} \times \frac{Mz}{m'} = \frac{Mz}{M + \delta m}$$

$$I' - I = m'\bar{z}'^2 + (m + \delta m)\bar{z}^2 - m'z'^2 - mz^2$$

$$= \frac{(m + \delta m)^2 M^2}{m'(M + \delta m)^2} z^2 + \frac{(m + \delta m)M^2}{(M + \delta m)^2} z^2 - \frac{m^2 z^2}{m'} - mz^2$$

$$= \frac{M\delta m}{M + \delta m} \times z^2 \quad \text{[after some rearrangement]}$$

We now write $\delta m = M' - M$, when

$$I' - I = \frac{(M' - M)M}{M'} z^2 = z^2 \, \Delta M$$

Now, $B = \dfrac{\hbar}{4\pi c I}$ and $B' = \dfrac{\hbar}{4\pi c I'}$

and so

$$I' - I = \frac{\hbar}{4\pi c}\left(\frac{1}{B'} - \frac{1}{B}\right) = \frac{\hbar}{4\pi c}\left(\frac{B - B'}{BB'}\right) = \frac{\hbar \, \Delta B}{4\pi c BB'}$$

and

$$z^2 = \frac{\hbar \, \Delta B}{4\pi c BB' \, \Delta M}$$

Now express the quantities numerically:

$$z^2 = \frac{1.054\,57 \times 10^{-34}\ \mathrm{J\,s}}{4\pi \times 2.9979 \times 10^{10}\ \mathrm{cm\,s^{-1}}} \times \frac{(\Delta B/\mathrm{cm^{-1}}) \times \mathrm{cm}}{(B/\mathrm{cm^{-1}})(B'/\mathrm{cm^{-1}})} \times \frac{1}{\Delta M/\mathrm{u}}$$

$$\times \frac{1}{1.6605 \times 10^{-27}\ \mathrm{kg}}$$

$$= 1.6858 \times 10^{-19}\ \mathrm{m^2} \times \frac{(\Delta B/\mathrm{cm^{-1}})}{(B/\mathrm{cm^{-1}})(B'/\mathrm{cm^{-1}})} \times \frac{1}{\Delta M/\mathrm{u}}$$

But $\Delta M/\mathrm{u} = \Delta M/(\mathrm{g\,mol^{-1}})$ if ΔM is now interpreted as the molar mass (as distinct from the molecular mass); so

$$(z/\mathrm{pm})^2 = 1.6858 \times 10^5 \frac{\Delta B/\mathrm{cm^{-1}}}{(B/\mathrm{cm^{-1}})(B'/\mathrm{cm^{-1}})(\Delta M/\mathrm{g\,mol^{-1}})}$$

[The general case is discussed in the original reference, *Amer. J. Phys.* **21**, 17 (1953).]

By multiplication of the right hand side by c^2/c^2, we obtain

$$(z/\mathrm{pm})^2 = \frac{5.053\,80 \times 10^9 (c\,\Delta B/\mathrm{MHz})}{(cB/\mathrm{MHz})(cB'/\mathrm{MHz})(\Delta M/\mathrm{g\,mol^{-1}})}$$

which we can use for the analysis of the data. Since $\Delta\nu(J) = 2(J+1)cB$, for $J = 10$ we can write

(a) $cB(^{35}\mathrm{Cl}^{126}\mathrm{TeF}_5) = \dfrac{30\,711.18\ \mathrm{MHz}}{22} = 1395.96\ \mathrm{MHz}$

(b) $cB(^{35}\text{Cl}^{125}\text{TeF}_5) = \dfrac{30\,713.24\text{ MHz}}{22} = 1396.06\text{ MHz}$

(c) $cB(^{37}\text{Cl}^{126}\text{TeF}_5) = \dfrac{29\,990.54\text{ MHz}}{22} = 1363.21\text{ MHz}$

$M(^{35}\text{Cl}^{126}\text{TeF}_5) = 34.9688 + 125.0331 + 5 \times 18.9984 = 254.9939\text{ g mol}^{-1}$

$M(^{35}\text{Cl}^{125}\text{TeF}_5) = 254.0051\text{ g mol}^{-1}$

$M(^{37}\text{Cl}^{126}\text{TeF}_5) = 256.9902\text{ g mol}^{-1}$

From (a, b), $c\,\Delta B/\text{MHz} = 0.10$, $\Delta M = 0.9850\text{ g mol}^{-1}$

$$z(\text{Te}) = \left(\frac{5.053\,80 \times 10^9 \times 0.10}{0.9850 \times 1395.96 \times 1396.06}\right)^{1/2}\text{pm} = \underline{16\text{ pm}}$$

From (a, c), $c\,\Delta B/\text{MHz} = 32.75$, $\Delta M = 1.9808\text{ g mol}^{-1}$

$$z(\text{Cl}) = \left(\frac{5.053\,80 \times 10^9 \times 32.75}{1.9808 \times 1396.06 \times 1363.21}\right)^{1/2}\text{pm} = \underline{210\text{ pm}}$$

Therefore, the distance between the Te and Cl atoms is $\underline{226\text{ pm}}$

16.16 $S(v, J) = (v + \frac{1}{2})\tilde{\nu} + BJ(J+1)$

$\Delta S_J^{\text{O}} = \tilde{\nu} - 2B(2J-1) \quad [\Delta v = 1,\ \Delta J = -2]$

$\Delta S_J^{\text{S}} = \tilde{\nu} + 2B(2J+3) \quad [\Delta v = 1,\ \Delta J = +2]$

The transition of maximum intensity corresponds, approximately, to the transition with the most probable value of J, which was calculated in Problem 16.13:

$$J_{\max} = \left(\frac{kT}{2hcB}\right)^{1/2} - \frac{1}{2}$$

The peak-to-peak separation is then

$$\Delta S = \Delta S_{J_{\max}}^{\text{S}} - \Delta S_{J_{\max}}^{\text{O}} = 2B(2J_{\max}+3) - \{-2B(2J_{\max}-1)\}$$
$$= 8B(J_{\max} + \tfrac{1}{2})$$
$$= 8B\left(\frac{kT}{2hcB}\right)^{1/2} = \underline{\left(\frac{32BkT}{hc}\right)^{1/2}}$$

To analyze the data we rearrange the relation to

$$B = \frac{hc(\Delta S)^2}{32kT}$$

and convert to a bond length using

$$R = \left(\frac{\hbar}{4\pi\mu c B}\right)^{1/2} = \frac{2}{\pi c\,\Delta S}\left(\frac{kT}{\mu}\right)^{1/2}$$

Jı∧⟩We can now draw up the following table:

	$HgCl_2$	$HgBr_2$	HgI_2
T/K	555	565	565
μ/u	30.13	57.14	77.73
$\Delta S/\text{cm}^{-1}$	23.8	15.2	11.4
R/pm	349	401	458

Hence, the three bond lengths are approximately 350, 400, and 460 pm,

17. Electronic transitions

Exercises

17.1 $\lg \frac{I'}{I} = -\varepsilon[\mathrm{J}]l$ [1c]

$$= -855\ \mathrm{M}^{-1}\,\mathrm{cm}^{-1} \times 3.25 \times 10^{-3}\ \mathrm{M} \times 0.25\ \mathrm{cm} = -0.69\overline{5}$$

Hence $I'/I = 0.20$, and the reduction in intensity is <u>80 per cent</u>.

17.2 $\varepsilon = -\frac{1}{[\mathrm{J}]l} \lg \frac{I'}{I}$ [1c]

$$= \frac{-1}{6.67 \times 10^{-4}\ \mathrm{M} \times 0.35\ \mathrm{cm}} \lg 0.655 = 78\overline{7}\ \mathrm{M}^{-1}\,\mathrm{cm}^{-1}$$

$$= 78\overline{7}\ \mathrm{dm}^3\,\mathrm{mol}^{-1}\,\mathrm{cm}^{-1} = 78\overline{7} \times 10^3\ \mathrm{cm}^3\,\mathrm{mol}^{-1}\,\mathrm{cm}^{-1}\ [1\ \mathrm{dm} = 10\ \mathrm{cm}]$$

$$= \underline{7.9 \times 10^5\ \mathrm{cm}^2\,\mathrm{mol}^{-1}}$$

17.3 $[\mathrm{J}] = -\frac{1}{\varepsilon l} \lg \frac{I'}{I}$ [1c]

$$= \frac{-1}{286\ \mathrm{M}^{-1}\,\mathrm{cm}^{-1} \times 0.65\ \mathrm{cm}} \lg(1 - 0.465) = \underline{1.5\ \mathrm{mM}}$$

17.4 $\mathcal{A} = \int \varepsilon\, \mathrm{d}\nu$ [2]

The absorption begins at $\nu = \frac{c}{\lambda} = 1.30 \times 10^{15}$ Hz (at 230 nm) and extends to 1.03×10^{15} Hz. The integral is therefore approximately

$$\mathcal{A} = \tfrac{1}{2} \times 1.21 \times 10^4\ \mathrm{M}^{-1}\,\mathrm{cm}^{-1} \times (1.30 - 1.03) \times 10^{15}\ \mathrm{s}^{-1}$$

$$= 1.63 \times 10^{18}\ \mathrm{M}^{-1}\,\mathrm{cm}^{-1}\,\mathrm{s}^{-1} \quad [\text{Area of triangle} = \tfrac{1}{2} \times \text{base} \times \text{height}]$$

Then the oscillator strength is

$$f = 1.44 \times 10^{-19} \times \mathcal{A}/(\mathrm{cm}^2\,\mathrm{mol}^{-1}\,\mathrm{s}^{-1})$$

We write

$$\mathcal{A}=1.63\times10^{18}\ \mathrm{dm^3\ mol^{-1}\ cm^{-1}\ s^{-1}}$$
$$=1.63\times10^{18}\times10^{3}\ \mathrm{cm^3}\times10^{-3}\ \mathrm{mmol^{-1}\ cm^{-1}\ s^{-1}}$$
$$=1.63\times10^{18}\ \mathrm{cm^2\ mmol^{-1}\ s^{-1}}$$

and hence obtain

$$f=1.44\times10^{-19}\times1.63\times10^{18}=\underline{0.235}$$

17.5 $f=\dfrac{8\pi^2 m_e\nu}{3he^2}|\mu_{fi}|^2\quad[3b]=\dfrac{\nu|\mu_{fi}|^2}{7.095\times10^{-43}\ \mathrm{m^2\ s^{-1}\ C^2}}$ [Example 17.3]

For $\tilde{\nu}=35\,000\ \mathrm{cm^{-1}}$, $\nu=c\tilde{\nu}=1.05\times10^{15}$ Hz, and

$$f=\frac{1.05\times10^{15}\ \mathrm{Hz}\times(2.65\times10^{-30}\ \mathrm{C\ m})^2}{7.095\times10^{-43}\ \mathrm{Hz\ (C\ m)^2}}=\underline{0.0104}$$

17.6 A strong transition has $f\approx1$, a weak transition has $f\approx10^{-3}$, and a forbidden transition has f much smaller than 10^{-3}. Hence (a) weak, (b) strong, (c) forbidden, (d) forbidden, (e) strong.

17.7 Conjugation of double bonds in the diene causes the absorption characteristic of the bond [Table 17.2] to shift to longer wavelengths [electron in a box behavior]. Hence the absorption at 243 nm is due to the diene and that at 192 nm to the butene.

17.8 The weak absorption at 30 000 cm^{-1} is typical of a carbonyl group [Table 17.2]. The strong C=C absorption, which is typically at about 180 nm, has been shifted to longer wavelength (213 nm) by the conjugation of the double bond and the CO group.

17.9 The internuclear distance in H_2^+ is greater than that in H_2. The change in bond length and the corresponding shift in the molecular potential energy curves reduces the Franck–Condon factor for transitions between the two ground vibrational states. It creates a better overlap between $v=2$ of H_2^+ and $v=0$ of H_2, and so increases the Franck–Condon factor of that transition.

17.10 $\varepsilon=-\dfrac{1}{[\mathrm{J}]l}\lg\dfrac{I'}{I}$ with $l=0.20$ cm

We use this formula to draw up the following table:

$[Br_2]/M$	0.0010	0.0050	0.0100	0.0500	
I'/I	0.814	0.356	0.127	3.0×10^{-5}	
$\varepsilon/(M^{-1}\,cm^{-1})$	447	449	448	452	mean: $44\bar{9}$

Hence, the molar absorption coefficient is $\varepsilon = \underline{450\ M^{-1}\ cm^{-1}}$.

17.11 $\varepsilon = -\dfrac{1}{[J]l}\lg\dfrac{I'}{I}$ [1c]

$$= \frac{-1}{0.010\ M\times 0.20\ cm}\lg 0.48 = \underline{159\ M^{-1}\ cm^{-1}}$$

$$\frac{I'}{I} = 10^{-[J]\varepsilon l} = 10^{-0.010\,M\times 159\,M^{-1}\,cm^{-1}\times 0.40}$$

$$= 10^{-0.63\bar{6}} = 0.23\text{, or } \underline{23\text{ per cent}}$$

17.12 $l = \dfrac{-1}{\varepsilon[J]}\lg\dfrac{I'}{I}$

For water, $[H_2O] \approx \dfrac{1.00\ kg}{18.02\ g\ mol^{-1}}\Big/ L = 55.5\ M$

and $\varepsilon[J] = 55.5\ M\times 6.2\times10^{-5}\ M^{-1}\ cm^{-1} = 3.4\times10^{-3}\ cm^{-1}$

$= 0.34\ m^{-1}$, so $1/\varepsilon[J] = 2.9\ m$

Hence, $l/m = -2.9\times\lg\dfrac{I'}{I}$

(a) $I'/I = 0.5$, $l = -2.9\ m\times\lg 0.5 = \underline{0.9\ m}$

(b) $I'/I = 0.1$, $l = -2.9\ m\times\lg 0.1 = \underline{3\ m}$

17.13 $\mathcal{A} = \displaystyle\int \varepsilon\, d\nu$ [2]; refer to Fig. 17.1

From the illustration,

$$\mathcal{A} = \tfrac{1}{2}\times\varepsilon_{max}\times 2\Delta\nu_{1/2} \quad [\text{area} = \tfrac{1}{2}\times\text{height}\times\text{base}]$$

$$= \varepsilon_{max}\Delta\nu_{1/2} = c\varepsilon_{max}\Delta\tilde{\nu}_{1/2}$$

$$\approx 2.998\times10^{10}\ cm\ s^{-1}\times 5000\ cm^{-1}\times\varepsilon_{max} = 1.5\times10^{14}\ s^{-1}\times\varepsilon_{max}$$

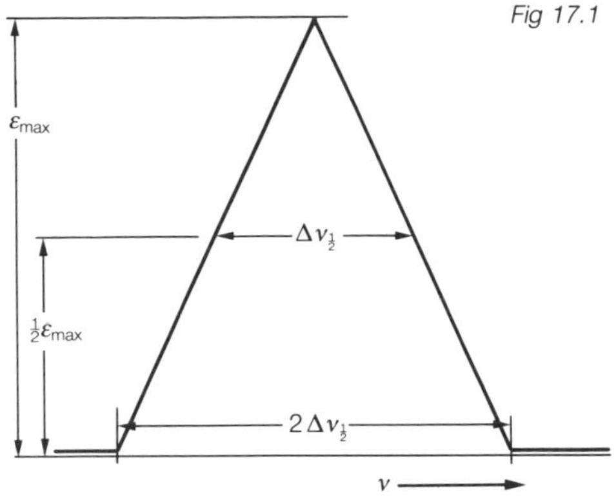

Fig 17.1

(a) $\mathcal{A} \approx 1.5 \times 10^{14}\ \mathrm{s}^{-1} \times 1 \times 10^{4}\ \mathrm{M}^{-1}\ \mathrm{cm}^{-1} = \underline{1.5 \times 10^{18}\ \mathrm{M}^{-1}\ \mathrm{cm}^{-1}\ \mathrm{s}^{-1}}$

which is equivalent [Exercise 17.4] to $1.\overline{5} \times 10^{18}\ \mathrm{cm}^2\ \mathrm{mmol}^{-1}\ \mathrm{s}^{-1}$. Hence

$f = 1.44 \times 10^{-19} \times 1.\overline{5} \times 10^{18} = \underline{0.2}$

(b) $\mathcal{A} \approx 1.5 \times 10^{14}\ \mathrm{s}^{-1} \times 5 \times 10^{2}\ \mathrm{M}^{-1}\ \mathrm{cm}^{-1} = \underline{7.5 \times 10^{16}\ \mathrm{M}^{-1}\ \mathrm{cm}^{-1}\ \mathrm{s}^{-1}}$

which is equivalent to $7.\overline{5} \times 10^{16}\ \mathrm{cm}^2\ \mathrm{mmol}^{-1}\ \mathrm{s}^{-1}$. Therefore,

$f = 1.44 \times 10^{-19} \times 7.\overline{5} \times 10^{16} = \underline{0.01}$

Problems

17.1 $\left[\mathrm{J}\right] = \dfrac{-1}{\varepsilon l} \lg \dfrac{I'}{I}$ [1c]

Suppose I' lies in the range $I'' \pm \Delta I$, then

$$[\mathrm{J}]_{\mathrm{max}} = -\frac{1}{\varepsilon l} \lg \frac{I'' - \Delta I}{I}$$

$$[\mathrm{J}]_{\mathrm{min}} = -\frac{1}{\varepsilon l} \lg \frac{I'' + \Delta I}{I}$$

$$\Delta[\mathrm{J}] = [\mathrm{J}]_{\mathrm{max}} - [\mathrm{J}]_{\mathrm{min}} = -\frac{1}{\varepsilon l} \lg \left(\frac{I'' - \Delta I}{I'' + \Delta I}\right)$$

$$= -\frac{1}{\varepsilon l} \lg \left(\frac{1 - \Delta I/I''}{1 + \Delta I/I''}\right) \approx -\frac{1}{\varepsilon l} \lg \left(1 - \frac{2\Delta I}{I''}\right)$$

since $\frac{1}{1+x} \approx 1-x$ if $x \ll 1$ and $\frac{1-x}{1+x} \approx (1-x)^2 \approx 1-2x$.

We then use

$$\lg(1-z) = \frac{1}{2.30}\ln(1-z) \approx \frac{-z}{2.30} \quad [z \ll 1]$$

to write

$$\lg\left(1-\frac{2\Delta I}{I''}\right) \approx \frac{-2\Delta I}{2.30 I''}$$

Hence,

$$\Delta[\mathrm{J}] \approx \frac{2}{2.30\varepsilon l} \times \frac{\Delta I}{I''}$$

$$\approx \frac{2}{2.30 \times 275\ \mathrm{M^{-1}\,cm^{-1}} \times 0.15\ \mathrm{cm}} \times 0.02 = \underline{4 \times 10^{-4}\ \mathrm{M}}$$

17.2 $\varepsilon = \varepsilon_{max}\,\mathrm{e}^{-\nu^2/2\Gamma}$ $[\nu = 0$ at band center, Γ a constant$]$ $\varepsilon = \frac{1}{2}\varepsilon_{max}$ when $\nu^2 = 2\Gamma \ln 2$. Therefore, the width at half height is

$$\Delta\nu_{1/2} = 2 \times (2\Gamma \ln 2)^{1/2}, \text{ implying that } \Gamma = \frac{\Delta\nu_{1/2}^2}{8 \ln 2}$$

Now we carry out the integration:

$$\mathcal{A} = \int \varepsilon\, \mathrm{d}\nu = \varepsilon_{max} \int_{-\infty}^{\infty} \mathrm{e}^{-\nu^2/2\Gamma}\, \mathrm{d}\nu$$

$$= \varepsilon_{max}(2\pi\Gamma)^{1/2} \quad \left[\int_{-\infty}^{\infty} \mathrm{e}^{-x^2}\,\mathrm{d}x = \pi^{1/2}\right]$$

$$= \varepsilon_{max}\left(\frac{2\pi\,\Delta\nu_{1/2}^2}{8 \ln 2}\right)^{1/2} = \left(\frac{\pi}{4 \ln 2}\right)^{1/2} \varepsilon_{max}\,\Delta\nu_{1/2}$$

$$= 1.0645\varepsilon_{max}\,\Delta\nu_{1/2}$$

In terms of wavenumbers, $\Delta\nu_{1/2} = c\,\Delta\tilde{\nu}_{1/2}$, so

$$\mathcal{A} = \underline{1.0645 c \varepsilon_{max}\,\Delta\tilde{\nu}_{1/2}}$$

From Fig. 17.41 of the text we estimate $\varepsilon_{max} \approx 9.5\ \mathrm{M^{-1}\,cm^{-1}}$ and $\Delta\tilde{\nu}_{1/2} \approx 4760\ \mathrm{cm^{-1}}$. Then

$$\mathcal{A} \approx 1.0645 \times 2.998 \times 10^{10}\ \mathrm{cm\,s^{-1}} \times 9.5\ \mathrm{M^{-1}\,cm^{-1}} \times 4760\ \mathrm{cm^{-1}}$$

$$\approx \underline{1.4 \times 10^{15}\ \mathrm{M^{-1}\,cm^{-1}\,s^{-1}}}$$

Then $f \approx 1.44 \times 10^{-19} \times 1.4 \times 10^{15} = \underline{2.0 \times 10^{-4}}$.

The area under the curve on the printed page is about 1288 mm^2; each mm^2 corresponds to about 190.5 cm$^{-1} \times 0.189$ M^{-1} cm^{-1}, and so $\int \varepsilon \, d\tilde{\nu} \approx 4.64 \times 10^4$ M^{-1} cm^{-2}. Then $\mathcal{A} = c \int \varepsilon \, d\tilde{\nu} = 1.4 \times 10^{15}$ M^{-1} cm^{-1} s^{-1}, corresponding to $f = 2.0 \times 10^{-4}$ as before. We can conclude that the transition is <u>forbidden</u>.

17.3 $\Delta\tilde{\nu}_{1/2} = \dfrac{1}{\lambda'} - \dfrac{1}{\lambda''}$ where λ' and λ'' are the wavelengths corresponding to $\frac{1}{2}\varepsilon_{max}$ on the short and long wavelength sides of the peak. From Fig. 17.42 of the text we can estimate the following values:

<u>280 nm peak</u>: $\lambda' \approx 260$ nm, $\lambda'' \approx 300$ nm

$$\Delta\tilde{\nu}_{1/2} \approx \left(\frac{1}{260} - \frac{1}{300}\right) \times 10^9 \text{ m}^{-1} = 5.13 \times 10^3 \text{ cm}^{-1}$$

Then, since $\varepsilon_{max} \approx 11$ M^{-1} cm^{-1}, from Problem 17.3

$$\begin{aligned}\mathcal{A} = 1.0645c\varepsilon_{max}\Delta\tilde{\nu}_{1/2} &= 1.0645 \times 2.998 \times 10^{10} \text{ cm s}^{-1} \\ &\quad \times 11 \text{ M}^{-1} \text{ cm}^{-1} \times 5.13 \times 10^3 \text{ cm}^{-1} \\ &\approx \underline{1.8 \times 10^{15} \text{ M}^{-1} \text{ cm}^{-1} \text{ s}^{-1}}\end{aligned}$$

and

$$f \sim 1.44 \times 10^{-19} \times 1.8 \times 10^{15} = \underline{2.6 \times 10^{-4}}$$

<u>430 nm peak</u>: $\lambda' \approx 390$ nm, $\lambda'' \approx 455$ nm

$$\Delta\tilde{\nu}_{1/2} \approx \left(\frac{1}{390} - \frac{1}{455}\right) \times 10^9 \text{ m}^{-1} = 3.66 \times 10^3 \text{ cm}^{-1}$$

Then, since $\varepsilon_{max} \approx 18$ M^{-1} cm^{-1}, from Problem 17.3

$$\begin{aligned}\mathcal{A} &= 1.0645 \times 2.998 \times 10^{10} \text{ cm s}^{-1} \times 18 \text{ M}^{-1} \text{ cm}^{-1} \times 3.66 \times 10^3 \text{ cm}^{-1} \\ &= \underline{2.1 \times 10^{15} \text{ M}^{-1} \text{ cm}^{-1} \text{ s}^{-1}}\end{aligned}$$

$$f = 1.44 \times 10^{-19} \times 2.1 \times 10^{15} = \underline{3.0 \times 10^{-4}}$$

For the second approach, we transfer the spectra to a wavenumber scale by drawing up the following table:

λ/nm	250	260	270	280	290	300	310	320	330	340
$\tilde{\nu}/(1000 \text{ cm}^{-1})$	40.0	38.5	37.0	35.7	34.5	33.3	32.3	31.3	30.3	29.4
$\varepsilon/(\text{M}^{-1} \text{ cm}^{-1})$	3	4	6	10	11	8	5	3	1	1

λ/nm	350	360	370	380	390	400	410	420	430	440
$\tilde{\nu}/(1000\ \text{cm}^{-1})$	28.6	27.8	27.0	26.3	25.6	25.0	24.4	23.8	23.3	22.7
$\varepsilon/(\text{M}^{-1}\ \text{cm}^{-1})$	1	3	5	8	11	14	17	17	16	16

λ/nm	450	460	470
$\tilde{\nu}/(1000\ \text{cm}^{-1})$	22.2	21.7	21.3
$\varepsilon/(\text{M}^{-1}\ \text{cm}^{-1})$	14	1	0

These points are plotted in Fig. 17.2. The area under the '280 nm' peak is

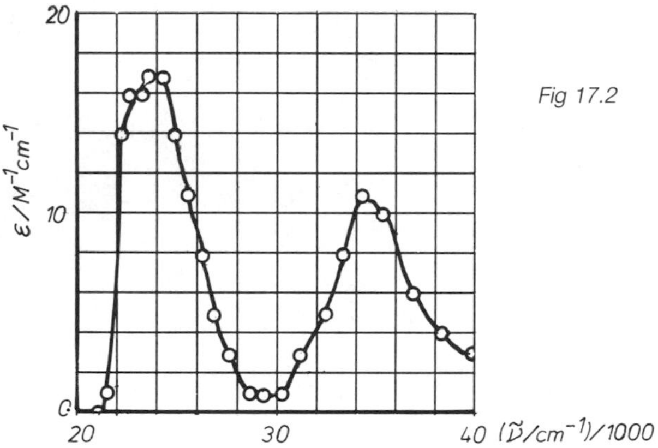

Fig 17.2

$5.72\times10^4\ \text{M}^{-1}\ \text{cm}^{-2}$ and that under the '430 nm' peak is $6.80\times10^4\ \text{M}^{-1}\ \text{cm}^{-2}$. It follows that

$$\mathcal{A}(280\ \text{nm})\approx 2.998\times10^{10}\ \text{cm s}^{-1}\times5.72\times10^4\ \text{M}^{-1}\ \text{cm}^{-2}$$

$$\approx \underline{1.7\times10^{15}\ \text{M}^{-1}\ \text{cm}^{-1}\ \text{s}^{-1}}$$

$$\mathcal{A}(430\ \text{nm})\approx 2.998\times10^{10}\ \text{cm s}^{-1}\times6.80\times10^4\ \text{M}^{-1}\ \text{cm}^{-2}$$

$$\approx \underline{2.0\times10^{15}\ \text{M}^{-1}\ \text{cm}^{-1}\ \text{s}^{-1}}$$

These two values correspond to

$f(280\text{ nm}) = \underline{2.5\times 10^{-4}}$, $f(430\text{ nm}) = \underline{2.9\times 10^{-4}}$

For the final part, we write $\nu = c/\lambda$, so $d\nu = -c\, d\lambda/\lambda^2$; then

$$\mathcal{A} = \int_0^\infty \varepsilon\, d\nu = c\int_0^\infty \frac{\varepsilon\, d\lambda}{\lambda^2} = c\varepsilon_{max}\int_0^\infty \frac{e^{-(\lambda-\lambda_0)^2/2\gamma}}{\lambda^2}\, d\lambda$$

where $e^{-(\lambda-\lambda_0)^2/2\gamma}$ is a gaussian centered on λ_0 with width determined by γ:

$$\gamma = \frac{\Delta\lambda_{1/2}^2}{8\ln 2}\quad \text{[as in Problem 17.2]}$$

The integral may be evaluated numerically, or approximated by setting $\lambda^2 \approx \lambda_0^2$ in the denominator and extending the lower limit to $-\infty$ (neither of which introduces much error if the lines are narrow). Then

$$\mathcal{A} \approx \frac{c\varepsilon_{max}}{\lambda_0^2}\int_{-\infty}^{\infty} e^{-(\lambda-\lambda_0)^2/2\gamma}\, d\lambda = \frac{c\varepsilon_{max}(2\pi\gamma)^{1/2}}{\lambda_0^2}$$

Therefore,

$$\mathcal{A} \approx \left(\frac{2\pi\,\Delta\lambda_{1/2}^2}{8\ln 2}\right)^{1/2}\frac{c\varepsilon_{max}}{\lambda_0^2} = \left(\frac{\pi}{4\ln 2}\right)^{1/2}\frac{c\varepsilon_{max}\,\Delta\lambda_{1/2}}{\lambda_0^2}$$

$$\approx 1.0645\,\frac{c\varepsilon_{max}\,\Delta\lambda_{1/2}}{\lambda_0^2}$$

For the 280 nm peak, $\Delta\lambda_{1/2} \approx 40$ nm

$$\mathcal{A} \approx \frac{1.0645\times 2.998\times 10^8\text{ m s}^{-1}\times 11\text{ M}^{-1}\text{ cm}^{-1}\times 60\times 10^{-9}\text{ m}}{(280\times 10^{-9}\text{ m})^2}$$

$$\approx \underline{1.8\times 10^{15}\text{ M}^{-1}\text{ cm}^{-1}\text{ s}^{-1}}$$

$$f \approx 1.44\times 10^{-19}\times 1.8\times 10^{15} = \underline{2.7\times 10^{-4}}$$

For the 430 nm peak, $\Delta\lambda_{1/2} \approx 65$ nm

$$\mathcal{A} \approx \frac{1.0645\times 2.998\times 10^8\text{ m s}^{-1}\times 18\text{ M}^{-1}\text{ cm}^{-1}\times 65\times 10^{-9}\text{ m}}{(430\times 10^{-9}\text{ m})^2}$$

$$\approx \underline{2.0\times 10^{15}\text{ M}^{-1}\text{ cm}^{-1}\text{ s}^{-1}}$$

$$f \approx 1.44\times 10^{-19}\times 2.0\times 10^{15} = \underline{2.9\times 10^{-4}}$$

17.4 One procedure is to use the formula developed in the last part of Problem 17.3:

$$\mathcal{A} = 1.0645\frac{c\varepsilon_{\max}\Delta\lambda_{1/2}}{\lambda_0^2}$$

From Fig. 17.43 of the text, we find $\Delta\lambda_{1/2} = 38$ nm with $\lambda_0 = 290$ nm and $\varepsilon_{\max} \approx 235\ \text{M}^{-1}\,\text{cm}^{-1}$; hence

$$\mathcal{A} = \frac{1.0645 \times 2.998 \times 10^8\ \text{m s}^{-1} \times 235\ \text{M}^{-1}\,\text{cm}^{-1} \times 38 \times 10^{-9}\ \text{m}}{(290 \times 10^{-9}\ \text{m})^2}$$

$$= 3.4 \times 10^{16}\ \text{M}^{-1}\,\text{cm}^{-1}\,\text{s}^{-1}$$

$$f = 1.44 \times 10^{-19} \times 3.4 \times 10^{16} = \underline{4.9 \times 10^{-3}}$$

The transition appears to be weakly forbidden. Since the dipole moment components transform as $A_1(z)$, $B_1(x)$, and $B_2(y)$, excitations from A_1 to A_1, B_1, and B_2 terms are allowed.

17.5 The absorbance A is defined as $\varepsilon[\text{J}]l$ [Section 17.1]. When only HIn is present at a concentration C

$A = \varepsilon Cl$ where ε is the molar absorption coefficient of HIn.

When all the HIn is present as In^-

$A'' = \varepsilon'' Cl$ where ε'' is the molar absorption coefficient if In^-.

The absorbance of the mixture is

$$A' = \varepsilon(1-\alpha)Cl + \varepsilon''\alpha Cl$$

where α is the degree of ionization of HIn. Therefore,

$$A' = \varepsilon Cl + (\varepsilon'' - \varepsilon)\alpha Cl$$

$$= A + \alpha(A'' - A)$$

which solves to

$$\alpha = \underline{\frac{A' - A}{A'' - A}}$$

Since $K_a = \frac{[\text{In}^-][\text{H}^+]}{[\text{InH}]} = \frac{\alpha[\text{H}^+]}{1-\alpha}$ [since $[\text{H}^+]$ is determined by any other acid present]

we know that

$$[\text{H}^+] = \left(\frac{1-\alpha}{\alpha}\right)K_a$$

and so

$$\underline{\mathrm{pH} = \mathrm{p}K_a - \lg \frac{1-\alpha}{\alpha}} \text{ with } \alpha = \frac{A' - A}{A'' - A}$$

When $A'' = 0$,

$$\alpha = 1 - \frac{A'}{A}, \frac{1-\alpha}{\alpha} = \frac{A'}{A - A'}$$

Hence

$$\frac{A'}{A} = (1 + 10^{\mathrm{pH} - \mathrm{p}K_a})^{-1}$$

and we can draw up the following table:

pH	1	2	3	3.5	4	4.5	5	6	7
A'/A	1.00	0.90	0.91	0.76	0.50	0.24	0.09	0.01	0.001

These points are plotted in Fig. 17.3.

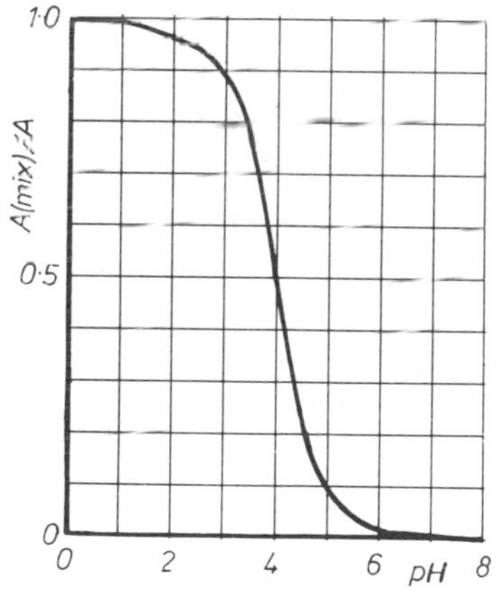

Fig 17.3

From the data, $\varepsilon = 8.33 \times 10^3\ \mathrm{M}^{-1}\ \mathrm{cm}^{-1}$, $\varepsilon'' = 18.33 \times 10^3\ \mathrm{M}^{-1}\ \mathrm{cm}^{-1}$, and $A = (1-\alpha)Cl\varepsilon$, $A'' = \alpha Cl\varepsilon''$. The ratios A/Cl and A''/Cl are the effective molar absorption coefficients of HIn and In′, and we write them $\bar{\varepsilon}$ *and* $\bar{\varepsilon}''$. We draw up the following table:

pH	4	5	6	7	8	9	10
$\bar{\varepsilon}/\varepsilon = 1-\alpha$	1	1	0.92	0.50	0.05		
α	0	0	0.08	0.50	0.95		
$\bar{\varepsilon}''/\varepsilon'' = \alpha$			0.09	0.50	0.95	1.00	1.00
Average α	0	0	0.08	0.50	0.95	1.00	1.00

Then we form

$$\mathrm{pH} = \mathrm{p}K_\mathrm{a} - \lg\frac{\alpha}{1-\alpha}$$

and draw up the following table:

pH	6.0	7.0	8.0	
$\mathrm{p}K_\mathrm{a}$	7.1	7.0	6.7	mean: 6.9

17.6 Use the technique described in Example 16.9 [the Birge–Sponer extrapolation method]. Plot the differences $\Delta\tilde{\nu}_v$ against v, Fig. 17.4. The

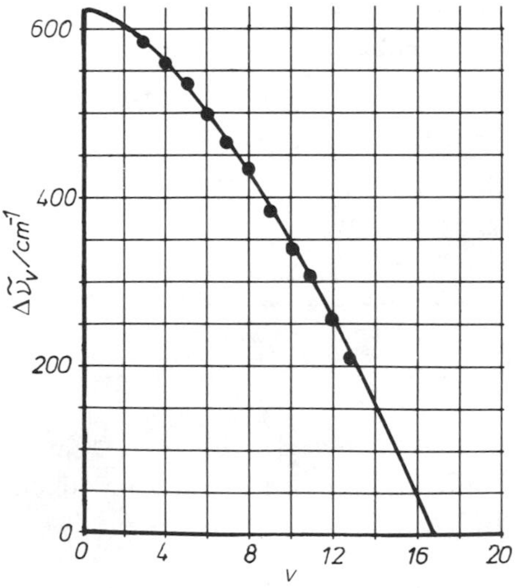

Fig 17.4

separation between neighboring lines vanishes at $v = 17$. Each square corresponds to 100 cm^{-1}. Therefore, since the area under the line is 68.0 squares, the dissociation energy is 6800 cm^{-1}. The $^3\Sigma_u^- \leftarrow X$ excitation energy (where X denotes the ground state) to $v = 0$ is 50 062.6 cm^{-1}, which corresponds to 6.21 eV. The $^3\Sigma_u^-$ dissociation energy, for

$$O_2(^3\Sigma_u^-) \rightarrow O + O^*$$

is 6800 cm^{-1}, or 0.85 eV. Therefore, the energy of

$$O_2(X) \rightarrow O + O^*$$

is $6.21 + 0.85$ eV $= 7.06$ eV. Since $O^* \rightarrow O$ is -190 kJ mol^{-1}, corresponding to -1.97 eV, the energy of

$$O_2(X) \rightarrow 2O$$

is $7.06\ \text{eV} - 1.97\ \text{eV} = 5.09\ \text{eV}$.

17.7 We draw up the following table:

	Line E_K/eV	Binding energy/eV	Assignment
N_2	5.6	15.6	$2p\sigma_g$
	4.5	16.7	$2p\pi_u$
	2.4	18.8	$2s\sigma_u^*$
CO	7.2	14.0	$2p\sigma$
	4.9	16.3	$2p\pi$
	1.7	19.5	$2s\sigma^*$

The spacing of the 4.5 eV lines in N_2 is 0.24 eV, or about 1940 cm^{-1}. The spacing of the 4.9 eV lines in CO is 0.23 eV, or about 1860 cm^{-1}. These are estimates from the illustrations of the separation of the vibrational levels of the N_2^+ and CO^+ ions in their excited states.

17.8 The electron configuration of NO is $(2s\sigma^*)^2(2p\pi)^4(2p\sigma)^2(2p\pi^*)^1$. The data refer to the kinetic energies of the ejected electrons, and so the ionization energies are 16.52 eV, 15.65 eV, and 9.21 eV. The 16.52 eV line refers to ionization of a $2p\sigma$ electron, and the 15.65 eV line (with its long vibrational progression) to ionization of a $2p\pi$ electron. The line at 9.21 eV refers to the ionization of the least strongly attached electron, that is $2p\pi^*$.

17.9 (a) Ethene (ethylene) belongs to D_{2h}. In this group the x, y, and z components of the dipole moment transform as B_{3u}, B_{2u}, and B_{1u} respectively.

[See a more extensive set of character tables than in the text.] The π orbital is B_{1u} (like z, the axis perpendicular to the plane) and π^* is B_{3g}. Since $B_{3g} \times B_{1u} = B_{2u}$ and $B_{2u} \times B_{2u} = A_{1g}$, the transition is allowed (and is y-polarized).

(b) Regard the CO group with its attached groups as locally C_{2v}. The dipole moment has components that transform as $A_1(z)$, $B_1(x)$, and $B_2(y)$, with the z-axis along the C=O direction and x perpendicular to the R_2CO plane. The n orbital is p_y (in the R_2CO plane), and hence transforms as B_2. The π^* orbital is p_x (perpendicular to the R_2CO plane), and hence transforms as B_1. Since $\Gamma_f \times \Gamma_i = B_1 \times B_2 = A_2$, but no component of the dipole moment transforms as A_2, the transition is forbidden.

17.10 (a) Vibrational energy spacings of the lower state is determined by the spacing of the peaks of A. From the spectrum, $\tilde{\nu} \approx 1800\ \text{cm}^{-1}$ [the scale is about $1\ \text{cm} \triangleq 11745\ \text{cm}^{-1}$]. (b) Nothing can be said about the spacing of the upper state levels (without a detailed analysis of the intensities of the lines). For the second part of the question, we note that after some vibrational decay the benzophenone (which does absorb near 360 nm) can transfer its energy to naphthalene. The latter then emits the energy radiatively.

17.11 The fluorescence spectrum gives the vibrational splitting of the lower state. The wavelengths stated correspond to the wavenumbers 22 730, 24 390, 25 640, 27 030 cm^{-1}, indicating spacings of 1660, 1250, and 1390 cm^{-1}. The absorption spectrum spacing gives the separation of the vibrational levels of the upper state. The wavenumbers of the absorption peaks are 27 800, 29 000, 30 300, and 32 800 cm^{-1}. The vibrational spacings are therefore 1200, 1300, and 2500 cm^{-1}.

17.12 $f = \dfrac{8\pi^2 m_e \nu}{3he^2}|\mu^2|$ [3b]

$$\mu_x = -e\int_0^L \psi_{n'}(x)x\psi_n(x)\,\mathrm{d}x, \quad \psi_n = \left(\frac{2}{L}\right)^{1/2}\sin\left(\frac{n\pi x}{L}\right)$$

$$= -\frac{2e}{L}\int_0^L x\sin\left(\frac{n'\pi x}{L}\right)\sin\left(\frac{n\pi x}{L}\right)\mathrm{d}x$$

$$= \begin{cases} 0 & \text{if } n' = n+2 \\ -\left(\dfrac{8eL}{\pi^2}\right)\dfrac{n(n+1)}{(2n+1)^2} & \text{if } n' = n+1 \end{cases}$$

The integral is standard, but may also be evaluated using $2\sin A \sin B = \cos(A-B) - \cos(A+B)$.

$$h\nu = E_{n+1} - E_n = (2n+1)\frac{h^2}{8m_eL^2}$$

Therefore, for the transition $n+1 \leftarrow n$,

$$f = \left(\frac{8\pi^2}{3}\right)\left(\frac{m_e}{he^2}\right)\left(\frac{h}{8m_eL^2}\right)(2n+1)\left(\frac{8eL}{\pi^2}\right)^2\frac{n^2(n+1)^2}{(2n+1)^4}$$

$$= \left(\frac{64}{3\pi^2}\right)\left\{\frac{n^2(n+1)^2}{(2n+1)^3}\right\}$$

For the transition $n+2 \leftarrow n$, $f = \underline{0}$.

For $R = 140$ pm,

$$\nu = \frac{(2n+1)h}{8m_eL^2} \text{ with } L \approx 22R$$

The highest filled orbital (the HOMO) has $n = 11$ [there are 22 electrons to accommodate], so $2n+1 = 23$. Therefore,

$$\nu = \frac{23h}{8m_eL^2} = \frac{23 \times 6.626 \times 10^{-34}\ \text{J s}}{8 \times 9.109 \times 10^{-31}\ \text{kg} \times (22 \times 140 \times 10^{-12}\ \text{m})^2}$$

$$= 2.2 \times 10^{14}\ \text{Hz}$$

which corresponds to $\tilde{\nu} = \nu/c = 7400\ \text{cm}^{-1}$. This wavenumber suggests that carotene absorbs in the infrared, which it does, but not for this reason (infrared absorption is by vibrational excitation). In order to obtain a carrot color (orange), we need absorption in the blue. The oscillator strength of the $12 \leftarrow 11$ transition is

$$f = \left(\frac{64}{3\pi^2}\right)\left\{\frac{121 \times 144}{23^3}\right\} = 3.1$$

and hence

$$\mathcal{A} = \frac{f}{1.44 \times 10^{-19}}\ \text{M}^{-1}\ \text{cm}^{-1}\ \text{s}^{-1} = 2.2 \times 10^{19}\ \text{M}^{-1}\ \text{cm}^{-1}\ \text{s}^{-1}$$

Therefore, if we take $\Delta\tilde{\nu} \approx 5000\ \text{cm}^{-1}$, corresponding to $\Delta\nu = 1.5 \times 10^{14}$ Hz,

$$\varepsilon \approx \frac{\mathcal{A}}{\Delta\nu} \approx \frac{\mathcal{A}}{1.5 \times 10^{14}\ \text{s}^{-1}} \approx 1.4 \times 10^5\ \text{M}^{-1}\ \text{cm}^{-1}$$

Then for $T = 50$ per cent

$$l=-\frac{1}{[\mathrm{J}]\varepsilon}\lg T=\frac{\lg 2}{1.0\times10^{-3}\,\mathrm{M}\times1.4\times10^{5}\,\mathrm{M}^{-1}\,\mathrm{cm}^{-1}}=\underline{2.2\times10^{-3}\,\mathrm{cm}}$$

17.13 $f\propto\dfrac{n^2(n+1)^2}{(2n+1)^3}$ [Problem 17.12]

The value of n depends on the number of bonds: each π bond supplies two π electrons and so n increases by 1. For large n,

$$f\propto\frac{n^4}{8n^3}\to\frac{n}{8}\text{ and }f\propto n$$

Therefore, for the longest wavelength transitions f increases as the chain length is increased. The energy of the transition is proportional to $(2n+1)/L^2$; but as $n\propto L$, this energy is proportional to $1/L$. Therefore, the transition moves toward the red as L is increased and the apparent color of the dye becomes bluer.

17.14 $\mu=-e\displaystyle\int\psi_{v'}x\psi_v\,\mathrm{d}x$

From Problem 12.13,

$$\mu_{10}=-e\int\psi_1x\psi_0\,\mathrm{d}x=-e\left\{\frac{\hbar}{2(m_ek)^{1/2}}\right\}^{1/2}$$

Hence,

$$f=\frac{8\pi^2m_e\nu}{3he^2}\times\frac{e^2\hbar}{2(m_ek)^{1/2}}=\underline{\frac{1}{3}}\quad\left[2\pi\nu=\left(\frac{k}{m_e}\right)^{1/2}\right]$$

17.15 $\mu=-eSR$ [given]

$$S=\left\{1+\frac{R}{a_0}+\frac{1}{3}\left(\frac{R}{a_0}\right)^2\right\}\mathrm{e}^{-R/a_0}\text{ [eqn 10, Section 14.4]}$$

$$f=\frac{8\pi^2m_e\nu}{3he^2}\mu^2=\frac{8\pi^2m_e\nu}{3h}R^2S^2$$

$$=\frac{8\pi^2m_e\nu a_0^2}{3h}\left(\frac{RS}{a_0}\right)^2=\left(\frac{RS}{a_0}\right)^2f_0$$

We then draw up the following table:

R/a_0	0	1	2	3	4	5	6	7	8
f/f_0	0	0.737	1.376	1.093	0.573	0.233	0.08	0.02	0.01

These points are plotted in Fig. 17.5.

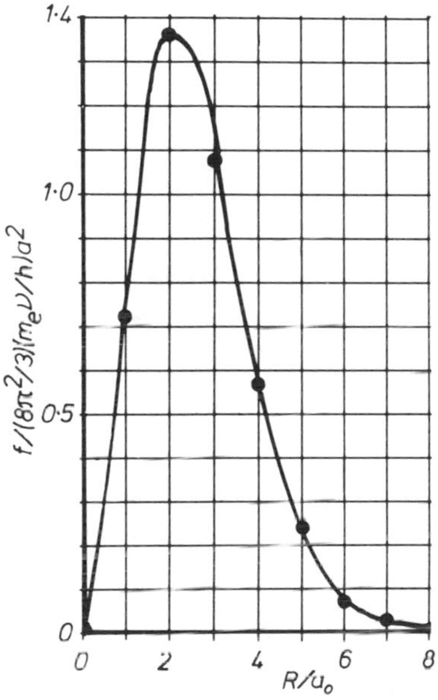

Fig 17.5

The maximum in f occurs at the maximum of RS:

$$\frac{\mathrm{d}}{\mathrm{d}R}(RS) = S + R\frac{\mathrm{d}S}{\mathrm{d}R}$$

$$= \left\{1 + \frac{R}{a_0} - \frac{1}{3}\left(\frac{R}{a_0}\right)^3\right\} \mathrm{e}^{-R/a_0} = 0 \text{ at } R = R^*$$

That is,

$$1 + \frac{R^*}{a_0} - \frac{1}{3}\left(\frac{R}{a_0}\right)^3 = 0$$

This equation may be solved either numerically or analytically [see Abramowitz and Stegun, *Handbook of mathematical functions*, Section 3.8.2], and $\underline{R^* = 2.103\,80a_0}$.

As $R \to 0$, the transition becomes $s \to s$, which is forbidden. As $R \to \infty$, the electron is confirmed to a single atom because its wavefunction does not extend to the other.

17.16 From the work in Problem 17.5, we know that

$$A' = A + \alpha(A'' - A)$$

in the notation defined there. There exists some wavelength at which $A'' = A$. At that wavelength A' is independent of α. This is the isosbestic point.

17.17 Use the Clebsch–Gordan series [Chapter 13] to compound the two resultant angular momenta, and impose the conservation of angular momentum on the composite system.

(a) O_2 has $S = 1$ [it is a spin triplet]. The configuration of an O atom is [He]$2s^2 2p^4$, which is equivalent to a Ne atom with two electron-like 'holes'. The atom may therefore exist is a spin singlet or as a spin triplet. Since $S_1 = 1$ and $S_2 = 0$, or $S_1 = 1$ and $S_2 = 1$ may each combine to give a resultant with $S = 1$, both may be the products of the reaction. Hence multiplicities $\underline{3+1}$ and $\underline{3+3}$ may be expected.

(b) N_2, $S = 0$. The configuration of an N atom is [He] $2s^2 2p^3$. The atoms may have $S = \frac{3}{2}$ or $\frac{1}{2}$. Then we note that $S_1 = \frac{3}{2}$ and $S_1 = \frac{3}{2}$ can combine to give $S = 0$; $S_1 = \frac{1}{2}$ and $S_2 = \frac{1}{2}$ can also combine to give $S = 0$ (but $S_1 = \frac{3}{2}$ and $S_2 = \frac{1}{2}$ cannot). Hence, the multiplicities $\underline{4+4}$ and $\underline{2+2}$ may be expected.

18. Magnetic resonance

Exercises

18..1 $E=-g_I\mu_N m_I B$ with $m_I=\frac{3}{2}, \frac{1}{2}, -\frac{1}{2}, -\frac{3}{2}$ $[1, \gamma\hbar=g_I\mu_N]$

$$=-0.4289\times 5.051\times 10^{-27}\,\mathrm{J\,T^{-1}}\times 7.500\,\mathrm{T}\times m_I$$

$$=\underline{-1.625\times 10^{-26}\,\mathrm{J}\times m_I}$$

18.2 $|\Delta E|=|-g_I\mu_N B(-1-1)|$ $[I=1, m_I(\mathrm{max})=+1, m_I(\mathrm{min})=-1]$

$$=2g_I\mu_N B$$

$$=2\times 0.4036\times 5.051\times 10^{-27}\,\mathrm{J\,T^{-1}}\times 15.00\,\mathrm{T}$$

$$=\underline{6.116\times 10^{-26}\,\mathrm{J}}$$

18.3 $B=\dfrac{h\nu}{g_I\mu_N}$ $[3, \gamma\hbar=\gamma_I\mu_N]$

$$=\frac{6.626\times 10^{-34}\,\mathrm{J\,Hz^{-1}}\times 150.0\times 10^{6}\,\mathrm{Hz}}{5.586\times 5.051\times 10^{-27}\,\mathrm{J\,T^{-1}}}=\underline{3.523\,\mathrm{T}}$$

18.4 $B=\dfrac{h\nu}{g_I\mu_N}=\dfrac{6.626\times 10^{-34}\,\mathrm{J\,Hz^{-1}}}{5.0508\times 10^{-27}\,\mathrm{J\,T^{-1}}}\times\dfrac{\nu}{g_I}$

$$=1.3119\times 10^{-7}\frac{(\nu/\mathrm{Hz})}{g_I}\,\mathrm{T}=0.13119\frac{(\nu/\mathrm{MHz})}{g_I}\,\mathrm{T}$$

We can draw up the following table:

B/T	^{1}H	^{2}H	^{13}C	^{14}N	^{19}F	^{31}P
g_I	5.5857	0.85745	1.4046	0.40356	5.2567	2.2634
(a) 60 MHz	1.4	9.2	5.6	19.5	1.5	3.5
(b) 300 MHz	7.05	45.9	28.0	97.5	7.49	17.4

18.5 $\dfrac{N_\alpha - N_\beta}{N_\alpha + N_\beta} = \dfrac{N_\alpha - N_\alpha\,\mathrm{e}^{-\Delta E/kT}}{N_\alpha + N_\alpha\,\mathrm{e}^{-\Delta E/kT}}$ [Boltzmann distribution]

$$= \frac{1-\mathrm{e}^{-\Delta E/kT}}{1+\mathrm{e}^{-\Delta E/kT}} \approx \frac{1-(1-\Delta E/kT)}{1+1}$$

$$\approx \frac{\Delta E}{2kT} = \frac{g_I\mu_N B}{2kT}$$

That is,

$$\frac{\Delta N}{N} \approx \frac{g_I\mu_N B}{2kT} = \frac{5.5857\times 5.0508\times 10^{-27}\ \mathrm{J\,T^{-1}}\times B}{2\times 1.38066\times 10^{-23}\ \mathrm{J\,K^{-1}}\times 298\ \mathrm{T}}$$

$$\approx 3.43\times 10^{-6} B/\mathrm{T}$$

(a) $B = 0.3\ \mathrm{T}$, $\delta N/N = \underline{1\times 10^{-6}}$

(b) $B = 1.5\ \mathrm{T}$, $\delta N/N = \underline{5.1\times 10^{-6}}$

(c) $B = 10\ \mathrm{T}$, $\delta N/N = \underline{3.4\times 10^{-5}}$

18.6 $B_{\mathrm{loc}} = (1-\sigma)B$ [Section 18.2]

$|\Delta B_{\mathrm{loc}}| = |(\Delta\sigma)|B \approx |\{\delta(\mathrm{CH_3}) - \delta(\mathrm{CHO})\}|B$

$= |(2.20 - 9.80)| \times 10^{-6} B = 7.60\times 10^{-6} B$

(a) $B = 1.5\ \mathrm{T}$, $|\Delta B_{\mathrm{loc}}| = 7.60\times 10^{-6}\times 1.5\ \mathrm{T} = \underline{11\ \mu\mathrm{T}}$

(b) $B = 7.0\ \mathrm{T}$, $|\Delta B_{\mathrm{loc}}| = 7.60\times 10^{-6}\times 7.0\ \mathrm{T} = \underline{53\ \mu\mathrm{T}}$

18.7 $|\Delta\nu| = |\Delta\delta| \times \nu_0$ [46] $= 7.60\times 10^{-6}\nu_0$

(a) $\nu_0 = 60\ \mathrm{MHz}$, $|\Delta\nu| = 7.60\times 10^{-6}\times 60\ \mathrm{MHz} = \underline{460\ \mathrm{Hz}}$

(b) $\nu_0 = 350\ \mathrm{MHz}$, $|\Delta\nu| = 7.60\times 10^{-6}\times 350\ \mathrm{MHz} = \underline{2.66\ \mathrm{kHz}}$

18.8 (a) The spectrum is shown in Fig. 18.1. (b) When the frequency is changed to 350 MHz, the separation of the CH_3 and CHO resonance increases

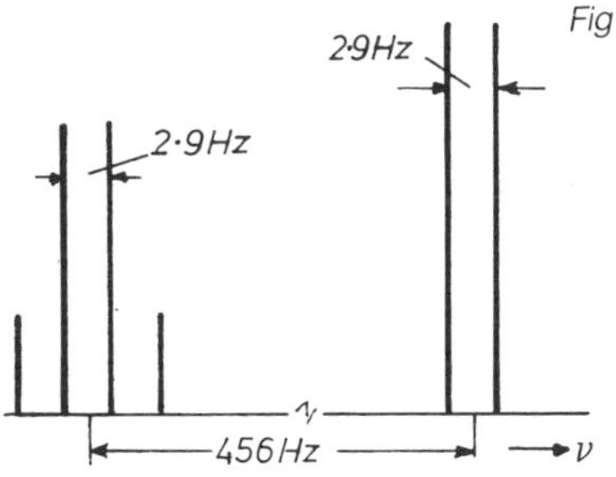

Fig 18.1

by a factor of 5.8, the fine structure (the splitting within the groups) remains unchanged, and the intensity increases (because $\delta N/N$ increases by a factor of 5.8).

18.9 $\tau \approx \dfrac{1}{2\pi\delta}$ [11] $= \dfrac{1}{2\pi\nu_0(\delta' - \delta)}$

$$\approx \frac{1}{2\pi \times 60 \times 10^6\,\text{Hz} \times (5.2 - 4.0) \times 10^{-6}} \approx 2.2\,\text{ms}$$

Therefore, the signals merge when the lifetime of each isomer is less than about 2.2 ms, corresponding to a conversion rate of $\underline{5 \times 10^2\,\text{s}^{-1}}$.

18.10 The four equivalent ^{19}F nuclei ($I = \frac{1}{2}$) give a single line. However, the ^{10}B nucleus ($I = 3$, 19.6 per cent abundant) results in $2 \times 3 + 1 = 7$ lines and the ^{11}B nucleus ($I = \frac{3}{2}$, 80.4 per cent abundant) results in $2 \times \frac{3}{2} + 1 = 4$ lines. The splitting arising from the ^{11}B nucleus will be larger than that arising from the ^{10}B nucleus (since its magnetic moment is larger, by a factor of 1.5, Table 18.1). Moreover, the total intensity of the 4 lines due to the ^{11}B nuclei will be greater (by a factor of $80.4/19.6 \approx 4$) than the total intensity of the 8 lines due to the ^{10}B nuclei. The individual line intensities will be in the ratio 8:1 (half the number of lines, and four times as abundant). The spectrum is sketched in Fig. 18.2.

18.11 The A, M, and X resonances lie in those distinctively different groups. The A resonance is split into a 1:2:1 triplet by the M nuclei, and each line of that triplet in split into a 1:4:6:4:1 quintet by the X nuclei, (with $J_{AM} > J_{AX}$). The M resonance is split into a 1:3:3:1 quartet by the A nuclei and each line is split into a quintet by the X nuclei (with $J_{AM} > J_{MX}$). The X resonance is split into a quartet by the A nuclei and then each line is split into a triplet by the M nuclei (with $J_{AX} > J_{MX}$). The spectrum is sketched in Fig. 18.3.

18.12 (a) If there is rapid rotation about the axis, the H nuclei are both chemically and magnetically equivalent. (b) Since $J_{cis} \neq J_{trans}$, the H nuclei are

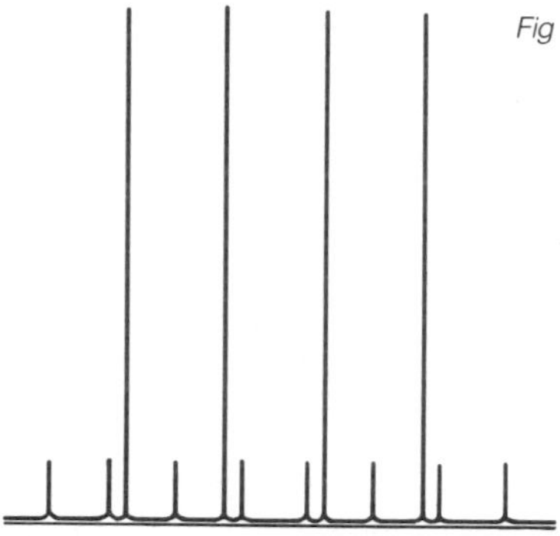

Fig 18.2

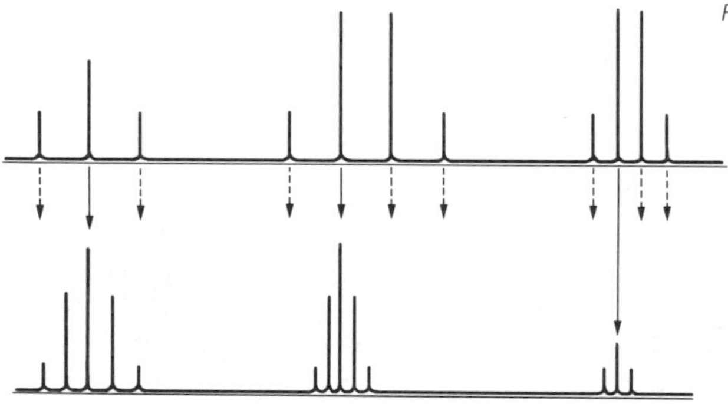

Fig 18.3

chemically but not magnetically equivalent. (c) Since all J_{HF} are equal in this molecule (the CH_2 group is perpendicular to the CF_2 group), the H and F nuclei are both chemically and magnetically equivalent.

18.13 (a) $B=\dfrac{h\nu}{g_I\mu_N}=\dfrac{6.626\times10^{-34}\,\text{J Hz}^{-1}\times9\times10^{9}\,\text{Hz}}{5.5857\times5.051\times10^{-27}\,\text{J T}^{-1}}$

$=\underline{2\times10^{2}\,\text{T}}$

(b) $B=\dfrac{h\nu}{g_e\mu_N}=\dfrac{6.626\times10^{-34}\,\text{J Hz}^{-1}\times60\times10^{6}\,\text{Hz}}{2.0023\times9.274\times10^{-24}\,\text{J T}^{-1}}$

$=\underline{2\,\text{mT}}$

18.14 $B=\dfrac{h\nu}{g_e\mu_B}=\dfrac{hc}{g_e\mu_B\lambda}$

$=\dfrac{6.626\times10^{-34}\,\text{J s}\times2.998\times10^{8}\,\text{m s}^{-1}}{2\times9.274\times10^{-24}\,\text{J T}^{-1}\times8\times10^{-3}\,\text{m}}=\underline{1.\bar{3}\,\text{T}}$

18.15 $n = \frac{10^{10}}{N_A} = \frac{10^{10}}{6 \times 10^{23}\,\text{mol}^{-1}} = 2 \times 10^{-14}\,\text{mol cm}^{-3}.$

which corresponds to $2 \times 10^{-14} \times 10^{3}\,\text{mol dm}^{-3}$, or $\underline{2 \times 10^{-11}\,\text{M}}$

18.16 $\frac{\delta N}{N} \approx \frac{g_e \mu_B B}{2kT}$ [Example 18.15 with $\mu_N \rightarrow \mu_B$, $g_I \rightarrow g_e$]

$$\approx \frac{2 \times 9.274 \times 10^{-24}\,\text{J T}^{-1} \times 0.3\,\text{T}}{2 \times 1.381 \times 10^{-23}\,\text{J K}^{-1} \times 298\,\text{K}} = 7 \times 10^{-4}$$

Therefore, the difference in population is

$$\delta N \approx 7 \times 10^{-4} \times 2.5 \times 10^{14} = \underline{2 \times 10^{11}}$$

18.17 $g = \frac{h\nu}{\mu_B B}$

We shall often need the value

$$\frac{h}{\mu_B} = \frac{6.62608 \times 10^{-34}\,\text{J Hz}^{-1}}{9.27402 \times 10^{-24}\,\text{J T}^{-1}} = 7.14478 \times 10^{-11}\,\text{T Hz}^{-1}$$

Then, in this case

$$g = \frac{7.14478 \times 10^{-11}\,\text{T Hz}^{-1} \times 9.2231 \times 10^{9}\,\text{Hz}}{329.12 \times 10^{-3}\,\text{T}}$$

$$= \underline{2.0022}$$

18.18 $a = B(\text{line 1}) - B(\text{line 2})$

$$= 357.3 - 306.6\,\text{mT} = \underline{50.7\,\text{mT}}$$

18.19 $a = B(\text{line 3}) - B(\text{line 2}) = B(\text{line 2}) - B(\text{line 1})$

$$\left.\begin{array}{l} B_3 - B_2 = 334.8 - 332.5\,\text{mT} = 2.3\,\text{mT} \\ B_2 - B_1 = 332.5 - 330.2\,\text{mT} = 2.3\,\text{mT} \end{array}\right\} a = \underline{2.3\,\text{mT}}$$

Use the center line to calculate g:

$$g = \frac{h\nu}{\mu_B B} = 7.14478 \times 10^{-11}\,\text{T Hz}^{-1} \times \frac{9.319 \times 10^{9}\,\text{Hz}}{332.5 \times 10^{-3}\,\text{T}}$$

$$= \underline{2.002\bar{5}}$$

18.20 The center of the spectrum will occur at 332.5 mT. Proton 1 splits the line into two components with separation 2.0 mT and hence at 332.5 ± 1.0 mT. Proton 2 splits these two hyperfine lines into two, each with separation 2.6 mT, and hence the lines occur at $332.5 \pm 1.0 \pm 1.3$ mT. The spectrum therefore consists of four lines of equal intensity at the fields 330.2 mT, 332.2 mT, 332.8 mT, 334.8 mT.

18.21 We construct Fig. 18.4a for CH_3 and Fig. 18.4b for CD_3.

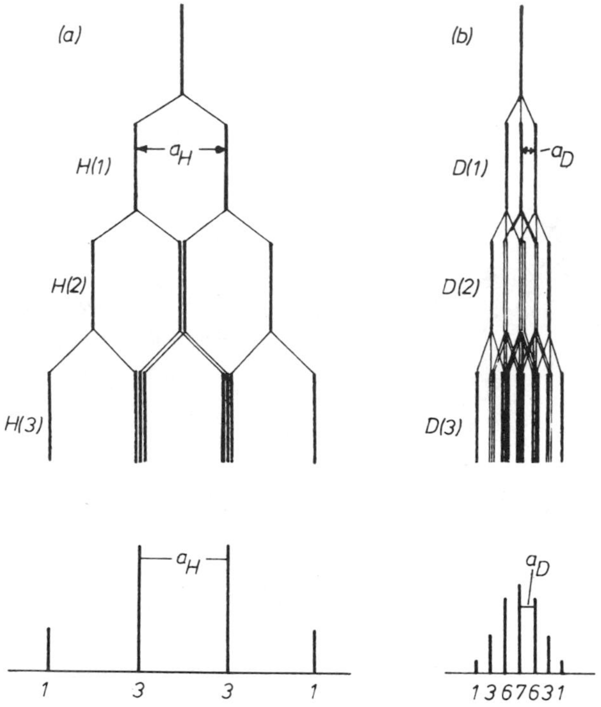

Fig 18.4

18.22

$$B = \frac{h\nu}{g\mu_B} = \frac{7.14478 \times 10^{-11}}{2.0025}\ \mathrm{T\,Hz^{-1}} \times \nu$$

$$= 35.68\ \mathrm{mT} \times (\nu/\mathrm{GHz})$$

(a) $\nu = 9.302$ GHz, $B = 331.9$ mT

(b) $\nu = 33.67$ GHz, $B = 1201$ mT

18.23 $\left.\begin{array}{l}\delta B = B_{\text{local}} - B = -\sigma B \\ g = g_e(1-\sigma)\end{array}\right\} \delta B = \left(\dfrac{g - g_e}{g_e}\right) B$

Therefore, $\delta B = \dfrac{2.0102 - 2.0023}{2.0023} \times B = 3.9 \times 10^{-3} B$

(a) $\delta B = 3.9 \times 10^{-3} \times 0.34\,\text{T} = \underline{1.3\,\text{mT}}$

(b) $\delta B = 3.9 \times 10^{-3} \times 1.23\,\text{T} = \underline{4.8\,\text{mT}}$

18.24 $\tau_J > \dfrac{1}{2\pi\delta\nu}$ if the lines are to be resolved.

$\tau_J = 200$ ms and

$$\frac{1}{2\pi\delta\nu} = \frac{1}{2\pi \times 90.0\,\text{Hz}} = 2\,\text{ms}$$

Since $\tau_J > 2$ ms, the two resonances will be resolved.

18.25 Since the number of hyperfine lines arising from a nucleus of spin I is $2I+1$, we solve $2I+1=4$ and find that $\underline{I=\frac{3}{2}}$.

18.26 The X nucleus produces six lines of equal intensity. The pair of H nuclei in XH_2 split each of these lines into a 1:2:1 triplet (Fig. 18.5a). The pair of D nuclei ($I=1$) in XD_2 split each line into a 1:2:3:2:1 quintet (Fig. 18.5b).

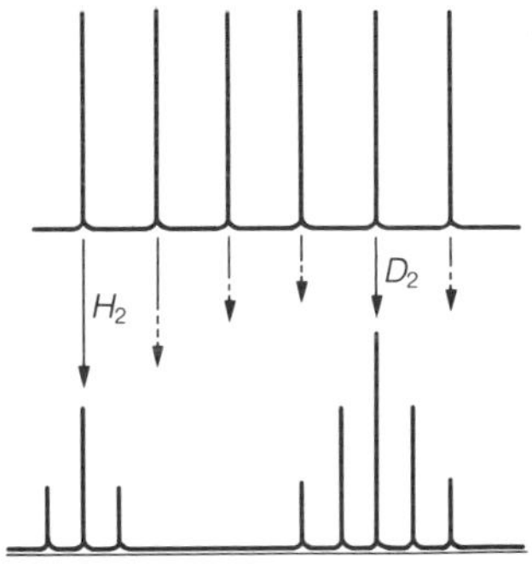

Fig 18.5

Problems

18.1 $g_I = -3.8260$

$$B = \frac{h\nu}{g_I \mu_N} = \frac{6.626 \times 10^{-34}\,\text{J Hz}^{-1} \times \nu}{(-)\,3.8260 \times 5.0508 \times 10^{-27}\,\text{J T}^{-1}}$$

$$= 3.429 \times 10^{-8} (\nu/\text{Hz})\,\text{T}$$

Therefore, with $\nu = 60\,\text{MHz}$,

$$B = 3.429 \times 10^{-8} \times 60 \times 10^{6}\,\text{T} = \underline{2.1\,\text{T}}$$

$$\frac{\delta N}{N} \approx \frac{g_I \mu_N B}{2kT} = \frac{-3.8260 \times 5.0508 \times 10^{-27}\,\text{J T}^{-1} \times 2.1\,\text{T}}{2 \times 1.381 \times 10^{-23}\,\text{J K}^{-1} \times 298\,\text{K}}$$

$$\approx \underline{-5 \times 10^{-6}}$$

Since $g_I < 0$ (as for an electron, the magnetic moment is antiparallel to its spin), the β state ($m_I = -\frac{1}{2}$) lies lower.

18.2 $$\tau_J \approx \frac{1}{2\pi\delta\nu} = \frac{1}{2\pi \times (5.2 - 4.0) \times 10^{-6} \times 60 \times 10^{6}\,\text{Hz}}$$

$\approx 2.2\,\text{ms}$, corresponding to a rate of jumping of $450\,\text{s}^{-1}$

When $\nu = 300\,\text{MHz}$

$$\tau_J \approx \frac{1}{2\pi \times (5.2 - 4.0) \times 300\,\text{Hz}} = 0.44\,\text{ms}$$

corresponding to a jump rate of $2.3 \times 10^{3}\,\text{s}^{-1}$. Assume an Arrhenius-like jumping process

$$\text{rate} \propto e^{-E_a/RT}$$

Then

$$\ln\left\{\frac{\text{rate}(T')}{\text{rate}(T)}\right\} = \frac{-E_a}{R}\left(\frac{1}{T'} - \frac{1}{T}\right)$$

and therefore

$$E_a = \frac{R\ln(r'/r)}{\dfrac{1}{T} - \dfrac{1}{T'}}$$

$$= \frac{8.314\ \mathrm{J\,K^{-1}\,mol^{-1}} \times \ln \dfrac{2.3\times 10^3}{450}}{\dfrac{1}{280\ \mathrm{K}} - \dfrac{1}{300\ \mathrm{K}}}$$

$$= \underline{57\ \mathrm{kJ\,mol^{-1}}}$$

18.3 $$g = \frac{h\nu}{\mu_B B} = \frac{7.14478\times 10^{-11}\ \mathrm{T} \times (\nu/\mathrm{Hz})}{B}$$

$$= \frac{7.14478\times 10^{-11}\ \mathrm{T}\times 9.302\times 10^9}{B}$$

$$= \frac{0.6646\bar{1}}{B/\mathrm{T}}$$

(a) $g_\parallel = \dfrac{0.6646\bar{1}}{0.33364} = \underline{1.992}$

(b) $g_\perp = \dfrac{0.6646\bar{1}}{0.33194} = \underline{2.002}$

18.4 Refer to Fig. 18.4 constructed previously. The width of the CH_3 spectrum is $3a_H = \underline{6.9\ \mathrm{mT}}$. The width of the CD_3 spectrum is $6a_D$. The splittings are proportional to the nuclear g values, hence

$$a_D \approx \frac{0.85745}{5.5857} \times a_H = 0.1535 a_H = 0.35\ \mathrm{mT}$$

Therefore, the overall width is $6a_D = \underline{2.1\ \mathrm{mT}}$

18.5 Construct the spectrum by taking into account first the two equivalent ^{14}N splitting (producing a 1:2:3:2:1 quintet) and then the splitting of each of these lines into a 1:4:6:4:1 quintet by the four equivalent protons. The resulting 25-line spectrum is shown in Fig. 18.6.

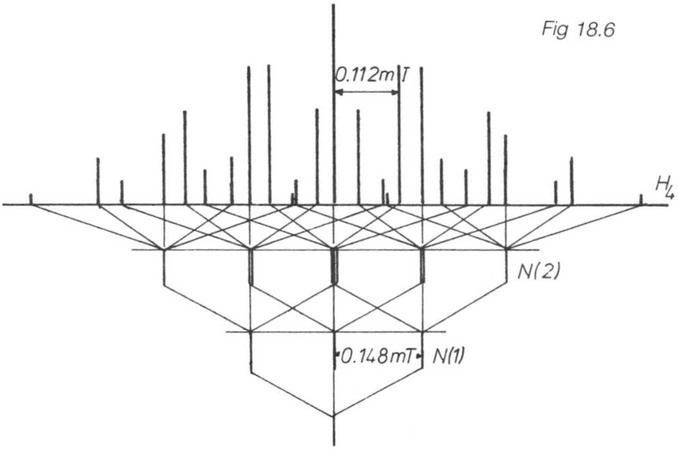

18.6 We write $P(\mathrm{N}2s) = \dfrac{5.7\ \mathrm{mT}}{55.2\ \mathrm{mT}} = \underline{0.10}$ (10 per cent of its time)

$$P(\mathrm{N}2p_z) = \frac{1.3\ \mathrm{mT}}{3.4\ \mathrm{mT}} = \underline{0.38} \text{ (38 per cent of its time).}$$

The total probability is

(a) $P(\mathrm{N}) = 0.10 + 0.38 = \underline{0.48}$ (48 per cent of its time).

(b) $P(\mathrm{O}) = 1 - P(\mathrm{N}) = \underline{0.52}$ (52 per cent of its time).

The hybridization ratio is

$$\frac{P(\mathrm{N}2p)}{P(\mathrm{N}2s)} = \frac{0.38}{0.10} = \underline{3.8}$$

The unpaired electron therefore occupies an orbital that resembles an sp^3 hybrid on N, in accord with the radical's nonlinear shape.

From the discussion in Section 14.9 we can write

$$a'^2 = \frac{1 + \cos\Phi}{1 - \cos\Phi} \text{ [eqn 20 of Section 14.9]}$$

$$b'^2 = 1 - a'^2 = \frac{-2\cos\Phi}{1 - \cos\Phi}$$

$$\lambda = \frac{b'^2}{a'^2} = \frac{-2\cos\Phi}{1 + \cos\Phi}, \text{ implying that } \cos\Phi = -\frac{\lambda}{2 + \lambda}$$

Then, since $\lambda = 3.8$, $\cos\Phi = -0.66$, so $\Phi = \underline{131°}$.

18.7 For $C_6H_6^-$, $a = Q\rho$ with $Q = 2.25$ mT [15]. Hence, we can construct the following maps:

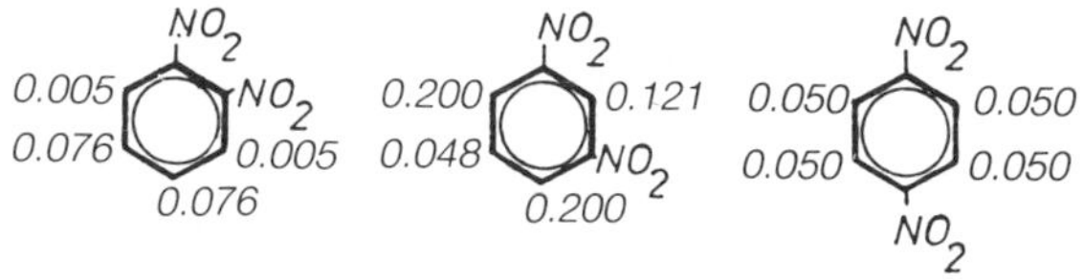

18.8 We use the same procedure is in Problem 18.7, and construct the following maps:

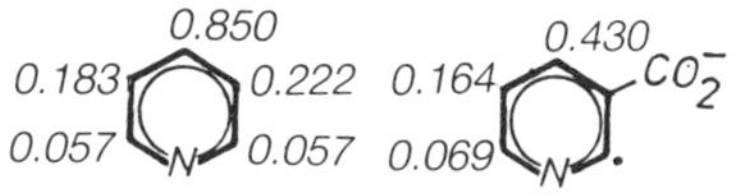

18.9 Rotation about the bond modulates the hyperfine coupling from 113.1 MHz to 11.2 MHz. Then use $\tau \lesssim 1/2\pi\delta\nu$:

$$\tau \lesssim \frac{1}{2\pi \times (113.1 - 11.2) \times 10^6\ \text{s}^{-1}} = 1.6\ \text{ns}$$

That is, at 115 K, it rotates around the parallel axis so as to change from one orientation (113.1 MHz coupling) to the other (11.2 MHz) in about <u>1.6 ns</u>.

18.10 $B = \dfrac{-g_I\mu_N\mu_0}{4\pi R^3}(1 - 3\cos^2\theta)m_I \quad [6] = \dfrac{g_I\mu_N\mu_0}{4\pi R^3} \quad [m_I = +\tfrac{1}{2},\ \theta = 0]$

which rearranges to

$$R = \left(\frac{g_I\mu_N\mu_0}{4\pi B}\right)^{1/3}$$

$$= \left(\frac{5.5857 \times 5.0508 \times 10^{-27}\ \text{J T}^{-1} \times 4\pi \times 10^{-7}\ \text{T}^2\ \text{J}^{-1}\ \text{m}^3}{4\pi \times 0.715 \times 10^{-3}\ \text{T}}\right)^{1/3}$$

$$= (3.946 \times 10^{-30}\ \text{m}^3)^{1/3} = \underline{158\ \text{pm}}$$

18.11 $\langle B \rangle \propto \displaystyle\int_0^{\pi} (1 - 3\cos^2\theta)\sin\theta\, d\theta \int_0^{2\pi} d\phi$

$$\propto \int_{-1}^{1} (1 - 3x^2)\, dx \times 2\pi \quad [x = \cos\theta,\ dx = -\sin\theta\, d\theta]$$

$$\propto (x - x^3)\big|_{-1}^{1} = \underline{0}$$

18.12 $$\langle B_{\text{nucl}}\rangle = \frac{-g_I\mu_N\mu_0 m_I}{4\pi R^3}\,\frac{\int_0^{\theta_{\max}}(1-3\cos^2\theta)\sin\theta\,d\theta}{\int_0^{\theta_{\max}}\sin\theta\,d\theta}$$

The denominator is the normalization constant, and ensures that the total probability of being between 0 and $\theta_{\max}$ is 1.

$$= \frac{-g_I\mu_N\mu_0 m_I}{4\pi R^3}\,\frac{\int_1^{x_{\max}}(1-3x^2)\,dx}{\int_1^{x_{\max}}dx} \qquad [x_{\max}=\cos\theta_{\max}]$$

$$= \frac{-g_I\mu_N\mu_0 m_I}{4\pi R^3}\cdot\frac{x_{\max}(1-x_{\max}^2)}{x_{\max}} = \underline{\frac{-g_I\mu_N\mu_0 m_I}{4\pi R^3}\sin^2\theta_{\max}}$$

If $\theta_{\max}=\pi$ [complete rotation], $\sin\theta_{\max}=0$ and $\langle B_{\text{nucl}}\rangle=0$. If $\theta_{\max}=30°$, $\sin^2\theta_{\max}=0.25$, and

$$\langle B_{\text{nucl}}\rangle = \frac{-5.5857\times 5.0508\times 10^{-27}\,\text{J T}^{-1}\times 4\pi\times 10^{-7}\,\text{T}^2\,\text{J}^{-1}\,\text{m}^3\times 0.25}{4\pi\times(1.58\times 10^{-10}\,\text{m})^3\times 2}$$

$$= \underline{-0.89\,\mu\text{T}}$$

18.13 $$I(\omega) = A\,\text{re}\int_0^{\infty} G(t)\,e^{i\omega t}\,dt$$

$$= A\,\text{re}\int_0^{\infty}\cos\omega_0 t\,e^{-t/\tau+i\omega t}\,dt$$

$$= \tfrac{1}{2}A\,\text{re}\int_0^{\infty}(e^{i\omega_0 t}+e^{-i\omega_0 t})\,e^{-t/\tau+i\omega t}\,dt$$

$$= \tfrac{1}{2}A\,\text{re}\int_0^{\infty}\{e^{i(\omega_0+\omega+i/\tau)t}+e^{-i(\omega_0-\omega-i/\tau)t}\}$$

$$= -\tfrac{1}{2}A\,\text{re}\left\{\frac{1}{i(\omega_0+\omega+i/\tau)}-\frac{1}{i(\omega_0-\omega-i/\tau)}\right\}$$

When ω and ω_0 are similar to magnetic resonance frequencies (or higher), only the second term in brackets is significant [because $1/(\omega_0+\omega)\ll 1$ but $1/(\omega_0-\omega)$ may be large if $\omega\approx\omega_0$]. Therefore,

$$I(\omega)\approx\tfrac{1}{2}A\ \mathrm{re}\,\frac{1}{\mathrm{i}(\omega_0-\omega)+1/\tau}$$

$$=\tfrac{1}{2}A\ \mathrm{re}\,\frac{-\mathrm{i}(\omega_0-\omega)+1/\tau}{(\omega_0-\omega)^2+1/\tau^2}$$

$$=\tfrac{1}{2}A\,\frac{1/\tau}{(\omega_0-\omega)^2+1/\tau^2}=\underline{\frac{\tfrac{1}{2}A\tau}{1+(\omega_0-\omega)^2\tau^2}}$$

which is a Lorentzian line centered on ω_0, of amplitude $\tfrac{1}{2}A\tau$ and width $2/\tau$ at half height.

18.14 We have seen [Problem 18.13] that if $G\propto\cos\omega_0 t$, then $I(\omega)\propto 1/\{1+(\omega_0-\omega)^2\tau^2\}$, which peaks at $\omega\approx\omega_0$. Therefore, if

$$G(t)\propto a\cos\omega_1 t+b\cos\omega_2 t$$

we can anticipate that

$$I(\omega)\propto\frac{a}{1+(\omega_1-\omega)^2\tau^2}+\frac{b}{1+(\omega_2-\omega)^2\tau^2}$$

and explicit calculation shows this to be so. Therefore, $I(\omega)$ consists of two absorption lines, one peaking at $\omega\approx\omega_1$ and the other at $\omega\approx\omega_2$.

19. Statistical thermodynamics: the concepts

Exercises

19.1 From the Boltzmann distribution

$$\frac{N_+}{N_-} = e^{-\beta\varepsilon} = 1 \text{ when } \beta = 0, \text{ which occurs when } \underline{T = \infty}.$$

19.2 $q = \left(\dfrac{2\pi mkT}{h^2}\right)^{1/2}$ [10]

$$= \left\{\frac{2\pi \times 120 \times 10^{-3}\,\text{kg mol}^{-1} \times 1.381 \times 10^{-23}\,\text{J K}^{-1} \times T}{6.022 \times 10^{23}\,\text{mol}^{-1} \times (6.626 \times 10^{-34}\,\text{J s})^2}\right\}^{3/2}$$

$$\times 2.00 \times 10^{-6}\,\text{m}^3$$

$$= 4.94 \times 10^{23}(T/\text{K})^{3/2}$$

(a) $T = 300\,\text{K}$, $q = 4.94 \times 10^{23} \times (300)^{3/2} = \underline{2.57 \times 10^{27}}$

(b) $T = 400\,\text{K}$, $q = 4.94 \times 10^{23} \times 10^{23} \times (400)^{3/2} = \underline{3.95 \times 10^{27}}$

19.3 (a) $\Lambda = h\left(\dfrac{\beta}{2\pi m}\right)^{1/2}$ $[10] = h\left(\dfrac{1}{2\pi mkT}\right)^{1/2}$

$$= 6.626 \times 10^{-34}\,\text{J s}$$

$$\times \left(\frac{1}{2\pi \times 39.95 \times 1.6605 \times 10^{-27}\,\text{kg} \times 1.381 \times 10^{-23}\,\text{J K}^{-1} \times T}\right)^{1/2}$$

$$= \frac{276\,\text{pm}}{(T/\text{K})^{1/2}}$$

(b) $q = \dfrac{V}{\Lambda^3} = \dfrac{1.00 \times 10^{-6}\,\text{m}^3(T/\text{K})^{3/2}}{(2.76 \times 10^{-10}\,\text{m})^3} = 4.76 \times 10^{22}(T/\text{K})^{3/2}$

(i) $T = 300\,\text{K}$, $\Lambda = 1.59 \times 10^{-11}\,\text{m} = \underline{15.9\,\text{pm}}$, $q = \underline{2.47 \times 10^{26}}$

(ii) $T = 3000\,\text{K}$, $\Lambda = \underline{5.04\,\text{pm}}$, $q = \underline{7.82 \times 10^{27}}$.

19.4 $q = \dfrac{V}{\Lambda^3}$, implying that $\dfrac{q}{q'} = \left(\dfrac{\Lambda'}{\Lambda}\right)^3$.

However, as $\Lambda \propto 1/m^{1/2}$, $\dfrac{q}{q'} = \left(\dfrac{m}{m'}\right)^{3/2}$

Therefore,

$$\frac{q(\mathrm{D_2})}{q(\mathrm{H_2})} = 2^{3/2} = \underline{2.83} \quad [m(\mathrm{D_2}) = 2m(\mathrm{H_2})]$$

19.5 $q = \sum_i \mathrm{e}^{-\beta\varepsilon_i} = 3 + \mathrm{e}^{-\beta\varepsilon_1} + 3\mathrm{e}^{-\beta\varepsilon_2}$

$$\beta\varepsilon = \frac{hc\tilde{\nu}}{kT} = \frac{1.4388(\tilde{\nu}/\mathrm{cm^{-1}})}{T/\mathrm{K}} \quad \text{[inside front cover]}$$

Therefore,

$$\begin{aligned} q &= 3 + \mathrm{e}^{-1.4388 \times 3500/1900} + 3\mathrm{e}^{-1.4388 \times 4700/1900} \\ &= 3 + 0.0706 + 0.085 = \underline{3.156} \end{aligned}$$

19.6 $$\frac{U - U(0)}{N} = \frac{\sum_i \varepsilon_i \mathrm{e}^{-\beta\varepsilon_i}}{q} \quad \text{[Section 19.3]} = \frac{hc}{q}\sum_i \tilde{\nu}_i \mathrm{e}^{-\beta hc\tilde{\nu}_i}$$

$$\begin{aligned} &= \frac{hc}{3.156} \times (0 + 3500\ \mathrm{cm^{-1}} \times \mathrm{e}^{-1.4388 \times 3500/1900} \\ &\qquad + 3 \times 4700\ \mathrm{cm^{-1}} \times \mathrm{e}^{-1.4388 \times 4700/1900}) \\ &= hc \times 204.9\ \mathrm{cm^{-1}}, \text{ corresponding to } \underline{2.45\ \mathrm{kJ\ mol^{-1}}}. \end{aligned}$$

19.7 $\dfrac{N_i}{N} = \dfrac{\mathrm{e}^{-\beta\varepsilon_i}}{q}$ [6a] which implies that $\dfrac{N_+}{N_-} = \mathrm{e}^{-\beta\varepsilon}$

for a two-level system ($N_+ + N_- = N$; $\varepsilon_- = 0$, $\varepsilon_+ = \varepsilon$). Therefore,

$$\beta = \frac{1}{\varepsilon}\ln\frac{N_-}{N_+}, \text{ which implies that } T = \frac{\varepsilon}{k\ln\left(\dfrac{N_-}{N_+}\right)}$$

Therefore,

$$T=\frac{hc\tilde{\nu}/k}{\ln\dfrac{N_-}{N_+}}=\frac{1.4388\text{ cm K}\times 540\text{ cm}^{-1}}{\ln(0.90/0.10)}=\underline{354\text{ K}}$$

19.8 The exact and approximate values are as follows:

x	5	10	15	
$x!$	120	3 628 800 (3.629×10^6)	$1.307\,674\times10^{12}$	
Approximation 1:	21	4.54×10^5	1.3395×10^{11}	$x!\approx e^{x\ln x-x}$
Approximation 2:	118	3.599×10^6	1.3004×10^{12}	[in question]

19.9 $q=\sum_i e^{-\beta\varepsilon_i}=\underline{1+e^{-2\mu_B\beta B}}$ [energies measured from lower state]

$$\langle\varepsilon\rangle=-\frac{1}{q}\left(\frac{\partial q}{\partial\beta}\right)\ [11a]=\underline{\frac{2\mu_B B\,e^{-2\mu_B\beta B}}{1+e^{-2\mu_B\beta B}}}$$

We write $x=2\mu_B\beta B$, then $\dfrac{\langle\varepsilon\rangle}{2\mu_B B}=\dfrac{e^{-x}}{1+e^{-x}}=\dfrac{1}{e^x+1}$

This function is plotted in Fig. 19.1. For the partition function we plot

$$q=1+e^{-x}$$

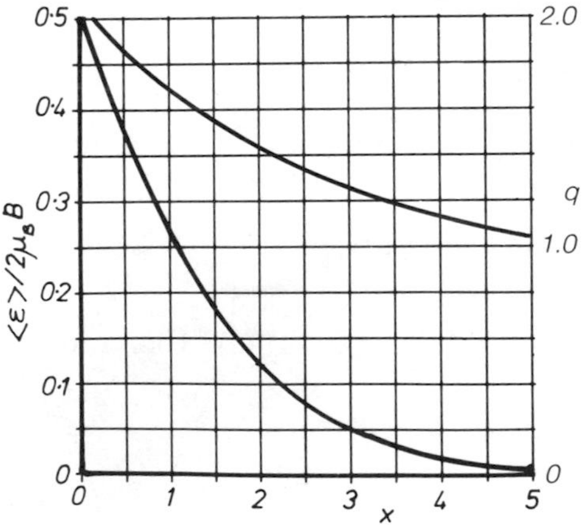

Fig 19.1

The relative populations are

$$\frac{N_+}{N_-}=\mathrm{e}^{-x},\ x=2\mu_\mathrm{B}\beta B=\frac{2\times 9.274\times 10^{-24}\,\mathrm{J\,T^{-1}}\times 1.0T}{1.381\times 10^{-23}\,\mathrm{J\,K^{-1}}\times T}=1.343/(T/\mathrm{K})$$

(a) $T=4\,\mathrm{K},\ \dfrac{N_+}{N_-}=\mathrm{e}^{-1.343/4}=\underline{0.72}$

(b) $T=298\,\mathrm{K},\ \dfrac{N_+}{N_-}=\mathrm{e}^{-1.343/298}=\underline{0.996}$

19.10 $q=\sum \mathrm{e}^{-\beta\varepsilon_i}=\underline{1+\mathrm{e}^{-x}+\mathrm{e}^{-2x}},\ x=g_I\mu_\mathrm{N}\beta B\quad [I=1]$

$$\frac{\mathrm{d}q}{\mathrm{d}\beta}=g_I\mu_\mathrm{N}B\frac{\mathrm{d}q}{\mathrm{d}x}=-g_I\mu_\mathrm{N}B(\mathrm{e}^{-x}+2\mathrm{e}^{-2x})$$

and so

$$\langle\varepsilon\rangle=-\frac{1}{q}\frac{\mathrm{d}q}{\mathrm{d}\beta}=\underline{\frac{g_I\mu_\mathrm{N}B(1+2\mathrm{e}^{-x})\,\mathrm{e}^{-x}}{1+\mathrm{e}^{-x}+\mathrm{e}^{-2x}}}$$

19.11 $S_\mathrm{m}^\ominus=R\ln\left(\dfrac{\mathrm{e}^{5/2}kT}{p^\ominus\Lambda^3}\right)\quad$ [23b with $p=p^\ominus$]

$$\Lambda=\left(\frac{h^2}{2\pi mkT}\right)^{1/2}=\frac{6.626\times 10^{-34}\,\mathrm{J\,s}}{(2\pi\times 20.18\times 1.6605\times 10^{-27}\,\mathrm{kg}\times 1.381\times 10^{-23}\,\mathrm{J\,K^{-1}}\,T)^{1/2}}$$

$$=\frac{3.886\times 10^{-10}\,\mathrm{m}}{(T/\mathrm{K})^{1/2}}$$

$$S_\mathrm{m}^\ominus=R\ln\frac{\mathrm{e}^{5/2}\times 1.381\times 10^{-23}\,\mathrm{J\,K^{-1}}\,T}{1\times 10^5\,\mathrm{Pa}\times(3.886\times 10^{-10}\,\mathrm{m})^3}\times\left(\frac{T}{\mathrm{K}}\right)^{3/2}$$

$$=R\ln 28.67\times(T/\mathrm{K})^{5/2}$$

(a) $T=200\,\mathrm{K},\ S_\mathrm{m}^\ominus=8.314\,\mathrm{J\,K^{-1}\,mol^{-1}}\times\ln 28.67\times(200)^{5/2}$

$=\underline{138\,\mathrm{J\,K^{-1}\,mol^{-1}}}$

(b) $T=298.15\,\mathrm{K},\ S_\mathrm{m}^\ominus=8.314\,\mathrm{J\,K^{-1}\,mol^{-1}}\times\ln 28.67\times(298.15)^{5/2}$

$=\underline{146\,\mathrm{J\,K^{-1}\,mol^{-1}}}$

19.12 $q=\dfrac{1}{1-e^{-\beta\varepsilon}}$ [8] $=\dfrac{1}{1-e^{-hc\beta\tilde{\nu}}}$

$$hc\beta\tilde{\nu}=\frac{1.4388\text{ cm K}\times 560\text{ cm}^{-1}}{500\text{ K}}=1.611$$

Therefore, $q=\dfrac{1}{1-e^{-1.611}}=1.249$

The internal energy due to vibrational excitation is

$$U-U(0)=\frac{N\varepsilon\,e^{-\beta\varepsilon}}{1-e^{-\beta\varepsilon}}\quad\text{[Example 19.6]}$$

$$=\frac{Nhc\tilde{\nu}\,e^{-hc\tilde{\nu}\beta}}{1-e^{-hc\tilde{\nu}\beta}}=\frac{Nhc\tilde{\nu}}{e^{hc\tilde{\nu}\beta}-1}$$

$$=1.249\times Nhc\times 560\text{ cm}^{-1}$$

and hence

$$S_m/N_Ak=\frac{U-U(0)}{N_AkT}+\ln q\quad[15]$$

$$=0.249\times\frac{hc}{kT}\times 560\text{ cm}^{-1}+\ln 1.249$$

$$=\frac{0.249\times 1.4388\text{ K cm}\times 560\text{ cm}^{-1}}{500\text{ K}}+\ln 1.249$$

$$=0.401+0.222=0.623$$

Hence, $S_m=0.623R=\underline{5.18\text{ J K}^{-1}\text{ mol}^{-1}}$

19.13 (a) Yes; He atoms indistinguishable and mobile. (b) Yes; CO molecules indistinguishable and mobile. (c) No; CO molecules can be identified by their locations. (d) Yes; H_2O molecules indistinguishable and mobile. (e) No; H_2O molecules can be identified by their locations.

19.14 (a) $S_m=R\ln\dfrac{A}{p}$ [23b, A constant if T is constant]

Therefore, at constant temperature

$$\Delta S_m = R \ln \frac{A}{p_f} - R \ln \frac{A}{p_i} = R \ln \frac{p_i}{p_f}$$

(b) $S_m = R \ln BT^{3/2}$ [23a, B constant if V is constant]

At constant volume

$$\Delta S = R \ln BT_f^{3/2} - R \ln BT_i^{3/2} = R \ln \left(\frac{T_f}{T_i}\right)^{3/2}$$

$$= \tfrac{3}{2} R \ln \frac{T_f}{T_i}$$

For a monatomic gas, $C_V = \tfrac{3}{2}R$, so

$$\Delta S_m = C_V \ln \frac{T_f}{T_i}$$

in accord with thermodynamics. Similarly, at constant pressure,

$$S_m = R \ln CT^{5/2} \quad [23b]$$

and $\Delta S = \tfrac{5}{2} R \ln \dfrac{T_f}{T_i}$

For a perfect gas $C_p = C_V + R = \tfrac{5}{2}R$, so

$$\Delta S = C_p \ln \frac{T_f}{T_i}$$

also in accord with thermodynamics.

Problems

19.1 $\dfrac{N_+}{N_-} = \tfrac{4}{2} \times e^{-hc\tilde{\nu}\beta}$ at thermal equilibrium [Boltzmann]

$$= 2e^{-1.4388 \times 450/300} = 0.23$$

The observed ratio is $\dfrac{0.30}{0.70} = 0.43$. Hence the populations are not at equilibrium.

19.2 $q=\dfrac{V}{\Lambda^3},\ \Lambda=\dfrac{h}{(2\pi mkT)^{1/2}}\quad [10,\ \beta=1/kT]$

and hence

$$T=\frac{h^2}{2\pi mk}\left(\frac{q}{V}\right)^{2/3}$$

$$=\frac{(6.626\times10^{-34}\ \mathrm{J\ s})^2}{2\pi\times39.95\times1.6605\times10^{-27}\ \mathrm{kg}\times1.381\times10^{-23}\ \mathrm{J\ K^{-1}}}\left(\frac{10}{1.0\times10^{-6}\ \mathrm{m^3}}\right)^{2/3}$$

$$=\underline{3.5\times10^{-15}\ \mathrm{K}}$$

The exact partition function in one dimension is

$$q=\sum_{n=1}^{\infty}\mathrm{e}^{-(n^2-1)h^2\beta/8mL^2}$$

For an Ar atom in a cubic box of side 1.0 cm,

$$\frac{h^2\beta}{8mL^2}$$

$$=\frac{(6.626\times10^{-34}\ \mathrm{J\ s})^2}{8\times39.95\times1.6605\times10^{-27}\ \mathrm{kg}\times1.381\times10^{-23}\ \mathrm{J\ K^{-1}}\times3.5\times10^{-15}\ \mathrm{K}\times(1.0\times10^{-2}\ \mathrm{m})}$$

$$=0.17\bar{1}$$

Then

$$q=\sum_{n=1}^{\infty}\mathrm{e}^{-0.17\bar{1}(n^2-1)}=1.00+0.60+0.25+0.08+0.02+\cdots=1.95$$

The partition function for motion in three dimensions is therefore

$$q=(1.95)^3=\underline{7.41}$$

19.3 (a) $q=\sum_{\mathrm{i}}\mathrm{e}^{-\beta\varepsilon_{\mathrm{i}}}=\sum_{\mathrm{i}}\mathrm{e}^{-hc\beta\tilde{\nu}_{\mathrm{i}}}$

We use $hc\beta = 1/(207\ \mathrm{cm}^{-1})$ at 298 K and $1/(3475\ \mathrm{cm}^{-1})$ at 5000 K. Therefore,

(i) $q = 5 + \mathrm{e}^{-4707/207} + 3\mathrm{e}^{-4751/207} + 5\mathrm{e}^{-10559/207}$

$= 5 + 1.3 \times 10^{-10} + 3.2 \times 10^{-10} + 2.7 \times 10^{-22} = \underline{5.00}$

(ii) $q = 5 + \mathrm{e}^{-4707/3475} + 3\mathrm{e}^{-4751/3475} + 5\mathrm{e}^{-10559/3475}$

$= 5 + 0.26 + 0.76 + 0.24 = \underline{6.25}$

(b) $P_i = \dfrac{g_i\,\mathrm{e}^{-\beta\varepsilon_i}}{q} = \dfrac{g_i\,\mathrm{e}^{-hc\beta\tilde{\nu}_i}}{q}$ [g_i is the degeneracy]

Therefore,

$$P_0 = \frac{5}{q} = 1.00 \text{ at 298 K and 0.80 at 5000 K}$$

$$P_2 = \frac{3\mathrm{e}^{-4751/207}}{5.00} = 6.5 \times 10^{-11} \text{ at 298 K}$$

$$P_2 = \frac{3\mathrm{e}^{-4751/3475}}{6.25} = 0.12 \text{ at 5000 K}$$

(c) We need $U - U(0)$, and evaluate it by explicit summation:

(i) $\dfrac{U_m - U_m(0)}{N_A hc} = \dfrac{1}{5.00}\{0 + 4707\ \mathrm{cm}^{-1} \times \mathrm{e}^{-4707/207} + \cdots\} = 4.32 \times 10^{-7}\ \mathrm{cm}^{-1}$

(ii) $\dfrac{U_m - U_m(0)}{N_A hc} = \dfrac{1}{6.25}\{0 + 4707\ \mathrm{cm}^{-1} \times \mathrm{e}^{-4707/3475} + \cdots\} = 1178\ \mathrm{cm}^{-1}$

Hence, at 298 K

$$U_m - U_m(0) = 4.88 \times 10^{-6}\ \mathrm{J\ mol^{-1}}$$

and at 5000 K

$$U_m - U_m(0) = 14.10\ \mathrm{kJ\ mol^{-1}}$$

It follows that

(i) $S_m = \dfrac{4.88 \times 10^{-6}\ \mathrm{J\ mol^{-1}}}{298\ \mathrm{K}} + 8.3144\ \mathrm{J\ K^{-1}} \times \ln 5.00$

$= \underline{13.38\ \mathrm{J\ K^{-1}\ mol^{-1}}}$ [essentially $R \ln 5$]

(ii) $S_m = \dfrac{14.10 \times 10^{3}\ \mathrm{J\ mol^{-1}}}{5000\ \mathrm{K}} + 8.314\ \mathrm{J\ K^{-1}\ mol^{-1}} \ln 6.25$

$= \underline{18.07\ \mathrm{J\ K^{-1}\ mol^{-1}}}$

19.4 We measure energies from the lower states, and write

$$q = 2 + 2e^{-hc\beta\tilde{\nu}} = 2 + 2e^{-1.4388 \times 121.1/(T/K)}$$

$$= 2 + 2e^{-174.2/(T/K)}$$

This function is plotted in Fig. 19.2.

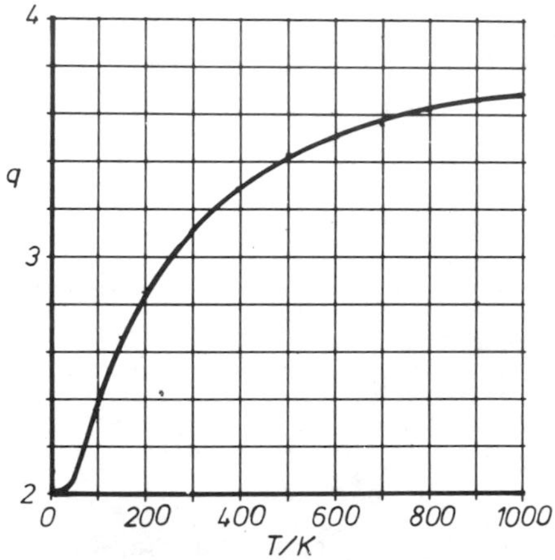

Fig 19.2

(a) At 300 K

$$P_0 = \frac{2}{q} = \frac{1}{1 + e^{-174.2/300}} = \underline{0.64}$$

$$P_1 = 1 - P_0 = \underline{0.36}$$

(b) The electronic contribution to U is

$$\frac{U - U(0)}{Nhc} = \frac{121.1 \text{ cm}^{-1} \times e^{-174.2/300}}{1 + e^{-174.2/300}} = 43.45 \text{ cm}^{-1}$$

which corresponds to $\underline{0.52 \text{ kJ mol}^{-1}}$.

For the electronic contribution to the molar entropy, we need

	300 K	500 K
$U - U(0) =$	0.518 kJ mol^{-1}	0.599 kJ mol^{-1}
$q =$	3.120	3.412

Then we form

$$S_m = \frac{U_m - U_m(0)}{T} + R \ln q$$

At 300 K: $S_m = \dfrac{518\ \mathrm{J\ mol^{-1}}}{300\ \mathrm{K}} + 8.314\ \mathrm{J\ K^{-1}\ mol^{-1}} \ln 3.120$

$$= 11.2\ \mathrm{J\ K^{-1}\ mol^{-1}}$$

At 500 K: $S_m = \dfrac{599\ \mathrm{J\ mol^{-1}}}{500\ \mathrm{K}} + 8.314\ \mathrm{J\ K^{-1}\ mol^{-1}} \ln 3.412$

$$= 11.4\ \mathrm{J\ K^{-1}\ mol^{-1}}$$

19.5 $q = \sum_i e^{-\beta\varepsilon_i} = \sum_i e^{-hc\beta\tilde{\nu}_i}$

At 100 K, $hc\beta = 1/(69.50\ \mathrm{cm^{-1}})$ and at 298 K, $hc\beta = 1/(207.22\ \mathrm{cm^{-1}})$. Therefore, at 100 K

(a) $q = 1 + e^{-213.30/69.50} + e^{-435.39/69.50} + e^{-636.27/69.50}$

$$+ e^{-845.93/69.50} + e^{-1054.38/69.50} = \underline{1.049}$$

and at 298 K

(b) $q = 1 + e^{-213.30/207.22} + e^{-425.39/207.22} + e^{-636.27/207.22}$

$$+ e^{-636.27/207.22} + e^{-1054.38/207.22} = \underline{1.56}$$

In each case

$$P_0 = \frac{1}{q} = \text{(a) } 0.953, \text{ (b) } 0.641$$

$$P_1 = \frac{e^{-hc\beta\tilde{\nu}_1}}{q} = \text{(a) } 0.044, \text{ (b) } 0.230$$

$$P_2 = \frac{e^{-hc\beta\tilde{\nu}_2}}{q} = \text{(a) } 0.002, \text{ (b)} = 0.083$$

For the molar entropy we need to form $U_m - U_m(0)$ by explicit summation:

$$U_m - U_m(0) = \frac{1}{q} \sum_i \varepsilon_i e^{-\beta\varepsilon_i} = \frac{1}{q} \sum_i hc\tilde{\nu}_i e^{-hc\beta\tilde{\nu}_i}$$

and find (a) 125 J mol^{-1} at 100 K and (b) 1400 J mol^{-1} at 298 K. It follows from

$$S_m = \frac{U_m - U_m(0)}{T} + R \ln q$$

that (a) $S_m = \frac{125\ \text{J mol}^{-1}}{100\ \text{K}} + R \ln 1.049 = \underline{1.65\ \text{J K}^{-1}\ \text{mol}^{-1}}$

$$\text{(b)}\ S_m = \frac{1400\ \text{J mol}^{-1}}{298\ \text{K}} + R \ln 1.56 = \underline{8.37\ \text{J K}^{-1}\ \text{mol}^{-1}}$$

19.6 (a) $W = \frac{N!}{n_1!n_2!\cdots}\ [1] = \frac{5!}{5!0!\cdots} = 1$

(b) We draw up the following table:

0	ε	2ε	3ε	4ε	5ε	$W = N!/n_1!n_2!\cdots$
4	0	0	0	0	1	5
3	1	0	0	1	0	20
3	0	1	1	0	0	20
2	2	0	1	0	0	30
2	1	2	0	0	0	30
1	3	1	0	0	0	20
0	5	0	0	0	0	1

The most probable configurations are {2, 2, 0, 1, 0, 0} and {2, 1, 2, 0, 0, 0} jointly.

19.7 We draw up the following table:

0	ε	2ε	3ε	4ε	5ε	6ε	7ε	8ε	9ε	W
8	0	0	0	0	0	0	0	0	1	9
7	1	0	0	0	0	0	0	1	0	72
7	0	1	0	0	0	0	1	0	0	72
7	0	0	1	0	0	1	0	0	0	72
7	0	0	0	1	1	0	0	0	0	72
6	2	0	0	0	0	0	1	0	0	252
6	0	2	0	0	1	0	0	0	0	252
6	0	0	3	0	0	0	0	0	0	84
6	1	0	0	2	0	0	0	0	0	252
6	1	1	0	0	0	1	0	0	0	504
6	1	0	1	0	1	0	0	0	0	504
6	0	1	1	1	0	0	0	0	0	504
5	3	0	0	0	0	1	0	0	0	504
5	0	3	1	0	0	0	0	0	0	504
5	2	1	0	0	1	0	0	0	0	1512
5	2	0	1	1	0	0	0	0	0	1512
5	1	2	0	1	0	0	0	0	0	1512
5	1	1	2	0	0	0	0	0	0	1512
4	4	0	0	0	1	0	0	0	0	630
4	3	1	0	1	0	0	0	0	0	2520
4	3	0	2	0	0	0	0	0	0	1260
4	2	2	1	0	0	0	0	0	0	3780
3	5	0	0	1	0	0	0	0	0	504
3	4	1	1	0	0	0	0	0	0	2520
2	6	0	1	0	0	0	0	0	0	252
2	5	2	0	0	0	0	0	0	0	756
1	7	1	0	0	0	0	0	0	0	72
0	9	0	0	0	0	0	0	0	0	1

The most probable configuration is the 'almost exponential' $\{4, 2, 2, 1, 0, 0, 0, 0, 0, 0\}$.

19.8 (a) $\dfrac{n_j}{n_0} = e^{-\beta j\varepsilon}$, which implies that $-j\beta\varepsilon = \ln n_j - \ln n_0$

and therefore that $\underline{\ln n_j = \ln n_0 - \dfrac{j\varepsilon}{kT}}$

Therefore, a plot of $\ln n_j$ against j should be a straight line with slope $-\varepsilon/kT$. Alternatively, plot $\ln p_j$ against j, since

$$\underline{\ln p_j = -j\varepsilon/kT}$$

We draw up the following table using the information in Problem 19.7:

j	0	1	2	3	
n_j	4	2	2	1	[most probable configuration]
$\ln n_j$	1.39	0.69	0.69	0	

These points are plotted in Fig. 19.3 (full line). The slope is -0.46, and since $\varepsilon/hc = 50\ \text{cm}^{-1}$, the slope corresponds to a temperature

$$T = \frac{50\ \text{cm}^{-1} \times 2.998 \times 10^{10}\ \text{cm s}^{-1} \times 6.626 \times 10^{-34}\ \text{J s}}{0.46 \times 1.381 \times 10^{-23}\ \text{J K}^{-1}}$$

$$= \underline{160\ \text{K}}$$

[A better estimate, 104 K, is found in Problem 19.9.]

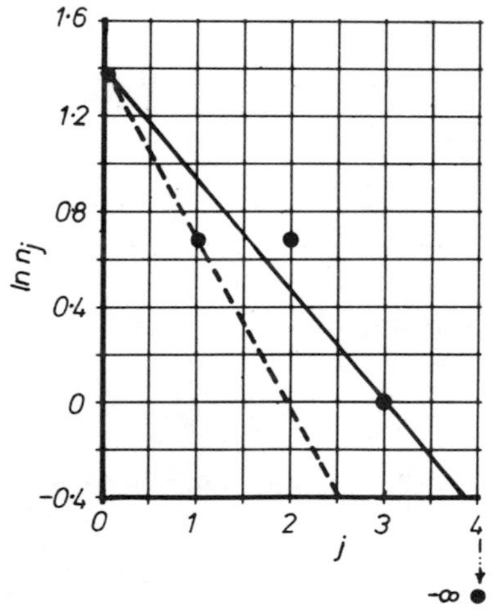

Fig 19.3

(b) Choose one of the weight 2520 configurations and one of the weight 504 configurations, and draw up the following table:

	j	0	1	2	3	4
$W=2520$	n_j	4	3	1	0	1
	$\ln n_j$	1.39	1.10	0	$-\infty$	0
$W=504$	n_j	6	0	1	1	1
	$\ln n_j$	1.79	$-\infty$	0	0	0

Inspection confirms that these data give very crooked lines.

19.9 (a) $U-U(0)=-N\dfrac{\mathrm{d}\ln q}{\mathrm{d}\beta}$ with $q=\dfrac{1}{1-\mathrm{e}^{\beta\varepsilon}}$

$$\frac{\mathrm{d}\ln q}{\mathrm{d}\beta}=\frac{1}{q}\frac{\mathrm{d}q}{\mathrm{d}\beta}=\frac{-\varepsilon\,\mathrm{e}^{-\beta\varepsilon}}{1-\mathrm{e}^{-\beta\varepsilon}}$$

$$a\varepsilon=\frac{U-U(0)}{N}=\frac{\varepsilon\,\mathrm{e}^{-\beta\varepsilon}}{1-\mathrm{e}^{-\beta\varepsilon}}=\frac{\varepsilon}{\mathrm{e}^{\beta\varepsilon}-1}$$

Hence, $\mathrm{e}^{\beta\varepsilon}=\dfrac{1+a}{a}$, implying that $\underline{\beta=\dfrac{1}{\varepsilon}\ln\left(1+\dfrac{1}{a}\right)}$

For $a=1$, $\beta=\dfrac{1}{\varepsilon}\ln 2$, implying that

$$T=\frac{\varepsilon}{k}\ln 2=50\ \mathrm{cm}^{-1}\times\frac{hc}{k}\ln 2=\underline{104\ \mathrm{K}}$$

(b) $q=\dfrac{1}{1-\mathrm{e}^{-\beta\varepsilon}}=\dfrac{1}{1-\left(\dfrac{a}{1+a}\right)}=\underline{1+a}$

(c) $$S/Nk=\frac{U-U(0)}{NkT}+\ln q$$

$$=a\beta\varepsilon+\ln q$$

$$=a\ln\left(1+\frac{1}{a}\right)+\ln(1+a)$$

$$=a\ln(1+a)-a\ln a+\ln(1+a)$$

$$=\underline{(1+a)\ln(1+a)-a\ln a}$$

When the mean energy is ε, $a=1$ and then $\underline{S/Nk=2\ln 2}$.

19.10 $$\frac{P_+}{P_-}=\mathrm{e}^{-\beta\varepsilon}$$

When $P_+>P_-$ it is necessary for $\beta<0$. For a negative temperature to describe a three-level system, the populations are specifically inverted as $T\to -T$ only if the separations $\varepsilon_2-\varepsilon_1$ and $\varepsilon_1-\varepsilon_0$ are equal.

20. Statistical thermodynamics: the machinery

Exercises

20.1 $C_V = \frac{1}{2}(3 + \nu_R^* + 2\nu_V^*)R$ [18]

with a mode active if $T > \theta_M$.

(a) $\nu_R^* = 2$, $\nu_V \approx 0$; hence $C_V = \frac{1}{2}(3+2)R = \underline{\frac{5}{2}R}$ [Experimental: $3.4R$]

(b) $\nu_R^* = 3$, $\nu_V \approx 0$; hence $C_V = \frac{1}{2}(3+3)R = \underline{3R}$ [Experimental: $3.2R$]

(c) $\nu_R^* = 3$, $\nu_V \approx 0$; hence $C_V = \frac{1}{2}(3+3)R = \underline{3R}$ [Experimental: $8.8R$]

Some of benzene's 30 vibrational modes must be at least partly active.

20.2 $$q = \frac{0.6950}{\sigma} \times \frac{T/\mathrm{K}}{(B/\mathrm{cm}^{-1})} \quad \text{[Table 20.2]}$$

$$= \frac{0.6950 \times (T/\mathrm{K})}{10.59} \quad [\sigma = 1] = 0.06563(T/\mathrm{K})$$

(a) $q = 0.06563 \times 298 = \underline{19.6}$

(b) $q = 0.06563 \times 523 = \underline{34.3}$

20.3 Look for the rotational subgroup of the molecule (the group of the molecule composed only of the identity and the rotational elements, and assess its order).

(a) CO. Full group $C_{\infty v}$; subgroup C_1; hence $\sigma = 1$

(b) O_2. Full group $D_{\infty h}$; subgroup C_2; hence $\sigma = 2$

(c) H_2S. Full group C_{2v}; subgroup C_2; hence $\sigma = 2$

(d) SiH_4. Full group T_d; subgroup T; hence $\sigma = 12$

(e) $CHCl_3$. Full group C_{3v}; subgroup C_3; hence $\sigma = 3$

20.4 $$q = \frac{1.0270}{\sigma} \frac{(T/\mathrm{K})^{3/2}}{(ABC/\mathrm{cm}^{-3})^{1/2}} \quad \text{[Table 20.2]}$$

$$= \frac{1.0270 \times 298^{3/2}}{2 \times (27.878 \times 14.509 \times 9.287)^{1/2}} \quad [\sigma = 2] = \underline{43.1}$$

The high temperature approximation is valid if $T > \theta_R$, where

$$\theta_R = \frac{hcB}{k} = 1.4388\ \text{cm K} \times B \quad \text{[inside front cover]}$$

$$= 1.4388\ \text{K} \times 27.878 \quad \text{[choose the 'worst case']}$$

$$= 40\ \text{K}$$

Therefore, the approximation is valid so long as T is substantially greater than $\underline{40\ \text{K}}$.

20.5 (a) $q = \sum_{JMK} \mathrm{e}^{-\beta E_J} \approx \frac{1}{\sigma} \sum_J (2J+1)^2\, \mathrm{e}^{-hcB\beta J(J+1)}$

$$hcB\beta = \frac{1.4388\ \text{K} \times 5.28}{T} = \frac{7.59\bar{7}}{T/\text{K}}, \quad \sigma = 12$$

$$q = \frac{1}{12} \sum_J (2J+1)^2\, \mathrm{e}^{-7.59\bar{7}J(J+1)/(T/\text{K})}$$

$$= \frac{1}{12}(1.0000 + 8.5526 + 21.4543 + 36.0863 + \cdots)$$

$$= \frac{1}{12} \times 439.27 = \underline{36.61} \text{ at } 298\ \text{K}$$

Similarly, at 500 K

$$q = \frac{1}{12}(1.0000 + 8.7306 + 22.8218 + 40.8335 + \cdots)$$

$$= \frac{1}{12} \times 950.06 = \underline{79.17}$$

[Note that the results are still approximate because the symmetry number is a valid corrector only at high temperatures. To get exact values of q we should do a detailed analysis of the rotational states allowed by the Pauli principle.]

(b) $q \approx \frac{1.0270}{\sigma} \times \frac{(T/\text{K})^{3/2}}{(B/\text{cm}^{-1})^{3/2}}$ [Table 20.2, $A = B = C$]

$$= \frac{1.0270}{12} \times \frac{(T/\text{K})^{3/2}}{(5.28)^{3/2}} = 7.054 \times 10^{-3} \times (T/\text{K})^{3/2}$$

At 298 K, $q=7.054\times10^{-3}\times298^{3/2}=\underline{36.3}$

At 500 K, $q=7.054\times10^{-3}\times500^{3/2}=\underline{78.9}$

20.6 $q=\dfrac{kT}{\sigma hcB}$ [9a], $B=\dfrac{\hbar}{4\pi cI}$, $I=\mu R^2$

Hence $q=\dfrac{8\pi^2kTI}{\sigma h^2}=\dfrac{8\pi^2kT\mu R^2}{\sigma h^2}$

For O_2, $\mu=\frac{1}{2}m(\mathrm{O})=\frac{1}{2}\times16.00\,\mathrm{u}=8.00\,\mathrm{u}$

and $\sigma=2$; therefore

$$q=\frac{8\pi^2\times1.381\times10^{-23}\,\mathrm{J\,K^{-1}}\times300\,\mathrm{K}\times8.00\times1.6605\times10^{-27}\,\mathrm{kg}\times(1.20\times10^{-10}\,\mathrm{m})^2}{2\times(6.626\times10^{-34}\,\mathrm{J\,s})^2}$$

$$=\underline{71.2}$$

20.7 $q=\dfrac{1.0270}{\sigma}\cdot\dfrac{(T/\mathrm{K})^{3/2}}{(ABC/\mathrm{cm}^{-3})^{1/2}}$ [Table 20.2, $\sigma=1$]

$$=\frac{1.0270\times(T/\mathrm{K})^{3/2}}{(3.1752\times0.3951\times0.3505)^{1/2}}=1.549\times(T/\mathrm{K})^{3/2}$$

(a) $q=1.549\times298^{3/2}=\underline{7.97\times10^3}$

(b) $q=1.549\times373^{3/2}=\underline{1.12\times10^4}$

20.8 $C_V/R=f^2,\ f=\left(\dfrac{\theta_V}{T}\right)\left(\dfrac{e^{-\frac{1}{2}\theta_V/T}}{1-e^{-\theta_V/T}}\right)$ [17]

We write $x=\theta_V/T$; then

$$C_V/R=\frac{x^2\,e^{-x}}{(1-e^{-x})^2}$$

This function is plotted in Fig. 20.1. For the acetylene (ethyne) calculation, use the expression above for each mode. We draw up the following table using $kT/hc=207\,\mathrm{cm}^{-1}$ at 298 K and $348\,\mathrm{cm}^{-1}$ at 500 K, and $\theta_V/T=hc\tilde{\nu}/kT$.

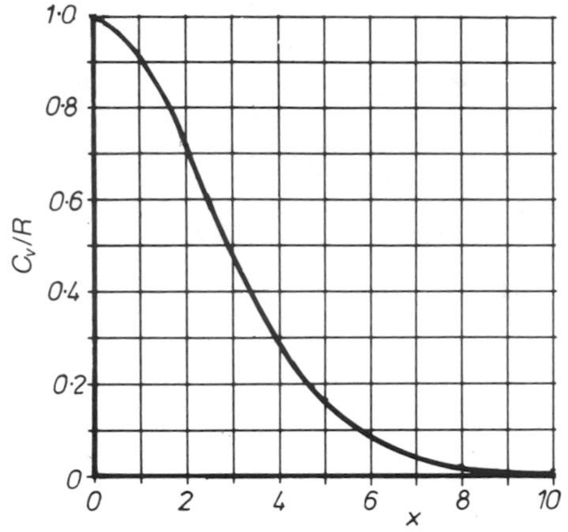

Fig 20.1

	x		C_V/R	
$\tilde{\nu}/\mathrm{cm}^{-1}$	298 K	500 K	298 K	500 K
612	2.96	1.76	0.505	0.777
612	2.96	1.76	0.505	0.777
729	3.52	2.09	0.389	0.704
729	3.52	2.09	0.389	0.704
1974	9.54	5.67	0.007	0.112
3287	15.88	9.45	3.2×10^{-5}	0.007
3374	16.30	9.70	3.2×10^{-5}	0.006

The heat capacity of the molecule is the sum of these contributions, namely 1.796 at 298 K and 3.086 at 500 K.

20.9 $q=\sum_{i} \mathrm{e}^{-\beta\varepsilon_i}=\underline{1+\mathrm{e}^{-\beta\varepsilon}}$

$$U-U(0)=\frac{N}{q}\sum_{i}\varepsilon_i\,\mathrm{e}^{-\beta\varepsilon_i}=\frac{N\varepsilon\,\mathrm{e}^{-\beta\varepsilon}}{1+\mathrm{e}^{-\beta\varepsilon}}$$

$$C_V = \left(\frac{\partial U}{\partial T}\right)_V = -\frac{1}{kT^2}\left(\frac{\partial U}{\partial \beta}\right)_V = \left(\frac{N\varepsilon^2}{kT^2}\right)\frac{e^{-\beta\varepsilon}}{(1+e^{-\beta\varepsilon})^2}$$

Hence, for molar quantities

$$C_V/R = \frac{x^2 e^{-x}}{(1+e^{-x})^2}, \quad x = \beta\varepsilon = \frac{\varepsilon}{kT}$$

The three functions are drawn in Fig. 20.2.

Fig 20.2

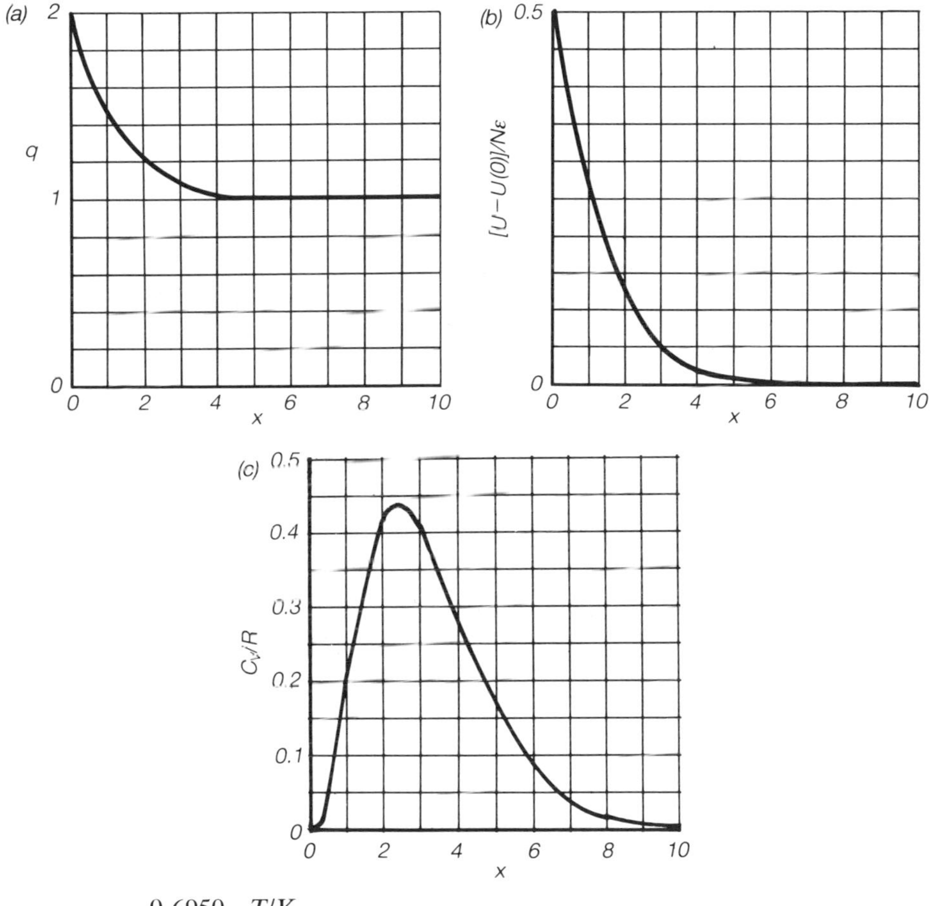

20.10 $q^R = \frac{0.6950}{\sigma}\frac{T/K}{B/cm^{-1}}$ [Table 20.2, $\sigma = 2$]

$$= \frac{0.6950 \times 298}{2 \times 0.3902} = 265$$

$$q^{\mathrm{V}}=\left(\frac{1}{1-\mathrm{e}^{-a}}\right)\left(\frac{1}{1-\mathrm{e}^{-b}}\right)^{2}\left(\frac{1}{1-\mathrm{e}^{-c}}\right) \quad \text{[Table 20.2]}$$

$$\text{with } a=\frac{1.4388\times 1388.2}{298}=6.70\overline{2}$$

$$b=\frac{1.4388\times 667.4}{298}=3.22\overline{2}$$

$$c=\frac{1.4388\times 2349.2}{298}=11.3\overline{4}$$

Hence,

$$q^{\mathrm{V}}=\frac{1}{1-\mathrm{e}^{-6.702}}\times\left(\frac{1}{1-\mathrm{e}^{-3.222}}\right)^{2}\times\frac{1}{1-\mathrm{e}^{-11.34}}=1.08\overline{6}$$

In each case the contribution to G is given by

$$G-G(0)=-nRT\ln q \quad \text{[Table 20.1]}$$

Therefore, the rotational contribution to the molar Gibbs functions is

$$-RT\ln q^{\mathrm{R}}=-8.314\ \mathrm{J\ K^{-1}\ mol^{-1}}\times 298\ \mathrm{K}\times\ln 265$$

$$=\underline{-13.8\ \mathrm{kJ\ mol^{-1}}}$$

and the vibrational contribution is

$$-RT\ln q^{\mathrm{V}}=-8.314\ \mathrm{J\ K^{-1}\ mol^{-1}}\times 298\ \mathrm{K}\times\ln 1.08\overline{6}$$

$$=\underline{-0.20\ \mathrm{kJ\ mol^{-1}}}$$

20.11 $q=4+2\mathrm{e}^{-\beta\varepsilon}$ [$^{2}\mathrm{P}_{3/2}$ has 4 states, $^{2}\mathrm{P}_{1/2}$ has 2]

$$U-U(0)=-\frac{N}{q}\frac{dq}{d\beta}=\frac{N\varepsilon\,e^{-\beta\varepsilon}}{2+e^{-\beta\varepsilon}}$$

$$C_V=\left(\frac{\partial U}{\partial T}\right)_V=-k\beta^2\left(\frac{\partial U}{\partial \beta}\right)_V$$

$$=\frac{2R(\varepsilon\beta)^2\,e^{-\beta\varepsilon}}{(2+e^{-\beta\varepsilon})^2}$$

Therefore, since at 500 K $\beta\varepsilon=2.53\bar{5}$

$$C_V/R=\frac{2\times 2.53\bar{5}^2\times e^{-2.53\bar{5}}}{(2+e^{-2.53\bar{5}})^2}=\underline{0.236}$$

At 900 K, when $\beta\varepsilon=1.408$,

$$C_V/R=\frac{2\times 1.408^2\times e^{-1.408}}{(2+e^{-1.408})^2}=\underline{0.193}$$

Note that C_V is smaller at 900 K than at 500 K, for then the temperature is higher than the peak in the 'two-level' heat capacity curve.

20.12 $q=3+2e^{-\beta\varepsilon}$ [the $^3\Sigma$ term is triply degenerate, and the $^1\Delta$ term is doubly (orbitally) degenerate]

$$\text{At 400 K, } \beta\varepsilon=\frac{1.4388\text{ cm K}\times 7918.1\text{ cm}^{-1}}{400\text{ K}}=28.48$$

Therefore, the contribution to G is

$$-RT\ln q=-8.314\text{ J K}^{-1}\text{ mol}^{-1}\times 400\text{ K}\times\ln(3+2\times e^{-28.48})$$

$$=-8.314\text{ J K}^{-1}\text{ mol}^{-1}\times 400\text{ K}\times\ln 3$$

$$=\underline{-3.65\text{ kJ mol}^{-1}}$$

20.13 The spin degeneracy of Co^{2+} is 4 [the ion is a spin quartet], so $q=4$. The contribution to the entropy is

$$R\ln q=8.314\text{ J K}^{-1}\text{ mol}^{-1}\times\ln 4=\underline{11.5\text{ J K}^{-1}\text{ mol}^{-1}}$$

20.14 $C_V=\frac{1}{2}(3+\nu_R^*+2\nu_V^*)R$ [18]

with $\nu_R^*=3$ and $\nu_V^*=0$. Hence $C_V=3R$; and since $C_p-C_V=R$, $C_p=4R=\underline{33.3\text{ J K}^{-1}\text{ mol}^{-1}}$. The experimental value is slightly greater, signifying a contribution either from the excitation of molecular vibration or from gas imperfections.

20.15 In each case $S_m = R \ln s$ [19]. Therefore,

(a) $S_m = R \ln 3 = 1.1R = \underline{9\ \text{J K}^{-1}\ \text{mol}^{-1}}$

(b) $S_m = R \ln 5 = 1.6R = \underline{13\ \text{J K}^{-1}\ \text{mol}^{-1}}$

(c) $S_m = R \ln 6 = 1.8R = \underline{15\ \text{J K}^{-1}\ \text{mol}^{-1}}$

20.16 Use $S_m = R \ln s$ [19]. Draw up the following table:

n:	0	1	2			3			4			5	6
			o	m	p	a	b	c	o	m	p		
s	1	6	6	6	6	3	6	6	6	6	3	6	1
S_m/R	0	1.8	1.8	1.8	1.8	1.1	1.8	1.8	1.8	1.8	1.1	1.8	0

where a is the 1, 2, 3 isomer, b the 1, 2, 4 isomer, and c the 1, 3, 5 isomer.

20.17 $$\frac{q^{\mathrm{T}}}{N_{\mathrm{A}}} = 2.561 \times 10^{-2} \times (T/\mathrm{K})^{5/2} \times (M/\mathrm{g\ mol^{-1}})^{3/2} \quad [\text{Table 20.2}]$$

$$= 2.561 \times 10^{-2} \times (298)^{5/2} \times (28.02)^{3/2} = 5.823 \times 10^{6}$$

$$q^{\mathrm{R}} = \tfrac{1}{2} \times 0.6950 \times \frac{298}{1.9987} \quad [\text{Table 20.2}] = 51.81$$

$$q^{\mathrm{V}} = \frac{1}{1 - \mathrm{e}^{-2358/207.2}} = 1.00$$

Therefore, $$\frac{q^{\ominus}}{N_{\mathrm{A}}} = 5.82\bar{3} \times 10^{6} \times 51.8\bar{1} \times 1.00 = 3.02 \times 10^{8}$$

$U_m - U_m(0) = \tfrac{3}{2}RT + RT = \tfrac{5}{2}RT \quad [T \gg \theta_T, \theta_R]$

Hence

$$S_m^{\ominus} = \frac{U_m - U_m(0)}{T} + R\left\{\ln \frac{q_m^{\ominus}}{N_{\mathrm{A}}} + 1\right\} \quad [\text{Table 20.1}]$$

$$= \tfrac{5}{2}R + R\{\ln 3.02 \times 10^{8} + 1\} = 23.03R$$

$$= \underline{191.4\ \mathrm{J\ K^{-1}\ mol^{-1}}}$$

The difference between the experimental and calculated values is negligible, indicating that the residual entropy is zero.

20.18 $q^{\mathrm{T}}/N_{\mathrm{A}} = 2.561 \times 10^{-2}(T/\mathrm{K})^{5/2}(M/\mathrm{g\ mol^{-1}})^{3/2}$ [Table 20.2]

$$q^{\mathrm{T}}(\mathrm{I_2})/N_{\mathrm{A}} = 2.561 \times 10^{-2} \times 1000^{5/2} + 253.8^{3/2} = 3.27 \times 10^{9}$$

$$q^{\mathrm{T}}(\mathrm{I})/N_{\mathrm{A}} = 2.561 \times 10^{-2} \times 1000^{5/2} + 126.9^{3/2} = 1.16 \times 10^{9}$$

$$q^{\mathrm{R}}(\mathrm{I_2}) = \frac{0.6950}{\sigma} \times \frac{T/\mathrm{K}}{B/\mathrm{cm^{-1}}}$$

$$= \tfrac{1}{2} \times 0.6950 \times \frac{1000}{0.0373} = 931\bar{6}$$

$$q^{\mathrm{V}}(\mathrm{I_2}) = \frac{1}{1-\mathrm{e}^{-a}},\ a = 1.4388\frac{\tilde{\nu}/\mathrm{cm^{-1}}}{T/\mathrm{K}} \quad \text{[Table 20.2]}$$

$$= \frac{1}{1-\mathrm{e}^{-214.36/695}} = 3.77$$

$$q^{\mathrm{E}}(\mathrm{I}) = 4$$

$$q^{\mathrm{E}}(\mathrm{I_2}) = 1$$

Hence $K_p = \dfrac{(q^{\ominus}(\mathrm{I})/N_{\mathrm{A}})^2}{q^{\ominus}(\mathrm{I_2})/N_{\mathrm{A}}}\mathrm{e}^{-D_e/RT}$ [22]

$$= \frac{(1.16 \times 10^{9} \times 4)^2\,\mathrm{e}^{-17.9}}{3.27 \times 10^{9} \times 9316 \times 3.77} = \underline{3.2 \times 10^{-3}}$$

20.19 We need to calculate

$$K_p = \frac{q^{\ominus}(^{79}\mathrm{Br_2})q^{\ominus}(^{81}\mathrm{Br_2})}{q^{\ominus}(^{79}\mathrm{Br}^{81}\mathrm{Br})^2}\mathrm{e}^{-\Delta E_0/RT}$$

The ratio of the translational partition functions is virtually 1 [because the masses nearly cancel; explicit calculation gives 0.999]. The same is true of the vibrational partition functions. Although the moments of inertia cancel in the rotational partition functions, the two homonuclear species each have $\sigma = 2$, so

$$\frac{q^{\mathrm{R}}(^{79}\mathrm{Br_2})q^{\mathrm{R}}(^{81}\mathrm{Br_2})}{q^{\mathrm{R}}(^{79}\mathrm{Br}^{81}\mathrm{Br})^2} = 0.25$$

The value of ΔE_0 is also very small compared with RT, so

$K_p \approx \underline{0.25}$

Problems

20.1 $q^{\mathrm{V}} = \dfrac{1}{1-\mathrm{e}^{-hc\tilde{\nu}\beta}}$ [Table 20.2]

which rearranges to

$$\tilde{\nu}=\frac{-kT}{hc}\ln\left\{\frac{1}{1-\dfrac{1}{q}}\right\}$$

Therefore, if $q=1.001$,

$$\tilde{\nu}=\frac{-500\text{ K}}{1.4388\text{ cm K}}\ln\left\{\frac{1}{1-\dfrac{1}{1.001}}\right\}=\underline{2.4\times10^{3}\text{ cm}^{-1}}$$

20.2 $q=2+2e^{-\beta\varepsilon}$

Therefore, $C_V/R=\dfrac{x^2e^{-x}}{(1+e^{-x})^2}$, $x=\beta\varepsilon$

We then draw up the following table:

T/K	50	298	500
$(kT/hc)/\text{cm}^{-1}$	34.8	207	348
x	3.46	0.585	0.348
C_V/R	0.354	0.079	0.029
$C_V/(\text{J K}^{-1}\text{ mol}^{-1})$	2.94	0.654	0.244

Note that the double degeneracies do not affect the results because the two factors of 2 in q cancel when U is formed. In the range of temperatures specified, the electronic contribution to the heat capacity decreases with increasing temperature.

20.3 $C_V/R=\dfrac{x^2e^{-x}}{(1+x)^2}$ [Problem 20.2], $x=2\mu_B B\beta$

Therefore, if $B=5.0$ T,

$$x=\frac{2\times9.274\times10^{-24}\text{ J T}^{-1}\times5.0\text{ T}}{1.381\times10^{-23}\text{ J K}^{-1}\times T}=\frac{6.72}{T/\text{K}}$$

(a) $T=50$ K, $x=0.134$, $C_V=4.47\times10^{-3}R$, implying that $C_V=$ $\underline{3.7\times10^{-2}\text{ J K}^{-1}\text{ mol}^{-1}}$. Since the equipartition value is about $3R$ $[\nu_R^*=3, \nu_V^*\approx0]$, the field brings about a change of about 0.1 per cent.

(b) $T=298$ K, $x=2.26\times10^{-2}$, $C_V=1.3\times10^{-4}R$, implying that $C_V=$ $\underline{1.1\ \text{mJ K}^{-1}\ \text{mol}^{-1}}$, a change of about 4×10^{-3} per cent.

20.4 $$q=\sum_{m=-\infty}^{\infty} e^{-m^2\hbar^2/2IkT}$$

$$\approx\frac{1}{\sigma}\int_{-\infty}^{\infty} e^{-m^2\hbar^2/2IkT}\,dm=\frac{1}{\sigma}\left(\frac{2IkT}{\hbar^2}\right)^{1/2}\int_{-\infty}^{\infty} e^{-x^2}\,dx$$

$$\approx\frac{1}{\sigma}\left(\frac{2\pi IkT}{\hbar^2}\right)^{1/2}$$

$$U-U(0)=-\frac{N}{q}\frac{\partial q}{\partial\beta}=\frac{N}{2\beta}=\tfrac{1}{2}NkT \quad \text{[or get by equipartition]}$$

$$C_V=\left(\frac{\partial U}{\partial T}\right)_V=\tfrac{1}{2}R=\underline{4.2\ \text{J K}^{-1}\ \text{mol}^{-1}}$$

$$S_m=\frac{U_m-U_m(0)}{T}+R\ln q \quad \text{[Table 20.1]}$$

$$=\tfrac{1}{2}R+R\ln\frac{1}{\sigma}\left(\frac{2\pi IkT}{\hbar^2}\right)^{1/2}$$

$$=\tfrac{1}{2}R+R\ln\frac{1}{3}\left(\frac{2\pi\times5.341\times10^{-47}\ \text{kg m}^2\times1.381\times10^{-23}\ \text{J K}^{-1}\times298}{(1.055\times10^{-34}\ \text{J s})^2}\right)^{1/2}$$

$$=\tfrac{1}{2}R+1.31R=\underline{1.81R}, \text{ or } 15\ \text{J K}^{-1}\ \text{mol}^{-1}$$

20.5 $q=1+5e^{-\beta\varepsilon}$

$$\varepsilon=E(J=2)-E(J=0)=6hcB \quad [E=hcBJ(J+1)]$$

$$\frac{U-U(0)}{N}=\frac{5\varepsilon\, e^{-\beta\varepsilon}}{1+5e^{-\beta\varepsilon}}$$

$$C_V/R=\frac{5\varepsilon^2\beta^2 e^{-\beta\varepsilon}}{(1+5e^{-\beta\varepsilon})^2}=\frac{180(hcB\beta)^2 e^{-6hcB\beta}}{(1+5e^{-6hcB\beta})^2}$$

$$\frac{hcB}{k}=1.4388\ \text{cm K}\times60.864\ \text{cm}^{-1}=87.571\ \text{K}$$

Hence,

$$C_V/R = \frac{1.380\times 10^6\,\mathrm{e}^{-525.4\,\mathrm{K}/T}}{(1+5\mathrm{e}^{-525.4\,\mathrm{K}/T})^2}$$

and the draw up the following table:

T/K	50	100	150	200	250	300	350	400	450	500
C_V/R	0.02	0.68	1.40	1.35	1.04	0.76	0.56	0.42	0.32	0.26

These points are plotted in Fig. 20.3.

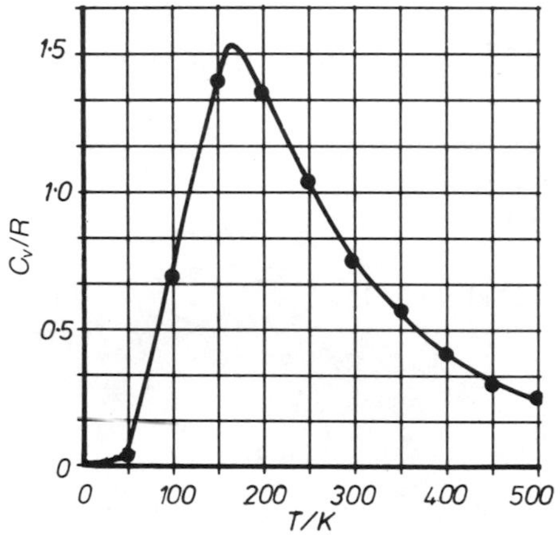

Fig 20.3

20.6 $$S_m = \frac{U_m + U_m(0)}{T} + R\ln q^R \quad \text{[Table 20.1, internal modes]}$$

$$q^R = \frac{\pi^{1/2}}{\sigma}\left\{\left(\frac{2I_\parallel kT}{\hbar^2}\right)\left(\frac{2I_\perp kT}{\hbar^2}\right)^2\right\}^{1/2} \quad \text{[Table 20.2]}$$

$$= \frac{1}{\sigma}\left\{8\pi I_\parallel I_\perp^2\left(\frac{kT}{\hbar^2}\right)^3\right\}^{1/2} \quad [\sigma = 12]$$

$$= \frac{1}{12}\{8\pi\times 2.93\times 10^{-45}\ \mathrm{kg\,m^2}\times(1.46\times 10^{-45}\ \mathrm{kg\,m^2})^2$$

$$\times\left(\frac{1.381\times 10^{-23}\ \mathrm{J\,K^{-1}}\times 362\ \mathrm{K}}{(1.055\times 10^{-34}\ \mathrm{J\,s})^2}\right)^3\Bigg\}^{1/2}$$

$$= 9950$$

$$\frac{U_m - U_m(0)}{T} = \tfrac{3}{2}R \quad \text{[from } q^R\text{, or by equipartition]}$$

Therefore, $S_m = \tfrac{3}{2}R + R \ln 9950$

$$= \underline{10.7R}, \text{ or } 89 \text{ J K}^{-1}\text{ mol}^{-1}.$$

In two dimensions (rotation about one axis)

$$q^R = \frac{1}{\sigma}\left(\frac{2\pi I_\| kT}{\hbar^2}\right)^{1/2} \quad \text{[Problem 20.4]}$$

$$= \frac{1}{6}\left\{\frac{2\pi \times 2.93\times 10^{-45}\text{ kg m}^2 \times 1.381\times 10^{-23}\text{ J K}^{-1}\times 362\text{ K}}{(1.055\times 10^{-34}\text{ J s})^2}\right\}^{1/2}$$

$$= 15.2$$

$$U_m - U_m(0) = \tfrac{1}{2}R \quad \text{[from } q^R\text{, or by equipartition]}$$

Therefore, $S_m = \tfrac{1}{2}R + R \ln 15.2$

$$= \underline{3.2R}, \text{ or } 27 \text{ J K}^{-1}\text{ mol}^{-1}$$

Hence, the change in rotational entropy on adsorption is

$$\Delta S_m = 27 - 89 \text{ J K}^{-1}\text{ mol}^{-1} = \underline{-62 \text{ J K}^{-1}\text{ mol}^{-1}}$$

The change in translational entropy on adsorption is

$$\Delta S_m^T = R \ln \frac{\sigma^\ominus}{V^\ominus}\left(\frac{h^2\beta}{2\pi m\,\text{e}}\right)^{1/2} \quad \text{[Problem 20.13]}$$

$$V^\ominus = \frac{1.0 \text{ mol} \times RT}{p^\ominus} = 8.21\times 10^{-5}\text{ m}^3(T/\text{K})$$

$$\sigma^\ominus = 1.0 \text{ mol} \times 4.08\times 10^{-18}\text{ m}^2 \times 6.022\times 10^{23}\text{ mol}^{-1} \times T/\text{K}$$

$$= 2.46\times 10^4\text{ m}^2(T/\text{K})$$

[The standard state of a mobile, two-dimensional film is defined so that the average separation of adsorbed molecules at 273 K is the same as in a three-dimensional gas at 273 K and 1 bar; see the original reference.]

$$\frac{\sigma^\ominus}{V^\ominus} = \frac{2.46\times 10^4\text{ m}^2(T/\text{K})}{8.21\times 10^{-5}\text{ m}^3(T/\text{K})} = 3.00\times 10^8\text{ m}^{-1}$$

$$\left(\frac{h^2\beta}{2\pi m\,\text{e}}\right)^{1/2} = \frac{6.626\times 10^{-34}\text{ J s}}{(2\pi\,\text{e}\times 78.12\times 1.6605\times 10^{-27}\text{ kg}\times 1.381\times 10^{-23}\text{ J K}^{-1}\times T)^{1/2}}$$

$$=\frac{1.20\times 10^{-10}\,\mathrm{m}}{(T/\mathrm{K})^{1/2}}$$

Therefore, $\Delta S_{\mathrm{m}}^{\mathrm{T}}=R\ln\dfrac{3.00\times 10^{8}\,\mathrm{m}^{-1}\times 1.20\times 10^{-10}\,\mathrm{m}}{362^{1/2}}$

$$=\underline{-6.3R},\text{ or }-52\,\mathrm{J\,K^{-1}\,mol^{-1}}.$$

Hence, the overall change in entropy is

$$\Delta S_{\mathrm{m}}=-52-62\,\mathrm{J\,K^{-1}\,mol^{-1}}=\underline{-114\,\mathrm{J\,K^{-1}\,mol^{-1}}}$$

which is in agreement with the experimental value ($-111\,\mathrm{J\,K^{-1}\,mol^{-1}}$) at low surface coverage, suggesting that the model of a mobile, single-axis roation layer is appropriate. (However, the data cannot identify which of the molecular axes is involved: we have assumed rotation about the figure axis.)

At higher surface coverages the change in entropy is only $-52\,\mathrm{J\,K^{-1}\,mol^{-1}}$, suggesting that rotation about all three axes is then possible, so that only the translational contribution ($\Delta S_{\mathrm{m}}^{\mathrm{T}}=-52\,\mathrm{J\,K^{-1}\,mol^{-1}}$) occurs.

20.7 The absorption lines are the values of $\{E(J+1)-E(J)\}/hc$ for $J=0, 1, \ldots$. Therefore, we can reconstruct the energy levels from the data using

$$hc\beta=\frac{hc}{kT}=207.223\,\mathrm{cm}^{-1}\quad\text{[inside front cover]}$$

$$q=\sum_{J=0}^{\infty}(2J+1)\,\mathrm{e}^{-\beta hcE(J)}$$

$$=1+3\mathrm{e}^{-21.19/207.223}+5\mathrm{e}^{-(21.19+42.37)/207.223}+7\mathrm{e}^{-(21.19+42.37+63.56)/207.223}+\cdots$$

$$=1+2.708+3.679+3.790+\cdots=\underline{19.89}$$

20.8 $K=\dfrac{q^{\ominus}(\mathrm{CHD_3})q^{\ominus}(\mathrm{DCl})}{q^{\ominus}(\mathrm{CD_4})q^{\ominus}(\mathrm{HCl})}\,\mathrm{e}^{-\beta\Delta E_0}\quad[22]$

The ratio of translational partition functions is

$$\frac{q^{\mathrm{T}}(\mathrm{CHD_3})q^{\mathrm{T}}(\mathrm{DCl})}{q^{\mathrm{T}}(\mathrm{CD_4})q^{\mathrm{T}}(\mathrm{HCl})}=\left\{\frac{M(\mathrm{CHD_3})M(\mathrm{DCl})}{M(\mathrm{CD_4})M(\mathrm{HCl})}\right\}^{3/2}$$

$$=\left\{\frac{19.06\times 37.46}{20.07\times 36.46}\right\}^{3/2}=0.964$$

The ratio of rotational partition functions is

$$\frac{q^R(CHD_s)q^R(DCl)}{q^R(CD_4)q^R(HCl)}=\frac{\sigma(CD_4)}{\sigma(CHD_3)}\frac{(B(CD_4)/\text{cm}^{-1})^{3/2}B(HCl)/\text{cm}^{-1}}{(A(CHD_3)B(CHD_3)^2/\text{cm}^{-3})^{1/2}B(DCl)/\text{cm}^{-1}}$$

$$=\frac{12}{3}\times\frac{2.63^{3/2}\times 10.59}{(2.63\times 3.28^2)^{1/2}\times 5.445}=6.24$$

The ratio of vibrational partition functions is

$$\frac{q^V(CHD_3)q^V(DCl)}{q^V(CD_4)q^V(HCl)}=\frac{q(2993)q(2142)q(1003)^3q(1291)^2q(1036)^2q(2145)}{q(2109)q(1092)^2q(2259)^3q(996)^3q(2991)}$$

where $q(x)=\dfrac{1}{1-e^{-1.4388x/(T/K)}}$

We also require ΔE_0, which is equal to the difference in zero point energies:

$$\Delta E_0/hc=\tfrac{1}{2}\{(2993+2142+3\times 1003+2\times 1291+2\times 1036+2145)$$
$$-(2109+2\times 1092\times 3\times 2259\times 3\times 996+2291)\}\ \text{cm}^{-1}$$
$$=-990\ \text{cm}^{-1}$$

Hence,

$$K=0.964\times 6.24\times Q\,e^{+1.4388\times 990/(T/K)}$$
$$=6.02Q\,e^{+1424/(T/K)}$$

where Q is the ratio of vibrational partition functions. We can now evaluate K (on a computer), and obtain the following values:

T/K	500	1000	1500	2000	2500	3000	3500	4000	4500	5000
K	110	34	26	23	22	22	21	21	21	21

20.9 $H_2O+DCl\rightleftharpoons HDO+HCl$

$$K=\frac{q^\ominus(HDO)q^\ominus(HCl)}{q^\ominus(H_2O)q^\ominus(DCl)}e^{-\beta\Delta E_0}$$

The ratio of translational partition functions [Table 20.2] is

$$\frac{q^T(HDO)q^T(HCl)}{q^T(H_2O)q^T(DCl)}=\left\{\frac{M(HDO)M(HCl)}{M(H_2O)M(DCl)}\right\}^{3/2}$$

$$=\left\{\frac{19.02\times 36.46}{18.02\times 37.46}\right\}^{3/2}=1.041$$

The ratio of rotational partition functions is

$$\frac{q^{\mathrm{R}}(\mathrm{HDO})q^{\mathrm{R}}(\mathrm{HCl})}{q^{\mathrm{R}}(\mathrm{H_2O})q^{\mathrm{R}}(\mathrm{DCl})}=2\times\frac{(27.88\times 14.51\times 9.29)^{1/2}\times 5.449}{(23.38\times 9.102\times 6.417)^{1/2}\times 10.59}=1.707$$

[$\sigma=2$ for H_2O, $\sigma=1$ for the other molecules].

The ratio of vibrational partition functions is

$$\frac{q^{\mathrm{V}}(\mathrm{HDO})q^{\mathrm{V}}(\mathrm{HCl})}{q^{\mathrm{V}}(\mathrm{H_2O})q^{\mathrm{V}}(\mathrm{DCl})}=\frac{q(2726.7)q(1402.2)q(3707.5)q(2991)}{q(3656.7)q(1594.8)q(3755.8)q(2145)}=Q$$

where $q(x)=\dfrac{1}{1-\mathrm{e}^{-1.4388\times x/(T/\mathrm{K})}}$

We also need ΔE_0 from the difference in zero-point energies:

$$\begin{aligned}\Delta E_0/hc&=\tfrac{1}{2}\{2726.7+1402.2+3707.5+2991)\\&\quad-(3656.7+1594.8+3755.8+2145)\}\ \mathrm{cm}^{-1}\\&=-162\ \mathrm{cm}^{-1}\end{aligned}$$

Therefore,

$$\begin{aligned}K&=1.041\times 1.707\times Q\times \mathrm{e}^{1.4388\times 162/(T/\mathrm{K})}\\&=1.777Q\,\mathrm{e}^{233/(T/\mathrm{K})}\end{aligned}$$

We then draw up the following table (using a computer):

T/K	100	200	300	400	500	600	700	800	900	1000
K	18.3	5.70	3.87	3.19	2.85	2.65	2.51	2.41	2.34	2.29

and specifically $K=\underline{3.89}$ at 298 K and $\underline{2.41}$ at 800 K.

21.10 $\Phi_0=\dfrac{G_{\mathrm{m}}(T)-H_{\mathrm{m}}(0)}{T}=\dfrac{G_{\mathrm{m}}(T)-G_{\mathrm{m}}(0)}{\mathrm{T}}$

$$=-R\ln\frac{q^{\mathrm{T}}q^{\mathrm{i}}}{N_{\mathrm{A}}}\quad\text{[Table 20.1]}$$

where q^{i} is the partition function for the internal modes.

(a) H_2: $\left(\dfrac{q^{\mathrm{T}}}{N_{\mathrm{A}}}\right)^{\ominus}=0.02561\times 1000^{5/2}\times 2.016^{3/2}=2.32\times 10^{6}$

$$q^{\mathrm{R}} = \frac{1}{2} \times \frac{0.6950 \times 1000}{60.864} = 5.711$$

$$q^{\mathrm{V}} = \frac{1}{1 - e^{-4400.39/695.3}} = 1.002$$

Hence $\Phi_0^{\ominus} = -R \ln 2.32 \times 10^6 \times 5.711 \times 1.002$

$$= -R \ln 1.33 \times 10^7 = \underline{-136 \text{ J K}^{-1} \text{ mol}^{-1}}$$

(b) $N_2 \left(\frac{q^{\mathrm{T}}}{N_{\mathrm{A}}}\right)^{\ominus} = 0.02561 \times 1000^{5/2} \times 28.02^{3/2} = 1.20 \times 10^8$

$$q^{\mathrm{R}} = \frac{1}{2} \times \frac{0.6950 \times 1000}{1.9987} = 173.9$$

$$q^{\mathrm{V}} = \frac{1}{1 - e^{-2358.07/695.3}} = 1.035$$

Hence $\Phi_0^{\ominus} = -R \ln 1.20 \times 10^8 \times 173.9 \times 1.035$

$$= -R \ln 2.16 \times 10^{10} = \underline{-198 \text{ J K}^{-1} \text{ mol}^{-1}}$$

(c) $NH_3 \left(\frac{q^{\mathrm{T}}}{N_{\mathrm{A}}}\right)^{\ominus} = 0.02561 \times 1000^{5/2} \times 17.03^{3/2} = 5.69 \times 10^7$

$$q^{\mathrm{R}} = \frac{1}{3} \times \frac{1.0270 \times 1000^{3/2}}{(6.34 \times 9.44^2)^{1/2}} = 455$$

$$q^{\mathrm{V}} = q(3336.7)q(950.4)q(3443.8)^2 q(1626.8)^2$$

where $q(x) = \frac{1}{1 - e^{-1.4388x/(T/\mathrm{K})}} = \frac{1}{1 - e^{-x/695.0}} = 1.68$

Hence

$$\Phi_0^{\ominus} = -R \ln 5.69 \times 10^7 \times 455 \times 1.68 = \underline{-204 \text{ J K}^{-1} \text{ mol}^{-1}}$$

For the equilibrium $N_2 + 3H_2 \rightleftharpoons 2NH_3$ we need

$$\Delta\Phi_0^{\ominus} = 2(-204) - (-198) - 3 \times (-136) \text{ J K}^{-1} \text{ mol}^{-1}$$

$$= +198 \text{ J K}^{-1} \text{ mol}^{-1}$$

Then proceed as in Section 9.4 (Example 9.6) using the data in Table 9.1. Specifically $\Delta H^{\ominus}(\mathcal{T}) = -92.2 \text{ kJ mol}^{-1}$ and

$$\Delta\{H_{\mathrm{m}}(\mathcal{T}) - H_{\mathrm{m}}(0)\} = 2 \times 9.92 - 8.669 - 3 \times 8.468 \text{ kJ mol}^{-1}$$

$$= -14.23 \text{ kJ mol}^{-1}$$

Hence

$$\frac{\Delta G_m^{\ominus}(T)}{T} = 198 + \frac{14.23 \times 10^3}{1000} - \frac{92.2 \times 10^3}{1000} \text{ J K}^{-1}\text{ mol}^{-1}$$

$$= +120 \text{ J K}^{-1}\text{ mol}^{-1}$$

and

$$K = e^{-120/8.314} = e^{-14.4} = \underline{5.6 \times 10^{-7}}$$

20.11 $\Phi_0 = -R \ln q$ and $q = \sum_J (2J+1)\, e^{-hc\beta\tilde{\nu}_J}$

since each J level is $(2J+1)$-fold degenerate. We then draw up the following table:

T/K	1000	2000	3000	4000	5000
$(kT/hc)/\text{cm}^{-1}$	695	1391	2085	2780	3475
q	2.000	2.000	2.002	2.014	2.053
$\Phi_0/(\text{J K}^{-1}\text{ mol}^{-1})$	−5.76	−5.76	−5.77	−5.82	−5.98

20.12 $Na_2(g) \rightleftharpoons 2Na(g)$, $K = \dfrac{q^{\ominus}(\text{Na})^2}{q^{\ominus}(\text{Na}_2)N_A} e^{-D_0/RT}$

$$q^T(\text{Na})/N_A = 0.02561 \times 1163^{5/2} \times 22.99^{3/2} = 130 \times 10^8$$

$$q^T(\text{Na}_2)/N_A = 3.68 \times 10^8$$

$$q^R(\text{Na}_2) = \tfrac{1}{2} \times 0.6950 \times \frac{1163}{0.1547} = 2612$$

$$q^V(\text{Na}_2) = \frac{1}{1 - e^{-159/808}} = 5.60$$

$q^E(\text{Na}) = 2.00$ [Problem 20.11]

Hence, $K = \dfrac{(2.00 \times 1.30 \times 10^8)^2}{3.68 \times 10^8 \times 2612 \times 5.60} \times e^{-70.4/9.67} = \underline{8.7}$

If the degree of dissociation is α at equilibrium, we have

$$\alpha=\left(\frac{K}{K+4p/p^{\ominus}}\right)^{1/2} \quad \text{[eqn 9 of Section 9.3]}$$

$$=\left(\frac{8.7}{8.7+4.0}\right)^{1/2}=0.83 \quad [p=p^{\ominus}]$$

Hence, at equilibrium the mole fractions are

$$x(\mathrm{Na_2})=\frac{1-\alpha}{1+\alpha}=\underline{0.095},\ x(\mathrm{Na})=\frac{2\alpha}{1+\alpha}=\underline{0.905}$$

20.13 $q^{\mathrm{T}}=q_x^{\mathrm{T}}q_y^{\mathrm{T}}$ with $q_x^{\mathrm{T}}=\left(\frac{2\pi mX^2}{\beta h^2}\right)^{1/2}$

Therefore,

$$q^{\mathrm{T}}=\left(\frac{2\pi m}{\beta h^2}\right)XY=\frac{2\pi m\sigma}{\beta h^2},\ \sigma=XY$$

$$U_{\mathrm{m}}-U_{\mathrm{m}}(0)=-\frac{N_{\mathrm{A}}}{q}\left(\frac{\partial q}{\partial \beta}\right)=RT$$

$$S_{\mathrm{m}}=\frac{U_{\mathrm{m}}-U_{\mathrm{m}}(0)}{T}+R(\ln q_{\mathrm{m}}-\ln N_{\mathrm{A}}+1) \quad \text{[Table 20.1]}$$

$$=R+R\ln(\mathrm{e}\,q_{\mathrm{m}}/N_{\mathrm{A}})=R\ln(\mathrm{e}^2\,q_{\mathrm{m}}/N_{\mathrm{A}})$$

$$=R\ln\left(\frac{2\pi\,\mathrm{e}^2\,m\sigma_{\mathrm{m}}}{h^2N_{\mathrm{A}}\beta}\right) \quad [\sigma_{\mathrm{m}}=\sigma/n]$$

Since in three dimensions

$$S_{\mathrm{m}}=R\ln\left\{\mathrm{e}^{5/2}\left(\frac{2\pi m}{h^2\beta}\right)^{3/2}\frac{V_{\mathrm{m}}}{N_{\mathrm{A}}}\right\} \quad \text{[Sackur–Tetrode equation]}$$

The entropy of condensation is the difference:

$$S_{\mathrm{m}}=\mathrm{R}\ln\frac{\mathrm{e}^2(2\pi m/h^2\beta)(\sigma_{\mathrm{m}}/N_{\mathrm{A}})}{\mathrm{e}^{5/2}(2\pi m/h^2\beta)^{3/2}(V_{\mathrm{m}}/N_{\mathrm{A}})}$$

$$=\underline{R\ln\left\{\left(\frac{\sigma_{\mathrm{m}}}{V_{\mathrm{m}}}\right)\left(\frac{h^2\beta}{2\pi m\,\mathrm{e}}\right)^{1/2}\right\}}$$

20.14 $q=\dfrac{1}{1-e^{-x}}$, $x=\hbar\omega\beta=hc\tilde{\nu}\beta=\dfrac{\theta_V}{T}$ [Table 20.2]

$$U-U(0)=-\frac{N}{q}\left(\frac{\partial q}{\partial \beta}\right)_V=-N(1-e^{-x})\frac{d}{d\beta}(1-e^{-x})^{-1}$$

$$=\frac{N\hbar\omega\, e^{-x}}{1-e^{-x}}=\underline{\frac{N\hbar\omega}{e^{x}-1}}$$

$$H-H(0)=U-U(0)=\frac{N\hbar\omega\, e^{-x}}{1-e^{-x}}=\underline{\frac{N\hbar\omega}{e^{x}-1}}$$

$$S=\frac{U-U(0)}{T}+nR\ln q=\frac{Nkx\, e^{-x}}{1-e^{-x}}-Nk\ln(1-e^{-x})$$

$$=\underline{Nk\left\{\frac{x}{e^{x}-1}-\ln(1-e^{-x})\right\}}$$

$$A-A(0)=G-G(0)=-nRT\ln q$$

$$=\underline{NkT\ln(1-e^{-x})}$$

The functions are plotted in Fig. 20.4.

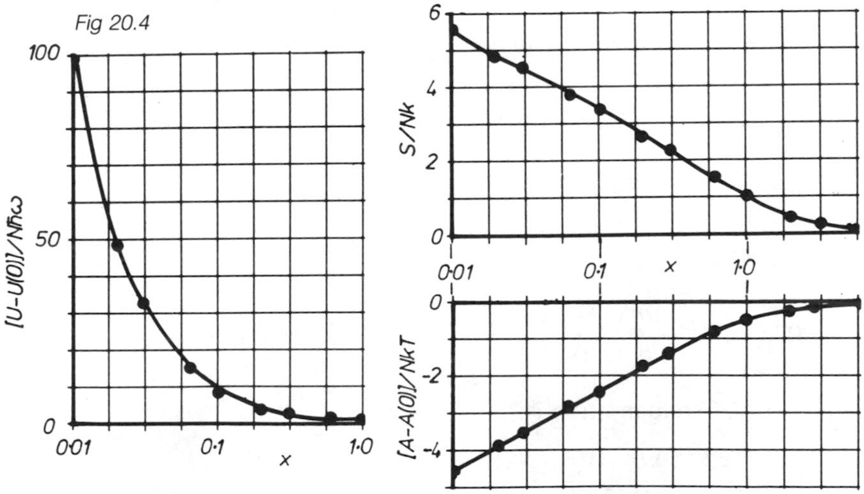

For several modes,

$$\Phi_0 = -R\sum_Q \ln q_Q = R\sum_Q \ln(1-\mathrm{e}^{-x_Q})$$

At 1000 K, $kT/hc = 695.03\ \mathrm{cm}^{-1}$, and so

$$x_1 = 4.80,\ x_2 = 1.37,\ x_3 = 4.95,\ x_4 = 2.34$$

and

$$\Phi_0 = R\ln\{(1-\mathrm{e}^{-4.80})(1-\mathrm{e}^{-1.37})(1-\mathrm{e}^{-4.95})^2(1-\mathrm{e}^{-2.34})^2\}$$

$$= -0.518R = \underline{-4.31\ \mathrm{J\,K^{-1}\,mol^{-1}}}$$

20.15 (a) $U - U(0) = -\dfrac{N}{q}\sum_j \varepsilon_j\,\mathrm{e}^{-\beta\varepsilon_j} = \dfrac{NkT}{q}\dot{q}$

$$= \underline{nRT\left(\frac{\dot{q}}{q}\right)}$$

$$C_V = \left(\frac{\partial U}{\partial T}\right)_V = \frac{\mathrm{d}\beta}{\mathrm{d}T}\left(\frac{\partial U}{\partial \beta}\right)_V = -\frac{1}{kT^2}\frac{\partial}{\partial\beta}\left\{\frac{N}{q}\sum_j \varepsilon_j\,\mathrm{e}^{-\beta\varepsilon_j}\right\}$$

$$= \left(\frac{N}{kT^2}\right)\left\{\frac{1}{q}\sum_j \varepsilon_j^2\,\mathrm{e}^{-\beta\varepsilon_j} + \frac{1}{q^2}\left(\frac{\partial q}{\partial\beta}\right)\sum_j \varepsilon_j\,\mathrm{e}^{-\beta\varepsilon_j}\right\}$$

$$= \left(\frac{N}{kT^2}\right)\left\{\frac{1}{q}\sum_j \varepsilon_j^2\,\mathrm{e}^{-\beta\varepsilon_j} - \frac{1}{q^2}\left(\sum_j \varepsilon_j\,\mathrm{e}^{-\beta\varepsilon_j}\right)^2\right\}$$

$$= \left(\frac{N}{kT^2}\right)\left\{\frac{k^2T^2\ddot{q}}{q} - \frac{k^2T^2}{q^2}\dot{q}^2\right\}$$

$$= \underline{nR\left\{\frac{\ddot{q}}{q} - \left(\frac{\dot{q}}{q}\right)^2\right\}}$$

$$S = \frac{U-U(0)}{T} + nR\ln\left(\frac{q}{N}+1\right) = nR\left\{\frac{\dot{q}}{q} + \ln\frac{\mathrm{e}\,q}{N}\right\}$$

(b) At 5000 K, $kT/hc = 3475\ \mathrm{cm}^{-1}$. We form the sums

$$q=\sum_j \mathrm{e}^{-\beta\varepsilon_j}=1+\mathrm{e}^{-21850/3475}+3\mathrm{e}^{-21870/3475}+\cdots=1.0167$$

$$\dot{q}=\sum_j \frac{\varepsilon_j}{kT}\mathrm{e}^{-\beta\varepsilon_j}=\frac{hc}{kT}\sum_j \nu_j \mathrm{e}^{-\beta\varepsilon_j}$$

$$=\left(\frac{1}{3475}\right)\{0+21850\,\mathrm{e}^{-21850/3475}+3\times 21870\,\mathrm{e}^{-21870/3475}+\cdots\}=0.1057$$

$$\ddot{q}=\sum_j \left(\frac{\varepsilon_j}{kT}\right)^2 \mathrm{e}^{-\beta\varepsilon_j}=\left(\frac{hc}{kT}\right)^2\sum_j \nu_j^2\,\mathrm{e}^{-\beta\varepsilon_j}$$

$$=\left(\frac{1}{3457}\right)^2\{0+21850^2\,\mathrm{e}^{-21850/3475}+3\times 21870^2\,\mathrm{e}^{-21870/3475}+\cdots\}=0.6719$$

Then the electronic contributions are

$$H_\mathrm{m}-H_\mathrm{m}(0)=U_\mathrm{m}-U_\mathrm{m}(0)=RT\frac{\dot{q}}{q}$$

$$=8.314\ \mathrm{J\,K^{-1}\,mol^{-1}}\times 5000\ \mathrm{K}\times\frac{0.1057}{1.0167}=\underline{4.32\ \mathrm{kJ\,mol^{-1}}}$$

$$C_V=R\left\{\frac{\ddot{q}}{q}-\left(\frac{\dot{q}}{q}\right)^2\right\}$$

$$=8.314\ \mathrm{J\,K^{-1}\,mol^{-1}}\times\left\{\frac{0.6719}{1.0167}-\left(\frac{0.1057}{1.0167}\right)^2\right\}=\underline{5.41\ \mathrm{J\,K^{-1}\,mol^{-1}}}$$

$$\Phi_0=-R\ln q$$
$$=-8.314\ \mathrm{J\,K^{-1}\,mol^{-1}}\times\ln 1.0167=\underline{-0.14\ \mathrm{J\,K^{-1}\,mol^{-1}}}$$

20.16 $q^\mathrm{E}=\sum_{M_J}\mathrm{e}^{-g\mu_\mathrm{B}\beta BM_J}$, $M_J=-\frac{3}{2},-\frac{1}{2},\frac{1}{2},\frac{3}{2}$; $g=\frac{4}{3}$

Since $g\mu_\mathrm{B}\beta B \ll 1$ for normally attainable fields,

$$g^\mathrm{E}=\sum_{M_J}\{1-g\mu_\mathrm{B}\beta BM_J+\tfrac{1}{2}(g\mu_\mathrm{B}\beta BM_J)^2+\cdots\}$$

$$=4+\tfrac{1}{2}(g\mu_\mathrm{B}\beta B)^2\sum_{M_J}M_J^2\quad\left[\sum_{M_J}M_J=0\right]$$

$$=4\left(1+\frac{10}{9}(\mu_\mathrm{B}\beta B)^2\right)\quad[g=\tfrac{4}{3}]$$

Therefore, if K is the actual equilibrium constant and K^0 is its value when $B=0$, we write

$$\frac{K}{K^0}=\left(1+\frac{10}{9}(\mu_B\beta B)^2\right)^2\approx 1+\frac{20}{9}\mu_B^2\beta^2B^2$$

For a shift of 1 per cent, we require

$$\frac{20}{9}\mu_B^2\beta^2B^2\approx 0.01,\text{ or }\mu_B\beta B\approx 0.067$$

Hence

$$B\approx\frac{0.067kT}{\mu_B}=\frac{0.067\times 1.381\times 10^{-23}\text{ J K}^{-1}\times 1000\text{ K}}{9.274\times 10^{-24}\text{ J T}^{-1}}$$

$$\approx \underline{100\text{ T}}$$

20.17 $c_s=\left(\frac{\gamma RT}{M}\right)^{1/2},\ \gamma=\frac{C_p}{C_V},\ C_p=C_V+R$

(a) $C_V=\frac{1}{3}R(3+\nu_R^*+2\nu_V^*)=\frac{1}{2}R(3+2)=\frac{5}{2}R$

$C_p=\frac{5}{2}R+R=\frac{7}{2}R$

$\gamma=\frac{7}{5}=1.40$; hence $\underline{c_s=\left(\frac{1.40RT}{M}\right)^{1/2}}$

(b) $C_V=\frac{1}{3}R(3+2)=\frac{5}{2}R,\ \gamma=1.40,\ \underline{c_s=\left(\frac{1.40RT}{M}\right)^{1/2}}$

(c) $C_V=\frac{1}{3}R(3+3)=3R$

$C_p=3R+R=4R,\ \gamma=\frac{4}{3},\ \underline{c_s=\left(\frac{4RT}{3M}\right)^{1/2}}$

For air, $M\approx 29\text{ g mol}^{-1}$, $J\approx 298\text{ K}$, $\gamma=1.40$

$$c_s\approx\left(\frac{1.40\times 2.48\text{ kJ mol}^{-1}}{29\times 10^{-3}\text{ kg mol}^{-1}}\right)^{1/2}=\underline{350\text{ m s}^{-1}}$$

21. Diffraction methods

Exercises

21.1 The points and planes are shown in Fig. 21.1a.

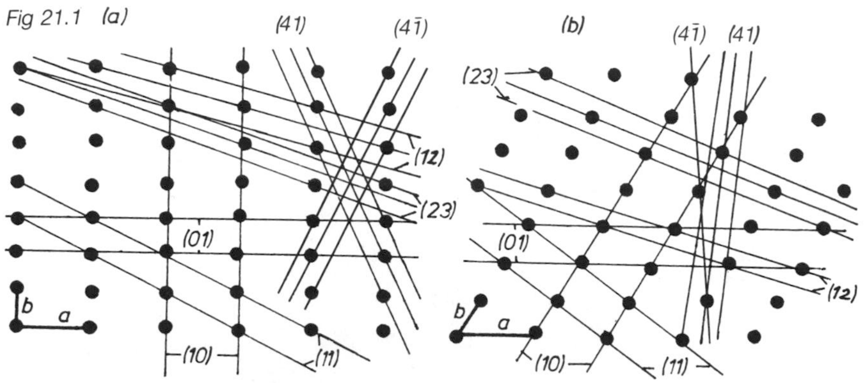

21.2 See Fig. 21.1b.

21.3 Draw up the following table, using the procedure set out in Section 21.2:

Original	Reciprocal	Clear fractions	Miller indices
$(2a, 3b, c)$ or $(2, 3, 1)$	$(\frac{1}{2}, \frac{1}{3}, 1)$	$(3, 2, 6)$	(326)
(a, b, c) or $(1, 1, 1)$	$(1, 1, 1)$	$(1, 1, 1)$	(111)
$(6a, 3b, 3c)$ or $(6, 3, 3)$	$(\frac{1}{6}, \frac{1}{3}, \frac{1}{3})$	$(1, 2, 2)$	(122)
$(2a, -3b, -3c)$ or $(2, -3, -3)$	$(\frac{1}{2}, -\frac{1}{3}, -\frac{1}{3})$	$(3, -2, -2)$	$(3\bar{2}\bar{2})$

21.4 The planes are drawn in Fig. 21.2a.

21.5 The planes are drawn in Fig. 21.2b.

21.6 $d_{khl} = \dfrac{a}{(h^2 + k^2 + l^2)^{1/2}}$ [1]

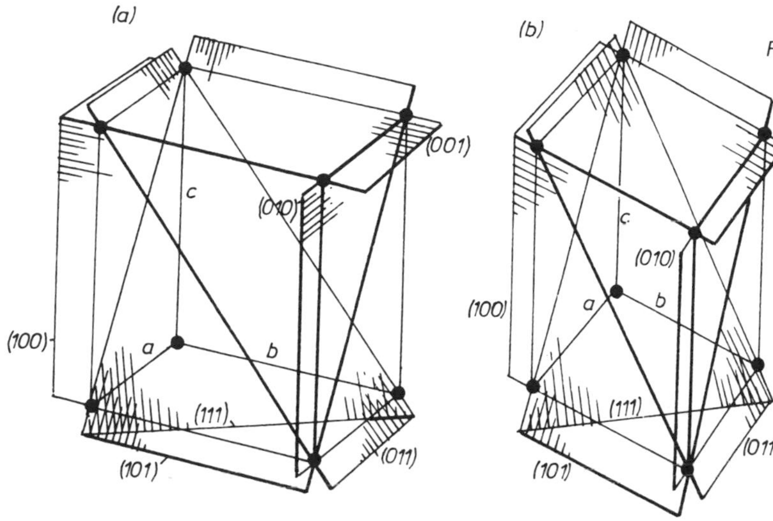

Therefore,

$$d_{111}=\frac{a}{3^{1/2}}=\frac{432\text{ pm}}{3^{1/2}}=\underline{249\text{ pm}}$$

$$d_{211}=\frac{a}{6^{1/2}}=\frac{432\text{ pm}}{6^{1/2}}=\underline{176\text{ pm}}$$

$$d_{100}=a=\underline{432\text{ pm}}$$

21.7 $\lambda=2d\sin\theta$ [2a]

$$=2\times 99.3\text{ pm}\times\sin 20.85°=\underline{70.7\text{ pm}}$$

21.8 $\theta=\arcsin\dfrac{\lambda}{2d}$ [2a, $\arcsin\equiv\sin^{-1}$]

$$\Delta\theta=\arcsin\frac{\lambda_1}{2d}-\arcsin\frac{\lambda_2}{2d}$$

$$=\arcsin\left(\frac{154.051\text{ pm}}{2\times 77.8\text{ pm}}\right)-\arcsin\left(\frac{154.433\text{ pm}}{2\times 77.8\text{ pm}}\right)=-1.07°$$

$$=-0.0187\text{ rad}$$

The separation of the components is therefore $2\times 5.74\text{ cm}\times 0.0187=\underline{0.21\text{ cm}}$.

21.9 $V = 651\ \text{pm} \times 651\ \text{pm} \times 934\ \text{pm} = \underline{3.96 \times 10^{-28}\ \text{m}^3}$

21.10 $\rho = \dfrac{NM}{VN_A}$ [N is the number of formula units per unit cell]

Therefore, $N = \dfrac{\rho V N_A}{M}$

$$= \frac{3.9 \times 10^6\ \text{g m}^{-3} \times 634 \times 784 \times 516 \times 10^{-36}\ \text{m}^3 \times 6.022 \times 10^{23}\ \text{mol}^{-1}}{154.77\ \text{g mol}^{-1}}$$

$$= 3.9$$

Therefore, $N = 4$ and the true calculated density (in the absence of defects) is

$$\rho = \frac{4 \times 154.77\ \text{g mol}^{-1}}{634 \times 784 \times 516 \times 10^{-30}\ \text{cm}^3 \times 6.032 \times 10^{23}\ \text{mol}^{-1}} = \underline{4.01\ \text{g cm}^{-3}}$$

21.11 $d_{hkl} = \left\{ \left(\dfrac{h}{a}\right)^2 + \left(\dfrac{k}{b}\right)^2 + \left(\dfrac{l}{c}\right)^2 \right\}^{-1/2}$ [1]

$$= \left\{ \left(\frac{4}{812}\right)^2 + \left(\frac{1}{947}\right)^2 + \left(\frac{1}{637}\right)^2 \right\}^{-1/2} \text{pm} = \underline{190\ \text{pm}}$$

21.12 The plane cuts the axes at $a/5$, $b/2$, and $c/3$, and so the intersection distances are $\underline{240\ \text{pm}}$, $\underline{606\ \text{pm}}$, and $\underline{395\ \text{pm}}$.

21.13 Since the reflection at 32.6° is (220), we know that

$$d_{220} = \frac{\lambda}{2 \sin \theta}\ [2] = \frac{154\ \text{pm}}{2 \sin 32.6} = 143\ \text{pm}$$

and hence, since

$$d_{220} = \frac{a}{(2^2 + 2^2)^{1/2}}\ [1] = \frac{a}{8^{1/2}}$$

it follows that

$a = 8^{1/2} \times 143\ \text{pm} = 404\ \text{pm}$

Therefore, we can draw up the following table:

θ	$10^5\left(\dfrac{2\sin\theta}{\lambda}\right)^2\Big/\text{pm}^2$	$h^2+k^2+l^2$	(hkl)	a/pm
19.4	1.86	3	(111)	401
22.5	2.47	4	(200)	402
32.6	4.90	8	(220)	404
39.4	6.80	11	(311)	402

The average value of a is $\underline{402\ \text{pm}}$.

21.14 $\theta_{hkl} = \arcsin\dfrac{\lambda}{2d_{hkl}}$

$$= \arcsin\frac{\lambda}{2}\left\{\left(\frac{h}{a}\right)^2 + \left(\frac{k}{b}\right)^2 + \left(\frac{l}{c}\right)^2\right\}^{1/2}$$

$$= \arcsin 77\left\{\left(\frac{h}{542}\right)^2 + \left(\frac{k}{917}\right)^2 + \left(\frac{l}{645}\right)^2\right\}^{1/2}$$

Therefore, $\theta_{100} = \arcsin\left(\dfrac{77}{542}\right) = \underline{8.17^\circ}$

$$\theta_{010} = \arcsin\left(\frac{77}{917}\right) = \underline{4.82^\circ}$$

$$\theta_{111} = \arcsin 77 \times \left\{\left(\frac{1}{542}\right)^2 + \left(\frac{1}{917}\right)^2 + \left(\frac{1}{645}\right)^2\right\}^{1/2}$$

$$= \arcsin\frac{77}{378} = \underline{11.75^\circ}$$

21.15 From the discussion of systematic absences [Section 21.4] we can conclude that the unit cell is face-centered cubic.

21.16 The lines with $h+k+l$ odd are absent; hence the cell is <u>body-centered cubic</u> [Section 21.4].

21.17 $F_{hkl}=\sum_i f_i\, e^{2\pi i(hx_i+ky_i+lz_i)}$ [6]

with $f_i=\frac{1}{8}$ [each atom is shared by eight cells]. Therefore,

$F_{hkl}=\frac{1}{8}f\{1+e^{2\pi ih}+e^{2\pi ik}+e^{2\pi il}+e^{2\pi i(h+k)}+e^{2\pi i(h+l)}+e^{2\pi i(k+l)}+e^{2\pi i(h+k+l)}\}$

However, $e^{2\pi i}=1$; h, k, and l are all integers. Hence all terms are unity, and

$$F_{hkl}=\underline{f}$$

21.18 The four values of $hx+ky+lz$ that occur in the exponential functions in F have the values 0, $\frac{5}{2}$, 3, and $\frac{7}{2}$, and so

$$F_{hkl}\propto 1+e^{5i\pi}+e^{6i\pi}+e^{7i\pi}=1-1+1-1=\underline{0}$$

21.19 Refer to Fig. 21.3. The hatched area is $3^{1/2}R\times 2R=2\sqrt{3}R^2$. The net

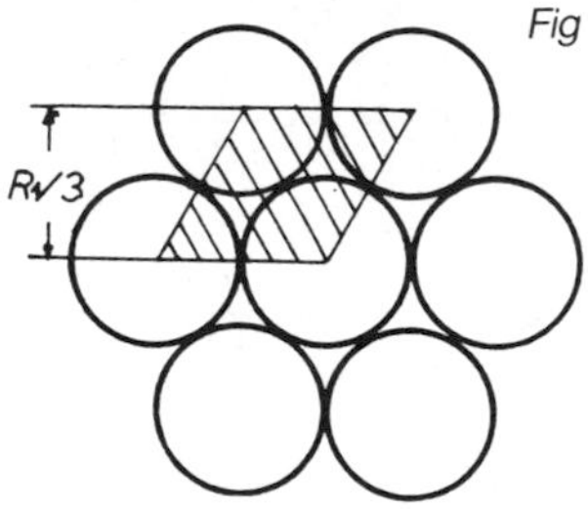

Fig 21.3

number of cylinders in a hatched area is 1, and the area of a cylinder's base is πR^2. The volume of the prism (of which the hatched area is the base) is $2\sqrt{3}R^2L$, and the volume occupied by the cylinders is πR^2L. Hence, the packing fraction is

$$f=\frac{\pi R^2L}{2\sqrt{3}R^2L}=\frac{\pi}{2\sqrt{3}}=\underline{0.9069}$$

21.20 $d_{100}=a=350$ pm

$\rho = \dfrac{NM}{VN_A}$, implying that

$$N = \frac{\rho V N_A}{M} = \frac{0.53\times10^6\ \mathrm{g\ m^{-3}}\times(350\times10^{-12}\ \mathrm{m})^3\times 6.022\times10^{23}\ \mathrm{mol^{-1}}}{6.94\ \mathrm{g\ mol^{-1}}}$$

$$= 1.97$$

An fcc cubic cell has $N=4$ and a bcc unit cell has $N=2$. Hence, lithium has a <u>bcc unit cell</u>.

21.21 $\theta_{khl} = \arcsin\left\{\dfrac{\lambda}{2a}(h^2+k^2+l^2)^{1/2}\right\}$

The systematic absences in an fcc structure are that (hkl) all even or all odd are the only permitted lines [Fig. 21.12 of the text]. Since $\lambda/2a = 0.213$, we expect the following lines:

(hkl):	111	200	220	311	...
θ	21°	25°	37°	45°	...

The density is calculated from

$$\rho = \frac{NM}{VN_A} = \frac{4\times 63.55\ \mathrm{g\ mol^{-1}}}{(361\ \mathrm{pm})^3\times 6.022\times10^{23}\ \mathrm{mol^{-1}}} = \underline{8.97\ \mathrm{g\ cm^{-3}}}$$

21.22 Draw points corresponding to the vectors joining each pair of atoms. Heavier atoms give more intense contributions than light atoms. Remember that there are two vectors joining any pair of atoms ($\overrightarrow{AB}$ and $\overleftarrow{AB}$); don't forget the AA zero vectors for the center point of the diagram. See Fig. 21.4 for (a) BF_3 and (b) C_6H_6.

21.23 (a) $E = \dfrac{p^2}{2m} = \dfrac{h^2}{2m\lambda^2}$ $[p = h/\lambda]$

$$= \frac{(6.626\times10^{-34}\ \mathrm{J\ s})^2}{2\times1.675\times10^{-27}\ \mathrm{kg}\times(70\times10^{-12}\ \mathrm{m})^2} = \underline{2.7\times10^{-20}\ \mathrm{J}}$$

(b) Write $E = \frac{1}{2}kT$ [equipartition], then

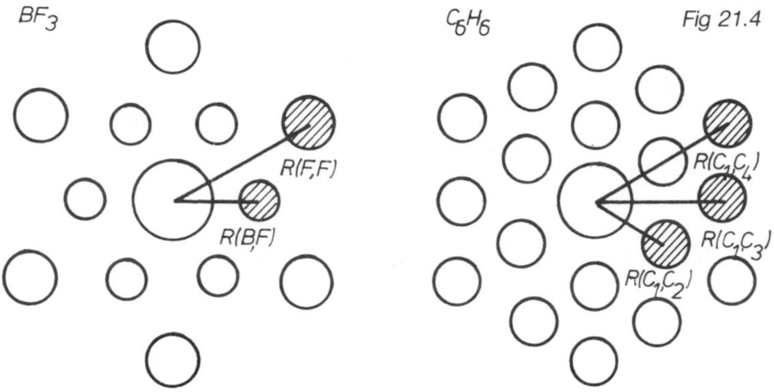

Fig 21.4

$$T=\frac{2E}{k}=\frac{2\times 2.7\times 10^{-20}\,\mathrm{J}}{1.381\times 10^{-23}\,\mathrm{J\,K^{-1}}}=\underline{3.9\times 10^{3}\,\mathrm{K}}$$

21.24 $\lambda=\frac{h}{p}=\frac{h}{mv}$, which implies that

$$v=\frac{h}{m\lambda}=\frac{6.626\times 10^{-34}\,\mathrm{J\,s}}{1.675\times 10^{-27}\,\mathrm{kg}\times 50\times 10^{-12}\,\mathrm{m}}=\underline{7.9\,\mathrm{km\,s^{-1}}}$$

21.25 Combine $E=\frac{1}{2}kT$ and $E=\frac{h^2}{2m\lambda^2}$, to obtain

$$\lambda=\frac{h}{(mkT)^{1/2}}=\frac{6.626\times 10^{-34}\,\mathrm{J\,s}}{(1.675\times 10^{-27}\,\mathrm{kg}\times 1.381\times 10^{-23}\,\mathrm{J\,K^{-1}}\times 300\,\mathrm{K})^{1/2}}$$

$$=\underline{252\,\mathrm{pm}}$$

21.26 $E=\frac{h^2}{2m\lambda^2}$ [Exercise 21.23] and $E=e\,\Delta\phi$

Therefore,

$$\Delta\phi=\frac{h^2}{2me\lambda^2}=\frac{(6.626\times 10^{-34}\,\mathrm{J\,s})^2}{2\times 9.109\times 10^{-31}\,\mathrm{kg}\times 1.602\times 10^{-19}\,\mathrm{C}\times(18\times 10^{-12}\,\mathrm{m})^2}$$

$$=\underline{4.6\,\mathrm{kV}}\quad [1\,\mathrm{J}=1\,\mathrm{C\,V}]$$

21.27 $\lambda=\frac{h}{p}=\frac{h}{m_e v}$

$$\tfrac{1}{2}m_e v^2 = e\,\Delta\phi, \text{ so } v = \left(\frac{2e\,\Delta\phi}{m_e}\right)^{1/2}$$

$$\text{and } \lambda = \left(\frac{h^2}{2m_e e\,\Delta\phi}\right)^{1/2}$$

$$= \frac{6.626\times10^{-34}\ \text{J s}}{(2\times9.109\times10^{-31}\ \text{kg}\times1.602\times10^{-19}\ \text{C}\times\Delta\phi)^{1/2}}$$

$$= \frac{1.227\ \text{nm}}{(\Delta\phi/\text{V})^{1/2}}$$

(a) $\Delta\phi = 1.0\ \text{kV},\ \lambda = \dfrac{1.227\ \text{nm}}{(1.0\times10^3)^{1/2}} = \underline{39\ \text{pm}}$

(b) $\Delta\phi = 10\ \text{kV},\ \lambda = \dfrac{1.227\ \text{nm}}{(1.0\times10^4)^{1/2}} = \underline{12\ \text{pm}}$

(c) $\Delta\phi = 40\ \text{kV},\ \lambda = \dfrac{1.227\ \text{nm}}{(4.0\times10^4)^{1/2}} = \underline{6.1\ \text{pm}}$

Problems

21.1 $\lambda = 2d_{hkl}\sin\theta_{hkl} = \dfrac{2a\sin\theta_{hkl}}{(h^2+k^2+l^2)^{1/2}}$

$$= 2a\sin 6.0° = 0.209a$$

In an NaCl unit cell (Fig. 21.5) the number of formula units is 4 [each corner ion is shared by 8 cells, each edge ion by 4, and each face ion by 2].

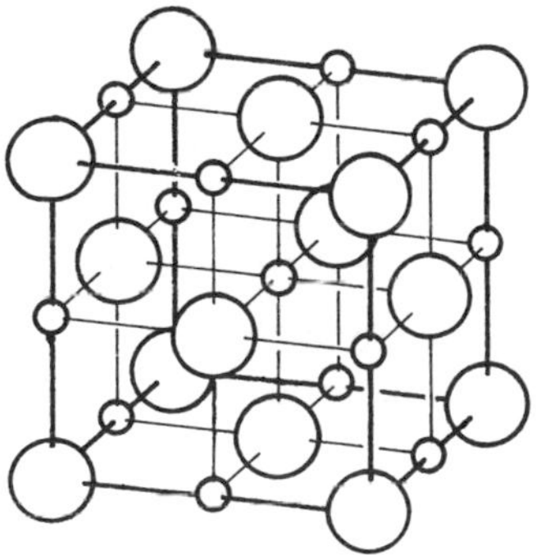

Fig 21.5

Therefore,

$$\rho = \frac{NM}{VN_A} = \frac{4M}{a^3 N_A}, \text{ implying that } a = \left(\frac{4M}{\rho N_A}\right)^{1/3}$$

$$a = \left(\frac{4 \times 57.44 \text{ g mol}^{-1}}{2.17 \times 10^6 \text{ g m}^{-3} \times 6.022 \times 10^{23} \text{ mol}^{-1}}\right)^{1/3} = 560\overline{2} \text{ pm}$$

and hence

$$\lambda = 0.209 \times 560.\overline{2} \text{ pm} = \underline{117 \text{ pm}}$$

21.2 Follow Example 21.3. Note that since $R = 28.7$ mm, $\theta/\text{deg} = (D/2R)(180/\pi) = D/\text{mm}$. Then proceed through the following sequence:

(1) Convert from distance to angle using $\theta/\text{deg} = D/\text{mm}$.
(2) Calculate $\sin^2\theta$.
(3) Find the common factor $A = \lambda^2/4a^2$ in $\sin^2\theta = (\lambda^2/4a^2)(h^3 + k^2 + l^2)$.
(4) Index the lines using $\sin^2\theta/A = h^2 + k^2 + l^2$.
(5) Solve $A = \lambda^2/4a^2$ for a.

We therefore draw up the following table:

D/mm	14.5	20.6	25.4	29.6	33.4	37.1	44.0
θ/deg	14.5	20.6	25.4	29.6	33.4	37.1	44.0
$10^3 \sin^2\theta$	62.7	124	184	244	303	364	483
$\sin^2\theta/A$	1.03	2.03	3.02	4.00	4.97	5.97	7.92
(hkl)	(001)	(011)	(111)	(002)	(012)	(112)	(022)

D/mm	47.5	50.9	54.4	58.2	62.1	66.4	78.1
θ/deg	47.5	50.9	54.4	58.2	62.1	66.4	78.1
$10^3 \sin^2\theta$	544	602	661	722	781	840	947
$\sin^2\theta/A$	8.92	9.87	10.84	11.84	12.80	13.77	16.69
(hkl)	(003) (122)	(013)	(113)	(222)	(023)	(123)	(004)

with $A = 61.0 \times 10^{-3}$. When we compare this sequence of indexes with Fig. 21.12 of the text, we conclude that the lattice is primitive cubic.

$$a = \frac{\lambda}{2A^{1/2}} = \frac{154 \text{ pm}}{2 \times (61.0 \times 10^{-3})^{1/2}} = \underline{213 \text{ pm}}$$

21.3 Measure the diffraction angles from the illustration, and then proceed as in Problem 21.2.

(a) D/cm	2.2	3.0	3.6	4.4	5.0	5.8	6.7	7.7
θ/deg	22	30	36	44	50	58	67	77
$10^3 \sin^2\theta$	140	250	345	482	587	719	847	949
$\sin^2\theta/A$	2.4	4.2	5.8	8.1	9.9	12.1	14.3	16.0
(hkl)	(011)	(002)	(112)	(022)	(013)	(222)	(123)	(004)

with $A = 0.0594$. Comparison with Fig. 21.12 of the text identifies the lattice as body-centered cubic.

$$a = \frac{\lambda}{2A^{1/2}} = \frac{154\text{ pm}}{2 \times 0.0594^{1/2}} = \underline{316\text{ pm}}$$

In a bcc lattice $4R = \sqrt{3}a$, so $\underline{R = 137\text{ pm}}$.

(b) D/cm	2.1	2.5	3.7	4.5	4.7	5.9	6.7	7.2
θ/deg	21	25	37	45	47	59	67	72
$10^3 \sin^2\theta$	128	179	362	500	535	735	847	905
$\sin^2\theta/A$	2.8	3.9	8.0	11.0	11.8	16.2	18.6	19.9
(hkl)	(111)	(002)	(022)	(113)	(222)	(004)	(133)	(204)

with $A = 0.0455$. Comparison with Fig. 21.12 of the text identifies the lattice as face-centered cubic.

$$a = \frac{\lambda}{2A^{1/2}} = \frac{154\text{ pm}}{2 \times 0.0455^{1/2}} = \underline{361\text{ pm}}$$

For such a lattice, $4R = \sqrt{2}a$, so $\underline{R = 128\text{ pm}}$.

21.4 $d_{hkl} = \dfrac{\lambda}{2\sin\theta_{hkl}}$ with $\lambda = 154$ pm

and $\dfrac{1}{d_{hkl}} = \left(\dfrac{h}{a}\right)^2 + \left(\dfrac{k}{b}\right)^2 + \left(\dfrac{l}{c}\right)^2$

We find that $d_{100} = a = \dfrac{\lambda}{2\sin\theta_{100}} = \dfrac{154\text{ pm}}{2\sin 7°\,25'} = \underline{597\text{ pm}}$

$$d_{010}=b=\frac{154\text{ pm}}{2\sin 3°\,28'}=\underline{1270\text{ pm}}$$

$$d_{001}=c=\frac{154\text{ pm}}{2\sin 10°\,13'}=\underline{434\text{ pm}}$$

Therefore, the volume of the unit cell is

$$V=abc=3.29\times10^{-28}\text{ m}^3$$

and its density is

$$\rho=\frac{NM}{VN_A}=\frac{\text{N}\times271.5\text{ g mol}^{-1}}{3.29\times10^{-22}\text{ cm}^3\times6.022\times10^{23}\text{ mol}^{-1}}$$

$$=1.37\times N\text{ g cm}^{-3}$$

However, experimentally $\rho=5.42\text{ g cm}^{-3}$; so $N==3.97$. That is, there are <u>four</u> $HgCl_2$ units in each unit cell.

21.5 When a very narrow X-ray beam (with a spread of wavelengths) is directed on the center of a genuine pearl, all the crystallites are irradiated parallel to a trigonal axis and the result is a Laue photograph with sixfold symmetry. In a cultured pearl the narrow beam will have an arbitrary orientation with respect to the crystallite axes (of the central core) and an unsymmetrical Laue photograph will result. [See J. Bijvoet *et al.*, *X-ray analysis of crystals*, Butterworth (1951).]

21.6 $\lambda=2a\sin\theta_{100}$ as $d_{100}=a$

Therefore, $a=\dfrac{\lambda}{2\sin\theta_{100}}$

and $\dfrac{a(\text{KCl})}{a(\text{NaCl})}=\dfrac{\sin\theta_{100}(\text{NaCl})}{\sin\theta_{100}(\text{KCl})}=\dfrac{\sin 6°\,0'}{\sin 5°\,23'}=1.114$

Therefore, $a(\text{KCl})=1.114\times564\text{ pm}=\underline{628\text{ pm}}$

$$\frac{\rho(\text{KCl})}{\rho(\text{NaCl})}=\frac{M(\text{KCl})}{M(\text{NaCl})}\times\left\{\frac{a(\text{NaCl})}{a(\text{KCl})}\right\}^3$$

$$=\frac{74.55}{58.44}\times\left\{\frac{564\text{ pm}}{628\text{ pm}}\right\}^3=0.924$$

Experimentally,

$$\frac{\rho(\mathrm{KCl})}{\rho(\mathrm{NaCl})}=\frac{1.99\ \mathrm{g\ cm^{-3}}}{2.17\ \mathrm{g\ cm^{-3}}}=0.917$$

and the measurements are broadly consistent.

21.7 $V=abc\sin\beta$

and the information given tells us that $a=1.377b$, $c=1.436b$, and $\beta=122°\,49'$; hence

$$V=1.377\times 1.436b^3\sin 122°\,49'=1.662b^3$$

Since $\rho=\dfrac{NM}{VN_A}=\dfrac{2M}{1.662b^3N_A}$,

we know that

$$b=\left(\frac{2M}{1.662\rho N_A}\right)^{1/3}$$

$$=\left(\frac{2\times 128.18\ \mathrm{g\ mol^{-1}}}{1.662\times 1.152\times 10^6\ \mathrm{g\ m^{-3}}\times 6.022\times 10^{23}\ \mathrm{mol^{-1}}}\right)^{1/3}$$

$$=605.8\ \mathrm{pm}$$

Therefore, $\underline{a=834\ \mathrm{pm}}$, $\underline{b=606\ \mathrm{pm}}$, $\underline{c=870\ \mathrm{pm}}$.

21.8 $d_{111}=\dfrac{\lambda}{2\sin\theta_{111}}=\dfrac{70.8\ \mathrm{pm}}{2\sin 8°\,44'}=233\ \mathrm{pm}$

$d_{111}=\dfrac{a}{\sqrt{3}}$ [1], so $a=233\times\sqrt{3}\ \mathrm{pm}=404\ \mathrm{pm}$

$\rho=\dfrac{NM}{VN_A}$ implies that $N_A=\dfrac{NM}{\rho V}$

Therefore,

$$N_A=\frac{4\times 25.94\ \mathrm{g\ mol^{-1}}}{2.601\times 10^6\ \mathrm{g\ m^{-3}}\times(404\times 10^{-12}\ \mathrm{m})^3}=\underline{6.05\times 10^{23}\ \mathrm{mol^{-1}}}$$

21.9 $\sin\theta_{hkl}=\dfrac{\lambda}{2a}(h^2+k^2+l^2)^{1/2}$

$$=\frac{154\ \mathrm{pm}}{2\times 334.5\ \mathrm{pm}}\times(h^2+k^2+l^2)^{1/2}$$

$$=0.230\times(h^2+k^2+l^2)^{1/2}$$

The indexes may vary over all integral values [Fig. 21.12 of the text], and so lines will occur at

(hkl)	(100)	(110)	(111)	(200)	(210)	...
θ_{hkl}	13° 17′	18° 59′	23° 28′	27° 23′	30° 57′	

The density is

$$\rho=\frac{NM}{VN_A}=\frac{M}{VN_A}=\frac{210\ \mathrm{g\ mol^{-1}}}{(334.5\times10^{-12}\ \mathrm{m})^3\times6.022\times10^{23}\ \mathrm{mol^{-1}}}$$

$$=9.32\times10^6\ \mathrm{g\ m^{-3}},\ \text{or}\ \underline{9.32\ \mathrm{g\ cm^{-3}}}$$

The radius of each atom is $\frac{1}{2}a=167.3$ pm. In an fcc lattice the diagonal would be $4\times167.3\ \mathrm{pm}=669.0$ pm [if we ignore the variation of metallic radius with coordination number], giving a side $a'=\frac{669.0}{\sqrt{2}}\ \mathrm{pm}=473.1$ pm. The density would then be

$$\rho=\frac{4\times210\ \mathrm{g\ mol^{-1}}}{(473.1\times10^{-12}\ \mathrm{m})^3\times6.022\times10^{23}\ \mathrm{mol^{-1}}}=\underline{13.2\ \mathrm{g\ cm^{-3}}}$$

21.10 $\theta(100\ \mathrm{K})=22°\,2'\,25''$, $\theta(300\ \mathrm{K})=21°\,57'\,59''$

$\sin\theta(100\ \mathrm{K})=0.37526$, $\sin\theta(300\ \mathrm{K})=0.37406$

$$\frac{\sin\theta(300\ \mathrm{K})}{\sin\theta(100\ \mathrm{K})}=0.99681=\frac{a(100\ \mathrm{K})}{a(300\ \mathrm{K})}$$

$$a(300\ \mathrm{K})=\frac{\lambda\sqrt{3}}{2\sin\theta}=\frac{154.062\ \mathrm{pm}\times\sqrt{3}}{2\times0.37406}=356.67\ \mathrm{pm}$$

$$a(100\ \mathrm{K})=0.99681\times356.67\ \mathrm{pm}=355.53\ \mathrm{pm}$$

$$\frac{\delta a}{a}=\frac{356.67-355.53}{355.53}=3.206\times10^{-3}$$

$$\frac{\delta V}{V}=\frac{356.67^3-355.53^3}{355.53^3}=9.650\times10^{-3}$$

$$\alpha_{\text{Volume}}=\frac{1}{V}\frac{\delta V}{\delta T}=\frac{9.650\times10^{-3}}{200\ \mathrm{K}}=\underline{4.8\times10^{-5}\ \mathrm{K^{-1}}}$$

$$\alpha_{\text{Linear}} = \frac{1}{a}\frac{\delta a}{\delta T} = \frac{3.206\times10^{-3}}{200\ \text{K}} = \underline{1.6\times10^{-5}\ \text{K}^{-1}}$$

21.11 $I = \sum_{i,j} f_i f_j \frac{\sin sR_{ij}}{sR_{ij}}, \quad s = \frac{4\pi}{\lambda}\sin\tfrac{1}{2}\theta \quad [8]$

$$= 4f_C f_{Cl}\frac{\sin sR_{CCl}}{sR_{CCl}} + 6f_{Cl}^2\frac{\sin sR_{ClCl}}{sR_{ClCl}}$$

$$= 4\times6\times17\times f^2\frac{\sin x}{x} + 6\times17^2\times f^2\frac{\sin\left(\frac{8}{3}\right)^{1/2}x}{\left(\frac{8}{3}\right)^{1/2}x} \quad [x = sR_{CCl}]$$

$$I/f^2 = 408\frac{\sin x}{x} + 1062\frac{\sin(8/2)^{1/2}x}{x}$$

This function is plotted in Fig. 21.6. We can find x_{max} and x_{min} from the graph,

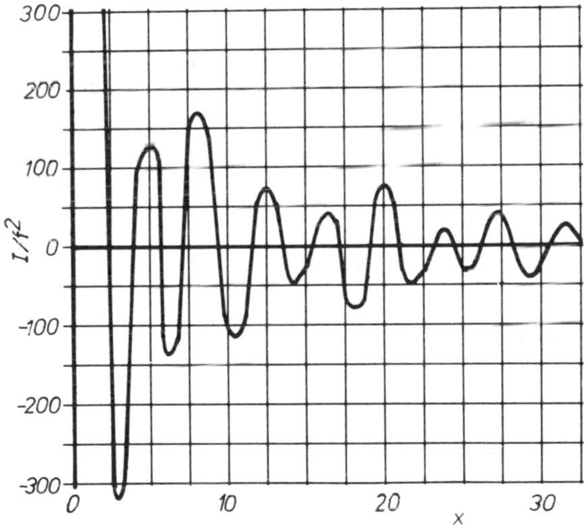

Fig 21.6

and s_{max} and s_{min} from the data. Then, since $x = sR_{CCl}$, we can take the ratio x/s to find the bond length R_{CCl}. We draw up the following table:

	Maxima			Minima			
θ(expt.)	3° 10′	5° 22′	7° 54′	1° 46′	4° 6′	6° 10′	9° 10′
s/pm^{-1}	0.0284	0.0480	0.0706	0.0158	0.0367	0.0597	0.0819
x(calc.)	5.0	8.5	12.5	2.8	6.5	10.5	14.5
(x/s)/pm	176	177	177	177	177	176	177

Hence, $R_{\text{CCl}} = \underline{177\ \text{pm}}$ and the experimental diffraction pattern is consistent with tetrahedral geometry.

21.12 Consider, for simplicity, the two-dimensional lattice and planes shown in Fig. 21.7. The (hk) planes cut the a and b axes at a/h and b/k, and we have

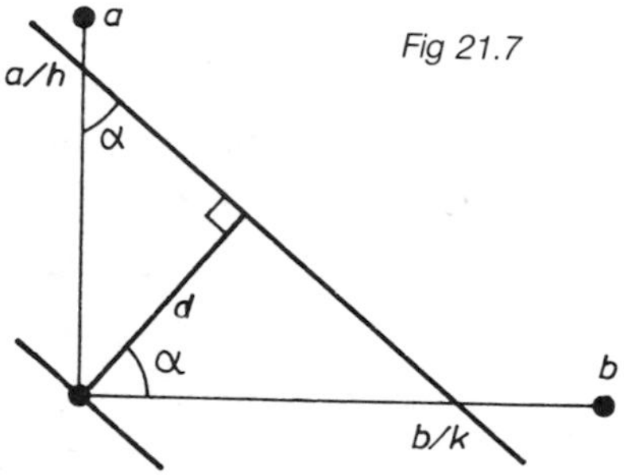

Fig 21.7

$$\sin\alpha = \frac{d}{(a/h)} = \frac{hd}{a}, \quad \cos\alpha = \frac{d}{(b/k)} = \frac{kd}{b}$$

Then, since $\sin^2\alpha + \cos^2\alpha = 1$, we can write

$$\left(\frac{hd}{a}\right)^2 + \left(\frac{kd}{b}\right)^2 = 1$$

and therefore

$$\frac{1}{d^2} = \left(\frac{h}{a}\right)^2 + \left(\frac{k}{b}\right)^2$$

The argument extends by analogy (or further trigonometry) to three dimensions, to give

$$\frac{1}{d^2}=\left(\frac{h}{a}\right)^2+\left(\frac{k}{b}\right)^2+\left(\frac{l}{c}\right)^2$$

21.13 If the sides of the unit cell define the vectors $\boldsymbol{a}$, $\boldsymbol{b}$, and $\boldsymbol{c}$, then its volume is $V=\boldsymbol{a}\cdot\boldsymbol{b}\wedge\boldsymbol{c}$ [given]. Introduce the orthogonal set of unit vectors $\hat{\mathbf{i}}$, $\hat{\mathbf{j}}$, $\hat{\mathbf{k}}$ so that

$$\mathbf{a}=a_x\hat{\mathbf{i}}+a_y\hat{\mathbf{j}}+a_z\hat{\mathbf{k}}$$

$$\mathbf{b}=b_x\hat{\mathbf{i}}+b_y\hat{\mathbf{j}}+b_z\hat{\mathbf{k}}$$

$$\mathbf{c}=c_x\hat{\mathbf{i}}+c_y\hat{\mathbf{j}}+c_z\hat{\mathbf{k}}$$

Then $V=\boldsymbol{a}\cdot\boldsymbol{b}\wedge\boldsymbol{c}=\begin{vmatrix} a_x & a_y & a_z \\ b_x & b_y & b_z \\ c_x & c_y & c_z \end{vmatrix}$

Therefore,

$$V^2=\begin{vmatrix} a_x & a_y & a_z \\ b_x & b_y & b_z \\ c_x & c_y & c_z \end{vmatrix}\begin{vmatrix} a_x & a_y & a_z \\ b_x & b_y & b_z \\ c_x & c_y & c_z \end{vmatrix}=\begin{vmatrix} a_x & a_y & a_z \\ b_x & b_y & b_z \\ c_x & c_y & c_z \end{vmatrix}\begin{vmatrix} a_x & b_x & c_x \\ a_y & b_y & c_y \\ a_z & b_z & c_z \end{vmatrix}$$

[interchange rows and columns, no change in value]

$$=\begin{vmatrix} a_xa_x+a_ya_y+a_za_z & a_xb_x+a_yb_y+a_zb_z & a_xc_x+a_yc_y+a_zc_z \\ b_xa_x+b_ya_y+b_za_z & b_xb_x+b_yb_y+b_zb_z & b_xc_x+b_yc_y+b_zc_z \\ c_xa_x+c_ya_y+c_za_z & c_xb_x+c_yb_y+c_zb_z & c_xc_x+c_yc_y+c_zc_z \end{vmatrix}$$

$$=\begin{vmatrix} a^2 & \boldsymbol{a}\cdot\boldsymbol{b} & \boldsymbol{a}\cdot\boldsymbol{c} \\ \boldsymbol{b}\cdot\boldsymbol{a} & b^2 & \boldsymbol{b}\cdot\boldsymbol{c} \\ \boldsymbol{c}\cdot\boldsymbol{a} & \mathbf{c}\cdot\mathbf{b} & c^2 \end{vmatrix}=\begin{vmatrix} a^2 & ab\cos\gamma & ac\cos\beta \\ ab\cos\gamma & b^2 & bc\cos\alpha \\ ac\cos\beta & bc\cos\alpha & c^2 \end{vmatrix}$$

$$=a^2b^2c^2(1-\cos^2\alpha-\cos^2\beta-\cos^2\gamma+2\cos\alpha\cos\beta\cos\gamma)^{1/2}$$

Hence,

$$\underline{V=abc(1-\cos^2\alpha-\cos^2\beta-\cos^2\gamma+2\cos\alpha\cos\beta\cos\gamma)^{1/2}}$$

For a monoclinic cell $\alpha=\gamma=90°$, and

$$V=abc(1-\cos^2\beta)^{1/2}=\underline{abc\sin\beta}$$

For an orthorhombic cell, $\alpha=\beta=\gamma=90°$, and

$$V=\underline{abc}$$

21.14 $f=\dfrac{NV_a}{V_c}$, where N is the number of atoms in each unit cell, V_a their individual volumes, and V_c the volume of the unit cell itself. Refer to Fig. 21.8.

Fig 21.8

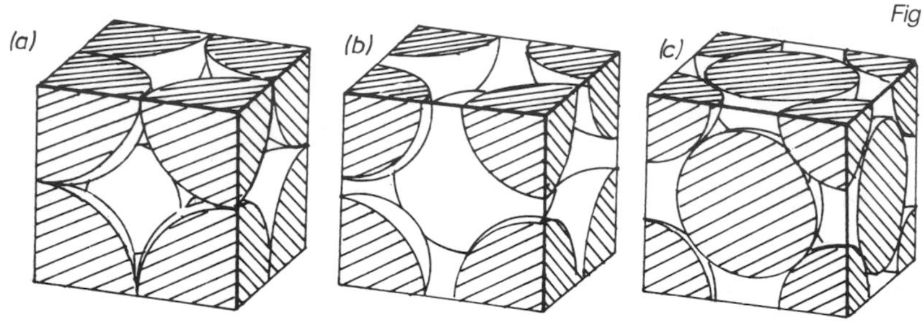

(a) $N=1,\ V_a=\frac{4}{3}\pi R^3,\ V_c=(2R)^3$

$$f=\tfrac{4}{3}\pi R^3/(2R)^3=\frac{\pi}{6}=\underline{0.5236}$$

(b) $N=2,\ V_a=\frac{4}{3}\pi R^3,\ V_c=\left(\dfrac{4R}{\sqrt{3}}\right)^3$

[body diagonal of a unit cube is $\sqrt{3}$]

$$f=\frac{2\times\frac{4}{3}\pi R^3}{(4R/\sqrt{3})^3}=\frac{\pi\sqrt{3}}{8}=\underline{0.6802}$$

(c) $N=4,\ V_a=\frac{4}{3}\pi R^3,\ V_c=(2\sqrt{2}R)^3$

$$f=\frac{4\times\frac{4}{3}\pi R^3}{(2\sqrt{2}R)^3}=\frac{\pi}{3\sqrt{2}}=\underline{0.7405}$$

21.15 $F_{hkl}=\sum_i f_i\,e^{2\pi i(hx_i+ky_i+lz_i)}$ [6]

For each A atom use $\frac{1}{8}f_A$ [each A atom shared by eight cells] but use f_B for the central atom [since it contributes solely to the cell].

$$F_{hkl}=\tfrac{1}{8}f_A\{1+e^{2\pi ih}+e^{2\pi ik}+e^{2\pi il}+e^{2\pi i(h+k)}+e^{2\pi i(h+l)}+e^{2\pi i(k+l)}+e^{2\pi i(h+k+l)}\}$$
$$+f_B\,e^{\pi i(h+k+l)}$$
$$=f_A+(-1)^{h+k+l}f_B \quad [h,\ k,\ l \text{ are all integers, } e^{i\pi}=-1]$$

(a) $f_A = f, f_B = 0$; $F_{hkl} = f$ [no systematic absences]

(b) $f_B = \frac{1}{2}f_A$; $F_{hkl} = f_A\{1 + \frac{1}{2}(-1)^{h+k+l}\}$

Therefore, when $h+k+l$ is odd, $F_{hkl} = f_A\{1 - \frac{1}{2}\} = \frac{1}{2}f_A$, and when $h+k+l$ is even, $F_{hkl} = \frac{3}{2}f_A$. That is, there is an alternation of intensity ($I \propto F^2$) according to whether $h+k+l$ is odd or even.

(c) $f_A = f_B = f$; $F_{h+k+l} = f\{1 + (-1)^{h+k+l}\} = 0$ if $h+k+l+$ is odd.

Thus, all $h+k+l$ odd lines are missing.

22. The electric and magnetic properties of molecules

Exercises

22.1 $C=\varepsilon_r C_0$ [Example 22.1] $=35.5\times 6.2\,\text{pF}=\underline{220\,\text{pF}}$

22.2 $\alpha+\dfrac{\mu^2}{3kT}=\dfrac{3\varepsilon_0 P_m}{N_A}$ [6a]

Therefore, $\dfrac{\mu^2}{3k}\left(\dfrac{1}{T}-\dfrac{1}{T'}\right)=\dfrac{3\varepsilon_0}{N_A}(P-P')$ [P at T, P' at T']

and hence

$$\mu^2=\frac{(9\varepsilon_0 k/N_A)(P-P')}{\dfrac{1}{T}-\dfrac{1}{T'}}$$

$$=\frac{9\times 8.854\times 10^{-12}\,\text{J}^{-1}\,\text{C}^2\,\text{m}^{-1}\times 1.381\times 10^{-23}\,\text{J K}^{-1}\times(70.62-62.47)\times 10^{-6}\,\text{m}^3\,\text{mol}^{-1}}{6.022\times 10^{23}\,\text{mol}^{-1}\times\left(\dfrac{1}{351.0\,\text{K}}-\dfrac{1}{423.2\,\text{K}}\right)}$$

$$=3.06\bar{4}\times 10^{-59}\,\text{C}^2\,\text{m}^2$$

and hence $\mu=\underline{5.5\times 10^{-30}\,\text{C m}}$, or 1.7 D.

Then $\alpha=\dfrac{3\varepsilon_0 P_m}{N_A}-\dfrac{\mu^2}{3kT}$

$$=\frac{3\times 8.854\times 10^{-12}\,\text{J}^{-1}\,\text{C}^2\,\text{m}^{-1}\times 70.62\times 10^{-6}\,\text{m}^3\,\text{mol}^{-1}}{6.022\times 10^{23}\,\text{mol}^{-1}}$$

$$-\frac{3.06\bar{4}\times 10^{-59}\,\text{C}^2\,\text{m}^2}{3\times 1.381\times 10^{-23}\,\text{J K}^{-1}\times 351.0\,\text{K}}$$

$$=\underline{1.01\times 10^{-39}\,\text{J}^{-1}\,\text{C}^2\,\text{m}^2}$$

corresponding to $\alpha' = \dfrac{\alpha}{4\pi\varepsilon_0} = \underline{9.1 \times 10^{-24}\,\text{cm}^3}$

22.3 $\dfrac{\varepsilon_r - 1}{\varepsilon_r + 2} = \dfrac{\rho P_m}{M}$ [6b] $= \dfrac{1.89\,\text{g cm}^{-3} \times 27.18\,\text{cm}^3\,\text{mol}^{-1}}{92.45\,\text{g mol}^{-1}}$

$= 0.556$

Hence, $\varepsilon_r = \dfrac{1 + 2 \times 0.556}{1 - 0.556} = \underline{4.8}$

22.4 A D_{3h} (trigonal planar) molecule is nonpolar; hence the second structure (with symmetry group C_{2v}) is more likely.

22.5 Follow Example 22.4

$R_m/(\text{cm}^3\,\text{mol}^{-1}) = 10 \times 1.65 + 2 \times 1.20 + 2 \times 1.41 = 21.72$

$V_m = \dfrac{74.12\,\text{g mol}^{-1}}{0.715\,\text{g cm}^{-3}} = 103.\bar{6}\,\text{cm}^3\,\text{mol}^{-1}$

$n_r = \left\{\dfrac{V_m + 2R_m}{V_m - R_m}\right\}^{1/2} = \left\{\dfrac{103.\bar{6} + 2 \times 21.72}{103.\bar{6} - 21.72}\right\}^{1/2} = \underline{1.34}$

The experimental value is 1.354.

22.6 $\alpha = \dfrac{3\varepsilon_0 R_m}{N_A}$ with $R_m = \dfrac{M}{\rho}\left\{\dfrac{n_r^2 - 1}{n_r^2 + 2}\right\}$ [9]

Therefore,

$$\alpha = \frac{3\varepsilon_0 M}{\rho N_A}\left\{\frac{n_r^2 - 1}{n_r^2 + 2}\right\}$$

$$= \frac{3 \times 8.854 \times 10^{-12}\,\text{J}^{-1}\,\text{C}^2\,\text{m}^2 \times 267.8\,\text{g mol}^{-1}}{3.32 \times 10^6\,\text{g m}^{-3} \times 6.022 \times 10^{23}\,\text{mol}^{-1}} \times \frac{1.732^2 - 1}{1.732^2 + 2}$$

$$= \underline{1.42 \times 10^{-39}\,\text{J}^{-1}\,\text{C}^2\,\text{m}^2}$$

and $\alpha' = 1.28 \times 10^{-23}\,\text{cm}^3$.

22.7 Refer to Fig. 22.2 of the text, and add moments vectorially [see diagram **2** of the text, Section 22.1].

(a) *p*-xylene: the resultant is zero, so $\mu = \underline{0}$

(b) *o*-xylene: $\mu = 0.4\ \mathrm{D}\cos 30° + 0.4\ \mathrm{D}\cos 30° = \underline{0.7\ \mathrm{D}}$

(c) *m*-xylene: $\mu = 0.4\ \mathrm{D}\cos 30° + 0.4\ \mathrm{D}\cos 60° = \underline{0.5\ \mathrm{D}}$

The *p*-xylene molecule belongs to the group D_{2h}, and so it is necessarily nonpolar.

22.8 $\mu = (\mu_1^2 + \mu_2^2 + 2\mu_1\mu_2\cos\theta)^{1/2}$ [Section 22.1]

$$= (1.5^2 + 0.80^2 + 2 \times 1.5 \times 0.80 \times \cos 109.5°)^{1/2}\ \mathrm{D}$$

$$= \underline{1.4\ \mathrm{D}}$$

22.9 $\mu^* = \alpha\mathscr{E}$ [1a] $= 4\pi\varepsilon_0\alpha'\mathscr{E}$ [3]

$$= 4\pi \times 8.854 \times 10^{-12}\ \mathrm{J^{-1}\ C^2\ m^2} \times 1.48 \times 10^{-30}\ \mathrm{m^3} \times 1.0 \times 10^5\ \mathrm{V\ m^{-1}}$$

$$= 1.6 \times 10^{-35}\ \mathrm{C\ m} \quad [\mathrm{I\ J} = 1\ \mathrm{C\ V}]$$

which corresponds to $\underline{4.9\ \mu\mathrm{D}}$.

22.10 $n_r = \left\{\dfrac{V_m + 2R_m}{V_m - R_m}\right\}^{1/2}$ [10]

$$R_m = \frac{4\pi}{3}\alpha' N_A \quad \text{[following 9]}$$

$$= \frac{4\pi}{3} \times 1.5 \times 10^{-24}\ \mathrm{cm^3} \times 6.022 \times 10^{23}\ \mathrm{mol^{-1}} = 3.8\ \mathrm{cm^3\ mol^{-1}}$$

$$V_m = \frac{M}{\rho} = \frac{18.02\ \mathrm{g\ mol^{-1}}}{1.00\ \mathrm{g\ cm^{-3}}} = 18.0\ \mathrm{cm^3\ mol^{-1}}$$

Hence,

$$n_r = \left\{\frac{18.0 + 2 \times 3.8}{18.0 - 3.8}\right\}^{1/2} = \underline{1.34}$$

Discrepancies may be due to a more complicated local field correction than has been assumed, and vibrational contributions.

22.11 $\dfrac{\varepsilon_r - 1}{\varepsilon_r + 2} = \dfrac{\rho N_A}{3\varepsilon_0 M}\left(\alpha + \dfrac{\mu^2}{3kT}\right)$ [6]

Hence, $\varepsilon_r = \dfrac{1+2x}{1-x}$ with $x = \dfrac{\rho N_A}{3\varepsilon_0 M}\left(\alpha + \dfrac{\mu^2}{3kT}\right)$

$$x = \frac{1.173\times10^6\ \mathrm{g\ m^{-3}}\times 6.022\times10^{23}\ \mathrm{mol^{-1}}}{3\times 8.854\times10^{-12}\ \mathrm{J^{-1}\ C^2\ m^2}\times 112.6\ \mathrm{g\ mol^{-1}}}$$

$$\times\left\{4\pi\times 8.854\times10^{-12}\ \mathrm{J^{-1}\ C^2\ m^2}\times 1.23\times10^{-29}\ \mathrm{m^3}\right.$$

$$\left.+\frac{(1.57\times 3.336\times10^{-30}\ \mathrm{C\ m})^2}{3\times 1.381\times10^{-23}\ \mathrm{J\ K^{-1}}\times 298.15\ \mathrm{K}}\right\}$$

$$= 0.848$$

Therefore, $\varepsilon_r = \dfrac{1 + 2\times 0.848}{1 - 0.848} = \underline{18}$

22.12 (a) $R_m(\mathrm{CaCl_2}) = 1.19 + 2\times 9.30\ \mathrm{cm^3\ mol^{-1}} = 19.79\ \mathrm{cm^3\ mol^{-1}}$

$$V_m(\mathrm{CaCl_2}) = \frac{111.0\ \mathrm{g\ mol^{-1}}}{2.15\ \mathrm{g\ cm^{-3}}} = 51.6\ \mathrm{cm^3\ mol^{-1}}$$

$$n_r = \left\{\frac{V_m + 2R_m}{V_m - R_m}\right\}^{1/2} = \left\{\frac{51.6 + 2\times 19.79}{51.6 - 19.79}\right\}^{1/2} = \underline{1.69}$$

(b) $R_m(\mathrm{NaCl}) = 0.46 + 9.30\ \mathrm{cm^3\ mol^{-1}} = 9.76\ \mathrm{cm^3\ mol^{-1}}$

$$V_m(\mathrm{NaCl}) = \frac{58.4\ \mathrm{g\ mol^{-1}}}{2.16\ \mathrm{g\ cm^{-3}}} = 27.0\ \mathrm{cm^3\ mol^{-1}},$$

which gives [as above] $n_r = \underline{1.64}$

(c) $R_m(\mathrm{Ar}) = 4.14\ \mathrm{cm^3\ mol^{-1}}$, $V_m = \dfrac{39.95\ \mathrm{g\ mol^{-1}}}{1.42\ \mathrm{g\ cm^{-3}}} = 28.1\ \mathrm{cm^3\ mol^{-1}}$

which gives $n_r = \underline{1.23}$

22.13 $F = -\frac{dV}{dr}$ with $V = 4\varepsilon\left\{\left(\frac{\sigma}{r}\right)^{12} - \left(\frac{\sigma}{r}\right)^{6}\right\}$

Therefore, $F = 4\varepsilon\left\{\frac{12\sigma^{12}}{r^{13}} - \frac{6\sigma^{6}}{r^{7}}\right\} = \underline{\frac{24\varepsilon}{\sigma}\left\{2\left(\frac{\sigma}{r}\right)^{13} - \left(\frac{\sigma}{r}\right)^{7}\right\}}$

The force is zero when

$$2\left(\frac{\sigma}{r}\right)^{13} = \left(\frac{\sigma}{r}\right)^{7}, \text{ or } \underline{r = 2^{1/6}\sigma}$$

22.14 $m = g_e\{S(S+1)\}^{1/2}\mu_B$ [Section 22.11, $g_e = 2$]

Therefore, since $m = 3.81\mu_B$

$S(S+1) = \frac{1}{4}\times 3.81^2 = 3.63$, implying that $S = 1.47$

Since $S \approx \frac{3}{2}$, there must be three unpaired spins.

22.15 $\chi_m = \chi V_m$ [24] $= \frac{\chi M}{\rho}$

$$= \frac{-7.2\times 10^{-7}\times 78.11 \text{ g mol}^{-1}}{0.879 \text{ g cm}^{-3}} = \underline{-6.4\times 10^{-5} \text{ cm}^3 \text{ mol}^{-1}}$$

22.16 $\chi_m = 6.3001 \times \frac{S(S+1)}{T/\text{K}} \text{ cm}^3 \text{ mol}^{-1}$ [Example 22.7]

Since Cu(II) is a d^9 species, it has one unpaired spin, and so $S = s = \frac{1}{2}$. Therefore,

$$\chi_m = \frac{6.3001 \times \frac{1}{2} \times \frac{3}{2}}{298} \text{ cm}^3 \text{ mol}^{-1} = \underline{+0.016 \text{ cm}^3 \text{ mol}^{-1}}$$

Problems

22.1 The positive (H) end of the dipole will lie closer to the (negative) anion. The potential arising from a point dipole is

$$\phi = \frac{-\mu}{4\pi\varepsilon_0 r^2} \quad [11, V = q_2\phi]$$

and since the electric field is the negative gradient of the potential,

$$\mathscr{E} = \frac{-\mathrm{d}\phi}{\mathrm{d}r} = \frac{-2\mu}{4\pi\varepsilon_0 r^3}$$

$$= \frac{-2\times 1.85\times 3.34\times 10^{-30}\,\mathrm{C\,m}}{4\pi\times 8.854\times 10^{-12}\,\mathrm{J^{-1}\,C^2\,m^{-1}}\times r^3}$$

$$= \frac{-1.11\times 10^{-19}\,\mathrm{V\,m^{-1}}}{(r/\mathrm{m})^3} = \frac{-1.11\times 10^{8}\,\mathrm{V\,m^{-1}}}{(r/\mathrm{nm})^3}$$

(a) $\mathscr{E} = \underline{-1.1\times 10^{8}\,\mathrm{V\,m^{-1}}}$ when $r = 1.0\,\mathrm{nm}$

(b) $\mathscr{E} = \dfrac{-1.11\times 10^{8}\,\mathrm{V\,m^{-1}}}{0.3^3} = \underline{4.\bar{1}\times 10^{9}\,\mathrm{V\,m^{-1}}}$

(c) $\mathscr{E} = \dfrac{-1.11\times 10^{8}\,\mathrm{V\,m^{-1}}}{30^3} = \underline{4.\bar{1}\,\mathrm{kV\,m^{-1}}}$

22.2 The energy of a dipole is initially $-\mu\mathscr{E}$ and becomes zero when it is perpendicular to the field. The energy of the dipole–ion pair is initially zero (when the dipole is perpendicular to the line of approach of the atom) but changes to $-\mu q/4\pi\varepsilon_0 r^2$ [11] when the dipole points toward the ion and has zero interaction with the applied field. We need to establish when the magnitude of the latter interaction energy exceeds that of the former. This occurs when

$$\frac{\mu q}{4\pi\varepsilon_0 r^2} = \mu\mathscr{E}, \quad q = e$$

and hence when

$$r = \left(\frac{e}{4\pi\varepsilon_0\mathscr{E}}\right)^{1/2} = \left(\frac{9.109\times 10^{-19}\,\mathrm{C}}{4\pi\times 8.854\times 10^{-12}\,\mathrm{J^{-1}\,C^2\,m^{-1}}\times 1.0\times 10^{3}\,\mathrm{V\,m^{-1}}}\right)^{1/2}$$

$$= \underline{2.9\,\mu\mathrm{m}}$$

22.3 $$P_\mathrm{m} = \frac{M}{\rho}\left(\frac{\varepsilon_\mathrm{r}-1}{\varepsilon_\mathrm{r}+2}\right)\ [6b] = V_\mathrm{m}\frac{\Delta/\tau}{3+\Delta/\tau}$$

$$= \frac{\tau V_\mathrm{m}^{\circ}\Delta}{3\tau+\Delta}, \quad V_\mathrm{m}^{\circ} = 2.24\times 10^{4}\,\mathrm{cm^3\,mol^{-1}}$$

Moreover,

$$P_m = \frac{N_A\alpha}{3\varepsilon_0} + \frac{N_A\mu^2}{9\varepsilon_0 kT} \quad [6a]$$

Therefore, evaluate P_m from the Δ, τ data, and plot P_m against $1/T$: the slope is $N_A\mu^2/9\varepsilon_0 k$ and the intercept at $1/T=0$ is $N_A\alpha/3\varepsilon_0$ $\left(\text{or } \frac{4\pi}{3}N_A\alpha'\right)$. We therefore draw up the following table:

θ/°C	0	100	200	300
T/K	273	373	473	573
$1000/(T/\text{K})$	3.66	2.68	2.11	1.75
$P_m(\text{HCl})/(\text{cm}^3\,\text{mol}^{-1})$	32.1	26.1	22.4	19.4
$P_m(\text{HBr})/(\text{cm}^3\,\text{mol}^{-1})$	23.1	19.4	17.2	15.7
$P_m(\text{HI})/(\text{cm}^3\,\text{mol}^{-1})$	17.2	16.4	15.7	15.7

The points are plotted in Fig. 22.1. The intercepts and slopes are

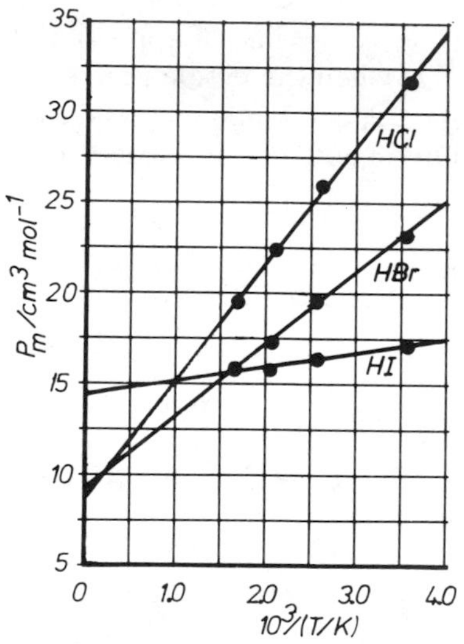

Fig 22.1

	HCl	HBr	HI
Intercept	8.9	9.3	14.1
Slope	6.4×10^3	3.8×10^3	8.3×10^2

It follows that, with $4\pi N_A/3 = 2.52\times10^{24}\ \text{mol}^{-1}$,

$$\alpha'(\text{HCl}) = \frac{8.9\ \text{cm}^3\ \text{mol}^{-1}}{4\pi N_A/3} = \underline{3.5\times10^{-24}\ \text{cm}^3}$$

$$\alpha'(\text{HBr}) = \frac{9.3\ \text{cm}^3\ \text{mol}^{-1}}{4\pi N_A/3} = \underline{3.7\times10^{-24}\ \text{cm}^3}$$

$$\alpha'(\text{HI}) = \frac{14.1\ \text{cm}^3\ \text{mol}^{-1}}{4\pi N_A/3} = \underline{5.6\times10^{-24}\ \text{cm}^3}$$

We also need

$$\mu = \left(\frac{9\varepsilon_0 k}{N_A}\right)^{1/2} \times (\text{slope}\times\text{cm}^3\ \text{mol}^{-1}\ \text{K})^{1/2}$$

$$= \left(\frac{9\times8.854\times10^{-12}\ \text{J}^{-1}\ \text{C}^2\ \text{m}^{-1}\times1.381\times10^{-23}\ \text{J K}^{-1}}{6.022\times10^{23}\ \text{mol}^{-1}}\right)^{1/2}$$

$$\times (\text{slope}\times\text{cm}^3\ \text{mol}^{-1}\ \text{K})^{1/2}$$

$$= 4.275\times10^{-29}\ \text{C}\times\left(\frac{\text{mol}}{\text{K m}}\right)^{1/2}\times(\text{slope}\times\text{cm}^3\ \text{mol}^{-1}\ \text{K})^{1/2}$$

$$= 4.275\times10^{-29}\ \text{C}\times(\text{slope}\times\text{cm}^3\ \text{m}^{-1})^{1/2}$$

$$= 4.275\times10^{-29}\ \text{C}\times(\text{slope}\times10^{-6}\ \text{m}^2)^{1/2}$$

$$= 4.275\times10^{-32}\ \text{C m}\times(\text{slope})^{1/2}$$

$$= 1.282\times10^{-2}\ \text{D}\times(\text{slope})^{1/2}$$

It follows that

$$\mu(\text{HCl}) = 1.282\times10^{-2}\ \text{D}\times(6.4\times10^3)^{1/2} = \underline{1.03\ \text{D}}$$

$$\mu(\text{HBr}) = 1.282\times10^{-2}\ \text{D}\times(3.8\times10^3)^{1/2} = \underline{0.80\ \text{D}}$$

$$\mu(\text{HI}) = 1.282\times10^{-2}\ \text{D}\times(8.3\times10^2)^{1/2} = \underline{0.36\ \text{D}}$$

22.4 $P_m = \dfrac{M}{\rho}\left(\dfrac{\varepsilon_r - 1}{\varepsilon_r + 2}\right)$ and $P_m = \dfrac{4\pi}{3}N_A\alpha' + \dfrac{N_A\mu^2}{9\varepsilon_0 kT}$

Therefore, we draw up the following table (with $M = 119.4\ \text{g mol}^{-1}$):

$\theta/°\text{C}$	−80	−70	−60	−40	−20	0	20
T/K	193	203	213	233	253	273	293
$1000/(T/\text{K})$	5.18	4.93	4.69	4.29	3.95	3.66	3.41
ε_r	3.1	3.1	7.0	6.5	6.0	5.5	5.0
$\dfrac{\varepsilon_r - 1}{\varepsilon_r + 2}$	0.41	0.41	0.67	0.65	0.63	0.60	0.57
$\rho/(\text{g cm}^{-3})$	1.65	1.64	1.64	1.61	1.57	1.53	1.50
$P_m/(\text{cm}^3\ \text{mol}^{-1})$	29.8	29.9	48.5	48.0	47.5	46.8	45.4

P_m is plotted against $1/T$ in Fig. 22.2. The (dang ously unreliable) intercept is

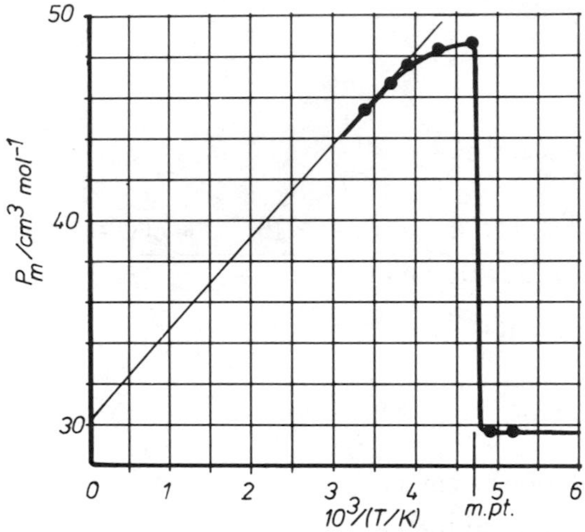

Fig 22.2

at 30 and the slope is 4.5×10^3. It follows that

$$\alpha' = \frac{3 \times 30\ \text{cm}^3\ \text{mol}^{-1}}{4\pi \times 6.022 \times 10^{23}\ \text{mol}^{-1}} = \underline{1.2 \times 10^{-23}\ \text{cm}^3}$$

and (using the conversion factor developed in Problem 22.3)

$$\mu = 1.282 \times 10^{-2}\ \text{D} \times (\text{slope})^{1/2}$$
$$= 1.282 \times 10^{-2}\ \text{D} \times (4.5 \times 10^3)^{1/2} = \underline{0.9\ \text{D}}$$

The sharp decrease in P_m occurs at the freezing point of chloroform (−63 °C), indicating that the dipole reorientation term no longer contributes. Note that P_m for the solid corresponds to the extrapolated, dipole free, value of P_m, so the extrapolation is less hazardous than it looks.

22.5 $P_m = \frac{M}{\rho}\left(\frac{\varepsilon_r - 1}{\varepsilon_r + 2}\right)$ and $P_m = \frac{4\pi}{3}N_A\alpha' + \frac{N_A\mu^2}{9\varepsilon_0 kT}$

The data have been corrected for the variation in methanol density, so use $\rho = 0.791$ g cm^{-3} for all the entries. Obtain μ and α' from the liquid range ($\theta > -95$ °C) results, but note that some molecular rotation occurs even below the freezing point (thus the -110 °C value is close to the -80 °C value). Draw up the following table using $M = 32.0$ g mol^{-1}.

θ/°C	−80	−50	−20	0	20
T/K	193	223	253	273	293
$1000/(T/\text{K})$	5.18	4.48	3.95	3.66	3.41
ε_r	57	49	42	38	34
$\frac{\varepsilon_r - 1}{\varepsilon_r + 2}$	0.949	0.941	0.932	0.925	0.917
$P_m/(\text{cm}^3\ \text{mol}^{-1})$	38.5	38.1	37.4	37.7	37.2

P_m is plotted against $1/T$ in Fig. 22.3. The extrapolated intercept at $1/T = 0$ is

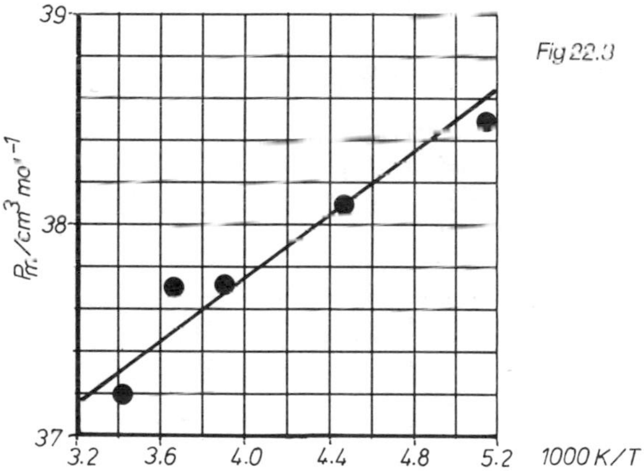

Fig 22.3

35.0 and the slope is 741 (from a least-squares analysis). It follows that

$$\alpha' = \frac{3 \times 35.0\ \text{cm}^3\ \text{mol}^{-1}}{4\pi \times 6.022 \times 10^{23}\ \text{mol}^{-1}} = \underline{1.38 \times 10^{-23}\ \text{cm}^3}$$

$$\mu = 1.282 \times 10^{-2}\ \text{D} \times (741)^{1/2} \quad \text{[from Problem 22.3]}$$

$$= \underline{0.35\ \text{D}}$$

22.6 $P_m = \frac{4\pi}{3} N_A \alpha' + \frac{N_A \mu^2}{9\varepsilon_0 kT}$

Therefore, draw up the following table:

T/K	292.9	309.0	333.0	387.0	413.0	446.0
$1000/(T/\text{K})$	3.42	3.24	3.00	2.58	2.42	2.24
$P_m/(\text{cm}^3\,\text{mol}^{-1})$	57.57	55.01	51.22	44.99	42.51	39.59

The points are plotted in Fig. 22.4. The extrapolated (least-squares) intercept

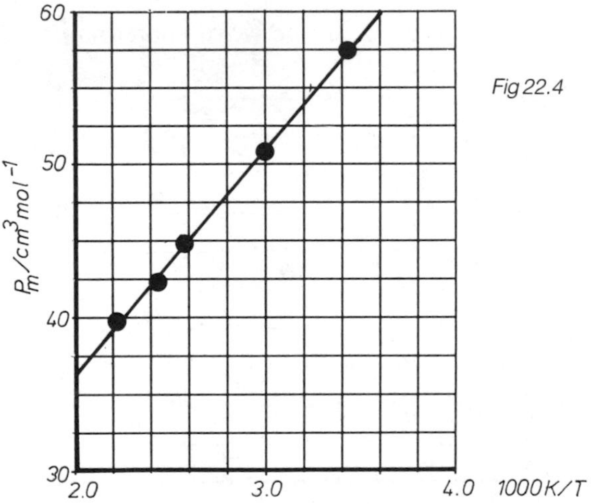

Fig 22.4

lies at 5.65, and so $\underline{\alpha' = 2.24 \times 10^{-24}\ \text{cm}^3}$ [see Problem 22.5 for the conversion]. The least-squares slope is 1.52×10^4, so [as in Problem 22.5], $\theta = \underline{1.58\ \text{D}}$.

22.7 Consider the arrangement shown in Fig. 22.5. The total potential energy of interaction of the two quadrupoles is

$$V = \frac{q_1 q_2}{4\pi\varepsilon_0}\left\{\left(\frac{1}{r} - \frac{2}{r-l} + \frac{1}{r-2l}\right) - 2\left(\frac{1}{r+l} - \frac{2}{r} + \frac{1}{r-l}\right) + \left(\frac{1}{r+2l} - \frac{2}{r+l} + \frac{1}{r}\right)\right\}$$

$$= \frac{q_1 q_2}{4\pi\varepsilon_0 r}\left\{\left(1 - \frac{2}{1-\lambda} + \frac{1}{1-2\lambda}\right) - 2\left(\frac{1}{1+\lambda} - 2 + \frac{1}{1-\lambda}\right)\right.$$

$$\left. + \left(\frac{1}{1+2\lambda} - \frac{2}{1+\lambda} + 1\right)\right\} \quad [\lambda = l/r \ll 1]$$

Expand each term using

$$\frac{1}{1+x} = 1 - x + x^2 - x^3 + x^4 - \cdots$$

and keep up to λ^4 [the preceding terms cancel]. The result is

$$V = \frac{q_1 q_2}{4\pi\varepsilon_0 r} \times 24\lambda^4 = \frac{6 q_1 q_2 l^4}{\pi\varepsilon_0 r^5}$$

Define the quadrupole moments of the two distributions as

$$Q_1 = q_1 l^2, \; Q_2 = q_2 l^2$$

and hence obtain

$$V = \frac{6 Q_1 Q_2}{\pi\varepsilon_0} \times \frac{1}{r^5}$$

22.8 $\dfrac{n_r^2 - 1}{n_r^2 + 2} = \dfrac{4\pi\alpha' N_A \rho}{3M}$ [9]

For a gas, $\rho = \dfrac{M}{V_m} = \dfrac{Mp}{RT}$

Fig 22.5

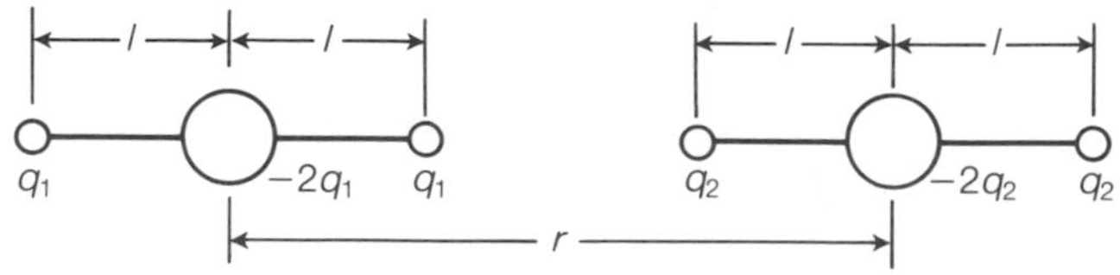

Therefore,

$$n_r = \left\{\frac{1 + 8\pi\alpha'\rho N_A/3M}{1 - 4\pi\alpha'\rho N_A/3M}\right\}^{1/2} = \left\{\frac{1 + 8\pi\alpha' p/3kT}{1 - 4\pi\alpha' p/3kT}\right\}^{1/2}$$

$$\approx \left\{\left(1 + \frac{8\pi\alpha' p}{3kT}\right)\left(1 + \frac{4\pi\alpha' p}{3kT}\right)\right\}^{1/2} \quad \left[\frac{1}{1-x} \approx 1 + x\right]$$

$$\approx \left\{1 + \frac{12\pi\alpha' p}{3kT} + \cdots\right\}^{1/2}$$

$$\approx 1 + \frac{2\pi\alpha' p}{kT} \quad [(1+x)^{1/2} \approx 1 + \tfrac{1}{2}x]$$

Hence, $\underline{n_r \approx 1 + \text{const.} \times p}$, with constant $= \underline{2\pi\alpha'/kT}$

From the first line above,

$$\alpha' = \frac{3M}{4\pi N_A \rho}\left(\frac{n_r^2 - 1}{n_r^2 + 2}\right) = \underline{\frac{3kT}{4\pi p}\left(\frac{n_r^2 - 1}{n_r^2 + 2}\right)}$$

22.9 The time-scale of the oscillations is about $1/(0.55\ \text{GHz}) = 2 \times 10^{-9}$ s for benzene and toluene, and 2.5×10^{-9} s for the additional oscillations in toluene. Toluene has a permanent dipole moment, benzene does not. Both have dipole moments induced by fluctuations in the solvent. Both have anisotropic polarizabilities (so that the refractive index is modulated by molecular reorientation).

22.10 The dimers should have a zero dipole moment. The strong molecular interactions in the pure liquid probably break up the dimers and produce hydrogen-bonded groups of molecules with a chainlike structure. In very dilute benzene solutions, the molecules should behave much like those in the gas and should tend to form planar dimers. Hence the relative permittivity should decrease as the dilution increases.

22.11 Consider a single molecule surrounded by $N-1$ ($\approx N$) others in a container of volume V. The number of molecules in a spherical shell of thickness $\mathrm{d}r$ at a distance r is $4\pi r^2 \times N/V$. Therefore, the interaction energy is

$$u=\int_d^R 4\pi r^2 \times \frac{N}{V} \times \left(\frac{-C_6}{r^6}\right) \mathrm{d}r = \frac{-4\pi N C_6}{V}\int_d^R \frac{\mathrm{d}r}{r^4}$$

where R is the radius of the container and d the molecular diameter (the distance of closest approach). Therefore,

$$u=\frac{4\pi}{3} \times \frac{N}{V} \times C_6 \times \left(\frac{1}{R^3}-\frac{1}{d^3}\right) \approx \frac{-4\pi N C_6}{3Vd^3}$$

because $d \ll R$. The mutual pairwise interaction energy of all N molecules is $U=\frac{1}{2}Nu$ [the $\frac{1}{2}$ appears because each pair must be counted only once; i.e. A with B but not A with B and B with A]. Therefore,

$$U=\frac{-2\pi N^2 C_6}{3Vd^3}$$

For a van der Waals gas,

$$\frac{n^2 a}{V^2}=\left(\frac{\partial U}{\partial V}\right)_T=\frac{2\pi N^2 C_6}{3V^2 d^3}$$

and therefore $a=\dfrac{2\pi N_A^2 C_6}{3d^3}$ $\quad [N=nN_A]$

22.12 $B=2\pi N_A \int_0^{\infty} \{1-\mathrm{e}^{-V/kT}\} r^2\,\mathrm{d}r \quad$ [22c]

$$=2\pi N_A \int_0^d r^2\,\mathrm{d}r + 2\pi N_A \int_d^{\infty} \{1-\mathrm{e}^{C_6/r^6 kT}\} r^2\,\mathrm{d}r$$

$$\approx \frac{2}{3}\pi N_A \mathrm{d}^3 - \frac{2\pi N_A C_6}{kT}\int_d^{\infty}\frac{\mathrm{d}r}{r^4} \quad [1-\mathrm{e}^x \approx x]$$

$$\approx \frac{2\pi}{3} N_A d^3 - \frac{2\pi}{3}\frac{N_A C_6}{kT} \times \frac{1}{d^3}$$

$$\approx \frac{2}{3}\pi N_A d^3\left(1-\frac{C_6}{kTd^6}\right)$$

22.13 An 'exponential–6' Lennard–Jones potential has the form

$$V = 4\varepsilon\left\{A\,\mathrm{e}^{-r/\sigma} - \left(\frac{\sigma}{r}\right)^6\right\}$$

and is sketched in Fig. 22.6. The minimum occurs where

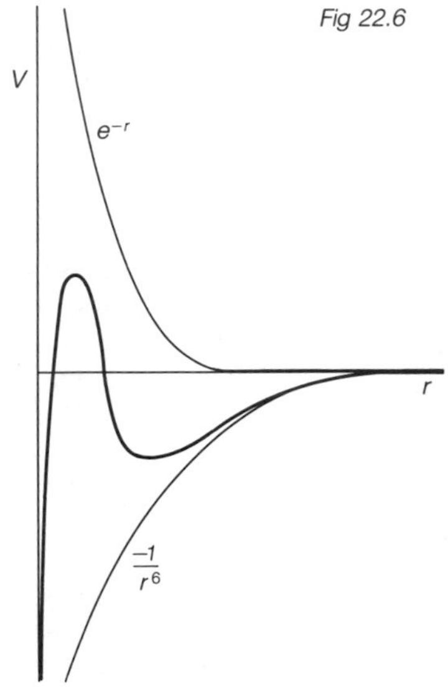

$$\frac{\mathrm{d}V}{\mathrm{d}r} = 4\varepsilon\left\{\frac{-A}{\sigma}\,\mathrm{e}^{-r/\sigma} + \frac{6\sigma^6}{r^7}\right\} = 0$$

which occurs at the solution of

$$\frac{\sigma^7}{r^7} = \frac{A}{6}\,\mathrm{e}^{-r/\sigma}$$

Solve this equation numerically. As an example, when $A = \sigma = 1$, a minimum occurs at $r = \underline{1.63}$.

22.14 $B = 2\pi N_A \int_0^\infty \{1 - \mathrm{e}^{-V/kT}\} r^2\,\mathrm{d}r$ [22c]

$$= 2\pi N_A \int_0^{\sigma_1} r^2\,\mathrm{d}r + 2\pi N_A \int_{\sigma_1}^{\sigma_2} \{1 - \mathrm{e}^{\varepsilon/kT}\} r^2\,\mathrm{d}r$$

$$= \frac{2\pi}{3} N_A \sigma_1^3 + \frac{2\pi}{3} N_A \{1 - \mathrm{e}^{\varepsilon/kT}\}(\sigma_2^3 - \sigma_1^3)$$

Suppose that $\varepsilon \ll kT$, then

$$B \approx \frac{2\pi}{3} N_A \sigma_1^3 - \frac{2\pi}{3} N_A \varepsilon(\sigma_2^3 - \sigma_1^3)/kT$$

For the van der Waals equation,

$$B = b - \frac{a}{RT}$$

Hence,

$$\underline{a = \frac{2\pi}{3} N_A \sigma_1^3}, \quad \underline{b = \frac{2\pi}{3} N_A^2 \varepsilon(\sigma_2^3 - \sigma_1^3)}$$

22.15 Numerical evaluation of B leads to the following values:

T/K	100	110	120	150	200	300	...	500
$B/(\text{cm}^3\,\text{mol}^{-1})$	−2.15	1.78	4.96	11.7	17.8	22.9		26.0

$B = 0$ at $T = 105$ K.

22.16 The number of molecules in a volume element $d\tau$ is $N\,d\tau/V = \mathcal{N}\,d\tau$. The energy of interaction of these molecules with one at a distance r is $\bar{V}\mathcal{N}\,d\tau$. The total interaction energy, taking into account the entire sample volume, is therefore

$$u = \int \bar{V}\mathcal{N}\,d\tau = \mathcal{N}\int \bar{V}\,d\tau \quad [\bar{V} \text{ is the interaction, not the volume}]$$

The total interaction energy of a sample of N molecules is $\frac{1}{2}Nu$ (the $\frac{1}{2}$ is included to avoid double counting), and so the cohesive energy density is

$$-\frac{U}{V} = \frac{-\frac{1}{2}Nu}{V} = -\tfrac{1}{2}\mathcal{N}u = -\tfrac{1}{2}\mathcal{N}^2\int \bar{V}\,d\tau$$

For $\bar{V} = -C_6/r^6$ and $d\tau = 4\pi r^2\,dr$,

$$\frac{-U}{V} = 2\pi\mathcal{N}^2 C_6 \int_d^\infty \frac{dr}{r^4} = \frac{2\pi}{3}\mathcal{N}^2 C_6/d^3$$

However, $\mathcal{N} = N_A\rho/M$, where M is the molar mass; therefore

$$-\frac{U}{V}=\frac{2\pi}{3}\left(\frac{N_A\rho}{M}\right)^2\frac{C_6}{d^3}$$

22.17 Refer to Fig. 22.7a. The scattering angle is $\theta=\pi-2\alpha$ if specular reflection occurs in the collision (angle of impact equal to angle of departure from the surface). For $b\leqslant R_1+R_2$, $\sin\alpha=b/(R_1+R_2)$:

$$\theta=\begin{cases}\pi-2\arcsin\left(\dfrac{b}{R_1+R_2}\right) & b\leqslant R_1+R_2\\ 0 & b>R_1+R_2\end{cases}$$

The function is plotted in Fig. 22.7b.

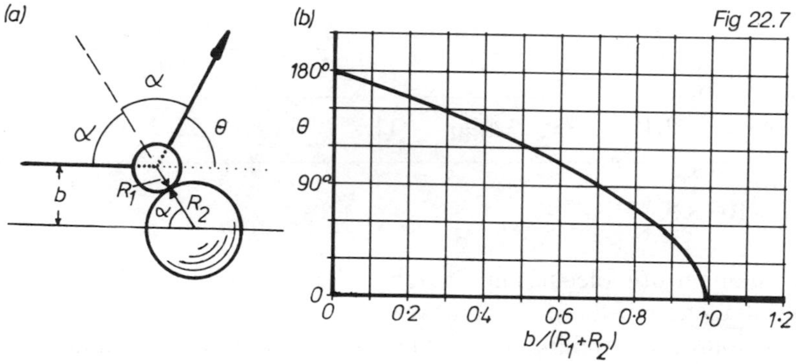

Fig 22.7

22.18 Once again [as in Problem 2.17] we can write

$$\theta(v)=\begin{cases}\pi-2\arcsin\left\{\dfrac{b}{R_1+R_2(v)}\right\} & b\leqslant R_1+R_2(v)\\ 0 & b>R_1+R_2(v)\end{cases}$$

but R_2 depends on v:

$$R_2(v)=R_2\,\mathrm{e}^{-v/v^*}.$$

Therefore, with $R_1=\frac{1}{2}R_2$ and $b=\frac{1}{2}R_2$

(a) $\theta(v)=\pi-2\arcsin\left\{\dfrac{1}{1+2\,\mathrm{e}^{-v/v^*}}\right\}$

[The restriction $b \leq R_1 + R_2(v)$ transforms into $\frac{1}{2}R_2 \leq \frac{1}{2}R_2 + R_2\,e^{-v/v^*}$, which is valid for all v.] This function is plotted in Fig. 22.8a. The kinetic energy of

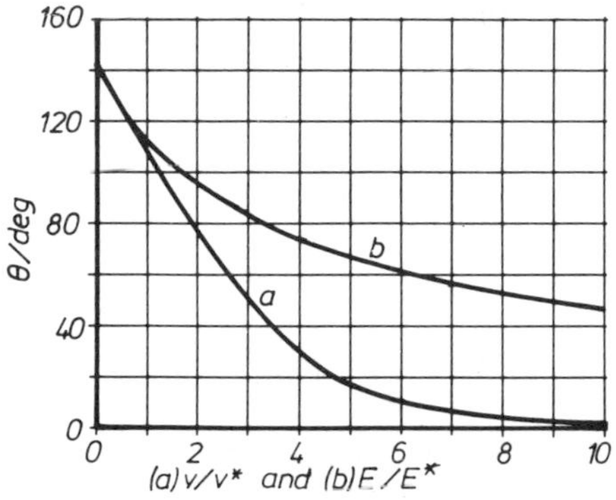

Fig 22.8

approach is $E = \frac{1}{2}mv^2$, and so

$$\text{(b)}\quad \theta(E) = \pi - 2\arcsin\left\{\frac{1}{1 + 2\,e^{-(E/E^*)^{1/2}}}\right\}$$

with $E^* = \frac{1}{2}mv^{*2}$. This function is plotted in Fig. 22.8b.

22.19 $\xi = \dfrac{-e^2}{6m_e}\langle r^2\rangle$

$$\langle r^2\rangle = \int_0^\infty r^2\psi^2\,d\tau \text{ with } \psi = \left(\frac{1}{\pi a_0^3}\right)^{1/2} e^{-r/a_0}$$

$$= 4\pi\int_0^\infty r^4\psi^2\,dr \quad [d\tau = 4\pi r^2\,dr] = \frac{4}{a_0^3}\int_0^\infty r^4\,e^{-2r/a_0}\,dr$$

$$= 3a_0^2 \quad \left[\int_0^\infty x^n\,e^{-ax}\,dx = \frac{n!}{a^{n+1}}\right]$$

Therefore,

$$\xi = \frac{-e^2a_0^2}{2m_e}$$

Then, since $\chi_m = N_A\mu_0\xi$ [25b, $m = 0$]

$$\chi_m = \frac{-N_A \mu_0 e^2 a_0^2}{2m_e}$$

22.20 If the proportion of molecules in the upper level is P, where they have a magnetic moment $2\mu_B$, the molar susceptibility

$$\chi_m = \frac{6.3001 \times S(S+1)}{T/\mathrm{K}}\ \mathrm{cm^3\ mol^{-1}} \quad \text{[Example 22.7]}$$

is changed to

$$\chi_m = \frac{6.3001 \times 4 \times P}{T/\mathrm{K}}\ \mathrm{cm^3\ mol^{-1}} = \frac{25.2P}{T/\mathrm{K}}\ \mathrm{cm^3\ mol^{-1}}$$

The proportion of molecules in the upper state is

$$P = \frac{e^{-hc\tilde{\nu}/kT}}{1+e^{-hc\tilde{\nu}/kT}} \quad \text{[Boltzmann distribution]}$$

$$= \frac{1}{1+e^{hc\tilde{\nu}/kT}}$$

and $hc\tilde{\nu}/kT = \dfrac{1.4388\ \mathrm{cm\ K} \times 121\ \mathrm{cm^{-1}}}{T} = \dfrac{174}{T/\mathrm{K}}$

Therefore,

$$\chi_m = \frac{25.2\ \mathrm{cm^3\ mol^{-1}}}{T/\mathrm{K} \times (1+e^{174/(T/\mathrm{K})})}$$

This function is plotted in Fig. 22.9.

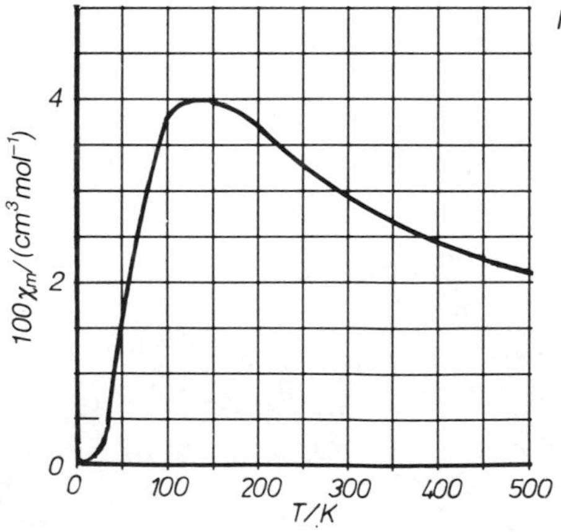

Fig 22.9

23. Macromolecules

Exercises

23.1 $$\langle M\rangle_N=\frac{N_1M_1+N_2M_2}{N}\quad[5]=\frac{62+78}{2}\text{ kg mol}^{-1}$$

$$=70\text{ kg mol}^{-1}$$

$$\langle M\rangle_M=\frac{m_1M_1+m_2M_2}{m}\quad[19a]$$

$$=\frac{n_1M_1^2+n_2M_2^2}{n_1M_1+n_2M_2}=\frac{M_1^2+M_2^2}{M_1+M_2}\quad[n_1=n_2]$$

$$=\frac{62^2+78^2}{62+78}\text{ kg mol}^{-1}=71\text{ kg mol}^{-1}$$

23.2 $$\Pi/c==\frac{RT}{M}\left\{1+B\frac{c}{M}+\cdots\right\}\quad[1b]$$

Therefore, to determine M and B we need to plot Π/c against c. We draw up the following table:

$c/(\text{g L}^{-1})$	1.21	2.72	5.08	6.60
$(\Pi/c)/(\text{Pa/g L}^{-1})$	111	118	129	136

The points are plotted in Fig. 23.1. A least-squares analysis gives an intercept of 105.$\bar{4}$ and a slope of 4.64. It follows that

$$\frac{RT}{M}=105.\bar{4}\text{ Pa g}^{-1}\text{ L}=105.\bar{4}\text{ Pa kg}^{-1}\text{ m}^3$$

and hence that

$$M=\frac{8.314\text{ J K}^{-1}\text{ mol}^{-1}\times 293\text{ K}}{105.\bar{4}\text{ Pa kg m}^3}=\underline{23.1\text{ kg mol}^{-1}}$$

The slope of the graph is equal to RTB/M^2, so

$$\frac{RTB}{M^2}=4.64\text{ Pa g}^{-2}\text{ L}^2=4.64\text{ Pa kg}^{-2}\text{ m}^6$$

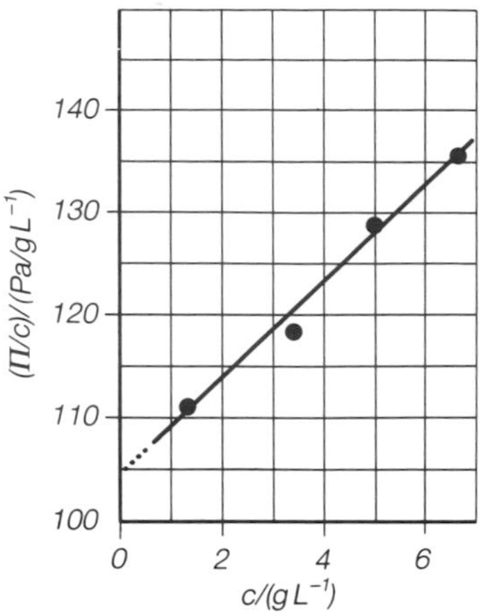

Fig 23.1

Therefore,

$$B=\frac{(23.1\ \text{kg mol}^{-1})^2\times 4.64\ \text{Pa kg}^{-2}\,\text{m}^6}{8.314\ \text{J K}^{-1}\,\text{mol}^{-1}\times 293\ \text{K}}=\underline{1.02\ \text{m}^3\,\text{mol}^{-1}}$$

23.3 $\Pi/c=(RT/M)\{1+(B/M)c\}$ [1b]

$\Pi=\rho gh$; so

$$\frac{h}{c}=\frac{RT}{\rho gM}+\frac{BRT}{\rho gM^2}\cdot c$$

and we should plot Π/h against c. Draw up the following table:

$c/(\text{mg cm}^{-3})$	3.2	4.8	5.7	6.88	7.94
h/cm	3.11	6.22	8.40	11.73	14.90
$(h/c)/(\text{cm}^4\,\text{mg}^{-1})$	0.97	1.30	1.47	1.70	1.90

The points are plotted in Fig. 23.2. The least-squares intercept is $0.35\bar{1}$ and the slope is 0.196. From the intercept

$$\frac{RT}{\rho gM}=0.35\bar{1}\ \text{cm}^4\,\text{mg}^{-1}=0.35\bar{1}\times 10^{-2}\ \text{m}^4\,\text{kg}^{-1}$$

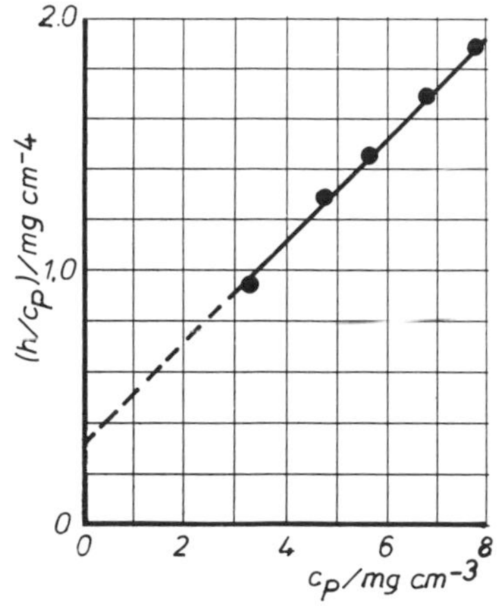

Fig 23.2

and hence

$$M = \frac{8.314\ \mathrm{J\ K^{-1}\ mol^{-1}} \times 298\ \mathrm{K}}{0.867 \times 10^3\ \mathrm{kg\ m^{-3}} \times 9.81\ \mathrm{m\ s^{-2}} \times 0.35\bar{1} \times 10^{-2}\ \mathrm{m^4\ kg^{-1}}}$$

$= \underline{83\ \mathrm{kg\ mol^{-1}}}$

23.4 We use the same procedure as in Exercise 23.3, and begin by drawing up the following table:

$c/(\mathrm{g}/100\ \mathrm{cm}^3)$	0.200	0.400	0.600	0.800	1.00
h/cm	0.48	1.12	1.86	2.76	3.88
$(h/c)/(100\ \mathrm{cm^4\ g^{-1}})$	2.4	2.80	3.10	3.45	3.88

The points are plotted in Fig. 23.3, and give a least-squares intercept at $2.04\bar{3}$ and a slope $1.80\bar{5}$. Therefore,

$$\frac{RT}{\rho g M} = 2.04\bar{3} \times 100\ \mathrm{cm^4\ g^{-1}} = 2.04\bar{3} \times 10^{-3}\ \mathrm{m^4\ kg^{-1}}$$

and hence

$$M = \frac{8.314\ \mathrm{J\ K^{-1}\ mol^{-1}} \times 298\ \mathrm{K}}{0.798 \times 10^3\ \mathrm{kg\ m^{-3}} \times 9.81\ \mathrm{m\ s^{-2}} \times 2.04\bar{3} \times 10^{-3}\ \mathrm{m^4\ kg^{-1}}}$$

$= \underline{155\ \mathrm{kg\ mol^{-1}}}$

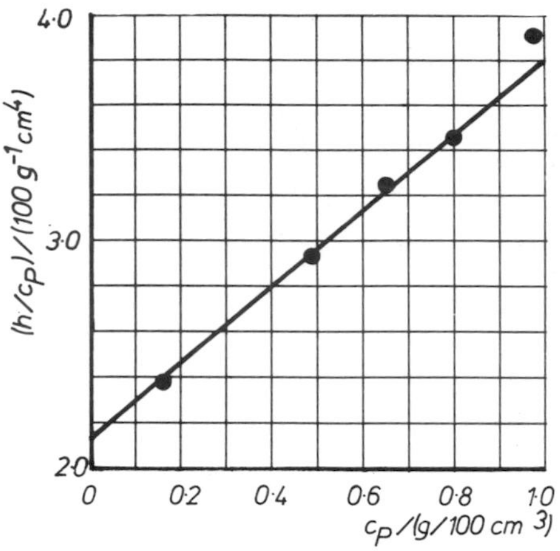

Fig 23.3

From the slope,

$$\frac{BRT}{\rho g M^2} = 1.80\bar{5} \times \frac{100\ \text{cm}^4\ \text{g}^{-1}}{\text{g}/(100\ \text{cm}^3)} = 1.80\bar{5} \times 10^4\ \text{cm}^7\ \text{g}^{-2}$$

$$= 1.80\bar{5} \times 10^{-4}\ \text{m}^7\ \text{kg}^{-2}$$

and hence

$$B = \left(\frac{\rho g M}{RT}\right) \times M \times 1.80\bar{5} \times 10^{-4}\ \text{m}^7\ \text{kg}^{-2}$$

$$= \frac{155\ \text{kg mol}^{-1} \times 1.80\bar{5} \times 10^{-4}\ \text{m}^7\ \text{kg}^{-2}}{2.04\bar{3} \times 10^{-3}\ \text{m}^4\ \text{kg}^{-1}}$$

$$= \underline{13.7\ \text{m}^3\ \text{mol}^{-1}}$$

23.5 $R_{\text{rms}} = N^{1/2} l$ [Section 23.6] $= 700^{1/2} \times 0.90\ \text{nm} = \underline{24\ \text{nm}}$

23.6 $R_g = \dfrac{N^{1/2} l}{\sqrt{3}}$ [constrained chains, Section 23.6]

$$N = 3\left(\frac{R_g}{l}\right)^2 = 3 \times \left(\frac{7.3\ \text{nm}}{0.154\ \text{nm}}\right)^2 = \underline{6.7 \times 10^3}$$

23.7 $[\eta] = \lim_{c \to 0} \left(\dfrac{\eta/\eta^* - 1}{c}\right)$ [16].

We begin by constructing the following table using $\eta^* = 0.985\ \mathrm{g\,m^{-1}\,s^{-1}}$:

$c/(\mathrm{g\,L^{-1}})$	1.32	2.89	5.73	9.17
$\left(\frac{\eta/\eta^* - 1}{c}\right) \Big/ (\mathrm{L\,g^{-1}})$	0.0731	0.0755	0.0771	0.0825

The points are plotted in Fig. 23.4. The least-squares intercept is at 0.0716, so $[\eta] = \underline{0.0716\ \mathrm{L\,g^{-1}}}$.

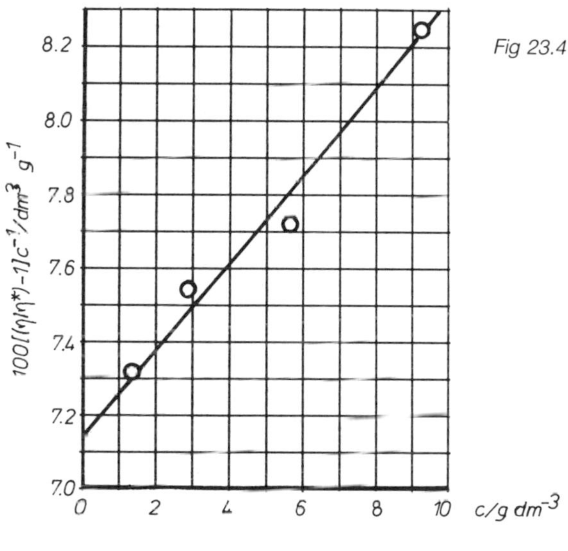

Fig 23.4

23.8 $S = \dfrac{s}{r\omega^2}$ [9a]

Since $s = \mathrm{d}r/\mathrm{d}t$, $\dfrac{s}{r} = \dfrac{1}{r}\dfrac{\mathrm{d}r}{\mathrm{d}t} = \dfrac{\mathrm{d}\ln r}{\mathrm{d}t}$

and if we plot $\ln r$ against t, the slope gives S through

$$S = \frac{1}{\omega^2}\frac{\mathrm{d}\ln r}{\mathrm{d}t}$$

The data are as follows:

t/min	15.5	29.1	36.4	58.2
r/cm	5.05	5.09	5.12	5.19
ln(r/cm)	1.619	1.627	1.633	1.647

The points are plotted in Fig. 23.5. The least-squares slope is 6.62×10^{-4}, so

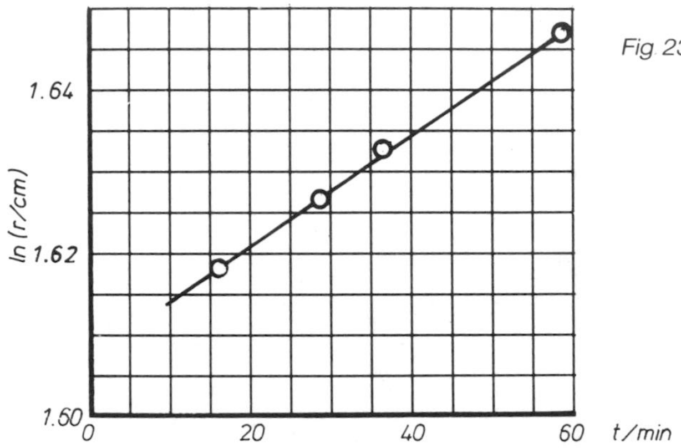

Fig. 23.5

$$S=\frac{6.62\times10^{-4}\ \text{min}^{-1}}{\omega^2}=\frac{6.62\times10^{-4}\times(1/60)\ \text{s}^{-1}}{(2\pi\times4.5\times10^4/60\ \text{s}^{-1})^2}$$

$$=4.9\overline{7}\times10^{-13}\ \text{s, or } \underline{5.0\ \text{Sv}}$$

23.9 Since $c\propto e^{+mb\omega^2r^2/2kT}$ [Sedimentation equilibrium, Section 23.2]

$$\ln c=\text{const.}+\frac{mb\omega^2r^2}{2kT}=\text{const.}+\frac{Mb\omega^2r^2}{2RT}$$

and a plot of $\ln c$ against r^2 should be a straight line of slope Mb/RT. We draw up the following table:

r/cm	5.0	5.1	5.2	5.3	5.4
c/(mg cm^{-3})	0.536	0.284	0.148	0.077	0.039
r^2/cm^2	25.0	26.0	27.0	28.1	29.2
ln(c/mg cm^{-3})	−0.624	−1.259	−1.911	−2.564	−3.244

The points are plotted in Fig. 23.6. The least-squares slope is −0.623. Therefore,

$$\frac{M(1-\rho v_s)\omega^2}{2RT} = -0.623\ \text{cm}^{-2} = -0.623\times10^4\ \text{m}^{-2}$$

It follows that

$$M = \frac{-0.623\times10^4\ \text{m}^{-2}\times2\times8.314\ \text{J K}^{-1}\ \text{mol}^{-1}\times293\ \text{K}}{(1-1.001\ \text{g cm}^{-3}\times1.112\ \text{cm}^3\ \text{g}^{-1})\times(2\pi\times322\ \text{s}^{-1})^2}$$

$$= \underline{65.6\ \text{kg mol}^{-1}}$$

23.10 $M = \dfrac{SRT}{bD}$ [13]

$$= \frac{3.2\times10^{-13}\ \text{s}\times8.314\ \text{J K}^{-1}\ \text{mol}^{-1}\times293\ \text{K}}{(1-0.656\times1.06)\times8.3\times10^{-11}\ \text{m}^2\ \text{s}^{-1}}$$

$$= \underline{31\ \text{kg mol}^{-1}}$$

23.11 (a) Osmometry gives the number-average molar mass, so

$$\langle M\rangle_N = \frac{N_1M_1+N_2M_2}{N_1+N_2} = \frac{\left(\dfrac{m_1}{M_1}\right)M_1+\left(\dfrac{m_2}{M_2}\right)M_2}{\left(\dfrac{m_1}{M_1}\right)+\left(\dfrac{m_2}{M_2}\right)}$$

$$= \frac{m_1+m_2}{\left(\dfrac{m_1}{M_1}\right)+\left(\dfrac{m_2}{M_2}\right)} = \frac{100\ \text{g}}{\left(\dfrac{30\ \text{g}}{30\ \text{kg mol}^{-1}}\right)+\left(\dfrac{70\ \text{g}}{15\ \text{kg mol}^{-1}}\right)}$$

$$= \underline{17.\bar{6}\ \text{kg mol}^{-1}}$$

(b) Light-scattering gives the mass-average molar mass, so

$$\langle M\rangle_M = \frac{m_1M_1+m_2M_2}{m_1+m_2} = 0.30\times30+0.70\times15\ \text{kg mol}^{-1}$$

$$= \underline{19.\bar{5}\ \text{kg mol}^{-1}}$$

23.12 $[\text{Na}^+]_\text{L} - [\text{Na}^+]_\text{R} = \dfrac{\nu[\text{P}][\text{Na}^+]_\text{L}}{2[\text{Cl}^-]+\nu[\text{P}]}$ [6a]

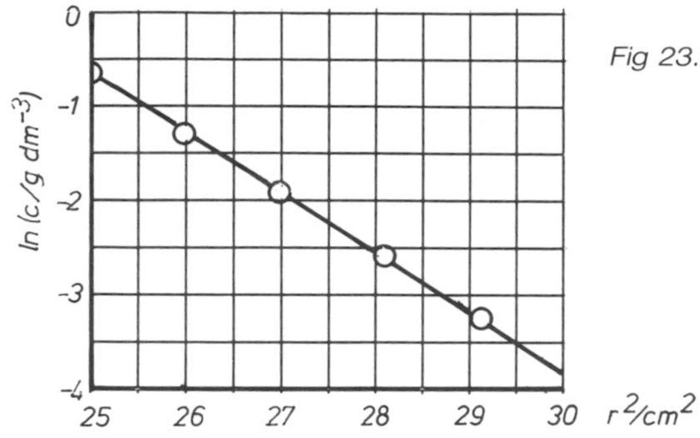

Fig 23.6

Hence

$$[\mathrm{Na^+}]_\mathrm{L} = \frac{[\mathrm{Na^+}]_\mathrm{R}}{1+\dfrac{\nu[\mathrm{P}]}{2[\mathrm{Cl^-}]+\nu[\mathrm{P}]}}$$

$$= \frac{0.0010\ \mathrm{M}}{1+\dfrac{20\times 1.00\times 10^{-4}\ \mathrm{M}}{2\times 0.0010\ \mathrm{M}+20\times 1.00\times 10^{-4}\ \mathrm{M}}} = 6.7\times 10^{-4}\ \mathrm{M}$$

where we have used

$$[\mathrm{P}] = \frac{1.00\ \mathrm{g}\times 10\ \mathrm{L^{-1}}}{100\times 10^3\ \mathrm{g\ mol^{-1}}} = 1.00\times 10^{-4}\ \mathrm{g\ L^{-1}}$$

Hence, $[\mathrm{Na^+}]_\mathrm{L} = \underline{6.7\times 10^{-4}\ \mathrm{M}}$

23.13 $[\mathrm{Cl^-}]_\mathrm{L} - [\mathrm{Cl^-}]_\mathrm{R} = \dfrac{-\nu[\mathrm{P}][\mathrm{Cl^-}]_\mathrm{L}}{[\mathrm{Cl^-}]_\mathrm{L}+[\mathrm{Cl^-}]_\mathrm{R}}$ [6b]

For simplicity, write $[\mathrm{Cl^-}]_\mathrm{L} = L$ and $[\mathrm{Cl^-}]_\mathrm{R} = R$. Then, since $\nu = 1$,

$$L - R = \frac{-[\mathrm{P}]L}{L+R},\ \text{implying that}\ L^2 - R^2 = -PL$$

Suppose an amount n mol of $\mathrm{Cl^-}$ ions migrate from the right hand compartment to the left, L becomes nM and R changes from 0.030 M to $(2\times 0.030 - n)/2$ M [since its volume is 2L]. Therefore, at equilibrium

$$n^2 + Pn - \left(\frac{0.060-n}{2}\right)^2 = 0 \quad \text{with}\ P = 0.100$$

This quadratic equation solves to $n = 6.7 \times 10^{-3}$; therefore, at equilibrium, $[Cl^-]_L = \underline{6.7\ \text{mM}}$.

23.14 Since $c \propto e^{Mb\omega^2 r^2/2RT}$ [Sedimentation equilibrium, Section 23.2],

$$\ln c = \text{const.} + \frac{Mb\omega^2 r^2}{2RT} \quad [b = 1 - \rho v_s]$$

and the slope of ln c against r^2 is equal to $Mb\omega^2/2RT$. Therefore,

$$M = \frac{2RT \times \text{slope}}{b\omega^2}$$

$$= \frac{2 \times 8.314\ \text{J K}^{-1}\ \text{mol}^{-1} \times 300\ \text{K} \times 729 \times 10^4\ \text{m}^{-2}}{(1 - 0.997 \times 0.61) \times (2\pi \times 50000/60\ \text{s}^{-1})^2}$$

$$= \underline{3.3\bar{9} \times 10^3\ \text{kg mol}^{-1}}$$

23.15 The force acting is $F = mr\omega^2$, and by Newton's second law of motion, $F = ma$,

$$a = r\omega^2 = 4\pi^2 r v^2$$

$$= 4\pi^2 \times 6.0 \times 10^{-2}\ \text{m} \times (80 \times 10^3/60\ \text{s})^2$$

$$= 4.2\bar{1} \times 10^6\ \text{m s}^{-2}$$

Then, since $g = 9.81\ \text{m s}^{-2}$, $a = \underline{4.3 \times 10^5\ g}$

23.16 $\tau = \dfrac{4\pi a^3 \eta}{3kT}$ [22]

(a) With $\eta(H_2O) = 0.8909 \times 10^{-3}\ \text{kg m}^{-1}\ \text{s}^{-1}$ and $a(\text{SA}) = 3.0\ \text{nm}$,

$$\tau = \frac{4\pi \times (3.0 \times 10^{-9}\ \text{m})^3 \times 0.8909 \times 10^{-3}\ \text{kg m}^{-1}\ \text{s}^{-1}}{3 \times 1.381 \times 10^{-23}\ \text{J K}^{-1} \times 298\ \text{K}} = \underline{2.4 \times 10^{-8}\ \text{s}}$$

(b) With $\eta(CCl_4) = 0.895 \times 10^{-3}\ \text{kg m}^{-1}\ \text{s}^{-1}$ and $a(CCl_4) = 250\ \text{pm}$,

$$\tau = \frac{4\pi \times (2.50 \times 10^{-10}\ \text{m})^3 \times 0.895 \times 10^{-3}\ \text{kg m}^{-1}\ \text{s}^{-1}}{3 \times 1.381 \times 10^{-23}\ \text{J K}^{-1} \times 298\ \text{K}} = \underline{1.4 \times 10^{-11}\ \text{s}}$$

23.17 $\left(\dfrac{\partial \gamma}{\partial c}\right)_T = \dfrac{-RT\Gamma_s}{c}$ [31]

Since $(\partial\gamma/\partial c)_T > 0$ [given], $\Gamma < 0$, which implies that the salt tends to avoid the surface.

Problems

23.1 $$\ln\frac{c_1}{c_2}=\frac{mb\omega^2(r_1^2-r_2^2)}{2kT} \quad [14]$$

$$=\frac{2\pi^2Mb\nu^2(r_1^2-r_2^2)}{RT} \quad [\omega=2\pi\nu]$$

and hence $$\nu=\left\{\frac{RT\ln(c_1/c_2)}{2\pi^2Mb(r_1^2-r_2^2)}\right\}^{1/2}$$

$$=\left\{\frac{8.314\ \mathrm{J\ K^{-1}\ mol^{-1}}\times 298\ \mathrm{K}\times\ln 5}{2\pi^2\times 1\times 10^2\ \mathrm{kg\ mol^{-1}}\times(1-0.75)\times(7.0^2-5.0^2)\times 10^{-4}\ \mathrm{m^2}}\right\}^{1/2}$$

$=58$ Hz, or $\underline{3500\ \text{rpm}}$.

23.2 $$[\mathrm{Na^+}]_\mathrm{L}-[\mathrm{Na^+}]_\mathrm{R}=\frac{\nu[\mathrm{P}][\mathrm{Na^+}]_\mathrm{L}}{[\mathrm{Na^+}]_\mathrm{L}+[\mathrm{Na^+}]_\mathrm{R}} \quad [6a]$$

Therefore, writing $[\mathrm{Na^+}]_\mathrm{L}=L$ and $[\mathrm{Na^+}]_\mathrm{R}=R$, and setting $\nu=2$, $(L+R)(L-R)=2[\mathrm{P}]L$

Suppose an amount $2n$ mol $\mathrm{Na^+}$ migrate from the left to the right hand compartments to reach equilibrium, then L changes from $0.030+0.010$ M to $0.040-n$ M and R changes from $0.030+0.010$ M to $0.040-n$ M and R changes from 0.0050 M to $0.0050+n$ M. We must therefore solve

$$0.045\times(0.035-2n)=0.030\times(0.040-n)$$

which gives $n=6.5\times10^{-3}$. Therefore, the concentration of $\mathrm{Na^+}$ ions at equilibrium are $L=0.034$ M, $R=0.012$ M. The potential difference across the membrane is therefore

$$E=\frac{RT}{F}\ln\frac{R}{L}=\frac{8.314\ \mathrm{J\ K^{-1}\ mol^{-1}}\times 300\ \mathrm{K}}{96.485\ \mathrm{kC\ mol^{-1}}}\ln\frac{0.012}{0.034}$$

$=\underline{-27\ \text{mV}}$

23.3 $$\Pi=RT[\mathrm{P}](1+B[\mathrm{P}]),\ B=\frac{\nu^2}{4[\mathrm{Cl^-}]+\nu[\mathrm{P}]} \quad [7]$$

$$B=\frac{400}{4\times 0.020\ \mathrm{M}} \quad [4[\mathrm{Cl^-}]\gg\nu[\mathrm{P}]]$$

$=5\times10^3\ \mathrm{L\ mol^{-1}}=\underline{5\ \mathrm{m^3\ mol^{-1}}}$

This value of B is comparable to the values calculated for nonelectrolyte solutions [Example 23.1], and so the two effects are comparable in this case.

23.4 $M=\dfrac{SRT}{bD}$ [13]

$$=\frac{4.5\times10^{-13}\,\text{s}\times8.314\,\text{J K}^{-1}\,\text{mol}^{-1}\times293\,\text{K}}{(1-0.75\times0.998)\times6.3\times10^{-11}\,\text{m}^2\,\text{s}^{-1}}$$

$$=\underline{69\,\text{kg mol}^{-1}}$$

Now combine $f=6\pi a\eta$ [10] with $f=kT/D$ [12]:

$$a=\frac{kT}{6\pi\eta D}=\frac{1.381\times10^{-23}\,\text{J K}^{-1}\times293\,\text{K}}{6\pi\times1.00\times10^{-3}\,\text{kg m}^{-1}\,\text{s}^{-1}\times6.3\times10^{-11}\,\text{m}^2\,\text{s}^{-1}}$$

$$=\underline{3.4\,\text{nm}}$$

23.5 $M=\dfrac{SRT}{bD}$ [13]

$$=\frac{5.01\times10^{-13}\,\text{s}\times8.314\,\text{J K}^{-1}\,\text{mol}^{-1}\times293\,\text{K}}{(1-1.0023\times0.734)\times6.97\times10^{-11}\,\text{m}^2\,\text{s}^{-1}}$$

$$=66.3\,\text{kg mol}^{-1}$$

$$f=\frac{kT}{D}\,[12]=\frac{1.381\times10^{-23}\,\text{J K}^{-1}\times293\,\text{K}}{6.97\times10^{-11}\,\text{m}^2\,\text{s}^{-1}}=5.81\times10^{-11}\,\text{kg s}^{-1}$$

$$V_m=v_s\times M=0.734\times10^{-3}\,\text{m}^3\,\text{kg}^{-1}\times66.3\,\text{kg mol}^{-1}$$

$$=4.87\times10^{-2}\,\text{m}^3\,\text{mol}^{-1}$$

$$\approx\frac{4\pi}{3}N_Aa^3$$

Hence,

$$a\approx\left(\frac{3V_m}{4\pi N_A}\right)^{1/3}=\left(\frac{3\times4.87\times10^{-2}\,\text{m}^3\,\text{mol}^{-1}}{4\pi\times6.022\times10^{23}\,\text{mol}^{-1}}\right)^{1/3}$$

$$\approx2.7\,\text{nm}$$

$$f_0=6\pi a\eta=6\pi\times2.7\times10^{-9}\,\text{m}\times1.00\times10^{-3}\,\text{kg m}^{-1}\,\text{s}^{-1}$$

$$=5.1\times10^{-11}\,\text{kg s}^{-1}$$

$$\frac{f}{f_0}=\frac{5.81\times 10^{-11}\ \mathrm{kg\,s^{-1}}}{5.1\times 10^{-11}\ \mathrm{kg\,s^{-1}}}=1.1\overline{4}$$

This ratio corresponds to an axial ratio of about 3.5 for a prolate ellipsoid [Table 23.1]. Therefore, with

$$a^3=a_{\parallel}a_{\perp}^2 \text{ and } a_{\parallel}\approx 3.5a_{\perp},\ a=2.7\ \mathrm{nm}$$

we conclude that

$$a_{\parallel}\approx \underline{6.2\ \mathrm{nm}},\ a_{\perp}\approx \underline{1.8\ \mathrm{nm}}$$

23.6 $S=\frac{s}{r\omega^2}$ [9a] $=\frac{1}{\omega^2}\frac{\mathrm{d}\ln r}{\mathrm{d}t}$ [Exercise 23.8]

Therefore, a plot of $\ln r$ against t will give S. We draw up the following table:

t/s	0	300	600	900	1200	1500	1800
r/cm	6.127	6.153	6.179	6.206	6.232	6.258	6.284
$\ln(r/\mathrm{cm})$	1.813	1.817	1.821	1.826	1.830	1.834	1.838

The least-squares slope is 1.408×10^{-5}, so

$$S=\frac{1.408\times 10^{-5}\ \mathrm{s^{-1}}}{(2\pi\times 50\times 10^3/60\ \mathrm{s^{-1}})^2}=5.14\times 10^{-13}\ \mathrm{s}$$

Then $M=\frac{SRT}{bD}$ [13]

$$=\frac{5.14\times 10^{-13}\ \mathrm{s}\times 8.314\ \mathrm{J\,K^{-1}\,mol^{-1}}\times 293\ \mathrm{K}}{(1-0.9981\times 0.728)\times 7.62\times 10^{-11}\ \mathrm{m^2\,s^{-1}}}$$

$$=\underline{60.1\ \mathrm{kg\,mol^{-1}}}$$

To assess the shape of the molecule we proceed as in Problem 23.5:

$$f=\frac{kT}{D}=\frac{1.381\times 10^{-23}\ \mathrm{J\,K^{-1}}\times 293\ \mathrm{K}}{7.62\times 10^{-11}\ \mathrm{m^2\,s^{-1}}}=5.31\times 10^{-11}\ \mathrm{kg\,s^{-1}}$$

$$V_{\mathrm{m}}=0.728\ \mathrm{cm^3\,g^{-1}}\times 60.1\times 10^3\ \mathrm{g\,mol^{-1}}=43.8\times 10^3\ \mathrm{cm^3\,mol^{-1}}$$

$$=4.38\times 10^{-2}\ \mathrm{m^3\,mol^{-1}}$$

Then,

$$a=\left(\frac{3V_{\mathrm{m}}}{4\pi N_{\mathrm{A}}}\right)^{1/3}=\left(\frac{3\times 4.38\times 10^{-2}\ \mathrm{m^3\ mol^{-1}}}{4\pi\times 6.022\times 10^{23}\ \mathrm{mol^{-1}}}\right)^{1/3}$$

$$=2.59\ \mathrm{nm}$$

$$f_0=6\pi a\eta=6\pi\times 2.59\times 10^{-9}\ \mathrm{m}\times 1.00\times 10^{-3}\ \mathrm{kg\ m^{-1}\ s^{-1}}$$

$$=4.89\times 10^{-11}\ \mathrm{kg\ s^{-1}}$$

which gives

$$\frac{f}{f_0}=\frac{5.31}{4.89}=1.09$$

Therefore, the molecule is either prolate or oblate, with an axial ratio of about 2.8 [Table 23.1].

23.7 $[\eta]=\lim_{c\to 0}\left(\frac{\eta/\eta^*-1}{c}\right)$ and $[\eta]=KM^a$ [Table 23.3]

We draw up the following table using $\eta^*=0.647\times 10^{-3}\ \mathrm{kg\ m^{-1}\ s^{-1}}$:

$c/(\mathrm{g}/100\ \mathrm{cm^3})$	0	0.2	0.4	0.6	0.8	1.0
$\eta/(10^{-3}\ \mathrm{kg\ m^{-1}\ s^{-1}})$	0.647	0.690	0.733	0.777	0.821	0.865
η/η^*-1	0	0.066	0.133	0.201	0.269	0.337
$\left(\frac{\eta/\eta^*-1}{c}\right)\Big/(100\ \mathrm{cm^3\ g^{-1}})$		0.332	0.332	0.335	0.336	0.337

The values are plotted in Fig. 23.7, and extrapolate to 0.330.

Hence

$$[\eta]=0.330\times 100\ \mathrm{cm^3\ g^{-1}}=33.0\ \mathrm{cm^3\ g^{-1}}$$

and

$$M=\left(\frac{33.0\ \mathrm{cm^3\ g^{-1}}}{8.3\times 10^{-2}\ \mathrm{cm^3\ g^{-1}}}\right)^{1/0.50}=158\times 10^3$$

That is, $M=\underline{158\ \mathrm{kg\ mol^{-1}}}$

23.8 $R_{\mathrm{g}}^2=\frac{1}{N}\sum_j R_j^2$

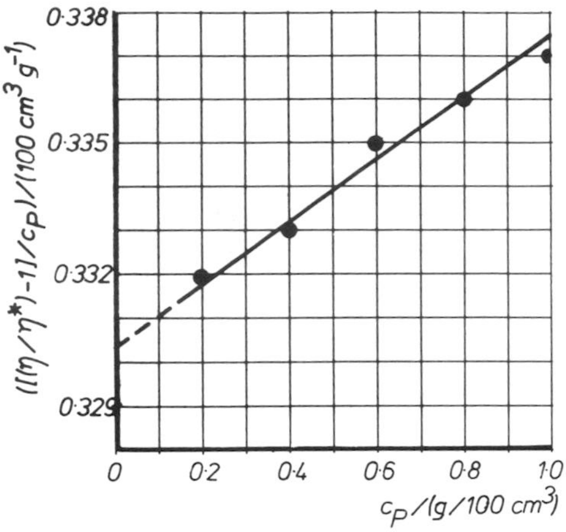

Fig 23.7

(a) Center of mass at center of sphere; therefore

$$R_g^2 = \frac{\int_0^a 4\pi r^4\,dr}{\int_0^a 4\pi r^2\,dr} = \frac{\frac{1}{5}a^5}{\frac{1}{3}a^3} = \frac{3}{5}a^2,\quad R_g = \left(\frac{3}{5}\right)^{1/2} a$$

(b) Center of mass at center of rod; therefore

$$R_g^2 = \frac{2\int_0^{1/2l} r^2\,dr}{2\int_0^{1/2l} dr} = \frac{\frac{1}{3}\left(\frac{1}{2}l\right)^3}{\frac{1}{2}l} = \frac{1}{12}l^2,\quad \underline{R_g = \frac{l}{2\sqrt{3}}}$$

For a sphere, $a = \left(\dfrac{3V_m}{4\pi N_A}\right)^{1/3} = \left(\dfrac{3v_s M}{4\pi N_A}\right)^{1/3}$

and so

$$R_g = \left(\frac{3}{5}\right)^{1/2}\left(\frac{3v_s M}{4\pi N_A}\right)^{1/3}$$

$$= \left(\frac{3}{5}\right)^{1/2}\left(\frac{3(v_s/\text{cm}^3\,\text{g}^{-1}) \times \text{cm}^3\,\text{g}^{-1} \times (M/\text{g mol}^{-1}) \times \text{g mol}^{-1}}{4\pi \times 6.022 \times 10^{23}\,\text{mol}^{-1}}\right)^{1/3}$$

$$= 5.690 \times 10^{-9}(v_s/\text{cm}^3\,\text{g}^{-1})^{1/3} \times (M/\text{g mol}^{-1})^{1/3}\,\text{cm}$$

$$= 5.690 \times 10^{-11}\,\text{m} \times \{(v_s/\text{cm}^3\,\text{g}^{-1})(M/\text{g mol}^{-1})\}^{1/3}$$

That is,

$$R_g/\text{nm} = \underline{0.056\,90 \times \{(v_s/\text{cm}^3\,\text{g}^{-1})(M/\text{g mol}^{-1})\}^{1/3}}$$

When $M = 100\ \text{kg mol}^{-1}$ and $v_s = 0.750\ \text{cm}^3\,\text{g}^{-1}$,

$$R_g/\text{nm} = 0.05690 \times \{0.750 \times 1.00 \times 10^5\}^{1/3} = \underline{2.40}$$

For a rod, $v_{\text{mol}} = \pi a^2 l$, so

$$R_g = \frac{v_{\text{mol}}}{2\pi a^2 \sqrt{3}} = \frac{v_s M}{N_A} \times \frac{1}{2\pi a^2 \sqrt{3}}$$

$$= \frac{0.750\ \text{cm}^3\,\text{g}^{-1} \times 1.00 \times 10^5\ \text{g mol}^{-1}}{6.022 \times 10^{23}\ \text{mol}^{-1} \times 2\pi \times (0.5 \times 10^{-7}\ \text{cm})^2 \times \sqrt{3}}$$

$$= 4.6 \times 10^{-6}\ \text{cm} = \underline{46\ \text{cm}}$$

23.9 Assume the solute particles are solid spheres; then

$$R_g = 0.05690 \times \{(v_s/\text{cm}^3\,\text{g}^{-1})(M/\text{g mol}^{-1})\}^{1/3}\ \text{nm} \quad \text{[Problem 23.8]}$$

and draw up the following table:

	$M/(\text{g mol}^{-1})$	$v_s/(\text{cm}^3\,\text{g}^{-1})$	$(R_g/\text{nm})_{\text{calc}}$	$(R_g/\text{nm})_{\text{expt}}$
SA	66×10^3	0.752	2.09	2.98
BSV	10.6×10^6	0.741	11.3	12.0
DNA	4×10^6	0.556	7.43	117.0

Therefore, SA and BSV resemble solid spheres, but DNA does not.

23.10 For a rigid rod, $R_g \propto l$ [Problem 23.8] $\propto M$, but for a random coil $R_g \propto N^{1/2} \propto M^{1/2}$. Therefore, poly($\gamma$-benzyl-L-glutamate) is rod-like whereas polystyrene is a random coil (in butanol).

23.11 $$\Gamma = \frac{-c}{RT}\left(\frac{\partial \gamma}{\partial c}\right)_T \quad [31] \quad = \frac{-[\text{A}]}{RT}\left(\frac{\partial \gamma}{\partial [\text{A}]}\right)_T \approx \frac{-[\text{A}]\,\Delta\gamma}{RT\,\Delta[\text{A}]}$$

Then we draw up the following table:

$[A]/\text{M}$	0	0.10	0.20	0.30	0.40	0.50
$-\left(\dfrac{\partial\gamma}{\partial[A]}\right)\Big/(\text{mN m}^{-1}\,\text{M}^{-1})$		26.0	25.0	26.0	23.0	30.0
$-[A]\left(\dfrac{\partial\gamma}{\partial[A]}\right)\Big/(\text{mN m}^{-1})$		2.60	5.00	7.80	9.20	15.0
$10^{10}\Gamma/(\text{mol cm}^{-2})$	0	1.07	2.05	3.20	3.77	6.15

For the last line we have used

$$\Gamma = -\frac{[A]}{RT}\left(\frac{\partial\gamma}{\partial[A]}\right)_T \frac{\text{mN m}^{-1}}{\text{mN m}^{-1}}$$

$$= -[A]\left\{\left(\frac{\partial\gamma}{\partial[A]}\right)_T\Big/(\text{mN m}^{-1})\right\}\frac{10^{-3}\,\text{N m}^{-1}}{2437\,\text{J mol}^{-1}}$$

and $\dfrac{10^{-3}\,\text{N m}^{-1}}{2437\,\text{J mol}^{-1}} = 4.103\times10^{-7}\,\text{mol m}^{-2} = 4.103\times10^{-11}\,\text{mol cm}^{-2}$

The surface pressure obeys $\pi = RT\Gamma$, with $\pi = \gamma^* - \gamma$. Therefore, we draw up the following table using $\gamma^* = 72.8\,\text{mN m}^{-1}$ and $RT = 2437\,\text{J mol}^{-1}$:

$[A]/\text{M}$	0	0.10	0.20	0.30	0.40	0.50
$10^{6}\Gamma/(\text{mol m}^{-2})$	0	1.07	2.05	3.20	3.77	6.15
$RT\Gamma/(\text{mN m}^{-1})$	0	2.60	5.02	7.81	9.21	15.0
$(\gamma^* - \gamma)/(\text{mN m}^{-1})$	0	2.6	5.1	7.7	10.0	13.0

The agreement is quite good, confirming that $\pi = RT\Gamma$.

23.12 $\Gamma = -\dfrac{c}{RT}\left(\dfrac{\partial\gamma}{\partial c}\right)_T$ [31]

and $\gamma = \gamma^* + (c/\text{M})\,\Delta\gamma$, $\left(\dfrac{\partial\gamma}{\partial c}\right) = \dfrac{\Delta\gamma}{\text{M}}$

Hence,

$$\Gamma = -\frac{c\,\Delta\gamma/\text{M}}{RT} = -(c/\text{M})(\Delta\gamma/\text{mN m}^{-1}) \times \frac{10^{-3}\,\text{N m}^{-1}}{RT}$$

$$= -(c/\text{M})(\Delta\gamma/\text{mN m}^{-1}) \times 4.103 \times 10^{-11}\,\text{mol cm}^{-2}$$

We then draw up the following table with $c \approx 1$ M:

	KCl	NaCl	Na_2CO_3
$\Delta\gamma/(\text{mN m}^{-1})$	1.4	1.64	2.7
$10^{11}\Gamma/(\text{mol cm}^{-2})$	−5.7	−6.7	−11.1

23.13 $dN \propto e^{-(M-\bar{M})^2/2\Gamma}\,dM$

We write the constant of proportionality as K, and evaluate it by requiring that $\int dN = N$. Put $M - \bar{M} = (2\Gamma)^{1/2}x$, so

$dM = (2\Gamma)^{1/2}\,dx$ and

$$N = K(2\Gamma)^{1/2}\int_a^\infty e^{-x^2}\,dx \quad [a = -M/(2\Gamma)^{1/2}]$$

$$\approx K(2\Gamma)^{1/2}\int_0^\infty e^{-x^2}\,dx \quad [a \approx 0] \quad = K(2\Gamma)^{1/2}\tfrac{1}{2}\pi$$

Hence, $K = \left(\dfrac{2}{\pi\Gamma}\right)^{1/2} N$

It then follows that

$$\langle M\rangle_N = \left(\frac{2}{\pi\Gamma}\right)^{1/2}\int_0^\infty M\,e^{-(M-\bar{M})^2/2\Gamma}\,dM$$

$$= \left(\frac{2}{\pi\Gamma}\right)^{1/2}(2\Gamma)\int_0^\infty \left\{x\,e^{-x^2} + \frac{\bar{M}}{(2\Gamma)^{1/2}}\,e^{-x^2}\right\}dx$$

$$= \left(\frac{8\Gamma}{\pi}\right)^{1/2}\left\{\frac{1}{2} + \left(\frac{\pi}{8\Gamma}\right)^{1/2}\bar{M}\right\} = \bar{M} + \left(\frac{2\Gamma}{\pi}\right)^{1/2}$$

23.14 The center of the spheres cannot approach more closely than $2a$; hence the excluded volume is

$$v_P = \tfrac{4}{3}\pi(2a)^3 = 8(\tfrac{4}{3}\pi a^3) = \underline{8v_{mol}}$$

where v_{mol} is the molecular volume. Since $B = \tfrac{1}{2}N_A v_P$ [4],

$$B(\text{BSV}) = \tfrac{1}{2}N_A \times \frac{32}{3}\pi a^3 = \frac{16}{3}\pi a^3 N_A$$

$$= \frac{16\pi}{3} \times 6.022 \times 10^{-23}\ \text{mol}^{-1} \times (14.0 \times 10^{-9}\ \text{m})^3$$

$$= \underline{28\ \text{m}^3\ \text{mol}^{-1}}$$

$$B(\text{Hb}) = \frac{16\pi}{3} \times 6.022 \times 10^{-23}\ \text{mol}^{-1} \times (3.2 \times 10^{-9}\ \text{m})^3$$

$$= \underline{0.33\ \text{m}^3\ \text{mol}^{-1}}$$

Since $\Pi = RT[\text{P}] + BRT[\text{P}]^2$ [1a]

if we write $\Pi° = RT[\text{P}]$,

$$\frac{\Pi - \Pi°}{\Pi°} = \frac{BRT[\text{P}]^2}{RT[\text{P}]} = B[\text{P}]$$

For BSV, $[\text{P}] = \dfrac{1.0\ \text{g}}{M} \times 10\ \text{L}^{-1} = \dfrac{10\ \text{g L}^{-1}}{1.07 \times 10^7\ \text{g mol}^{-1}}$

$$= 9.35 \times 10^{-7}\ \text{mol L}^{-1} = 9.35 \times 10^{-4}\ \text{mol m}^{-3}$$

and $\dfrac{\Pi - \Pi°}{\Pi°} = 28\ \text{m}^3\ \text{mol}^{-1} \times 9.35 \times 10^{-4}\ \text{mol m}^{-3} = 2.6 \times 10^{-2}$ corresponding to <u>2.6 per cent</u>.

For Hb, $[\text{P}] = \dfrac{10\ \text{g L}^{-1}}{66.5 \times 10^3\ \text{g mol}^{-1}} = 0.15\ \text{mol m}^{-3}$

and $\dfrac{\Pi - \Pi°}{\Pi°} = 0.15\ \text{mol m}^{-3} \times 0.33\ \text{m}^3\ \text{mol}^{-1} = 5.0 \times 10^{-2}$

which corresponds to <u>5 per cent</u>.

23.15 $B = \tfrac{1}{2}N_A v_P$ [4] $= 4N_A v_{mol}$ [Problem 23.14]

$$= \frac{16\pi}{3}N_A a_{eff}^3 = \frac{16\pi}{3}N_A \gamma^3 R_g^3 \quad [a_{eff} = \gamma R_g]$$

(a) $R_g = N^{1/2}l/\sqrt{6}$ [26]

$$B = \frac{16\pi}{3\times 6^{3/2}}\gamma^3 l^3 N^{3/2} N_A = \underline{4.22\times 10^{23}\ \text{mol}^{-1}\times (l\sqrt{N})^3}$$

$$= 4.22\times 10^{23}\ \text{mol}^{-1}\times (154\times 10^{-12}\ \text{m}\times\sqrt{4000})^3 = \underline{0.39\ \text{m}^3\ \text{mol}^{-1}}$$

(b) $R_g = 2^{1/2}\times R_g(\text{free})$ [27]

$$B = 2^{3/2}\times B(\text{free}) = \underline{1.19\times 10^{24}\ \text{mol}^{-1}\times (l\sqrt{N})^3}$$

$$= 2^{3/2}\times 0.39\ \text{m}^3\ \text{mol}^{-1} = \underline{1.1\ \text{m}^3\ \text{mol}^{-1}}$$

23.16 $$[\text{Na}^+]_L - [\text{Na}^+]_R = \frac{\nu[\text{P}][\text{Na}^+]_L}{[\text{Na}^+]_L + [\text{Na}^+]_R} \quad [6a]$$

which rearranges to

$$[\text{Na}^+]_L^2 - [\text{Na}^+]_R^2 = \nu[\text{P}][\text{Na}^+]_L$$

and hence to the quadratic equation

$$[\text{Na}^+]_L^2 - \nu[\text{P}][\text{Na}^+]_L - [\text{Na}^+]_R^2 = 0$$

Therefore, if $[\text{Na}^+]_R$ is constant,

$$[\text{Na}^+]_L = \tfrac{1}{2}\{\nu[\text{P}] \pm (\nu^2[\text{P}]^2 + 4[\text{Na}^+]_R^2)^{1/2}\}$$

and hence

$$\frac{[\text{Na}^+]_L}{[\text{Na}^+]_R} = \frac{\nu[\text{P}]}{2[\text{Na}^+]_R} \pm \left(1 + \left\{\frac{\nu[\text{P}]}{2[\text{Na}^+]_R}\right\}^2\right)^{1/2}$$

We write $x = \nu[\text{P}]/2[\text{Na}^+]_R$, and hence obtain

$$\frac{[\text{Na}^+]_L}{[\text{Na}^+]_R} = \underline{x + (1+x^2)^{1/2}}$$

[Ratio = 1 when $x = 0$, so choose + sign.] This function is plotted in Fig. 23.8.

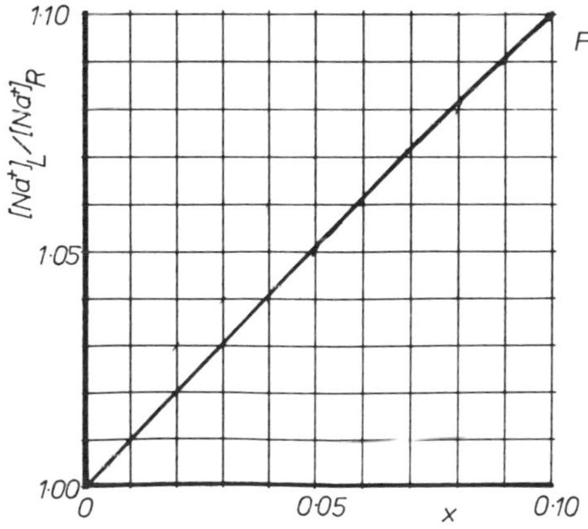

Fig 23.8

23.17 $G=U-TS-tl$ [given]

Hence $\mathrm{d}G=\mathrm{d}U-T\,\mathrm{d}S-S\,\mathrm{d}T-l\,\mathrm{d}t-t\,\mathrm{d}l$

$$=T\,\mathrm{d}S+t\,\mathrm{d}l-T\,\mathrm{d}S-S\,\mathrm{d}T-l\,\mathrm{d}t-t\,\mathrm{d}l=\underline{-S\,\mathrm{d}T-l\,\mathrm{d}t}$$

$A=U-TS=G+tl$

Hence $\mathrm{d}A=\mathrm{d}G+t\,\mathrm{d}l+l\,\mathrm{d}t=-S\,\mathrm{d}T-l\,\mathrm{d}t+t\,\mathrm{d}l+l\,\mathrm{d}t$

$$=\underline{-S\,\mathrm{d}T+t\,\mathrm{d}l}$$

Since $\mathrm{d}G$ and $\mathrm{d}A$ are both exact differentials,

$$\left(\frac{\partial S}{\partial l}\right)_T=-\left(\frac{\partial t}{\partial T}\right)_l \text{ and } \left(\frac{\partial S}{\partial t}\right)_T=\left(\frac{\partial l}{\partial T}\right)_t \quad \text{[Box 3.1]}$$

Since $\mathrm{d}U=T\,\mathrm{d}S+t\,\mathrm{d}l$ [given],

$$\left(\frac{\partial U}{\partial l}\right)_T=T\left(\frac{\partial S}{\partial l}\right)_T+t \quad \text{[Box 3.1, Relation 1]}$$

$$=\underline{-T\left(\frac{\partial t}{\partial T}\right)_l+t} \quad \text{[Maxwell relation, above]}$$

23.18 Write $t=aT$, then

$$\left(\frac{\partial t}{\partial T}\right)_l=a, \left(\frac{\partial U}{\partial l}\right)_T=t-aT \quad \text{[above]} \quad =0$$

and the internal energy is independent of the extension. Therefore,

$$t=-T\left(\frac{\partial S}{\partial l}\right)_T$$

and the tension is proportional to the variation of entropy with extension. The extension reduces the disorder of the chains, and they tend to revert to their disorderly (nonextended) state.

23.19 Refer to Fig. 23.9. Since $\boldsymbol{R}_i=\boldsymbol{R}_1+\boldsymbol{h}_i$ and $\sum_i \boldsymbol{R}_i=0$,

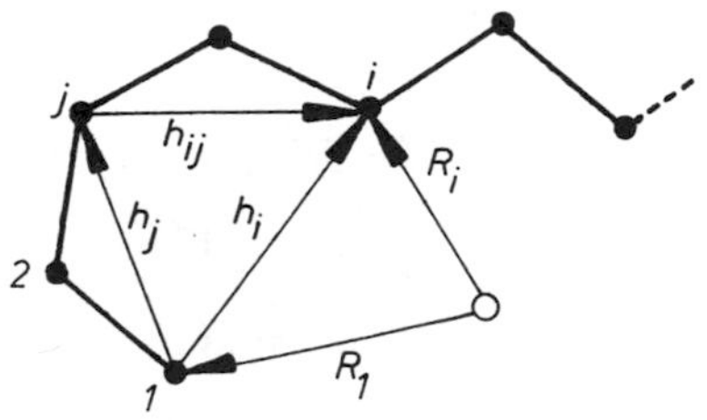

Fig 23.9

$$N\boldsymbol{R}_1+\sum_i \boldsymbol{h}_i=0$$

and hence $\boldsymbol{R}_1=-\dfrac{1}{N}\sum_i \boldsymbol{h}_i$

$$R_1^2=\frac{1}{N^2}\sum_{ij}\boldsymbol{h}_i\cdot\boldsymbol{h}_j,\quad \boldsymbol{R}_1\cdot\sum_i\boldsymbol{h}_i=-\frac{1}{N}\sum_{ij}\boldsymbol{h}_i\cdot\boldsymbol{h}_j$$

$$R_g^2=\frac{1}{N}\sum_i R_i^2 \quad \text{[new definition]}$$

$$=\frac{1}{N}\sum_i\{(\boldsymbol{R}_1+\boldsymbol{h}_i)\cdot(\boldsymbol{R}_1+\boldsymbol{h}_i)\}$$

$$=\frac{1}{N}\left\{NR_1^2+\sum_i h_i^2+2\boldsymbol{R}_1\cdot\sum_i\boldsymbol{h}_i\right\}$$

$$=\frac{1}{N}\left\{\sum_i \boldsymbol{h}_i^2-\frac{1}{N}\sum_{ij}\boldsymbol{h}_i\cdot\boldsymbol{h}_j\right\}$$

Since $\boldsymbol{h}_i\cdot\boldsymbol{h}_j=\frac{1}{2}(h_i^2+h_j^2-h_{ij}^2)$ [cosine rule]

$$R_g^2=\frac{1}{N}\left\{\sum_i h_i^2+\frac{1}{2N}\sum_{ij}h_{ij}^2-\frac{1}{2}\sum_i h_i^2-\frac{1}{2}\sum_j h_j^2\right\}$$

[In the last two terms, the summation over the second index contributes a factor N.]

$$=\underline{\frac{1}{2N^2}\sum_{ij}h_{ij}^2} \quad \text{[the original definition]}$$

23.20 (a) $R_{\text{rms}}^2=4\pi\left(\dfrac{a}{\pi^{1/2}}\right)^3\displaystyle\int_0^\infty r^4\,\mathrm{e}^{-a^2r^2}\,\mathrm{d}r$

$$=4\pi\left(\frac{a}{\pi^{1/2}}\right)^3\times\frac{3}{8}\left(\frac{\pi}{a^{10}}\right)^{1/2}=\frac{3}{2a^2}=Nl^2$$

Hence, $R_{rms} = \underline{lN^{1/2}}$.

(b) $R_{mean} = \int_0^\infty f(r)r\,dr = 4\pi\left(\frac{a}{\pi^{1/2}}\right)^3 \int_0^\infty r^3\,e^{-a^2r^2}\,dr$

$$= 4\pi\left(\frac{a}{\pi^{1/2}}\right)^3 \times \frac{1}{2a^4} = \frac{2}{a\pi^{1/2}} = \underline{\left(\frac{8N}{3\pi}\right)^{1/2} l}$$

(c) $\frac{df}{dr} = 4\pi\left(\frac{a}{\pi^{1/2}}\right)^3 \{2r - 2a^2r^2\}\,e^{-a^2r^2} = 0$ when $a^2r^2 = 1$.

Therefore, the most probable separation is

$$R^* = \frac{1}{a} = \underline{l\left(\frac{2}{3}N\right)^{1/2}}$$

When $N = 4000$ and $l = 154$ pm,

(a) $R_{rms} = \underline{9.74\text{ nm}}$, (b) $R_{mean} = \underline{8.97\text{ nm}}$, (c) $R^* = \underline{7.95\text{ nm}}$

23.21 A simple procedure is to generate numbers in the range 1 to 8, and to step north for 1 or 2, east for 3 or 4, south for 5 or 6, and west for 7 or 8 on a uniform grid. One such walk is shown in Fig. 23.10.

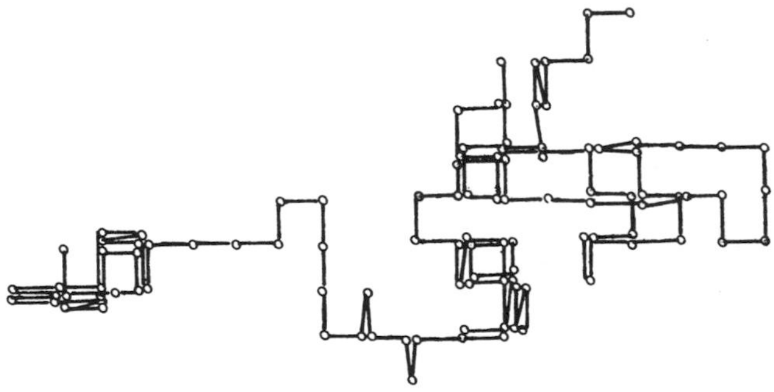

Fig 23.10

23.22 $P(\theta) = \frac{1}{N^2}\sum_{ij} \frac{\sin sR_{ij}}{sR_{ij}}, \; s = \frac{4\pi}{\lambda}\sin\tfrac{1}{2}\theta$ [21]

There are N terms in the sums for which $R_{ij} = 0$, $2(N-1)$ terms for which $R_{ij} = l$, $2(N-2)$ terms for which $R_{ij} = 2l, \ldots$ and $2(N-k)$ terms for which $R_{ij} = kl$. Therefore,

$$P(\theta) = \frac{1}{N^2}\sum_{k=0}^{N-1}\left\{2(N-k)\frac{\sin skl}{skl}\right\} - \frac{1}{N}$$

$$\approx \frac{2}{N}\int_0^{N-1} \frac{\sin skl}{skl}\,dk - \frac{2}{N^2sl}\int_0^{N-1} \sin skl\,dk - \frac{1}{N}$$

Write $x = skl$, $dk = dx/sl$, $Nl = L$ (the length of the rod):

$$P(\theta) \approx \frac{2}{sL}\int_0^{(N-1)sl}\left(\frac{\sin x}{x}\right)dx - \frac{2}{s^2L^2}\int_0^{(N-1)sl}\sin x\, dx - \frac{1}{N}$$

$$\approx \frac{2}{sL}\int_0^{(N-1)sl}\left(\frac{\sin x}{x}\right)dx + \frac{2}{s^2L^2}\{\cos(N-1)sl - 1\} - \frac{1}{N}$$

Since the rod is long, $(N-1)sl \approx Nsl = sL$ and $1/N \ll 1$.

Therefore, as $\cos\theta = 1 - 2\sin^2\frac{1}{2}\theta$,

$$P(\theta) \approx \frac{2}{sL}\int_0^{sL}\left(\frac{\sin x}{x}\right)dx - \left\{\frac{\sin\frac{1}{2}sL}{\frac{1}{2}sL}\right\}^2$$

$$\approx \frac{2}{sL}\operatorname{Si}(sL) - \left\{\frac{\sin\frac{1}{2}sL}{\frac{1}{2}sL}\right\}^2$$

For $L = \lambda$, $sL - 4\pi\sin\frac{1}{2}\theta$ and

$$P(\theta) \approx \frac{\operatorname{Si}(4\pi\sin\frac{1}{2}\theta)}{2\pi\sin\frac{1}{2}\theta} - \left\{\frac{\sin(2\pi\sin\frac{1}{2}\theta)}{2\pi\sin\frac{1}{2}\theta}\right\}^2$$

This function is plotted in Fig. 23.11.

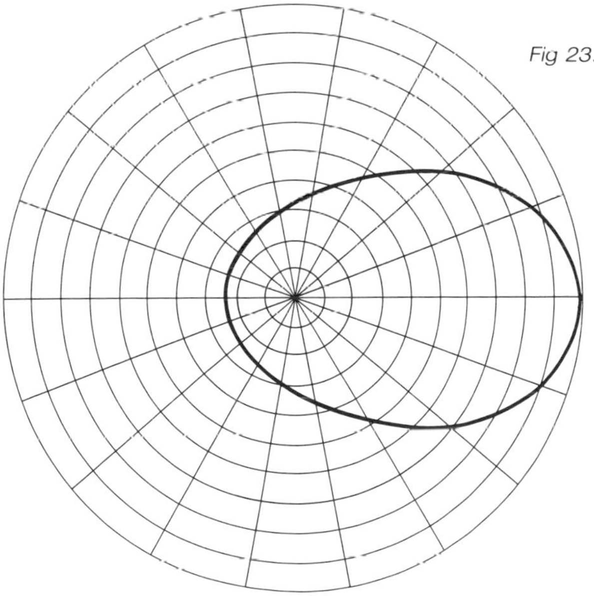

Fig 23.11

PART 3: CHANGE

24. The kinetic theory of gases

Exercises

24.1 $\bar{c}=\left(\frac{8kT}{\pi m}\right)^{1/2}$ [7b] $=\left(\frac{8RT}{\pi M}\right)^{1/2}$

$$=\left(\frac{8\times 8.314\ \mathrm{J\ K^{-1}\ mol^{-1}}\times T}{\pi\times(M/\mathrm{g\ mol^{-1}})\ \mathrm{g\ mol^{-1}}}\right)^{1/2}$$

$$=145.5\ \mathrm{m\ s^{-1}}\times\left(\frac{T/\mathrm{K}}{M/\mathrm{g\ mol^{-1}}}\right)^{1/2}\quad [\mathrm{J\ g^{-1}}=1000\ \mathrm{m^2\ s^{-2}}]$$

Therefore, we can draw up the following table with $M(\mathrm{He})=4.00\ \mathrm{g\ mol^{-1}}$ and $M(\mathrm{CH_4})=16.04\ \mathrm{g\ mol^{-1}}$:

T/K	77	298	1000
$\bar{c}(\mathrm{He})/\mathrm{m\ s^{-1}})$	640	1260	2300
$\bar{c}(\mathrm{CH_4})/(\mathrm{m\ s^{-1}})$	320	630	1150

24.2 $\lambda=\frac{kT}{2^{1/2}\sigma p}$ [12b] implies that $p=\frac{kT}{2^{1/2}\sigma\lambda}$

With $\lambda\approx 10\ \mathrm{cm}$

$$p=\frac{1.381\times 10^{-23}\ \mathrm{J\ K^{-1}}\times 298.15\ \mathrm{K}}{2^{1/2}\times 0.36\times 10^{-18}\ \mathrm{m^2}\times 0.10\ \mathrm{m}}=\underline{0.081\ \mathrm{Pa}}$$

This pressure corresponds to 8.0×10^{-7} atm.

24.3 $p=\frac{kT}{2^{1/2}\sigma\lambda}$ [Exercise 24.2] , with $\lambda\approx\sigma^{1/2}$

Hence,

$$p=\frac{1.381\times 10^{-23}\ \mathrm{J\ K^{-1}}\times 298.15\ \mathrm{K}}{2^{1/2}\times(0.36\times 10^{-18}\ \mathrm{m^2})^{3/2}}=\underline{1.4\times 10^{7}\ \mathrm{Pa}}$$

which corresponds to about 130 atm.

24.4 $\lambda = \dfrac{kT}{2^{1/2}\sigma p}$ [12b]

$$= \frac{1.381 \times 10^{-23}\ \mathrm{J\ K^{-1}} \times 217\ \mathrm{K}}{2^{1/2} \times 0.43 \times 10^{-18}\ \mathrm{m^2} \times 0.05 \times 1.013 \times 10^5\ \mathrm{Pa}}$$

$$= \underline{970\ \mathrm{nm}}$$

24.5 $z = \dfrac{2^{1/2}\sigma \bar{c} p}{kT}$ [9] $= 2^{1/2}\sigma\left(\dfrac{8kT}{\pi m}\right)^{1/2} \dfrac{p}{kT}$ [7b]

$$= \left(\frac{16}{\pi mkT}\right)^{1/2} \sigma p$$

$$= \left(\frac{16}{\pi \times 39.95 \times 1.6605 \times 10^{-27}\ \mathrm{kg} \times 1.381 \times 10^{-23}\ \mathrm{J\ K^{-1}} \times 298\ \mathrm{K}}\right)^{1/2}$$

$$\times 0.36 \times 10^{-18}\ \mathrm{m^2} \times p$$

$$= 4.92 \times 10^4\ \mathrm{s^{-1}} \times (p/\mathrm{Pa})$$

$$= 4.92 \times 10^4\ \mathrm{s^{-1}} \times 1.0133 \times 10^5 \times (p/\mathrm{atm})$$

$$= 4.98 \times 10^9\ \mathrm{s^{-1}} \times (p/\mathrm{atm})$$

Therefore (a) $z = \underline{5 \times 10^{10}\ \mathrm{s^{-1}}}$ when $p = 10$ atm, (b) $z = \underline{5 \times 10^9\ \mathrm{s^{-1}}}$ when $p =$ 1 atm, and (c) $z = \underline{5 \times 10^3\ \mathrm{s^{-1}}}$ when $p = 10^{-6}$ atm.

24.6 $Z_{AA} = \dfrac{zp}{2kT}$ [Example 24.4, based on eqn 10]

$$\frac{p}{2kT} = \frac{(p/\mathrm{atm}) \times 1.0133 \times 10^5\ \mathrm{Pa}}{2 \times 1.381 \times 10^{-23}\ \mathrm{J\ K^{-1}} \times 298\ \mathrm{K}} = 1.231 \times 10^{25}\ \mathrm{m^{-3}} \times (p/\mathrm{atm})$$

and therefore

$$Z_{AA} = 1.231 \times 10^{25}\ \mathrm{m^{-3}} \times 4.98 \times 10^9\ \mathrm{s^{-1}} \times (p/\mathrm{atm})^2$$
$$= 6.13 \times 10^{34} (p/\mathrm{atm})^2\ \mathrm{m^{-3}\ s^{-1}}$$

Therefore, in 1 L, the collision frequency is

$$Z_{AA} \times 10^{-3}\ \mathrm{m^3} = 6.13 \times 10^{31} (p/\mathrm{atm})^2\ \mathrm{s^{-1}}$$

(a) At 10 atm, there are $\underline{6.1 \times 10^{33}}$ collisions per second.

(b) At 1 atm, there are $\underline{6 \times 10^{31}}$ collisions per second.

(c) At 1 μatm, there are $\underline{6 \times 10^{19}}$ collisions per second.

Note that $Z \propto p^2$.

24.7 $z = \left(\dfrac{16}{\pi m k T}\right)^{1/2} \sigma p \quad$ [9, and Exercise 24.5]

$$= \frac{4 \times 0.43 \times 10^{-18}\,\text{m}^2 \times 0.05 \times 1.013 \times 10^5\,\text{Pa}}{(\pi \times 28.02 \times 1.6605 \times 10^{-27}\,\text{kg} \times 1.381 \times 10^{-23}\,\text{J K}^{-1} \times 217\,\text{K})^{1/2}}$$

$= \underline{4 \times 10^8\,\text{s}^{-1}}$

24.8 $Z_{AA} = \dfrac{\sigma \bar{c}}{2^{1/2}}\left(\dfrac{N}{V}\right)^2 \quad [10a] \quad = \sigma\left(\dfrac{4kT}{\pi m}\right)^{1/2}\left(\dfrac{N}{V}\right)^2$

$$= \sigma\left(\frac{4kT}{\pi m}\right)^{1/2}\left(\frac{N_A p}{RT}\right)^2 \quad [N = nN_A,\ pV = nRT]$$

$$= \sigma\left(\frac{4}{\pi k^3 T^3 m}\right)^{1/2} p^2 = \frac{2\sigma p^2}{(\pi m k^3 T^3)^{1/2}}$$

$$Z_{AB} = \sigma\left(\frac{8kT}{\pi\mu}\right)^{1/2}\left(\frac{NN'}{V^2}\right) \quad [11] \quad = \sigma\left(\frac{8}{\pi\mu k^3 T^3}\right)^{1/2} pp'$$

For O_2, $\sigma \approx \pi \times (357\,\text{pm})^2 = 4.00 \times 10^{-19}\,\text{m}^2$

For O_2, N_2 collisions, $\sigma \approx \pi \times (178 + 185\,\text{pm})^2 = 4.14 \times 10^{-19}\,\text{m}^2$

$m(O_2) = 32.00\,\text{u} = 5.32 \times 10^{-26}\,\text{kg}$

$$\mu(O_2, N_2) = \frac{32.00 \times 28.02\,\text{u}}{32.00 + 28.02} = 2.48 \times 10^{-26}\,\text{kg}$$

$p(O_2) = 0.210\,\text{atm} \quad$ [Example 1.6] $\quad = 21.3\,\text{kPa}$

$p(N_2) = 0.781\,\text{atm} \quad$ [Example 1.6] $\quad = 79.1\,\text{kPa}$

$$\frac{8}{\pi k^3 T^3} = \frac{8}{\pi \times (1.381 \times 10^{-23}\,\text{J K}^{-1} \times 298.15\,\text{K})^3} = 3.65 \times 10^{61}\,\text{J}^{-3}$$

Therefore,

$$Z(O_2, O_2) = 4.00 \times 10^{-19}\,\text{m}^2 \times \left(\frac{1.83 \times 10^{61}\,\text{J}^{-3}}{5.32 \times 10^{-26}\,\text{kg}}\right)^{1/2} \times (2.13 \times 10^4\,\text{Pa})^2$$

$$= \underline{3.3 \times 10^{33}\,\text{m}^{-3}\,\text{s}^{-1}}$$

$$Z(O_2, N_2) = 4.14 \times 10^{-19}\,\text{m}^2 \times \left(\frac{3.65 \times 10^{61}\,\text{J}^{-3}}{2.48 \times 10^{-26}\,\text{kg}}\right)^{1/2} \times 2.13 \times 10^4\,\text{Pa} \times 7.91 \times 10^4\,\text{Pa}$$

$$= \underline{2.7 \times 10^{34}\,\text{m}^{-3}\,\text{s}^{-1}}$$

24.9 $Z_{AA}=\dfrac{2\sigma p^2}{(\pi m k^3T^3)^{1/2}}$ [Exercise 24.8]

$m\approx 0.2m(O_2)+0.8m(N_2)\approx 29\ \mathrm{u}=4.8\times 10^{-26}\ \mathrm{kg}$

$\sigma\approx 4.0\times 10^{-19}\ \mathrm{m^2}$ [Exercise 24.8]

$$Z_{AA}\approx 4.0\times 10^{-19}\ \mathrm{m^2}\times\left(\frac{1.83\times 10^{61}\ \mathrm{J^{-3}}}{4.8\times 10^{-26}\ \mathrm{kg}}\right)^{1/2}\times\left(\frac{1.2\times 1.013\times 10^5\ \mathrm{Pa}}{760}\right)^2$$

$$=2.0\times 10^{29}\ \mathrm{m^{-3}\ s^{-1}}$$

Therefore, in $1.0\ \mathrm{cm^3}$, there are $\underline{2.0\times 10^{23}}$ collisions per second.

24.10 The average kinetic energy of one molecule is $\frac{1}{2}m\bar{c}^2$, so the molar internal energy is $\frac{1}{2}m\bar{c}^2N_A=\frac{1}{2}m(3kT/m)N_A=\frac{3}{2}RT$ [or by equipartition]. At 300 K,

$$U_m=\tfrac{3}{2}\times 8.314\ \mathrm{J\ K^{-1}\ mol^{-1}}\times 300\ \mathrm{K}=\underline{3.7\ \mathrm{kJ\ mol^{-1}}}$$

independent of the pressure and the identity of the molecules.

24.11 $\lambda=\dfrac{kT}{2^{1/2}\sigma p}$ [12b]

$$=\frac{1.381\times 10^{-23}\ \mathrm{J\ K^{-1}}\times 298.15\ \mathrm{K}}{2^{1/2}\times 0.43\times 10^{-18}\ \mathrm{m^2}\times p}$$

$$=\frac{6.8\times 10^{-3}\ \mathrm{m}}{(p/\mathrm{Pa})}=\frac{6.7\times 10^{-8}\ \mathrm{m}}{p/\mathrm{atm}}$$

(a) When $p=10$ atm, $\lambda=6.7\times 10^{-9}$ m, or $\underline{6.7\ \mathrm{nm}}$.

(b) When $p=1$ atm, $\lambda=\underline{67\ \mathrm{nm}}$.

(c) When $p=10^{-6}$ atm, $\lambda=\underline{6.7\ \mathrm{cm}}$.

24.12 $f(v)=4\pi\left(\dfrac{m}{2\pi kT}\right)^{3/2}v^2\,e^{-mv^2/2kT}$ [6]

$$\frac{m}{2kT}=\frac{28.0\times 1.6605\times 10^{-27}\ \mathrm{kg}}{2\times 1.381\times 10^{-23}\ \mathrm{J\ K^{-1}}\times 500\ \mathrm{K}}=3.37\times 10^{-6}\ \mathrm{m^{-2}\ s^2}$$

Therefore, at the center of the range,

$$f(295\ \mathrm{m\ s^{-1}})=4\pi\times\left(\frac{3.37\times 10^{-6}\ \mathrm{m^{-2}\ s^2}}{\pi}\right)^{3/2}\times(295\ \mathrm{m\ s^{-1}})^2$$

$$\times e^{-3.37\times 10^{-6}\times 295^2}$$

$$=9.06\times 10^{-4}\ \mathrm{m^{-1}\ s}$$

Therefore, the fraction of molecules in the specified range is

$$f \times \Delta v = 9.06 \times 10^{-4}\ \mathrm{m^{-1}\,s} \times 10\ \mathrm{m\,s^{-1}} = \underline{9.06 \times 10^{-3}}$$

corresponding to 0.91 per cent.

24.13 $Z_w = \dfrac{p}{(2\pi mkT)^{1/2}}$ [13b]

$$= \frac{90\ \mathrm{Pa}}{(2\pi \times 39.95 \times 1.6605 \times 10^{-27}\ \mathrm{kg} \times 1.381 \times 10^{-23}\ \mathrm{J\,K^{-1}} \times 500\ \mathrm{K})^{1/2}}$$

$$= 1.7 \times 10^{24}\ \mathrm{m^{-2}\,s^{-1}}$$

Therefore, the number of collisions is

$$N = 1.7 \times 10^{24}\ \mathrm{m^{-2}\,s^{-1}} \times (2.5 \times 3.0 \times 10^{-6}\ \mathrm{m^2}) \times 15\ \mathrm{s}$$

$$= \underline{1.9 \times 10^{20}}$$

24.14 $Z_{AB} = \sigma \left(\dfrac{8kT}{\pi\mu}\right)^{1/2} \left(\dfrac{NN'}{V^2}\right)$

$$T = \frac{pV}{nR} = \frac{2.00 \times 10^3\ \mathrm{Pa} \times 5.00 \times 10^{-3}\ \mathrm{m^3}}{4.50 \times 10^{-3}\ \mathrm{mol} \times 8.314\ \mathrm{J\,K^{-1}\,mol^{-1}}}$$

$$= 267\ \mathrm{K}$$

$d_{12} = \frac{1}{2}(d_1 + d_2)$

We obtain d from each σ [Table 24.2], writing $\sigma = \pi d^2$:

$$\sigma_{12} = \pi \times \left\{\frac{1}{2}\left(\frac{\sigma_1}{\pi}\right)^{1/2} + \frac{1}{2}\left(\frac{\sigma_2}{\pi}\right)^{1/2}\right\}^2 = \frac{1}{4}\{\sigma_1 + \sigma_2 + 2\surd(\sigma_1\sigma_2)\}$$

$$= \tfrac{1}{4}\{0.27 + 0.43 + 2 \times (0.27 \times 0.43)^{1/2}\}\ \mathrm{nm^2}$$

$$= 0.35\ \mathrm{nm^2}$$

$$\mu = \frac{2.02 \times 28.0\ \mathrm{u}}{2.02 \times 28.0} = 1.88\ \mathrm{u} = 3.13 \times 10^{-27}\ \mathrm{kg}$$

Therefore,

$$Z = 0.35 \times 10^{-18}\ \mathrm{m^2} \times \left(\frac{8 \times 1.381 \times 10^{-23}\ \mathrm{J\,K^{-1}} \times 267\ \mathrm{K}}{\pi \times 3.13 \times 10^{-27}\ \mathrm{kg}}\right)^{1/2}$$

$$\times \frac{1.50 \times 10^{-3}\ \mathrm{mol} \times 3.00 \times 10^{-3}\ \mathrm{mol} \times (6.022 \times 10^{23}\ \mathrm{mol^{-1}})^2}{(5.00 \times 10^{-3}\ \mathrm{m^3})^2}$$

$$= 4.0 \times 10^{31}\ \mathrm{m^{-3}\,s^{-1}}$$

Therefore, the number of collisions in 1.0 ns is

$$N = 4.0\times10^{31}\ \text{m}^{-3}\,\text{s}^{-1}\times5.00\times10^{-3}\ \text{m}^{3}\times1.0\times10^{-3}\ \text{s}$$

$$= \underline{2.0\times10^{32}}$$

24.15 $\lambda = \dfrac{kT}{2^{1/2}\sigma p}$ [12b]

But at constant volume, the pressure changes as the temperature is varied, and $p = nRT/V$; therefore

$$\lambda = \frac{kTV}{n2^{1/2}\sigma RT} = \frac{V}{n2^{1/2}\sigma N_A}$$

and λ is <u>independent</u> of temperature.

24.16 $\Delta m = Z_W A_0 m\,\Delta t$ [Example 24.7]

$$= \frac{pA_0 m\,\Delta t}{(2\pi mkT)^{1/2}} = pA_0\,\Delta t\left(\frac{m}{2\pi kT}\right)^{1/2}$$

$$= pA_0\,\Delta t\left(\frac{M}{2\pi RT}\right)^{1/2}$$

From the data, with $A_0 = \pi r^2$,

$$\Delta m = 0.835\ \text{Pa}\times\pi\times(1.25\times10^{-3}\ \text{m})^2\times7.20\times10^{3}\ \text{s}$$

$$\times\left(\frac{260\times10^{-3}\ \text{kg mol}^{-1}}{2\pi\times8.314\ \text{J K}^{-1}\,\text{mol}^{-1}\times400\ \text{K}}\right)^{1/2}$$

$$= 1.04\times10^{-4}\ \text{kg, or } \underline{104\ \text{mg}}$$

24.17 $J_z = -\kappa\dfrac{dT}{dz}$ [16]

$$= \frac{-0.163\ \text{mJ cm}^{-2}\,\text{s}^{-1}}{\text{K cm}^{-1}}\times(-2.5\ \text{K m}^{-1})\quad\text{[Table 24.4]}$$

$$= 0.41\ \text{mJ cm}^{-2}\,\text{s}^{-1}\times\text{cm/m}$$

$$= 0.41\times10^{-2}\ \text{mJ cm}^{-2}\,\text{s}^{-1} = \underline{4.1\ \mu\text{J cm}^{-2}\,\text{s}^{-1}}$$

24.18 $\kappa = \frac{1}{3}\lambda\bar{c}C_V[\text{A}]$ [20b]

$$\bar{c}=\left(\frac{8RT}{\pi M}\right)^{1/2} \text{ and } \lambda=\frac{kT}{2^{1/2}\sigma p}=\frac{V}{2^{1/2}\sigma n N_A}=\frac{1}{2^{1/2}\sigma N_A[A]}$$

Hence,

$$[A]\lambda\bar{c}=\left(\frac{8RT}{\pi M}\right)^{1/2}\frac{1}{2^{1/2}\sigma N_A}=\left(\frac{4RT}{\pi M}\right)^{1/2}\frac{1}{\sigma N_A}$$

and so

$$\kappa=\frac{1}{3\sigma N_A}\left(\frac{4RT}{\pi M}\right)^{1/2}C_V=\frac{1}{3\sigma N_A}\left(\frac{4RT}{\pi M}\right)^{1/2}\times\tfrac{3}{2}R \quad [C_V=\tfrac{3}{2}R]$$

$$=\frac{k}{2\sigma}\left(\frac{4RT}{\pi M}\right)^{1/2}$$

$$\sigma=\frac{k}{2\kappa}\left(\frac{4RT}{\pi M}\right)^{1/2}$$

$$=\frac{1.381\times10^{-23}\ \text{J K}^{-1}}{2\times0.0465\ \text{J s}^{-1}\text{K}^{-1}\text{m}^{-1}}\times\left(\frac{4\times8.314\ \text{J K}^{-1}\text{mol}^{-1}\times273\ \text{K}}{\pi\times20.2\times10^{-3}\text{kg mol}^{-1}}\right)^{1/2}$$

$$=\underline{5.6\times10^{-20}\ \text{m}^2},\ 0.056\ \text{nm}^2$$

The experimental value is 0.24 nm^2.

24.19 $\eta=\frac{1}{3}m\lambda\bar{c}N_A[A]\quad[21]$

$$=\frac{m}{3\sigma}\left(\frac{4RT}{\pi M}\right)^{1/2}\quad[\text{Exercise 24.18}]$$

Hence $\sigma=\dfrac{m}{3\eta}\left(\dfrac{4RT}{\pi M}\right)^{1/2}$

$$=\frac{20.2\times1.6605\times10^{-27}\ \text{kg}}{3\times2.98\times10^{-5}\ \text{kg m}^{-1}\text{s}^{-1}}\times\left(\frac{4\times8.314\ \text{J K}^{-1}\text{mol}^{-1}\times273\ \text{K}}{\pi\times20.2\times10^{-3}\ \text{kg mol}^{-1}}\right)^{1/2}$$

$$=\underline{1.42\times10^{-19}\ \text{m}^2},\ \text{or } 0.142\ \text{nm}^2$$

24.20 $\dfrac{dV}{dt}=\dfrac{(p_1^2-p_2^2)\pi r^4}{16l\eta p_0}\quad[2]$

which rearranges to

$$p_1^2 = p_2^2 + \left(\frac{16l\eta p_0}{\pi r^4}\right)\frac{dV}{dt}$$

$$= p_2^2 + \frac{16 \times 8.50\ \text{m} \times 1.76 \times 10^{-5}\ \text{kg m}^{-1}\,\text{s}^{-1} \times 1.00 \times 10^5\ \text{Pa}}{\pi \times (5.0 \times 10^{-3}\ \text{m})^4} \times \frac{9.5 \times 10^2\ \text{m}^3}{3600\ \text{s}}$$

$$= p_2^2 + 3.22 \times 10^{10}\ \text{Pa}^2$$

$$= (1.00 \times 10^5)^2\ \text{Pa}^2 + 3.22 \times 10^{10}\ \text{Pa}^2 = 4.22 \times 10^{10}\ \text{Pa}^2$$

Hence, $p_1 = \underline{205\ \text{kPa}}$, (2.05 bar).

24.21 $\eta = \frac{1}{3} m\lambda\bar{c}N_A[\text{A}]$ [21]

$$= \frac{m}{3\sigma}\left(\frac{4RT}{\pi M}\right)^{1/2}$$

$$= \frac{29 \times 1.6605 \times 10^{-27}\ \text{kg}}{3 \times 0.40 \times 10^{-18}\ \text{m}^2} \times \left(\frac{4 \times 8.314\ \text{J K}^{-1}\,\text{mol}^{-1} \times T}{\pi \times 29 \times 10^{-3}\ \text{kg mol}^{-1}}\right)^{1/2}$$

$$= 7.7 \times 10^{-7}\ \text{kg m}^{-1}\,\text{s}^{-1} \times (T/\text{K})^{1/2}$$

(a) At $T = 273$ K, $\eta = 1.3 \times 10^{-5}$ kg m^{-1} s^{-1}, or $\underline{130\ \mu\text{P}}$

(b) At $T = 298$ K, $\eta = \underline{130\ \mu\text{P}}$

(c) At $T = 1000$ K, $\eta = \underline{240\ \mu\text{P}}$

24.22 $\kappa = \frac{1}{3}\lambda\bar{c}C_V[\text{A}]$ [20b]

$$= \frac{k}{2\sigma}\left(\frac{4RT}{\pi M}\right)^{1/2} \quad \text{[Exercise 24.18]}$$

$$= \frac{1.381 \times 10^{-23}\ \text{J K}^{-1}}{2 \times (\sigma/\text{nm}^2) \times 10^{-18}\ \text{m}^2} \times \left(\frac{4 \times 8.314\ \text{J K}^{-1}\,\text{mol}^{-1} \times 300\ \text{K}}{\pi \times (M/g\ \text{mol}^{-1}) \times 10^{-3}\ \text{kg mol}^{-1}}\right)^{1/2}$$

$$= \frac{1.23 \times 10^{-2}\ \text{J K}^{-1}\,\text{m}^{-1}\,\text{s}^{-1}}{(\sigma/\text{nm}^2) \times (M/\text{g mol}^{-1})^{1/2}}$$

(a) For Ar,

$$\kappa = \frac{1.23 \times 10^{-2}\ \text{J K}^{-1}\,\text{m}^{-1}\,\text{s}^{-1}}{0.36 \times (39.95)^{1/2}} = \underline{5.4\ \text{mJ K}^{-1}\,\text{m}^{-1}\,\text{s}^{-1}}$$

(b) For He,

$$\kappa=\frac{1.23\times10^{-2}\,\mathrm{J\,K^{-1}\,m^{-1}\,s^{-1}}}{0.21\times(4.00)^{1/2}}=\underline{29\,\mathrm{mJ\,K^{-1}\,m^{-1}\,s^{-1}}}$$

The rate of flow of energy as heat is

$$\kappa A\,\frac{\mathrm{d}T}{\mathrm{d}z}=\kappa\times100\times10^{-4}\,\mathrm{m^2}\times150\,\mathrm{K\,m^{-1}}$$

$$=1.50\,\mathrm{K\,m}\times\kappa$$

$$=\underline{8.1\,\mathrm{mJ\,s^{-1}}}\text{ for Ar, }\underline{44\,\mathrm{mJ\,s^{-1}}}\text{ for He}$$

24.23 $\dfrac{\mathrm{d}V}{\mathrm{d}t}\propto\dfrac{1}{\eta}$ [2], which implies that

$$\frac{\eta(\mathrm{CO_2})}{\eta(\mathrm{Ar})}=\frac{\tau(\mathrm{CO_2})}{\tau(\mathrm{Ar})}=\frac{55\,\mathrm{s}}{83\,\mathrm{s}}=0.66\overline{3}$$

Therefore, $\eta(\mathrm{CO_2})=0.66\overline{3}\times\eta(\mathrm{Ar})=\underline{13\overline{8}\,\mu\mathrm{P}}$

For the molecular diameter of CO_2 we use

$$\sigma=\frac{m}{3\eta}\left(\frac{4RT}{\pi M}\right)^{1/2}\quad\text{[Exercise 24.19]}$$

$$=\frac{44.01\times1.6605\times10^{-27}\,\mathrm{kg}}{3\times1.3\overline{8}\times10^{-5}\,\mathrm{kg\,m^{-1}s^{-1}}}\times\left(\frac{4\times8.314\,\mathrm{J\,K^{-1}\,mol^{-1}}\times298\,\mathrm{K}}{\pi\times44.01\times10^{-3}\,\mathrm{kg\,mol^{-1}}}\right)^{1/2}$$

$$=4.7\times10^{-19}\,\mathrm{m^2}$$

$$\approx\pi d^2;\text{ therefore }d\approx\left(\frac{1}{\pi}\times4.7\times10^{-19}\,\mathrm{m^2}\right)^{1/2}=\underline{390\,\mathrm{pm}}$$

24.24 $D=\frac{1}{3}\lambda\bar{c}$ [19] $=\dfrac{2}{3p\sigma}\left(\dfrac{k^3T^3}{\pi m}\right)^{1/2}$

$$=\frac{2}{3p\times0.36\times10^{-18}\,\mathrm{m^2}}\times\left\{\frac{(1.381\times10^{-23}\,\mathrm{J\,K^{-1}})^3\times(298\,\mathrm{K})^3}{\pi\times39.95\times1.6605\times10^{-27}\,\mathrm{kg}}\right\}^{1/2}$$

$$=\frac{1.07\,\mathrm{m^2\,s^{-1}}}{(p/\mathrm{Pa})}=\frac{1.06\times10^{-5}\,\mathrm{m^2\,s^{-1}}}{(p/\mathrm{atm})}$$

Therefore, (a) at 10^{-6} atm, $D = \underline{11\ \text{m}^2\ \text{s}^{-1}}$, (b) at 1 atm, $D = \underline{1.1 \times 10^{-5}\ \text{m}^2\ \text{s}^{-1}}$, and (c) at 100 atm, $D = \underline{1.1 \times 10^{-7}\ \text{m}^2\ \text{s}^{-1}}$.

Problems

24.1 The time for a slot to coincide with the location of a neighboring slot is $\left(\dfrac{2}{360}\right)\Big/\nu$. If an atom passes through, it must have a speed

$$\frac{1.0\ \text{cm}}{\left(\dfrac{2}{360}\right)\Big/\nu} = 180\nu\ \text{cm} = 180(\nu/\text{Hz})\ \text{cm s}^{-1}$$

Hence, the distributions of the x-component of velocity are

ν/Hz	20	40	80	100	200
$v_x/(\text{cm s}^{-1})$	3600	7200	14 400	18 000	36 000
$I(40\ \text{K})$	0.846	0.513	0.069	0.015	0.002
$I(100\ \text{K})$	0.592	0.485	0.217	0.119	0.057

Theoretically,

$$f(v_x) = \left(\frac{m}{2\pi kT}\right)^{1/2} e^{-mv_x^2/2kT} \quad [5]$$

Therefore, as $I \propto f$, $I \propto \left(\dfrac{1}{T}\right)^{1/2} e^{-mv_x^2/2kT}$

Since

$$\frac{mv_x^2}{2kT} = \frac{83.8 \times 1.6605 \times 10^{-27}\ \text{kg} \times \{1.80(\nu/\text{Hz})\ \text{m s}^{-1}\}^2}{2 \times 1.381 \times 10^{-23}\ \text{J K}^{-1} \times T}$$

$$= \frac{1.63 \times 10^{-2}(\nu/\text{Hz})^2}{T/\text{K}}$$

we can write

$$I \propto \left(\frac{1}{T/\mathrm{K}}\right)^{1/2} \mathrm{e}^{-1.63\times 10^{-2}(\nu/\mathrm{Hz})^2/(T/\mathrm{K})}$$

and draw up the following table, obtaining the constant of proportionality by fitting I to the value at $T = 40$ K, $\nu = 80$ Hz:

ν/Hz	20	40	80	100	120
I(40 K)	0.80	0.49	(0.069)	0.016	0.003
I(100 K)	0.56	0.46	0.209	0.116	0.057

in fair agreement with the experimental data.

24.2 $\langle X\rangle = \sum_{i=1}^{N}\left(\frac{N_i}{N}\right)X_i$ [A1, $P_i = N_i/N$]

(a) $\langle v_x\rangle = \frac{1}{328}\{40\times 50 + 62\times 55 + \cdots + 2\times 70 + 38\times(-50)$

$+ 59\times(-55) + \cdots + 2\times(-70)\}$ mph

$= \underline{1.8 \text{ mph}}$ East

(b) $\langle |v_x|\rangle = \frac{1}{328}\{40\times 50 + 62\times 55 + \cdots + 2\times 70 + 38\times 50$

$+ 59\times 55 + \cdots + 2\times 70\}$ mph

$= \underline{56 \text{ mph}}$

(c) $\langle v_x^2\rangle = \frac{1}{328}\{40\times 50^2 + 62\times 55^2 + \cdots + 2\times 70^2\}\ (\text{mph})^2$

$= 3184(\text{mph})^2$

$\sqrt{\langle v_x^2\rangle} = \underline{56 \text{ mph}}$ [that $\sqrt{\langle v_x^2\rangle} = \langle |v_x|\rangle$ in this case is coincidental.]

24.3 $\langle X\rangle = \frac{1}{N}\sum_{i}^{N} N_iX_i$ [A1, $P_i = N_i/N$]

(a) $\langle h\rangle = \frac{1}{53}\{5'5'' + 2\times(5'6'') + \cdots + 6'2''\} = \underline{5'9\tfrac{1}{2}''}$

(b) $\langle h^2\rangle = \frac{1}{53}\{(5'5'')^2 + 2\times(5'6'')^2 + \cdots + (6'2'')^2\} = 33.54\ \text{ft}^2$

$\sqrt{\langle h^2\rangle} = 5.79\ \text{ft} = \underline{5'9\tfrac{1}{2}''}$

24.4 $\kappa \propto T^{1/2}C_V$, so $\frac{\kappa'}{\kappa} = \left(\frac{T'}{T}\right)^{1/2} \times \frac{C'_V}{C_V}$

At 300 K, $C_V \approx \frac{3}{2}R + R = \frac{5}{2}R$

At 10 K, $C_V \approx \frac{3}{2}R$ [Rotation not excited]

Therefore,

$$\frac{\kappa'}{\kappa} = \left(\frac{300}{10}\right)^{1/2} \times \frac{5}{3} = \underline{9.1}$$

24.5 Rate of energy transfer: $\frac{\mathrm{d}E}{\mathrm{d}t} = \kappa A \frac{\mathrm{d}T}{\mathrm{d}z}$

Therefore, with $\kappa \approx 0.241\ \text{mJ cm}^{-2}\ \text{s}^{-1}/(\text{K cm}^{-1})$ [Table 24.4]

$$\frac{\mathrm{d}E}{\mathrm{d}t} \approx \frac{0.241\ \text{mJ cm}^{-2}\ \text{s}^{-1}}{\text{K cm}^{-1}} \times 1.0\times 10^4\ \text{cm}^2 \times \frac{35\ \text{K}}{5.0\ \text{cm}}$$

$$\approx 17\times 10^3\ \text{mJ s}^{-1} = \underline{17\ \text{J s}^{-1}}, \text{ or } 17\ \text{W}$$

Therefore, a $\underline{28\ \text{W}}$ heater is required.

24.6 The pressure change follows the equation

$$p = p_0\,\mathrm{e}^{-t/\tau},\quad \tau = \left(\frac{2\pi m}{kT}\right)^{1/2} \frac{V}{A_0} \quad \text{[Example 24.6]}$$

Therefore, the time required for the pressure to fall from p_0 to p is

$$t = \tau \ln \frac{p_0}{p}$$

Consequently for two different gases at the same initial and final pressures

$$\frac{t'}{t} = \frac{\tau'}{\tau} = \left(\frac{M'}{M}\right)^{1/2}$$

and hence

$$M' = \left(\frac{t}{t'}\right)^2 M = \left(\frac{52}{42}\right)^2 \times 28.02\ \text{g mol}^{-1}$$

$$= \underline{43\ \text{g mol}^{-1}}$$

24.7 $Z_W = \dfrac{p}{(2\pi mkT)^{1/2}}$ [13b]

$$= \frac{(50/760) \times 1.013 \times 10^5\ \text{Pa}}{(2\pi \times 39.95 \times 1.6605 \times 10^{-27}\ \text{kg} \times 1.381 \times 10^{-23}\ \text{J K}^{-1} \times 1273\ \text{K})^{1/2}}$$

$$= 7.7\overline{8} \times 10^{25}\ \text{s}^{-1}\ \text{m}^2$$

Therefore, the collision frequency is

$$AZ_W = 2\pi \times 5.0 \times 10^{-2}\ \text{m} \times 1.0 \times 10^{-4}\ \text{m} \times 7.7\overline{8} \times 10^{25}\ \text{s}^{-1}\ \text{m}^{-2}$$

$$= \underline{2.4 \times 10^{21}\ \text{s}^{-1}}$$

24.8 $t = \tau \ln \dfrac{p_0}{p}$, $\tau = \left(\dfrac{2\pi m}{kT}\right)^{1/2} \dfrac{V}{A_0}$ [Example 24.6]

Since $\tau = \left(\dfrac{2\pi M}{RT}\right)^{1/2} \dfrac{V}{A_0} = \left(\dfrac{2\pi \times 32.0 \times 10^{-3}\ \text{kg mol}^{-1}}{8.314\ \text{J K}^{-1}\ \text{mol}^{-1} \times 298\ \text{K}}\right)^{1/2} \times \dfrac{3.0\ \text{m}^3}{\pi \times (1.0 \times 10^{-4}\ \text{m})^2}$

$$= 8.6 \times 10^5\ \text{s}$$

we find that

$$t = 8.6 \times 10^5 \times \ln \frac{0.80}{0.70} = \underline{1.1 \times 10^5\ \text{s}}\ (30\ \text{h})$$

24.9 $\dfrac{dN}{dt} = -Z_W A = \dfrac{-Ap}{(2\pi mkT)^{1/2}}$

where p is the (constant) vapor pressure of the solid. The change in the number of molecules inside the cell in an interval Δt is therefore $\Delta N = -Z_W A\ \Delta t$, and so the mass loss is

$$\Delta m = \Delta N m = -Ap\left(\frac{m}{2\pi kT}\right)^{1/2} \Delta t$$

$$= -Ap\left(\frac{M}{2\pi RT}\right)^{1/2} \Delta t$$

Therefore, the vapor pressure of the substance in the cell is

$$p=\frac{-\Delta m}{A\,\Delta t}\left(\frac{2\pi RT}{M}\right)^{1/2}$$

For the vapor pressure of germanium,

$$p=\frac{4.3\times10^{-8}\,\mathrm{kg}}{\pi\times(5.0\times10^{-4}\,\mathrm{m})^2\times7200\,\mathrm{s}}\times\left(\frac{2\pi\times8.314\,\mathrm{J\,K^{-1}\,mol^{-1}}\times1273\,\mathrm{K}}{72.5\times10^{-3}\,\mathrm{kg\,mol^{-1}}}\right)^{1/2}$$

$$=7.3\times10^{-3}\,\mathrm{Pa},\ \text{or}\ \underline{7.3\,\mathrm{mPa}}$$

24.10 $Z_W=\dfrac{p}{(2\pi mkT)^{1/2}}$

$$=\frac{(p/\mathrm{atm})\times1.0133\times10^5\,\mathrm{Pa}}{(2\pi\times32.0\times1.6605\times10^{-27}\,\mathrm{kg}\times1.381\times10^{-23}\,\mathrm{J\,K^{-1}}\times300\,\mathrm{K})^{1/2}}$$

$$=2.72\times10^{27}\,\mathrm{m^{-2}\,s^{-1}}\times(p/\mathrm{atm})$$

$$=2.72\times10^{23}\,\mathrm{cm^{-2}\,s^{-1}}\times(p/\mathrm{atm})$$

Hence, (a) at 1.0 atm, $Z_W=\underline{2.7\times10^{23}\,\mathrm{cm^{-2}\,s^{-1}}}$, (b) at 1.0×10^{-6} atm, $Z_W=\underline{2.7\times10^{16}\,\mathrm{cm^{-2}\,s^{-1}}}$, and (c) at 1.0×10^{-10} atm, $Z_W=2.7\times10^{13}\,\mathrm{cm^{-2}\,s^{-1}}$.

The nearest-neighbor distance in titanium is 291 pm, so the number of atoms per cm^2 is approximately 1.2×10^{15} (the precise value depends on the details of the packing, which is hcp, and the identity of the surface) The number of collisions per exposed atom is therefore $Z_W/(1.2\times10^{15}\,\mathrm{cm^{-2}})$:

(a) When $p==1.0$ atm, $Z_{\mathrm{atom}}=2.3\times10^8\,\mathrm{s^{-1}}$, (b) when $p=1.0\,\mu$atm, $Z_{\mathrm{atom}}=230\,\mathrm{s^{-1}}$, and (c) when $p=10^{-10}$ atm, $Z_{\mathrm{atom}}=0.02\,\mathrm{s^{-1}}$.

24.11 $\dfrac{dN}{dt}=k_r[\mathrm{Bk}]-Z_W A$ with $Z_W=\dfrac{p}{(2\pi mkT)^{1/2}}$

$[\mathrm{Bk}]=[\mathrm{Bk}]_0\,e^{-k_r t}$ and $p=\dfrac{nRT}{V}$

Therefore, the pressure of helium inside the container obeys

$$\frac{dp}{dt}=\frac{kT}{V}\frac{dN}{dt}=\frac{kk_rT}{V}[\mathrm{Bk}]_0\,e^{-k_rt}-\frac{pAkT/V}{(2\pi mkT)^{1/2}}$$

If we write $a=kk_rT[\mathrm{Bk}]_0/V$, $b=\dfrac{A}{V}\left(\dfrac{kT}{2\pi m}\right)^{1/2}$, the rate equation becomes

$$\frac{dp}{dt} = a\,e^{-k_r t} - bp, \; p = 0 \text{ at } t = 0$$

The solution is therefore

$$p = \left(\frac{a}{k_r - b}\right)\{e^{-bt} - e^{-k_r t}\}$$

Since $[Bk] = \frac{1}{2}[Bk]_0$ when $t = 4.4h$, it follows from the radioactive decay law ($[Bk] = [Bk]_0\,e^{-k_r t}$) that

$$k_r = \frac{\ln 2}{4.4 \times 3600\text{ s}} = 4.4 \times 10^{-5}\text{ s}^{-1}$$

We also know that

$$[Bk]_0 = \frac{1.0 \times 10^{-3}\text{ g}}{244\text{ g mol}^{-1}} \times 6.022 \times 10^{23}\text{ mol}^{-1} = 2.5 \times 10^{18}$$

$$a = \frac{kk_r T[Bk]_0}{V} = \frac{1.381 \times 10^{-23}\text{ J K}^{-1} \times 4.4 \times 10^{-5}\text{ s}^{-1} \times 298\text{ K} \times 2.5 \times 10^{18}}{1.0 \times 10^{-6}\text{ m}^3}$$

$$= 0.45\text{ Pa s}^{-1}$$

$$b = \frac{\pi \times (2.0 \times 10^{-6}\text{ m})^2}{1.0 \times 10^{-6}\text{ m}^3} \times \left(\frac{1.381 \times 10^{-23}\text{ J K}^{-1} \times 298\text{ K}}{2\pi \times 4.0 \times 1.6605 \times 10^{-27}\text{ kg}}\right)^{1/2}$$

$$= 3.9 \times 10^{-3}\text{ s}^{-1}$$

Hence,

$$p = \frac{0.45\text{ Pa s}^{-1}}{(4.4 \times 10^{-5} - 3.9 \times 10^{-3})\text{ s}^{-1}} \times \{e^{-3.9 \times 10^{-3}(t/\text{s})} - e^{-4.4 \times 10^{-5}(t/\text{s})}\}$$

$$= 120\text{ Pa} \times \{e^{-4.4 \times 10^{-5}(t/\text{s})} - e^{-3.9 \times 10^{-3}(t/\text{s})}\}$$

(a) $t = 1$ h, $p = 120\text{ Pa} \times \{e^{-0.16} - e^{-14}\} = \underline{100\text{ Pa}}$

(b) $t = 10$ h, $p = 120\text{ Pa} \times \{e^{-1.6} - e^{-140}\} = \underline{24\text{ Pa}}$

24.12 The time required is that for the H_2O molecules to effuse from the bulb through the circular hole representing the cold tube. We established in Problem 24.8 and Exercise 24.6 that

$$t = \tau \ln\frac{p_0}{p}, \; \tau = \left(\frac{2\pi m}{kT}\right)^{1/2}\frac{V}{A_0}$$

Therefore,

$$t=\left(\frac{2\pi\times 18.02\times 1.6605\times 10^{-27}\,\mathrm{kg}}{1.381\times 10^{-23}\,\mathrm{J\,K^{-1}}\times 300\,\mathrm{K}}\right)^{1/2}\times\frac{\left(\frac{4\pi}{3}\right)\times(5.0\times 10^{-2}\,\mathrm{m})^3}{\pi\times(3.0\times 10^{-3}\,\mathrm{m})^2}\times\ln\frac{1\,\mathrm{Torr}}{10\,\mu\mathrm{Torr}}$$

$$=0.12\,\mathrm{s}\ln 1.0\times 10^5=\underline{1.4\,\mathrm{s}}$$

24.13 The atomic current is the number of atoms emerging from the slit per second, which is $Z_W A$ with $A=1\times 10^{-7}\,\mathrm{m}^2$. We use

$$Z_W=\frac{p}{(2\pi mkT)^{1/2}}$$

$$=\frac{(p/\mathrm{kPa})\times 10^3\,\mathrm{Pa}}{(2\pi\times(M/\mathrm{g\,mol^{-1}})\times 1.6605\times 10^{-27}\,\mathrm{kg}\times 1.381\times 10^{-23}\,\mathrm{J\,K^{-1}}\times 380\,\mathrm{K})^{1/2}}$$

$$=1.35\times 10^{26}\,\mathrm{m^{-2}\,s^{-1}}\times\frac{p/\mathrm{kPa}}{(M/\mathrm{g\,mol^{-1}})^{1/2}}$$

(a) Cadmium:

$$Z_W A=1.35\times 10^{26}\,\mathrm{m^{-2}\,s^{-1}}\times 1\times 10^{-7}\,\mathrm{m}^2\times\frac{0.13\times 10^{-3}}{(112.4)^{1/2}}$$

$$=\underline{1.7\times 10^{14}\,\mathrm{s^{-1}}}$$

(b) Mercury:

$$Z_W A=1.35\times 10^{26}\,\mathrm{m^{-2}\,s^{-1}}\times 1\times 10^{-7}\,\mathrm{m}^2\times\frac{152}{(200.6)^{1/2}}$$

$$=\underline{1.4\times 10^{20}\,\mathrm{s^{-1}}}$$

24.14 $Z_{AA}=\sigma\left(\frac{4kT}{\pi m}\right)^{1/2}\left(\frac{N}{V}\right)^2$ [10] $=\sigma\left(\frac{4RT}{\pi M}\right)^{1/2}\left(\frac{p}{kT}\right)^2$

$$Z_{AB}=\sigma\left(\frac{8kT}{\pi\mu}\right)^{1/2}\left(\frac{pp'}{k^2T^2}\right)$$

$\sigma(H_2)=0.27\,\mathrm{nm}^2$, $\sigma(I_2)\approx 1.2\,\mathrm{nm}^2$

$$Z(H_2, H_2)=0.27\times 10^{-18}\,\mathrm{m}^2\times\left(\frac{4\times 8.314\,\mathrm{J\,K^{-1}\,mol^{-1}}\times 400\,\mathrm{K}}{\pi\times 2.02\times 10^{-3}\,\mathrm{kg\,mol^{-1}}}\right)^{1/2}$$

$$\times\left(\frac{0.5\times 1.0133\times 10^5\,\mathrm{Pa}}{1.381\times 10^{-23}\,\mathrm{J\,K^{-1}}\times 400\,\mathrm{K}}\right)^2$$

$$=\underline{3.3\times 10^{34}\,\mathrm{m^{-3}\,s^{-1}}}$$

Similarly, with $M(I_2)=254\ \mathrm{g\ mol^{-1}}$,

$$Z(I_2, I_2)=\underline{1.3\times10^{34}\ \mathrm{m^{-3}\ s^{-1}}}$$

For the H_2, I_2 collisions, we use

$$\mu=\frac{2.02\times254\ \mathrm{u}}{2.02+254}=2.00\ \mathrm{u}$$

$$\sigma(H_2, I_2)\approx\tfrac{1}{4}\{\sigma(H_2)+\sigma(I_2)+2(\sigma\sigma')^{1/2}\}\quad\text{[Example 24.14]}$$

$$\approx\tfrac{1}{4}\{0.27+1.2+2\times\surd(0.27\times1.2)\}\ \mathrm{nm^2}=0.65\ \mathrm{nm^2}$$

Hence,

$$Z(H_2, I_2)=0.65\ \mathrm{nm^2}\times\left(\frac{8\times8.314\ \mathrm{J\ K^{-1}\ mol^{-1}}\times400\ \mathrm{K}}{\pi\times2.00\times10^{-3}\ \mathrm{kg\ mol^{-1}}}\right)^{1/2}$$

$$\times\left(\frac{0.5\times1.0133\times10^{5}\ \mathrm{Pa}}{1.381\times10^{-23}\ \mathrm{J\ K^{-1}}\times400\ \mathrm{K}}\right)^{2}$$

$$=\underline{1.1\times10^{35}\ \mathrm{m^{-3}\ s^{-1}}}$$

24.15 The work required to go from a distance R from the center of a planet of mass m' to infinity is

$$w=\int_R^{\infty}\frac{Gmm'}{R^2}\mathrm{d}R=\frac{Gmm'}{R}$$

This can be expressed in terms of the gravitational acceleration g by considering the difference in work required to go from R and $R+h$:

$$\Delta w=\frac{Gmm'}{R}-\frac{Gmm'}{R+h}=\frac{Gmm'}{R}\left\{1-\frac{1}{1+h/R}\right\}$$

$$=\frac{Gmm'}{R}\left\{1-\left(1-\frac{h}{R}+\cdots\right)\right\}=\frac{Gmm'h}{R^2}+\cdots$$

Therefore, for small displacements,

$$\Delta w=\frac{Gmm'h}{R^2}$$

We write this

$$\Delta w=mgh$$

and hence identity g as Gm'/R^2

Next, the energy available after the initial boost is $E=\frac{1}{2}mv^2$; and so the minimum escape velocity is

$$v=\left(\frac{2Gm'}{R}\right)^{1/2}=(2gR)^{1/2}$$

(a) $v=(2\times 9.81\text{ m s}^{-2}\times 6.37\times 10^6\text{ m})^{1/2}=\underline{11.2\text{ km s}^{-1}}$

(b) $$g(\text{Mars})=\frac{m(\text{Mars})}{m(\text{Earth})}\times\frac{R(\text{Earth})^2}{R(\text{Mars})^2}\times g(\text{Earth})$$

$$=0.108\times\left(\frac{6.37}{3.38}\right)^2\times 9.81\text{ m s}^{-2}=\underline{3.73\text{ m s}^{-2}}$$

Hence,

$$v=(2\times 3.73\text{ m s}^{-2}\times 3.38\times 10^6\text{ m})^{1/2}=5.0\text{ km s}^{-1}$$

Since $\bar{c}=\left(\frac{8kT}{\pi m}\right)^{1/2}$

$$T=\frac{\pi m\bar{c}^2}{8k}=\frac{\pi M\bar{c}^2}{8R}$$

and we can draw up the following table:

$10^{-3}T/\text{K}$	H_2	He	O_2	
Earth	11.9	23.6	189	[$\bar{c}=11.2\text{ km s}^{-1}$]
Mars	2.4	4.8	39	[$\bar{c}=5.0\text{ km s}^{-1}$]

24.16 The probability of a molecule possessing an energy E is proportional to $e^{-E/kT}$ [Boltzmann, Section 19.1]. Consider a one dimensional system; then $E=\frac{1}{2}mv_x^2$. The probability of the molecule having a velocity in the range v_x to v_x+dv_x is therefore

$$f(v_x)\,dv_x=K\,e^{-mv_x^2/2kT}\,dv_x$$

The constant K is found in the same way as in the text (by normalization to 1), and we conclude that

$$f(v_x)=\left(\frac{m}{2\pi kT}\right)^{1/2}e^{-mv_x^2/2kT}$$

which is eqn 5.

24.17 Write the mean velocity initially as a, then in the emerging beam

$$\langle v_x \rangle = K \int_0^a v_x f(v_x)\,\mathrm{d}v_x$$

where K is a constant which ensures that the distribution in the emergent beam is also normalized. That is,

$$1 = K \int_0^a f(v_x)\,\mathrm{d}v_x = K\left(\frac{m}{2\pi kT}\right)^{1/2} \int_0^a \mathrm{e}^{-mv_x^2/2kT}\,\mathrm{d}v_x$$

$$= K\left(\frac{m}{2\pi kT}\right)^{1/2}\left(\frac{2kT}{m}\right)^{1/2} \int_0^b \mathrm{e}^{-x^2}\,\mathrm{d}x \quad [b = (m/2kT)^{1/2}a]$$

$$= \frac{K}{\pi^{1/2}} \int_0^b \mathrm{e}^{-x^2}\,\mathrm{d}x = \tfrac{1}{2}K\,\mathrm{erf}(b)$$

where erf(z) is the error function [Table 12.2]:

$$\mathrm{erf}(z) = \frac{2}{\pi^{1/2}} \int_0^z \mathrm{e}^{-x^2}\,\mathrm{d}x$$

Therefore, $K = \dfrac{2}{\mathrm{erf}(b)}$

The mean velocity of the emerging beam is

$$\langle v_x \rangle = K\left(\frac{m}{2\pi kT}\right)^{1/2} \int_0^a v_x\,\mathrm{e}^{-mv_x^2/2kT}\,\mathrm{d}v_x$$

$$= K\left(\frac{m}{2\pi kT}\right)^{1/2}\left(-\frac{kT}{m}\right) \int_0^a \frac{\mathrm{d}}{\mathrm{d}v_x}(\mathrm{e}^{-mv_x^2/2kT})\,\mathrm{d}v_x$$

$$= -K\left(\frac{kT}{2\pi m}\right)^{1/2}(\mathrm{e}^{-ma^2/2kT} - 1)$$

Now use

$$a = \langle v_x \rangle_{\mathrm{initial}} = \left(\frac{2kT}{m\pi}\right)^{1/2}$$

[Obtain this expression most quickly by setting $a = \infty$ in the expression for $\langle v_x \rangle_{\mathrm{final}}$, and erf($b$) = 1]. It follows that

$$e^{-ma^2/2kT} = e^{-1/\pi}$$

and $\mathrm{erf}(b) = \mathrm{erf}\left(\dfrac{1}{\pi^{1/2}}\right)$

Therefore,

$$\langle v_x \rangle = \left(\frac{2kT}{\pi m}\right)^{1/2} \left\{ \frac{1 - e^{-1/\pi}}{\mathrm{erf}\left(\dfrac{1}{\pi^{1/2}}\right)} \right\}$$

From tables of the error function [expanded versions of Table 12.2], $\mathrm{erf}(1/\pi^{1/2}) = \mathrm{erf}(0.56) = 0.57$ and $e^{-1/\pi} = 0.73$. Therefore,

$$\langle v_x \rangle = \underline{0.47 \langle v_x \rangle_{\text{initial}}}$$

24.18 $f(v) = 4\pi \left(\dfrac{m}{2\pi kT}\right)^{3/2} v^2 e^{-mv^2/2kT}$ [6]

The proportion of molecules with a speed less than c is

$$P = \int_0^c f(v)\,dv = 4\pi \left(\frac{m}{2\pi kT}\right)^{3/2} \int_0^c v^2 e^{-mv^2/2kT}\,dv$$

We write $a = m/2kT$; then

$$P = 4\pi \left(\frac{a}{\pi}\right)^{3/2} \int_0^c v^2 e^{-av^2}\,dv$$

$$= -4\pi \left(\frac{a}{\pi}\right)^{3/2} \frac{d}{da} \int_0^c e^{-av^2}\,dv = -4\pi \left(\frac{a}{\pi}\right)^{3/2} \frac{d}{da} \frac{1}{a^{1/2}} \int_0^{ca^{1/2}} e^{-x^2} dx$$

$$= -4\pi \left(\frac{a}{\pi}\right)^{3/2} \left\{ -\frac{1}{2}\left(\frac{1}{a}\right)^{3/2} \int_0^{ca^{1/2}} e^{-x^2}\,dx + \left(\frac{1}{a}\right)^{1/2} \frac{d}{da} \int_0^{ca^{1/2}} e^{-x^2}\,dx \right\}$$

Then we use

$$\int_0^{ca^{1/2}} e^{-x^2}\,dx = \left(\frac{\pi^{1/2}}{2}\right) \mathrm{erf}(ca^{1/2})$$

$$\frac{d}{da} \int_0^{ca^{1/2}} e^{-x^2}\,dx = \left(\frac{dca^{1/2}}{da}\right) \times e^{-c^2 a} \quad \left[\frac{d}{dx}\int_0^x f(y)\,dy = f(x)\right]$$

$$= \frac{1}{2}\left(\frac{c}{a^{1/2}}\right) e^{-c^2 a}$$

and hence

$$P = \operatorname{erf}(ca^{1/2}) - \frac{2ca^{1/2}}{\pi^{1/2}}\,e^{-c^2a}$$

Now, $c = \left(\frac{3kT}{m}\right)^{1/2}$, so $ca^{1/2} = \left(\frac{3kT}{m}\right)^{1/2}\left(\frac{m}{2kT}\right)^{1/2} = \left(\frac{3}{2}\right)^{1/2}$, and

$$P = \operatorname{erf}\left(\sqrt{\frac{3}{2}}\right) - \left(\frac{6}{\pi}\right)^{1/2} e^{-3/2} = 0.92 - 0.31 = \underline{0.61}$$

Therefore 61 per cent of the molecules have a speed less than the root mean square speed and 39 per cent have a speed greater than the root mean square speed.

For the proportions in terms of the mean speed $\bar{c}$, replace c by $\bar{c} = (8kT/\pi m)^{1/2} = (8/3\pi)^{1/2}c$, so $\bar{c}a^{1/2} = 2/\pi^{1/2}$. Then

$$P = \operatorname{erf}(\bar{c}a^{1/2}) - \frac{2\bar{c}a^{1/2}}{\pi^{1/2}}\,e^{-\bar{c}^2a}$$

$$= \operatorname{erf}\left(\frac{2}{\pi^{1/2}}\right) - \frac{4}{\pi}\,e^{-4/\pi} = 0.889 - 0.356 = \underline{0.533}$$

That is, 53 per cent of the molecules have a speed less than the mean, and 47 per cent have a speed greater than the mean.

24.19 Consider a range of speeds Δv around c^* and nc^*, then

$$\frac{f(nc^*)}{f(c^*)} = \frac{(nc^*)^2\,e^{-mn^2c^{*2}/2kT}}{c^{*2}\,e^{-mc^{*2}/2kT}} \quad [6]$$

$$= n^2\,e^{-(n^2-1)mc^{*2}/2kT} = \underline{n^2\,e^{(1-n^2)}} \quad [7a]$$

Therefore, $\frac{f(3c^*)}{f(c^*)} = 9 \times e^{-8} = \underline{3.02 \times 10^{-3}}$

$$\frac{f(4c^*)}{f(c^*)} = 16 \times e^{-15} = \underline{4.9 \times 10^{-6}}$$

24.20 The rate of growth of volume, dv/dt, is equal to the product of the collision frequency Z_W, the surface area, A, and the volume added by each arriving molecule, V_m/N_A. Therefore,

$$\frac{\mathrm{d}v}{\mathrm{d}t}=sZ_{\mathrm{W}}AV_{\mathrm{m}}/N_{\mathrm{A}}$$

where s is the sticking probability. For a spherical particle,

$v=\frac{4}{3}\pi r^3$ and $A=4\pi r^2$, so

$$\frac{\mathrm{d}v}{\mathrm{d}t}=4\pi r^2\frac{\mathrm{d}r}{\mathrm{d}t}=A\frac{\mathrm{d}r}{\mathrm{d}t}$$

Consequently,

$$\frac{\mathrm{d}r}{\mathrm{d}t}=sZ_{\mathrm{w}}V_{\mathrm{m}}/N_{\mathrm{A}}=\frac{spV_{\mathrm{m}}}{(2\pi mkT)^{1/2}N_{\mathrm{A}}}$$

We know the number density, not the pressure, so we use

$$p=\frac{nRT}{V}=\frac{nN_{\mathrm{A}}kT}{V}=\frac{N}{V}kT=\mathcal{N}kT$$

The molar volume is

$$V_{\mathrm{m}}=\frac{M}{\rho}$$

Therefore,

$$\frac{\mathrm{d}r}{\mathrm{d}t}=\frac{s\mathcal{N}}{\rho N_{\mathrm{A}}}\left(\frac{MRT}{2\pi}\right)^{1/2}$$

Since $\mathcal{N}\leqslant 3\times10^{15}\,\mathrm{cm^{-3}}=3\times10^{21}\,\mathrm{m^{-3}}$, $M=207\,\mathrm{g\,mol^{-1}}$, $\rho\approx11.5\,\mathrm{g\,cm^{-3}}$, $T=935\,\mathrm{K}$, and $s\approx1$, we obtain

$$\frac{\mathrm{d}r}{\mathrm{d}t}\leqslant\frac{3\times10^{21}\,\mathrm{m^{-3}}}{6.022\times10^{23}\,\mathrm{mol^{-1}}\times11.5\times10^{3}\,\mathrm{kg\,m^{-3}}}$$

$$\times\left(\frac{2.07\times10^{-3}\,\mathrm{kg\,mol^{-1}}\times8.314\,\mathrm{J\,K^{-1}\,mol^{-1}}\times935\,\mathrm{K}}{2\pi}\right)^{1/2}$$

$$=7\times10^{-6}\,\mathrm{m\,s^{-1}},\text{ or }\underline{7\times10^{-4}\,\mathrm{cm\,s^{-1}}}$$

Therefore, in 0.5 ms the growth in radius of the particle cannot exceed about $7\,\mu\mathrm{m\,s^{-1}}\times0.5\,\mathrm{ms}\approx\underline{4\,\mathrm{nm}}$.

25. Molecules in motion

Exercises

25.1 $\kappa = c\Lambda_m$ [1] $= 5.35 \times 10^{-2}\,\text{M} \times 135.5\ \text{S cm}^2\ \text{mol}^{-1}$

$= 7.25\ \text{S mol dm}^{-3}\ \text{cm}^2\ \text{mol}^{-1}$

$= 7.25 \times 10^{-3}\ \text{S cm}^{-1}$, or $\underline{7.25\ \text{mS cm}^{-1}}$

25.2 $\kappa = \dfrac{l}{RA}$ [Section 25.1]

$$= \frac{2.75\ \text{cm}}{351\ \Omega \times (2.2\ \text{cm})^2} = \underline{1.6\ \text{mS cm}^{-1}}$$

25.3 $\Lambda_m = \Lambda_m^{\circ} - \mathcal{K}c^{1/2}$ [2]

Therefore, for two concentrations c and c'

$$\Lambda_m' - \Lambda_m = -\mathcal{K}(c'^{1/2} - c^{1/2})$$

and $\mathcal{K} = -\dfrac{\Lambda_m' - \Lambda_m}{c'^{1/2} - c^{1/2}} = \dfrac{-(109.9 - 106.1)\ \text{S cm}^2\ \text{mol}^{-1}}{\{(6.2 \times 10^{-3})^{1/2} - (1.5 \times 10^{-2})^{1/2}\}\text{M}^{1/2}}$

$= 86.\overline{9}\ \text{S cm}^2\ \text{mol}^{-1}\ \text{M}^{1/2}$

Therefore,

$$\Lambda_m^{\circ} = \Lambda_m + \mathcal{K}c^{1/2}$$

$= 109.9\ \text{S cm}^2\ \text{mol}^{-1} + 86.\overline{9}\ \text{S cm}^2\ \text{mol}^{-1}\ \text{M}^{-1/2} \times (6.2 \times 10^{-3}\ \text{M})^{1/2}$

$= \underline{116.7\ \text{S cm}^2\ \text{mol}^{-1}}$

25.4 $\lambda = zuF$ [8]

$= 1 \times 6.85 \times 10^{-8}\ \text{m}^2\ \text{s}^{-1}\ \text{V}^{-1} \times 9.6485 \times 10^4\ \text{C mol}^{-1}$

$= 6.61 \times 10^{-3}\ \Omega^{-1}\ \text{m}^2\ \text{mol}^{-1}$ [$1\ \text{V} = 1\ \text{A}\ \Omega$, $1\ \text{A} = 1\ \text{C s}^{-1}$]

$= 6.61\ \text{mS m}^2\ \text{mol}^{-1} = \underline{66.1\ \text{S cm}^2\ \text{mol}^{-1}}$

25.5 $s = uE$ [7]

$$= 7.92 \times 10^{-8}\ \text{m}^2\ \text{s}^{-1}\ \text{V}^{-1} \times \frac{35.0\ \text{V}}{8.00 \times 10^{-3}\ \text{m}}$$

$= 3.47 \times 10^{-4}\ \text{m s}^{-1}$, or $\underline{347\ \mu\text{m s}^{-1}}$

25.6 $t_4 = \dfrac{u_+}{u_+ + u_-}$ [11] $= \dfrac{4.01}{4.01 + 8.09}$ [Table 25.2]

$= \underline{0.331}$

25.7 $\Lambda_m^\circ = \nu_+\lambda_+ + \nu_-\lambda_-$ [3]

$\Lambda_m^\circ(KCl) = \lambda(K^+) + \lambda(Cl^-) = 149.9\ S\ cm^2\ mol^{-1}$

$\Lambda_m^\circ(KNO_3) = \lambda(K^+) + \lambda(NO_3^-) = 145.0\ S\ cm^2\ mol^{-1}$

$\Lambda_m^\circ(AgNO_3) = \lambda(Ag^+) + \lambda(NO_3^-) = 133.4\ S\ cm^2\ mol^{-1}$

Hence $\Lambda_m^\circ(AgCl) = \Lambda_m^\circ(AgNO_3) + \Lambda_m^\circ(KCl) - \Lambda_m^\circ(KNO_3)$

$= 133.4 + 149.9 - 145.0\ S\ cm^2\ mol^{-1}$

$= \underline{138.3\ S\ cm^2\ mol^{-1}}$

25.8 $\Lambda_m' = \alpha\Lambda_m^\circ$ [4c], $\alpha = \dfrac{K_a}{2c}\left\{\left(1 + \dfrac{4c}{K_m}\right)^{1/2} - 1\right\}$

Hence, $\Lambda_m' = \left(\dfrac{1.91 \times 10^{-5}}{2 \times 0.040}\right) \times \left\{\left(1 + \dfrac{4 \times 0.040}{1.91 \times 10^{-5}}\right)^{1/2} - 1\right\}\Lambda_m^\circ$

$= 0.022\Lambda_m^\circ$

$= 0.022 \times (349.6 + 40.9)\ S\ cm^2\ mol^{-1} = \underline{8.59\ S\ cm^2\ mol^{-1}}$

$\kappa = c\Lambda_m' = 0.040\ mol\ dm^{-3} \times 8.59\ S\ cm^2\ mol^{-1}$

$= 3.4 \times 10^{-4}\ S\ cm^{-1}$, or $\underline{0.34\ mS\ cm^{-1}}$

$R = \dfrac{C}{\kappa} = \dfrac{0.206\ cm^{-1}}{3.4 \times 10^{-4}\ S\ cm^{-1}} = \underline{6.1 \times 10^2\ \Omega}$

25.9 $u = \dfrac{\lambda}{zF}$ [8]

$u(Li^+) = \dfrac{38.7\ S\ cm^2\ mol^{-1}}{9.6485 \times 10^4\ C\ mol^{-1}} = 4.01 \times 10^{-4}\ S\ C^{-1}\ cm^2$

$= \underline{4.01 \times 10^{-4}\ cm^2\ s^{-1}\ V^{-1}}$ [$1\ C\ \Omega = 1\ A\ s\ \Omega = 1\ V\ s$]

$$u(\mathrm{Na^+}) = \frac{50.1\ \mathrm{S\ cm^2\ mol^{-1}}}{9.6485 \times 10^4\ \mathrm{C\ mol^{-1}}} = \underline{5.19 \times 10^{-4}\ \mathrm{cm^2\ s^{-1}\ V^{-1}}}$$

$$u(\mathrm{K^+}) = \frac{73.5\ \mathrm{S\ cm^2\ mol^{-1}}}{9.6485 \times 10^4\ \mathrm{C\ mol^{-1}}} = \underline{7.62 \times 10^{-4}\ \mathrm{cm^2\ s^{-1}\ V^{-1}}}$$

25.10 $a = \dfrac{kT}{6\pi\eta D}$ [20 and Example 25.7]

$$= \frac{1.381 \times 10^{-23}\ \mathrm{J\ K^{-1}} \times 293\ \mathrm{K}}{6\pi \times 1.00 \times 10^{-3}\ \mathrm{kg\ m^{-1}\ s^{-1}} \times 7.1 \times 10^{-11}\ \mathrm{m^2\ s^{-1}}}$$

$$= 3.0\bar{2} \times 10^{-9}\ \mathrm{m}$$

$$M \approx \frac{4\pi}{3} a^3 \rho \times N_\mathrm{A} = \frac{4\pi a^3 N_\mathrm{A}}{3 v_\mathrm{s}}$$

$$\approx \frac{4\pi}{3} \times \frac{(3.0\bar{2} \times 10^{-9}\ \mathrm{m})^3 \times 6.022 \times 10^{23}\ \mathrm{mol^{-1}}}{0.75 \times 10^{-6}\ \mathrm{m^3\ g^{-1}}}$$

$$\approx 9.3 \times 10^4\ \mathrm{g\ mol^{-1}},\ \text{or}\ \underline{93\ \mathrm{kg\ mol^{-1}}}$$

25.11 $D = \dfrac{ukT}{ez} = \dfrac{uRT}{zF}$ [16]

$$= \frac{7.40 \times 10^{-8}\ \mathrm{m^2\ s^{-1}\ V^{-1}} \times 8.314\ \mathrm{J\ K^{-1}\ mol^{-1}} \times 298\ \mathrm{K}}{9.6485 \times 10^4\ \mathrm{C\ mol^{-1}}}$$

$$= \underline{1.90 \times 10^{-9}\ \mathrm{m^2\ s^{-1}}}$$

25.12 $a = \dfrac{kT}{6\pi\eta D}$ [20 and Example 25.7]

$$= \frac{1.381 \times 10^{-23}\ \mathrm{J\ K^{-1}} \times 293\ \mathrm{K}}{6\pi \times 1.00 \times 10^{-3}\ \mathrm{kg\ m^{-1}\ s^{-1}} \times 4.0 \times 10^{-11}\ \mathrm{m^2\ s^{-1}}}$$

$$= 5.4 \times 10^{-9},\ \text{or}\ \underline{5.4\ \mathrm{nm}}$$

25.13 $\langle x^2\rangle^{1/2}=(2Dt)^{1/2}$ [26b]

which implies that

$$t=\frac{\langle x^2\rangle}{2D}=\frac{(5.0\times10^{-3}\ \mathrm{m})^2}{2\times3.17\times10^{-9}\ \mathrm{m^2\,s^{-1}}}=\underline{3.9\times10^{3}\ \mathrm{s}}$$

25.14 $a=\dfrac{kT}{6\pi\eta D}$ [20 and Example 25.7]

$$=\frac{1.381\times10^{-23}\ \mathrm{J\,K^{-1}}\times298\ \mathrm{K}}{6\pi\times1.00\times10^{-3}\ \mathrm{kg\,m^{-1}\,s^{-1}}\times5.2\times10^{-10}\ \mathrm{m^2\,s^{-1}}}$$

$=4.2\times10^{-10}$ m, or $\underline{420\ \mathrm{pm}}$

25.15 $\tau=\dfrac{\lambda^2}{2D}$ [28] $\approx\dfrac{(300\times10^{-12}\ \mathrm{m})^2}{2\times2.13\times10^{-9}\ \mathrm{m^2\,s^{-1}}}$

$=\underline{21\ \mathrm{ps}}$

25.16 $\langle x^2\rangle^{1/2}=(2Dt)^{1/2}$ [26b]

(a) $\langle x^2\rangle^{1/2}=(2\times2.13\times10^{-9}\ \mathrm{m^2\,s^{-1}}\times1.0\ \mathrm{s})^{1/2}=\underline{65\ \mu\mathrm{m}}$

(b) $\langle x^2\rangle^{1/2}=(2\times5.21\times10^{-10}\ \mathrm{m^2\,s^{-1}}\times1.0\ \mathrm{s})^{1/2}=\underline{32\ \mu\mathrm{m}}$

[Data from Table 25.4.]

25.17 $t=\dfrac{\langle x^2\rangle}{2D}$

(a) Iodine: $t=\dfrac{(1.0\times10^{-3}\ \mathrm{m})^2}{2\times2.13\times10^{-9}\ \mathrm{m^2\,s^{-1}}}=\underline{240\ \mathrm{s}}$, about 4 min.

Sucrose: $t=\dfrac{(1.0\times10^{-3}\ \mathrm{m})^2}{2\times5.21\times10^{-10}\ \mathrm{m^2\,s^{-1}}}=\underline{960\ \mathrm{s}}$, about 16 min.

(b) Since $t\propto\langle x^2\rangle$, for a 10 fold increase in distance,

Iodine: $t=\underline{2.4\times10^{4}\ \mathrm{s}}$, about 7 h.

Sucrose: $t=\underline{9.6\times10^{4}\ \mathrm{s}}$, about 27 h.

Problems

Preliminary calculation:

$$\kappa=\frac{C}{R} \text{ and } \kappa=c\Lambda_m\text{; hence } C=\kappa R=c\Lambda_m R$$

Therefore, from the data

$$C=0.0200 \text{ mol dm}^{-3}\times 138.3 \text{ S cm}^2\text{ mol}^{-1}\times 74.58\ \Omega$$
$$=206.3 \text{ cm}^2\text{ dm}^{-3}=\underline{0.2063 \text{ cm}^{-1}}$$

25.1 $\dfrac{\kappa(CH_3COOH)}{\kappa(KCl)}=\dfrac{R(KCl)}{R(CH_3COOH)}=\dfrac{33.21\ \Omega}{300.0\ \Omega}$

Therefore,

$$\kappa(CH_3COOH)=\frac{33.21}{300.0}\times 1.1639\times 10^{-2}\text{ S cm}^{-1}=1.288\times 10^{-3}\text{ S cm}^{-1}$$

But this value includes a contribution of 7.6×10^{-4} S cm^{-1} from the water; hence the conductivity of the acetic acid itself is $(1.288-0.76)\times 10^{-3}$ S cm^{-1} = 5.3×10^{-4} S cm^{-1}. Therefore,

$$\Lambda_m=\frac{5.3\times 10^{-4}\text{ S cm}^{-1}}{0.100 \text{ mol dm}^{-3}}=\underline{5.3 \text{ S cm}^2\text{ mol}^{-1}}$$

25.2 $\Lambda_m=\Lambda_m^\circ-\mathcal{K}c^{1/2}$ [1], $\Lambda_m=C/cR$ where $C=0.2063$ cm^{-1}.
Therefore, we draw up the following table:

c/M	0.0005	0.001	0.005	0.010	0.020	0.050
$(c/\text{M})^{1/2}$	0.0224	0.032	0.071	0.100	0.141	0.224
R/Ω	3314	1668	342.1	174.1	89.08	37.14
$\Lambda_m/(\text{S cm}^2\text{ mol}^{-1})$	124.5	123.7	120.6	118.5	115.8	111.1

The value of Λ_m are plotted against $c^{1/2}$ in Fig. 25.1. The limiting value is $\Lambda_m^\circ=\underline{126 \text{ cm}^2\text{ mol}^{-1}}$. The slope is -76.5; hence $\mathcal{K}=\underline{76.5 \text{ S cm}^2\text{ mol}^{-1}\text{ M}^{-1/2}}$.

(a) $\Lambda_m=(50.1+76.8)\text{ S cm}^2\text{ mol}^{-1}-76.5\text{ S cm}^2\text{ mol}^{-1}\times(0.010)^{1/2}$
$=\underline{119.2 \text{ S cm}^2\text{ mol}^{-1}}$

(b) $\kappa=c\Lambda_m=0.010\text{ mol dm}^{-3}\times 119.2\text{ S cm}^2\text{ mol}^{-1}$
$=1.192\text{ S cm}^2\text{ dm}^{-3}=\underline{1.192\text{ mS cm}^{-1}}$

(c) $R=\dfrac{C}{\kappa}=\dfrac{0.2063\text{ cm}^{-1}}{1.192\times 10^{-3}\text{ S cm}^{-1}}=\underline{173.1\ \Omega}$

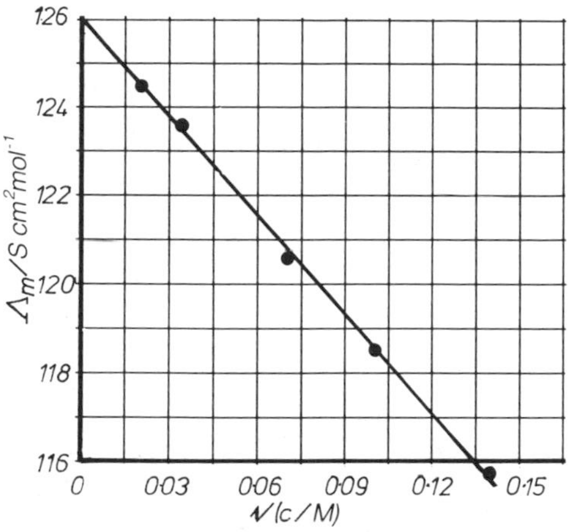

Fig 25.1

25.3 $c=\dfrac{\kappa}{\Lambda_m}\approx\dfrac{\kappa}{\Lambda_m^\circ}$ [c small, conductivity of water allowed for in the data.]

$$c\approx\frac{1.887\times10^{-6}\ \mathrm{S\ cm^{-1}}}{138.3\ \mathrm{S\ cm^2\ mol^{-1}}}\quad \text{[Exercise 25.7]}$$

$$\sim 1.36\times10^{-8}\ \mathrm{mol\ cm^{-3}}=\underline{1.36\times10^{-5}\ \mathrm{M}}$$

$K_{sp}\approx(1.36\times10^{-5})^2=\underline{1.86\times10^{-10}}$

We can correct for activities using $\gamma_\pm\approx10^{-A\sqrt{c}}\approx0.996$; hence

$$K_{sp}=\gamma_\pm^2\times1.86\times10^{-10}=\underline{1.85\times10^{-10}}$$

25.4 $\Lambda_m^\circ(\mathrm{NaCH_3CO_2})=\lambda(\mathrm{Na^+})+\lambda(\mathrm{CH_3CO_2^-})=91.0\ \mathrm{S\ cm^2\ mol^{-1}}$

$$\Lambda_m^\circ(\mathrm{HCl})=\lambda(\mathrm{H^+})+\lambda(\mathrm{Cl^-})=425.0\ \mathrm{S\ cm^2\ mol^{-1}}$$

$$\Lambda_m^\circ(\mathrm{NaCl})=\lambda(\mathrm{Na^+})+\lambda(\mathrm{Cl^-})=128.1\ \mathrm{S\ cm^2\ mol^{-1}}$$

$$\begin{aligned}\Lambda_m^\circ(\mathrm{CH_3COOH})&=\lambda(\mathrm{H^+})+\lambda(\mathrm{CH_3CO_2^-})\\&=\Lambda_m^\circ(\mathrm{HCl})+\Lambda_m^\circ(\mathrm{NaCH_3CO_3})-\Lambda_m^\circ(\mathrm{NaCl})\\&=(425.0+91.0-128.1)\ \mathrm{S\ cm^2\ mol^{-1}}\\&=\underline{387.9\ \mathrm{S\ cm^2\ mol^{-1}}}\end{aligned}$$

$$\alpha=\frac{\Lambda_m}{\Lambda_m^\circ}=\frac{\kappa}{c\Lambda_m^\circ}=\frac{C}{cR\Lambda_m^\circ}$$

$$=\frac{0.2063\ \mathrm{cm^{-1}}}{0.020\times10^{-3}\ \mathrm{mol\ cm^{-3}}\times888\ \Omega\times387.9\ \mathrm{S\ cm^2\ mol^{-1}}}$$

$$=\underline{0.030}$$

25.5 $$\frac{1}{\Lambda_m}=\frac{1}{\Lambda_m^\circ}+\frac{\Lambda_m c}{K_a(\Lambda_m^\circ)^2} \quad [5]$$

with $\Lambda_m^\circ=\lambda(H^+)+\lambda(CH_3CO_2^-)=390.5\ S\ cm^2\ mol^{-1}$. We draw up the following table using $\Lambda_m=\kappa/c=C/cR$ and $C=0.2063\ cm^{-1}$:

$10^3c/M$	0.49	0.99	1.98	15.81	63.23	252.9
$\Lambda_m/(S\ cm^2\ mol^{-1})$	68.5	49.5	35.6	13.0	6.56	3.22
$10^5c\Lambda_m/(S\ cm^{-1})$	3.36	4.90	7.05	20.6	41.5	81.4
$100/(\Lambda_m/S\ cm^2\ mol^{-1})$	1.46	2.02	2.81	7.69	15.2	31.1

We now plot $100/\Lambda_m$ against $10^5\ c\Lambda_m$ (Fig. 25.2). A least-squares fit of the data

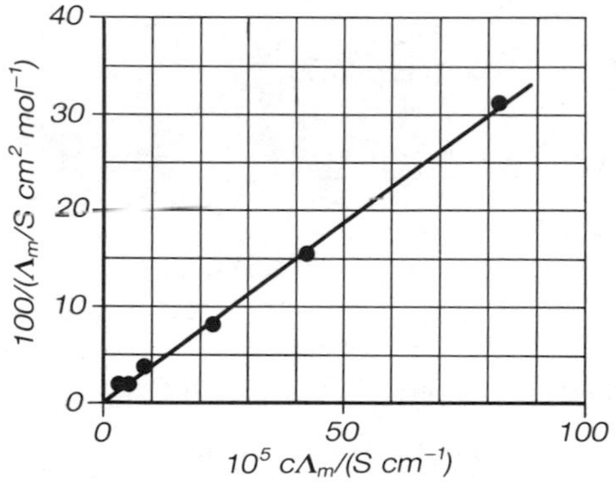

Fig 25.2

gives an intercept at 0.352 and a slope of 0.01559. Since we are actually plotting

$$\frac{100\ S\ cm^2\ mol^{-1}}{\Lambda_m}=\frac{100\ S\ cm^2\ mol^{-1}}{\Lambda_m^\circ}+\frac{10^2\ S\ cm^2\ mol^{-1}}{K_a(\Lambda_m^\circ)^2}\left(\frac{10^5\ c\Lambda_m}{S\ cm^{-1}}\right)\times\frac{S\ cm^{-1}}{10^5}$$

the slope of the plot is

$$\text{Slope}=\frac{10^2\ S^2\ cm\ mol^{-1}}{10^5\ K_a(\Lambda_m^\circ)^2}=\frac{10^{-3}\ S^2\ cm\ mol^{-1}}{K_a(\Lambda_m^\circ)^2}=0.352$$

Hence,

$$K_a = \frac{10^{-3}\ \mathrm{S^2\,cm\,mol^{-1}}}{0.352 \times (390.5\ \mathrm{S\,cm^2\,mol^{-1}})^2}$$

$$= 1.86 \times 10^{-8}\ \mathrm{mol\,cm^{-3}} = 1.86 \times 10^{-5}\ \mathrm{M}$$

Therefore, $\mathrm{p}K_a = -\lg 1.86 \times 10^{-5} = \underline{4.73}$

25.6 $s = uE$ [7] with $E = \dfrac{10\ \mathrm{V}}{1.00\ \mathrm{cm}} = 10\ \mathrm{V\,cm^{-1}}$

$s(\mathrm{Li^+}) = 4.01 \times 10^{-4}\ \mathrm{cm^2\,s^{-1}} \times 10\ \mathrm{V\,cm^{-1}} = \underline{4.0 \times 10^{-3}\ \mathrm{cm\,s^{-1}}}$

$s(\mathrm{Na^+}) = 5.19 \times 10^{-4}\ \mathrm{cm^2\,s^{-1}} \times 10\ \mathrm{V\,cm^{-1}} = \underline{5.2 \times 10^{-3}\ \mathrm{cm\,s^{-1}}}$

$s(\mathrm{K^+}) = 7.62 \times 10^{-4}\ \mathrm{cm^2\,s^{-1}} \times 10\ \mathrm{V\,cm^{-1}} = \underline{7.6 \times 10^{-3}\ \mathrm{cm\,s^{-1}}}$

$t = \dfrac{d}{s}$ with $d = 1.0$ cm:

$$t(\mathrm{Li^+}) = \frac{1.0\ \mathrm{cm}}{4.0 \times 10^{-3}\ \mathrm{cm\,s^{-1}}} = \underline{250\ \mathrm{s}}$$

$t(\mathrm{Na^+}) = \underline{190\ \mathrm{s}}$, $t(\mathrm{K^+}) = \underline{130\ \mathrm{s}}$ likewise.

For the distance moved during a half-cycle, write

$$d = \int_0^{1/2\nu} s\,\mathrm{d}t = \int_0^{1/2\nu} uE\,\mathrm{d}t = uE_0 \int_0^{1/2\nu} \sin(2\pi\nu t)\,\mathrm{d}t$$

$$= \frac{uE}{\pi\nu} = \frac{u \times 10\ \mathrm{V\,cm^{-1}}}{\pi \times 1.0 \times 10^3\ \mathrm{s^{-1}}} = 3.18 \times 10^{-3}\, u\ \mathrm{V\,s\,cm^{-1}}$$

That is, $d/\mathrm{cm} = 3.18 \times 10^{-3} \times (u/\mathrm{cm^2\,V^{-1}\,s^{-1}})$

Hence,

$d(\mathrm{Li^+}) = 3.18 \times 10^{-3} \times 4.0 \times 10^{-4}\ \mathrm{cm} = \underline{1.3 \times 10^{-6}\ \mathrm{cm}}$

$d(\mathrm{Na^+}) = \underline{1.7 \times 10^{-6}\ \mathrm{cm}}$, $d(\mathrm{K^+}) = \underline{2.4 \times 10^{-6}\ \mathrm{cm}}$

These correspond to about <u>43</u>, <u>55</u>, and <u>81</u> solvent molecule diameters respectively.

25.7 $t(\mathrm{H^+}) = \dfrac{u(\mathrm{H^+})}{u(\mathrm{H^+}) + u(\mathrm{Cl^-})}$ [11b]

$$= \frac{3.623}{3.623 + 0.791} = \underline{0.82}$$

When NaCl is added,

$$t(\mathrm{H}^+) = \frac{c(\mathrm{H}^+)u(\mathrm{H}^+)}{c(\mathrm{H}^+)u(\mathrm{H}^+ + c(\mathrm{Na}^+)u(\mathrm{Na}^+) + c(\mathrm{Cl}^-)u(\mathrm{Cl}^-)} \quad [10]$$

$$= \frac{1.0\times 10^{-3}\times 3.623}{1.0\times 10^{-3}\times 3.623 + 1.0\times 0.519 + 1.001\times 0.791}$$

$$= \underline{0.0028}$$

25.8 $t = \dfrac{zcVF}{I\,\Delta t}$ [Section 25.2] $= \dfrac{zcAFx}{I\,\Delta t}$

$$= \frac{21\ \mathrm{mol\,m^{-3}}\times\pi\times(2.073\times 10^{-3}\ \mathrm{m})^2\times 9.6485\times 10^4\ \mathrm{C\,mol^{-1}}}{18.2\times 10^{-3}\ \mathrm{A}}\times\frac{x}{\Delta t}$$

$$= 1.50\times 10^3\ \mathrm{m^{-1}\,s}\times\frac{x}{\Delta t}$$

$$= 1.50\left(\frac{x/\mathrm{mm}}{\Delta t/\mathrm{s}}\right)$$

Then we draw up the following table:

$\Delta t/\mathrm{s}$	200	400	600	800	1000
x/mm	64	128	192	254	318
t_+	0.48	0.48	0.48	0.48	0.48
$t_- = 1 - t_+$	0.52	0.52	0.52	0.52	0.52

Hence, we conclude that $t_+ = \underline{0.48}$ and $t_- = \underline{0.52}$.

For the mobility of K^+ we use

$$t_+ = \frac{\lambda_+}{\Lambda_m^\circ}\ [12] \quad = \frac{u_+F}{\Lambda_m^\circ}\ [8]$$

to obtain

$$u_+ = \frac{t_+\Lambda_m^\circ}{F} = \frac{0.48\times 149.9\ \mathrm{S\,cm^2\,mol^{-1}}}{9.6485\times 10^4\ \mathrm{C\,mol^{-1}}}$$

$$= \underline{7.5\times 10^{-4}\ \mathrm{cm^2\,s^{-1}\,V^{-1}}}$$

$\lambda_+ = t_+\Lambda_m^\circ$ [12] $= 0.48\times 149.9\ \mathrm{S\,cm^2\,mol^{-1}}$

$= \underline{72\ \mathrm{S\,cm^2\,mol^{-1}}}$

25.9 $t_+ = \frac{zcAF}{I} \times \frac{x}{\Delta t}$ [Problem 25.8]

Since the density of the solution is about $0.682\ \mathrm{g\ cm^{-3}}$, the concentration c is related to the molality m by

$$c/\mathrm{M} = \frac{1}{0.682} \times m/(\mathrm{mol\ kg^{-1}}) = 14.7m/(\mathrm{mol\ kg^{-1}})$$

$$A = \pi r^2 = \pi \times (2.073 \times 10^{-3}\ \mathrm{m})^2 = 1.350 \times 10^{-5}\ \mathrm{m^2}$$

$$\frac{czAF}{I\,\Delta t} = \frac{1.350 \times 10^{-5}\ \mathrm{m^2} \times 9.6485 \times 10^4\ \mathrm{C\ mol^{-1}}}{5.000 \times 10^{-3}\ \mathrm{A} \times 2500\ \mathrm{s}} \times c$$

$$= 0.1042\ \mathrm{m^2\ mol^{-1}} \times c$$

$$= 0.1042/\mathrm{mm} \times c/\mathrm{M} = 0.153/\mathrm{mm} \times m/(\mathrm{mol\ kg^{-1}})$$

and so

$$t_+ = 0.153 \times (x/\mathrm{mm}) \times m/(\mathrm{mol\ kg^{-1}})$$

(a) $t_+ = 0.153 \times 286.9 \times 0.013\,65 = 0.60$

(b) $t_+ = 0.153 \times 92.03 \times 0.042\,55 = 0.60$

Therefore, $t(\mathrm{H^+}) = 0.60$ and the mobility is not as abnormal as in water where $t(\mathrm{H^+}) = 0.82$.

25.10 $R = \frac{C}{\kappa} = \frac{0.2063\ \mathrm{cm^{-1}}}{5.5 \times 10^{-8}\ \mathrm{S\ cm^{-1}}} = \underline{3.75\ \mathrm{M\Omega}}$

$$\Lambda_\mathrm{m}^\circ = \lambda(\mathrm{H^+}) + \lambda(\mathrm{OH^-}) = 349.8 + 197.6\ \mathrm{S\ cm^2\ mol^{-1}} = 547.4\ \mathrm{S\ cm^2\ mol^{-1}}$$

and so $\alpha = \frac{\Lambda_\mathrm{m}}{\Lambda_\mathrm{m}^\circ} = \frac{\kappa}{c\Lambda_\mathrm{m}^\circ} = \frac{5.5 \times 10^{-8}\ \mathrm{S\ cm^{-1}}}{55.5\ \mathrm{mol\ dm^{-3}} \times 547.4\ \mathrm{S\ cm^2\ mol^{-1}}}$

$$= 1.8 \times 10^{-9}$$

We then write

$$K_\mathrm{w} = a(\mathrm{H^+})a(\mathrm{OH^-}) \approx c(\mathrm{H^+})c(\mathrm{OH^-})/\mathrm{M}^2$$

$$= \alpha^2 c(\mathrm{H_2O})^2/\mathrm{M}^2 = \alpha^2 \times (55.5)^2$$

$$= (1.8 \times 10^{-9})^2 \times (55.5)^2 = \underline{1.0 \times 10^{-14}}$$

$\mathrm{p}K_\mathrm{w} = -\lg K_\mathrm{w} = \underline{14.0}$
$\mathrm{pH} = -\lg a(\mathrm{H^+}) = -\lg K_\mathrm{w}^{1/2} = -\frac{1}{2}\lg K_\mathrm{w} = \underline{7.0}$

25.11 $\mathcal{F} = -\dfrac{RT}{c} \times \dfrac{\mathrm{d}c}{\mathrm{d}x}$ [15]

$$\frac{\mathrm{d}c}{\mathrm{d}x} = \frac{(0.05 - 0.10)\,\mathrm{M}}{0.10\ \mathrm{m}} = -0.50\ \mathrm{M\ m^{-1}}$$

$$RT = 2.48 \times 10^3\ \mathrm{J\ mol^{-1}} = 2.48 \times 10^3\ \mathrm{N\ m\ mol^{-1}}$$

(a) $\mathcal{F} = \dfrac{-2.48\ \mathrm{kN\ m\ mol^{-1}}}{0.10\ \mathrm{M}} \times (-0.50\ \mathrm{M\ m^{-1}})$

$= \underline{12\ \mathrm{kN\ mol^{-1}}}, \underline{2.1 \times 10^{-20}\ \mathrm{N\ molecule^{-1}}}$

(b) $\mathcal{F} = \dfrac{-2.48\ \mathrm{kN\ m\ mol^{-1}}}{0.075\ \mathrm{M}} \times (-0.50\ \mathrm{M\ m^{-1}})$

$= \underline{17\ \mathrm{kN\ mol^{-1}}}, \underline{2.8 \times 10^{-20}\ \mathrm{N\ molecule^{-1}}}$

(c) $\mathcal{F} = \dfrac{-2.48\ \mathrm{kN\ m\ mol^{-1}}}{0.05\ \mathrm{M}} \times (-0.50\ \mathrm{M\ m^{-1}})$

$= \underline{25\ \mathrm{kN\ mol^{-1}}}, \underline{4.1 \times 10^{-20}\ \mathrm{N\ molecule^{-1}}}$

25.12 $s = \dfrac{D}{kT}\mathcal{F}$ [Section 25.4]

$$= \frac{5.2 \times 10^{-10}\ \mathrm{m^2\ s^{-1}} \times \mathcal{F}}{1.381 \times 10^{-23}\ \mathrm{J\ K^{-1}} \times 298.15\ \mathrm{K}}$$

$$= 1.26 \times 10^{11}\ \mathrm{m\ s^{-1}}(\mathcal{F}/\mathrm{N})$$

[$\mathcal{F}$ is the force per molecule.]

(a) $s = 1.26 \times 10^{11}\ \mathrm{m\ s^{-1}} \times 2.1 \times 10^{-20} = \underline{2.7\ \mathrm{nm\ s^{-1}}}$

(b) $s = 1.26 \times 10^{11}\ \mathrm{m\ s^{-1}} \times 2.8 \times 10^{-20} = \underline{3.5\ \mathrm{nm\ s^{-1}}}$

(c) $s = 1.26 \times 10^{11}\ \mathrm{m\ s^{-1}} \times 4.1 \times 10^{-20} = \underline{5.2\ \mathrm{nm\ s^{-1}}}$

We could monitor the concentration by refractive index, optical rotation, infrared spectroscopy. The initial flux through a region is the same at every point because $\mathrm{d}c/\mathrm{d}x$ is a constant except at the left boundary and at the right, open side (Fig. 25.3a). The initial change is then as shown in Fig. 25.3b. This initial distortion is then magnified as time goes on, and as $\mathrm{d}c/\mathrm{d}x$ is no longer the same everywhere, $\mathrm{d}c/\mathrm{d}t$ changes everywhere (Fig. 25.3c). After a long time, the concentration becomes virtually uniform and sinks toward 0.075 M (Fig. 25.3d).

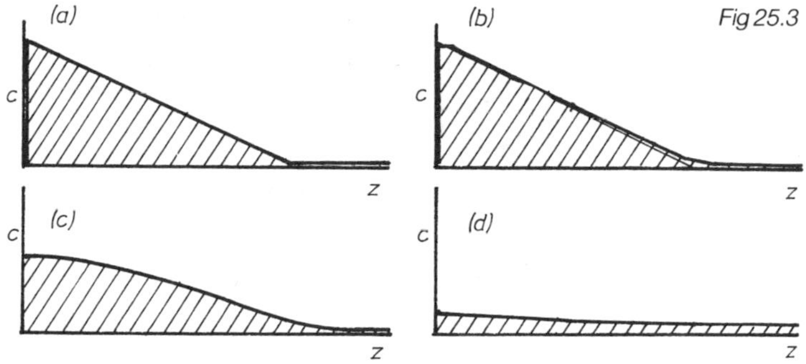

Fig 25.3

25.13 $D=\dfrac{uRT}{zF}$ [16] and $a=\dfrac{ze}{6\pi\eta u}$ [Example 25.7]

$$D=\frac{8.314\ \mathrm{J\,K^{-1}\,mol^{-1}}\times 298.15\ \mathrm{K}\times u}{9.6485\times 10^{4}\ \mathrm{C\,mol^{-1}}}$$

$$=2.569\times 10^{-2}\ \mathrm{V}\times u$$

so $D/(\mathrm{cm^2\,s^{-1}})=2.569\times 10^{-2}\times u/(\mathrm{cm^2\,s^{-1}\,V^{-1}})$

$$a=\frac{1.602\times 10^{-19}\ \mathrm{C}}{6\pi\times 1.00\times 10^{-3}\ \mathrm{kg\,m^{-1}\,s^{-1}}\times u}$$

$$=\frac{8.50\times 10^{-18}\ \mathrm{C\,kg^{-1}\,m\,s}}{u}$$

$$=\frac{8.50\times 10^{-18}\ \mathrm{V^{-1}\,m^{3}\,s^{-1}}}{u}\quad [1\ \mathrm{J}=1\ \mathrm{C\,V},\ 1\ \mathrm{J}=1\ \mathrm{kg\,m^2\,s^{-2}}]$$

and so

$$a/\mathrm{m}=8.50\times 10^{-14}/(u/\mathrm{cm^2\,s^{-1}\,V^{-1}})$$

and therefore

$$a/\mathrm{pm}=8.50\times 10^{-2}/(u/\mathrm{cm^2\,s^{-1}\,V^{-1}})$$

We can now draw up the following table using data from Table 25.2:

	Li^+	Na^+	K^+	Rb^+
$10^4\,u/(\mathrm{cm^2\,s^{-1}\,V^{-1}})$	4.01	5.19	7.62	7.92
$10^5\,D/\mathrm{cm^2}$	1.03	1.33	1.96	2.04
a/pm	212	164	112	107

The ionic radii themselves (i.e., their crystallographic radii) are

	Li^+	Na^+	K^+	Rb^+
r_+/pm	59	102	138	149

and it would seem that K^+ and Rb^+ have effective hydrodynamic radii that are smaller than their ionic radii. The effective hydrodynamic and ionic volumes of Li^+ and Na^+ are $\frac{4\pi}{8}\pi a^3$ and $\frac{4\pi}{3}\pi r_+^3$ respectively, and so the volumes occupied by hydrating water molecules are

$$\text{(a) } Li^+\text{: } \Delta V=\frac{4\pi}{3}\times(212^3-59^3)\times 10^{-36}\,\text{m}^3=3.9\times 10^{-29}\,\text{m}^3$$

$$\text{(b) } Na^+\text{: } \Delta V=\frac{4\pi}{3}\times(164^3-102^3)\times 10^{-36}\,\text{m}^3=1.4\times 10^{-29}\,\text{m}^3$$

The volume occupied by a single H_2O molecule is approximately $(4\pi/3)\times(150\,\text{pm})^3=1.4\times 10^{-29}\,\text{m}^3$. Therefore, Li^+ has about three firmly attached H_2O molecules whereas Na^+ has only one (according to this analysis).

25.14 If diffusion is an activated process, we expect

$$D\propto e^{-E_a/RT}$$

Therefore, if the diffusion constant is D at T and D' at T',

$$E_a=-\frac{R\ln(D'/D)}{\left(\frac{1}{T'}-\frac{1}{T}\right)}$$

$$=-\frac{8.314\,\text{J K}^{-1}\,\text{mol}^{-1}\times\ln\left(\frac{2.89}{2.05}\right)}{\frac{1}{298\,\text{K}}-\frac{1}{273\,\text{K}}}=9.3\,\text{kJ mol}^{-1}$$

That is, the activation energy for diffusion is $9.3\,\text{kJ mol}^{-1}$.

25.15 $c=\dfrac{n_0\,e^{-x^2/4Dt}}{A(\pi Dt)^{1/2}}$ [24]

and we know that $n_0=\dfrac{10\,\text{g}}{342\,\text{g mol}^{-1}}\times 6.022\times 10^{23}\,\text{mol}^{-1}=1.7\bar{6}\times 10^{22}$

$A = \pi R^2 = 19.6\ \text{cm}^2,\ D = 5.21 \times 10^{-6}\ \text{cm}^2\ \text{s}^{-1}$ [Table 25.4]

$$A(\pi Dt)^{1/2} = 19.6\ \text{cm}^2 \times (\pi \times 5.21 \times 10^{-6}\ \text{cm}^2\ \text{s}^{-1} \times t)^{1/2}$$

$$= 7.93 \times 10^{-2}\ \text{cm}^3 \times (t/\text{s})^{1/2}$$

$$\frac{x^2}{4Dt} = \frac{25\ \text{cm}^2}{4 \times 5.21 \times 10^{-6}\ \text{cm}^2\ \text{s}^{-1} \times t} = \frac{1.20 \times 10^6}{(t/\text{s})}$$

Therefore,

$$c = \frac{1.7\bar{6} \times 10^{22}}{7.93 \times 10^{-2}\ \text{cm}^3 \times (t/\text{s})^{1/2}} \times \text{e}^{-1.20 \times 10^6/(t/\text{s})}$$

$$= 2.22 \times 10^{23}\ \text{cm}^{-3} \times \left\{\frac{\text{e}^{-1.20 \times 10^6/(t/\text{s})}}{(t/\text{s})^{1/2}}\right\}$$

$$= 369\ \text{M} \times \left\{\frac{\text{e}^{-1.20 \times 10^6/(t/\text{s})}}{(t/\text{s})^{1/2}}\right\}$$

(a) $t = 10\ \text{s}$,

$$c = 369\ \text{M} \times \frac{\text{e}^{-1.2 \times 10^5}}{10^{1/2}} \approx 0$$

(b) $t = 1\ \text{yr} = 3.16 \times 10^7\ \text{s}$,

$$c = 369\ \text{M} \times \frac{\text{e}^{-0.038}}{(3.16 \times 10^7)^{1/2}} = \underline{0.063\ \text{M}}$$

25.16 $\langle x^2 \rangle = 2Dt$ [26b] , $D = \dfrac{kT}{6\pi a\eta}$ [Example 25.7]

Hence, $\eta = \dfrac{kT}{6\pi Da} = \dfrac{kTt}{3\pi a\langle x^2 \rangle}$

$$= \frac{1.381 \times 10^{-23}\ \text{J K}^{-1} \times 298.15\ \text{K} \times t}{3\pi \times 2.12 \times 10^{-7}\ \text{m} \times \langle x^2 \rangle}$$

$$= 2.06 \times 10^{-15}\ \text{J m}^{-1} \times \frac{t}{\langle x^2 \rangle}$$

and therefore

$$\eta/(\mathrm{kg\,m^{-1}\,s^{-1}}) = \frac{2.06 \times 10^{-11}(t/\mathrm{s})}{(\langle x^2\rangle/\mathrm{cm}^2)}$$

We draw up the following table:

t/s	30	60	90	120
$10^8\langle x^2\rangle/\mathrm{cm}^2$	88.2	113.5	128	144
$10^3\eta/(\mathrm{kg\,m^{-1}\,s^{-1}})$	0.701	1.09	1.45	1.72

Hence, the mean value is $\underline{1.2 \times 10^{-3}\ \mathrm{kg\,m^{-1}\,s^{-1}}}$.

25.17 The current I_j carried by an ion j is proportional to its concentration c_j, mobility u_j, and charge number $|z_j|$. Therefore,

$$I_j = Ac_ju_j|z_j|$$

where A is a constant. The total current passing through a solution is

$$I = \sum_j I_j = A\sum_j c_ju_j|z_j|$$

The transport number of the ion j is therefore

$$t_j = \frac{I_j}{I} = \frac{Ac_ju_j|z_j|}{A\sum_j c_ju_j|z_j|} = \frac{c_ju_j|z_j|}{\sum_j c_ju_j|z_j|}$$

If there are two cations in the mixture,

$$\frac{t'}{t''} = \frac{c'u'z'}{c''u''z''} = \underline{\frac{c'u'}{c''u''}} \text{ if } z' = z''$$

25.18 Consider the consequence of the passage of 1 mol of electrons through the cell

$$\mathrm{Ag|AgCl|HCl}(c_1)\mathrm{|HCl}(c_2)\mathrm{|AgCl|Ag}$$

Right compartment: 1 mol Cl^- are formed, but t_- mol migrate out across the junction, giving a net change of $(1-t_-)$ mol $= t_+$ mol.

Left compartment: 1 mol Cl^- is lost (by formation of solid AgCl), but t_- mol flows in across the junction, giving a net change of $(-1+t_+)$ mol $= -t_+$ mol.

The reaction Gibbs function is therefore

$$\Delta G = t_+\{\mu(Cl^-, c_2) - \mu(Cl^-, c_1)\}$$

$$= t_+ RT \ln\frac{a_2}{a_1}$$

Therefore, since $\Delta G = -FE$,

$$E_t = \frac{-t_+RT}{F}\ln\frac{a_2}{a_1}$$

For the same cell without transfer, the Nernst equation gives

$$E = \frac{-RT}{F}\ln\frac{a_2}{a_1}$$

Therefore, $\underline{E_t = t_+E}$

For electrodes reversible with respect to the cations, 1 mol M^+ is generated but t_+ mol migrates out, giving a net change of $(1-t_+)$ mol $= t_-$ mol. By the same argument,

$$\underline{E_t = E_-E}$$

25.19 $\dfrac{\partial c}{\partial t} = D\dfrac{\partial^2 c}{\partial x^2}$ [21] with $c = \dfrac{n_0\, e^{-x^2/4Dt}}{A(\pi Dt)^{1/2}}$ [24]

When $c = \dfrac{a}{t^{1/2}}\, e^{-bx^2/t}$, then

$$\frac{\partial c}{\partial t} = -\tfrac{1}{2}(a/t^{3/2})\, e^{-bx^2/t} + \frac{a}{t^{1/2}}\times\frac{bx^2}{t^2}\, e^{-bx^2/t}$$

$$= -\frac{c}{2t} + \frac{bx^2}{t^2}c$$

$$\frac{\partial c}{\partial x}=\frac{a}{t^{1/2}}\times\left(\frac{-2bx}{t}\right)\mathrm{e}^{-bx^2/t}$$

$$\frac{\partial^2 c}{\partial x^2}=-\left(\frac{2b}{t}\right)\left(\frac{a}{t^{1/2}}\right)\mathrm{e}^{-bx^2/t}+\left(\frac{a}{t^{1/2}}\right)\left(\frac{2bx}{t}\right)^2\mathrm{e}^{-bx^2/t}$$

$$=-\frac{2b}{t}c+\left(\frac{2bx}{t}\right)^2 c=-\left(\frac{1}{2Dt}\right)c+\left(\frac{bx^2}{Dt^2}\right)c$$

$$=D\frac{\partial c}{\partial t}\text{ as required.}$$

Initially the material is concentrated at $x=0$. Note that $c=0$ for $x>0$ when $t=0$ on account of the very strong exponential factor [$\mathrm{e}^{-bx^2/t}\to 0$ more strongly than $1/t^{1/2}\to\infty$]. When $x=0$, $\mathrm{e}^{-x^2/4Dt}=1$. We confirm the correct behavior by noting that $\langle x\rangle=0$ and $\langle x^2\rangle=0$ at $t=0$ [26], and so all the material must be at $x=0$ at $t=0$.

25.20 $P(x)=\dfrac{N!}{\frac{1}{2}(N+s)!\frac{1}{2}(N-s)!2^N}$ [A2] , $s=x/d$

$$P(6d)=\frac{N!}{\frac{1}{2}(N+6)!\frac{1}{2}(N-6)!2^N}$$

(a) $N=4$, $P(6d)=\underline{0}$ [$m!=\infty$ for $m<0$]

(b) $N=6$, $P(6d)=\dfrac{6!}{6!0!2^6}=\dfrac{1}{2^6}=\dfrac{1}{64}=\underline{0.016}$

(c) $N=12$, $P(6d)=\dfrac{12!}{9!3!2^{12}}=\dfrac{12\times 11\times 10}{3\times 2\times 2^{12}}=\underline{0.054}$

[NB $0!=1$]

25.21 Draw up the following table based on eqns A2 and A3:

N	4	6	8	10	20
$P(6\lambda)_{\text{Exact}}$	0	0.016	0.313	0.0439	0.0739
$P(6\lambda)_{\text{Approx.}}$	0.004	0.162	0.0297	0.0417	0.0725

N	30	40	60	100
$P(6\lambda)_{\text{Exact}}$	0.0806	0.0807	0.0763	0.0666
$P(6\lambda)_{\text{Approx.}}$	0.0799	0.0804	0.0763	0.0666

The points are plotted in Fig. 25.4. The discrepancy is less than 0.1 per cent

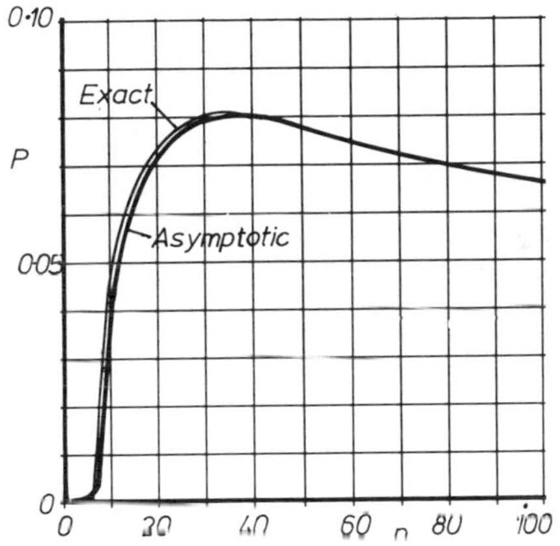

Fig 25.4

when $N > 60$.

26. The rates of chemical reactions

Exercises

26.1 $v = \frac{1}{\nu_J}\frac{d[J]}{dt}$ [1], so $\frac{d[J]}{dt} = \nu_J v$

The reaction has the form

$0 = 3C + D - A - 2B$

Rate of formation of $C = 3v = \underline{3.0\ \text{M s}^{-1}}$

Rate of formation of $D = v = \underline{1.0\ \text{M s}^{-1}}$

Rate of consumption of $A = v = \underline{1.0\ \text{M s}^{-1}}$

Rate of consumption of $B = 2v = \underline{2.0\ \text{M s}^{-1}}$

26.2 $v = \frac{1}{\nu_J}\frac{d[J]}{dt}$ [1]

For the reaction $2A + B \rightarrow 2C + 3D$, $\nu_C = +2$; hence

$v = \frac{1}{2} \times 1.0\ \text{M s}^{-1} = \underline{0.50\ \text{M s}^{-1}}$

Rate of formation of $D = 3v = \underline{1.5\ \text{M s}^{-1}}$

Rate of consumption of $A = 2v = \underline{1.0\ \text{M s}^{-1}}$

Rate of consumption of $B = v = \underline{0.50\ \text{M s}^{-1}}$

26.3 The rate is expressed in M s^{-1}; therefore

$\text{M s}^{-1} = [k] \times \text{M} \times \text{M}$

requires the units of k to be $\underline{\text{M}^{-1}\ \text{s}^{-1}}$

(a) Rate of formation of $A = v = \underline{k[A][B]}$

(b) Rate of consumption of $C = 3v = \underline{3k[A][B]}$

26.4 $\frac{d[C]}{dt} = k[A][B][C]$

$v = \frac{1}{\nu_J}\frac{d[J]}{dt}$ with $\nu_J = \nu_C = 2$

Therefore $v = \frac{1}{2}\frac{d[C]}{dt} = \underline{\tfrac{1}{2}k[A][B][C]}$

The units of k must satisfy

$$\text{M s}^{-1} = [k] \times \text{M} \times \text{M} \times \text{M} = [k]\,\text{M}^3$$

which requires k to have the units $\underline{\text{M}^{-2}\,\text{s}^{-1}}$

26.5 $2N_2O_5 \rightarrow 4NO_2 + O_2$, $v = k[N_2O_5]$

Therefore, rate of consumption of $N_2O_5 = 2v = 2k[N_2O_5]$

$$\frac{d[N_2O_5]}{dt} = -2k[N_2O_5]$$

$$[N_2O_5] = [N_2O_5]_0\,e^{-2kt}$$

which implies that

$$t = \frac{1}{2k}\ln\frac{[N_2O_5]_0}{[N_2O_5]}$$

and therefore that

$$t_{1/2} = \frac{1}{2k}\ln 2 = \frac{\ln 2}{2 \times 1.38 \times 10^{-5}\,\text{s}^{-1}} = \underline{2.51 \times 10^4\,\text{s}}$$

Since the partial pressure of N_2O_5 is proportional to its concentration,

$$p(N_2O_5) = p_0(N_2O_5)\,e^{-2kt}$$

(a) $p(N_2O_5) = 500\,\text{Torr} \times e^{-2.76 \times 10^{-5} \times 10^2} = \underline{499\,\text{Torr}}$

(b) $p(N_2O_5) = 500\,\text{Torr} \times e^{-2.76 \times 10^{-5} \times 6000} = \underline{424\,\text{Torr}}$

26.6 (a) For a second-order reaction, denoting the units of k by $[k]$:

$\text{M s}^{-1} = [k] \times \text{M}^2$, implying that $[k] = \underline{\text{M}^{-1}\,\text{s}^{-1}}$

For a third-order reaction,

$\text{M s}^{-1} = [k] \times \text{M}^3$, implying that $[k] = \underline{\text{M}^{2}\,\text{s}^{-1}}$

(b) For a second-order reaction

$\text{atm s}^{-1} = [k] \times \text{atm}^2$, implying that $[k] = \underline{\text{atm}^{-1}\,\text{s}^{-1}}$

For a third-order reaction

$\text{atm s}^{-1} = [k] \times \text{atm}^3$, implying that $[k] = \underline{\text{atm}^{-2}\,\text{s}^{-1}}$

26.7 $[^{14}C]=[^{14}C]_0\,e^{-kt},\ k=\dfrac{\ln 2}{t_{1/2}}$ [9]

$$t=\frac{1}{k}\ln\frac{[^{14}C]_0}{[^{14}C]}=\frac{t_{1/2}}{\ln 2}\times\ln\frac{[^{14}C]_0}{[^{14}C]}$$

$$=\frac{5730\text{ y}}{\ln 2}\times\ln\left(\frac{1.00}{0.72}\right)=\underline{27\overline{2}0\text{ y}}$$

26.8 $[^{90}Sr]=[^{90}Sr]_0\,e^{-kt},\ k=\dfrac{\ln 2}{t_{1/2}}$ [9]

$$k=\frac{\ln 2}{28.1\text{ y}}=0.0247\text{ y}^{-1}$$

Hence, with [Sr] replaced by its mass,

$$m=1.00\ \mu\text{g}\times e^{-0.0247(t/\text{y})}$$

(a) $m=1.00\,\mu\text{g}\times e^{-0.0247\times 18}=\underline{0.64\,\mu\text{g}}$

(b) $m=1.00\,\mu\text{g}\times e^{-0.0247\times 70}=\underline{0.18\,\mu\text{g}}$

26.9 $kt=\dfrac{1}{[B]_0-[A]_0}\ln\dfrac{[A]_0([B]_0-x)}{([A]_0-x)[B]_0}$ [7b]

which rearranges to

$$x=\frac{[A]_0[B]_0\{e^{k([B]_0-[A]_0)t}-1\}}{[B]_0\,e^{([B]_0-[A]_0)kt}-[A]_0}$$

$$=\frac{0.050\times 0.100\text{ M}\times\{e^{(0.100-0.050)\times 0.11\times t/\text{s}}-1\}}{0.100\times e^{(0.100-0.050)\times 0.11\times t/\text{s}}-0.050}$$

$$=\frac{0.100\text{ M}\times(e^{5.5\times 10^{-3}t/\text{s}}-1)}{2e^{5.5\times 10^{-3}t/\text{s}}-1}$$

(a) $x=\dfrac{0.100\text{ M}\times(e^{0.055}-1)}{2e^{0.055}-1}=5.1\times 10^{-3}\text{ M}$

which implies that $[\text{NaOH}]=0.050-0.0051\text{ M}=\underline{0.045\text{ M}}$ and $[CH_3COOC_2H_5]=0.100-0.0051\text{ M}=\underline{0.095\text{ M}}$

(b) $x=\dfrac{0.100\text{ M}\times(e^{3.3}-1)}{2e^{3.3}-1}=0.049\text{ M}$

Hence,

$$[\text{NaOH}] = 0.050 - 0.049\ \text{M} = \underline{0.001\ \text{M}}$$

$$[\text{CH}_3\text{COOC}_2\text{H}_5] = 0.100 - 0.049\ \text{M} = \underline{0.051\ \text{M}}$$

26.10 Rate of consumption of A $= k[\text{A}][\text{B}]$

$$= 3.67 \times 10^{-3}\ \text{M}^{-1}\,\text{s}^{-1} \times \frac{0.255\ \text{mol}}{1.70\ \text{L}} \times \frac{0.605\ \text{mol}}{1.70\ \text{L}}$$

$$= 1.96 \times 10^{-4}\ \text{M s}^{-1}$$

and hence

$$\frac{\text{d}[\text{A}]}{\text{d}t} = \underline{-1.96 \times 10^{-4}\ \text{M s}^{-1}}$$

Likewise,

$$\frac{\text{d}[\text{B}]}{\text{d}t} = -2k[\text{A}][\text{B}] = -2 \times (1.96 \times 10^{-4}\ \text{M s}^{-1})$$

$$= -3.92 \times 10^{-4}\ \text{M s}^{-1}$$

$$\frac{\text{d}[\text{P}]}{\text{d}t} = k[\text{A}][\text{B}] = \underline{1.96 \times 10^{-4}\ \text{M s}^{-1}}$$

$$\frac{\text{d}n_\text{B}}{\text{d}t} = \frac{\text{d}[B]}{\text{d}t} \times V = -3.92 \times 10^{-4}\ \text{M s}^{-1} \times 1.70\ \text{L}$$

$$= \underline{-6.66 \times 10^{-4}\ \text{mol s}^{-1}}$$

$$v_0 = k[\text{A}][\text{B}] = \underline{1.96 \times 10^{-4}\ \text{M s}^{-1}}$$

26.11 $v = k[\text{A}]^2$, $\nu_\text{A} = -2$

Hence,

$$\frac{\text{d}[\text{A}]}{\text{d}t} = -2k[\text{A}]^2$$

which solves to

$$\frac{1}{[A]}-\frac{1}{[A]_0}=2kt \quad [6a \text{ and } 6b]$$

Hence, $2kt_{1/2}=\frac{2}{[A]_0}-\frac{1}{[A]_0}=\frac{1}{[A]_0}$

and $t_{1/2}=\frac{1}{2k[A]_0}=\frac{1}{2\times 2.62\times 10^{-3}\,\text{M}^{-1}\,\text{s}^{-1}\times 1.70\,\text{M}}$

$$=\underline{112\,\text{s}}$$

26.12 The rate of consumption of A is

$$\frac{d[A]}{dt}=-2k[A]^2 \quad [\nu_A=-2]$$

which solves to

$$\frac{1}{[A]}-\frac{1}{[A]_0}=2kt \quad [6a \text{ and } 6b]$$

Therefore,

$$t=\frac{1}{2k}\left\{\frac{1}{[A]}-\frac{1}{[A]_0}\right\}$$

$$=\frac{1}{2\times 3.50\times 10^{-4}\,\text{M}^{-1}\,\text{s}^{-1}}\times\left\{\frac{1}{0.011\,\text{M}}-\frac{1}{0.260\,\text{M}}\right\}$$

$$=\underline{1.24\times 10^{5}\,\text{s}}$$

26.13 $[B]_0=\frac{1}{2}[A]_0$, hence $[A]_0=0.624\,\text{M}$. For the reaction $2A \rightarrow B$, $[A]=[A]_0-2[B]$. We can therefore draw up the following table

t/s	0	600	1200	1800	2400
[B]/M	0	0.089	0.153	0.200	0.230
[A]/M	0.624	0.446	0.318	0.224	0.164

The data are plotted in Fig. 26.1a. We see that the half-life of A from its initial concentration is approximately 1200 s, and that its half-life from the

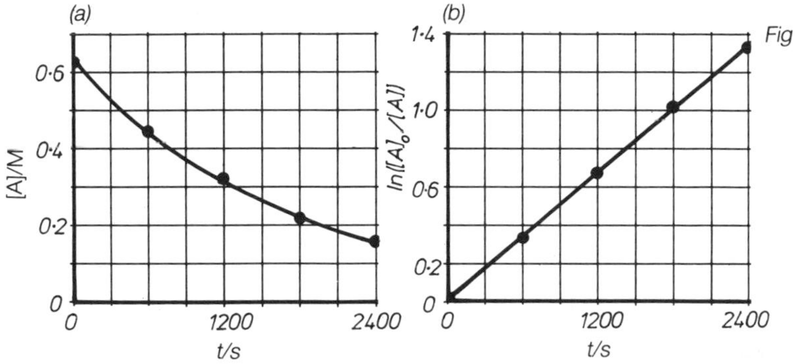

Fig 26.1

concentration at 1200 s is also 1200 s. This indicates a first-order reaction. We confirm this conclusion by plotting the data accordingly, using

$$\ln\frac{[A]_0}{[A]} = k_A t \text{ if } \frac{d[A]}{dt} = -k_A[A]$$

First, draw up the table:

t/s	0	600	1200	1800	2400
$\ln\frac{[A]_0}{[A]}$	0	0.34	0.67	1.02	1.34

and plot the points (Fig. 26.1b). The points lie as a straight line, which confirms first-order kinetics. Since the slope of the line is 5.6×10^{-4}, we conclude that $k_A = 5.6\times10^{-4}\,s^{-1}$. To express the rate law in the form

$$v = k[A]$$

we note that

$$v = -\frac{1}{2}\frac{d[A]}{dt} = -\tfrac{1}{2}\times(-k_A[A]) = \tfrac{1}{2}k_A[A]$$

and hence $k = \tfrac{1}{2}k_A = \underline{2.8\times10^{-4}\,s^{-1}}$

26.14 $\ln k = \ln A - \dfrac{E_a}{RT}$ [13a]

$$\ln k' = \ln A - \frac{E_a}{RT'}$$

$$\text{Hence, } E_a = \frac{R\ln(k'/k)}{\left(\frac{1}{T}-\frac{1}{T'}\right)} = \frac{8.314\ \text{J K}^{-1}\ \text{mol}^{-1}\times\ln\left(\frac{1.38\times10^{-2}}{2.80\times10^{-3}}\right)}{\frac{1}{303\ \text{K}}-\frac{1}{323\ \text{K}}}$$

$$= \underline{64.9\ \text{kJ mol}^{-1}}$$

For A, we use

$$A = k\times e^{E_a/RT}$$

$$= 2.80\times10^{-3}\ \text{M s}^{-1}\times e^{64.9\times10^3/8.314\times303}$$

$$= \underline{4.32\times10^{8}\ \text{M s}^{-1}}$$

26.15 The first step is rate-determining; hence

$$v = k[H_2O_2][Br^-]$$

The reaction is first-order in H_2O_2 and in Br^-, and second-order overall.

26.16 We assume a pre-equilibrium (as that step is fast), and write

$$K = \frac{[A]^2}{[A_2]},\ \text{implying that } [A] = K^{1/2}[A_2]^{1/2}$$

The rate-determining step then gives

$$v = \frac{d[P]}{dt} = k_2[A][B] = \underline{k_2K^{1/2}[A_2]^{1/2}[B]}$$

26.17 We assume a pre-equilibrium (as the initial step is fast), and write

$$K = \frac{[\text{Unstable helix}]}{[A][B]},\ \text{implying that } [\text{Unstable helix}] = K[A][B]$$

The rate-determining step then gives

$$v = \frac{d[\text{Double helix}]}{dt} = k_1[\text{Unstable helix}]$$

$$= \underline{k_1K[A][B]}$$

The equilibrium constant is the outcome of the two processes

$$A + B \underset{k_2'}{\overset{k_2}{\rightleftharpoons}} [\text{Unstable helix}],\ K = \frac{k_2}{k_2'}$$

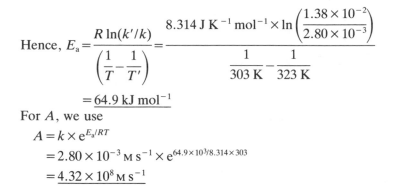

Therefore, with $v=k[\mathrm{A}][\mathrm{B}]$, $\underline{k=k_1k_2/k_2'}$.

26.18 The rate of change if [A] is

$$\frac{\mathrm{d}[\mathrm{A}]}{\mathrm{d}t}=-k[\mathrm{A}]^n$$

Hence, $\displaystyle\int_{[\mathrm{A}]_0}^{[\mathrm{A}]}\frac{\mathrm{d}[\mathrm{A}]}{[\mathrm{A}]^n}=-k\int_0^t \mathrm{d}t=-kt$

Therefore, $kt=\left(\dfrac{1}{n-1}\right)\left\{\dfrac{1}{[\mathrm{A}]^{n-1}}-\dfrac{1}{[\mathrm{A}]_0^{n-1}}\right\}$

and $kb_{1/2}=\left(\dfrac{1}{n-1}\right)\left\{\dfrac{2^{n-1}}{[\mathrm{A}]_0^{n-1}}-\dfrac{1}{[\mathrm{A}]_0^{n-1}}\right\}$

$$=\left(\frac{2^{n-1}-1}{n-1}\right)\times\frac{1}{[\mathrm{A}]_0^{n-1}}$$

Hence, $\underline{t_{1/2}\propto 1/[\mathrm{A}]_0^{n-1}}$.

26.19 Maximum velocity $=k_b[\mathrm{E}]_0$ [following eqn 24]

also $\dfrac{\mathrm{d}[\mathrm{P}]}{\mathrm{d}t}=k[\mathrm{E}]_0$, $k=\dfrac{k_b[\mathrm{S}]}{K_\mathrm{M}+[\mathrm{S}]}$ [24a]

Therefore, since

$$v=\frac{k_b[\mathrm{S}][\mathrm{E}]_0}{K_\mathrm{M}+[\mathrm{S}]}$$

we know that

$$k_b[\mathrm{E}]_0=\left\{\frac{K_\mathrm{M}+[\mathrm{S}]}{[\mathrm{S}]}\right\}v$$

$$=\left\{\frac{0.035+0.110}{0.110}\right\}\times 1.15\times 10^{-3}\ \mathrm{M\ s^{-1}}$$

$$=\underline{1.52\times 10^{-3}\ \mathrm{M\ s^{-1}}}$$

26.20 From Exercise 26.19, it follows that we require

$$\frac{[\mathrm{S}]}{K_\mathrm{M}+[\mathrm{S}]}=\tfrac{1}{2}$$

which is satisfied when $\underline{[\mathrm{S}]=K_{\mathrm{M}}}$

26.21 $\dfrac{1}{k}=\dfrac{1}{k_{\mathrm{a}}[\mathrm{A}]}+\dfrac{k_{\mathrm{a}}'}{k_{\mathrm{a}}k_{\mathrm{b}}}$ [28]

Therefore, with [A] interpreted as p, for two different pressures

$$\frac{1}{k}-\frac{1}{k'}=\frac{1}{k_{\mathrm{a}}}\left(\frac{1}{p}-\frac{1}{p'}\right)$$

and hence

$$k_{\mathrm{a}}=\frac{\dfrac{1}{p}-\dfrac{1}{p'}}{\dfrac{1}{k}-\dfrac{1}{k'}}=\frac{\dfrac{1}{12\ \mathrm{Pa}}-\dfrac{1}{1.30\times10^{3}\ \mathrm{Pa}}}{\dfrac{1}{2.10\times10^{-5}\ \mathrm{s}^{-1}}-\dfrac{1}{2.50\times10^{-4}\ \mathrm{s}^{-1}}}$$

$$=1.9\times10^{-6}\ \mathrm{Pa}^{-1}\,\mathrm{s}^{-1},\ \text{or}\ \underline{1.9\ \mathrm{MPa}^{-1}\,\mathrm{s}^{-1}}$$

26.22 $\mathrm{NH_4^+}(aq)+\mathrm{H_2O}(l)\rightleftharpoons\mathrm{NH_3}(aq)+\mathrm{H_3O^+}(aq)$, $\mathrm{p}K_{\mathrm{a}}=9.25$

$$\mathrm{NH_3}(aq)+\mathrm{H_2O}(l)\underset{k'}{\overset{k}{\rightleftharpoons}}\mathrm{NH_4^+}(aq)+\mathrm{OH^-}(aq),\ \mathrm{p}K_{\mathrm{b}}$$

$\mathrm{p}K_{\mathrm{b}}=\mathrm{p}K_{\mathrm{w}}-\mathrm{p}K_{\mathrm{a}}=14.00-9.25=4.75$

Therefore,

$$K_{\mathrm{b}}=\frac{k}{k'}=10^{-4.75}=1.78\times10^{-5}$$

and

$$k=k'K_{\mathrm{b}}=1.78\times10^{-5}\times4.0\times10^{10}\ \mathrm{M}^{-1}\,\mathrm{s}^{-1}=\underline{7.1\times10^{5}\ \mathrm{s}^{-1}}$$

$$\frac{1}{\tau}=k+k'([\mathrm{NH_4^+}]+[\mathrm{OH^-}])\quad[\text{Example 26.8}]$$

$$=k+2k'K_{\mathrm{b}}^{1/2}[\mathrm{NH_3}]^{1/2}\quad[[\mathrm{NH_4^+}]=[\mathrm{OH^-}]=(K_{\mathrm{b}}[\mathrm{NH_3}])^{1/2}]$$

$$=7.1\times10^{5}\ \mathrm{s}^{-1}+2\times4.0\times10^{10}\ \mathrm{M}^{-1}\,\mathrm{s}^{-1}\times(1.78\times10^{-5})^{1/2}\times(0.15\ \mathrm{M})^{1/2}$$

$$=1.31\times10^{8}\ \mathrm{s}^{-1},\ \text{hence}\ \underline{\tau=7.63\ \mathrm{ns}}$$

26.23 $\dfrac{1}{\tau}=k+k'([\mathrm{B}]+[\mathrm{C}])$ [Example 26.8]

$$K=\frac{k}{k'},\ \text{implying that}\ \frac{1}{\tau}=k\left\{1+\frac{[B]+[C]}{K}\right\}$$

and therefore that

$$k=\frac{1/\tau}{1+\dfrac{[B]+[C]}{K}}=\frac{(3.0\times10^{-6}\,\text{s})^{-1}}{1+\dfrac{2\times2.0\times10^{-4}\,\text{M}}{2.0\times10^{-16}\,\text{M}}}$$

$$=\underline{1.7\times10^{-7}\,\text{s}^{-1}}$$

and therefore

$$k'=\frac{k}{K}=\frac{1.7\times10^{-7}\,\text{s}^{-1}}{2.0\times10^{-16}\,\text{M}}=\underline{8.5\times10^{8}\,\text{M}^{-1}\,\text{s}^{-1}}$$

Problems

26.1 Inspection of the data suggests that the production of water is increasing as $1-e^{-kt}$, which suggests that we should test for first-order kinetics. For a first-order reaction of the form $A\rightarrow B+C$, with B the water,

$$\frac{d[B]}{dt}=k[A]=k\{[A]_0-[B]\}$$

which solves to

$$[B]=[A]_0(1-e^{-kt})=[B]_\infty(1-e^{-kt})$$

where $[B]_\infty$ is the concentration or (what is equivalent in this case) the volum when the reaction is complete. It follows that

$$\ln\left\{\frac{[B]_\infty}{[B]_\infty-[B]}\right\}=kt$$

We therefore draw up the following table:

t/s	30	60	90	120	150
$\dfrac{V_\infty}{V_\infty-V}$	2.0	3.3	5.0	6.7	10.0
$\ln\left\{\dfrac{V_\infty}{V_\infty-V}\right\}$	0.69	1.20	1.61	1.90	2.30

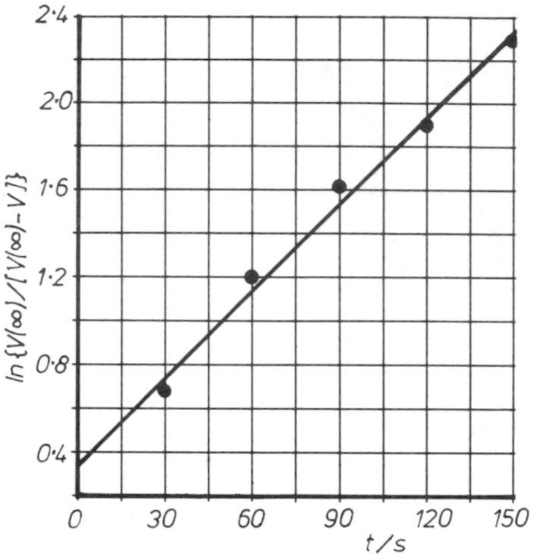

Fig 26.2

The points are plotted in Fig. 26.2. They fall on a straight line, confirming first-order kinetics. The slope is 1.31×10^{-2}, so $k = 1.31 \times 10^{-2}\ s^{-1}$. The C_4H_6 is probably reactive under the conditions of the experiment.

26.2 An Arrhenius plot tests the linearity of

$$\ln k = \ln A - \frac{E_a}{RT}$$

by plotting $\ln k$ against $1/T$. We therefore draw up the following table:

T/K	773.5	786	797.5	810	810	824	834
$10^3/(T/\mathrm{K})$	1.29	1.27	1.25	1.23	1.23	1.21	1.20
$-\ln(k/\mathrm{s}^{-1})$	6.42	5.83	5.48	4.81	4.80	4.21	3.81

The points are plotted in Fig. 26.3. The slope of the line is 2.9×10^4, implying that

$$E_a = 2.9 \times 10^4\ \mathrm{K} \times R = 240\ \mathrm{kJ\ mol^{-1}}$$

The extrapolated intercept lies at -30, implying that

$$A = e^{30}\ s^{-1} = 1.1 \times 10^{13}\ s^{-1}$$

26.3 If the reaction is first-order, the partial pressure of cyclopropane should obey

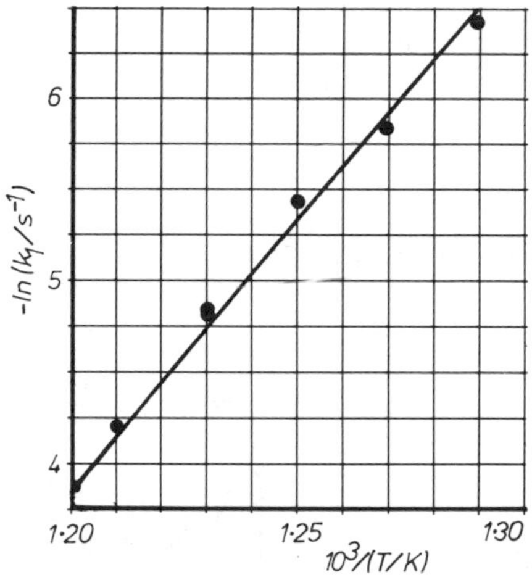

Fig 26.3

$$\ln\frac{p_0}{p}=kt$$

and $(1/t)\ln p_0/p$ should be a constant. We test this by drawing up the following table:

p_0/Torr	200	300	400	400	600	600
t/s	100	200	100	200	100	200
p/Torr	186	173	373	347	559	520
$10^4\left(\frac{1}{t/\mathrm{s}}\right)\ln\frac{p_0}{p}$	7.3	7.3	7.0	7.1	7.1	7.2

The values in the last row of the table are virtually constant, and so (in the pressure range spanned by the data) the reaction has first-order kinetics with $k=7.2\times10^{-4}\,\mathrm{s}^{-1}$.

26.4 $^{239}_{92}\mathrm{U}\xrightarrow{t_{1/2}}{}^{239}_{93}\mathrm{Np}\xrightarrow{t'_{1/2}}{}^{239}_{94}\mathrm{Pu}$

with $t_{1/2}=23.5$ min and $t'_{1/2}=2.35$ day.

$$\frac{[\mathrm{U}]}{[\mathrm{U}]_0}=e^{-kt}\quad\left[19\mathrm{a},\ k=\frac{\ln 2}{t_{1/2}}=0.0314\,\mathrm{min}^{-1}\right]$$

$$\frac{[\mathrm{Np}]}{[\mathrm{U}]_0}=\left(\frac{k}{k'-k}\right)(\mathrm{e}^{-kt}-\mathrm{e}^{-k't}) \quad \left[19\mathrm{b},\ k'=\frac{\ln 2}{t'_{1/2}}=0.295\ \mathrm{day}^{-1}\right]$$

$$\frac{[\mathrm{Pu}]}{[\mathrm{U}]_0}=1+\frac{k\,\mathrm{e}^{-k't}-k'\,\mathrm{e}^{-kt}}{k'-k}$$

These three functions are plotted in Fig. 26.4.

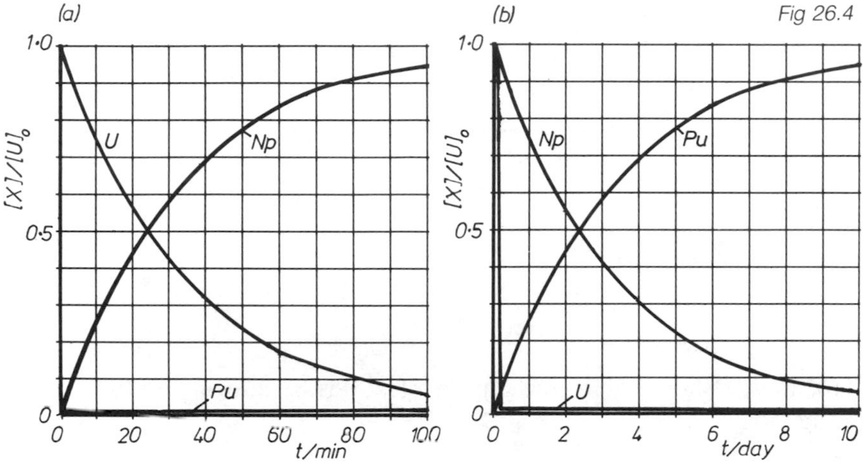

26.5 $\mathrm{A}+\mathrm{B}\rightarrow\mathrm{P},\ \frac{\mathrm{d}[\mathrm{P}]}{\mathrm{d}t}=k[\mathrm{A}]^m[\mathrm{B}]^n$

and for a short interval Δt,

$$\Delta[\mathrm{P}]\approx k[\mathrm{A}]^m[\mathrm{B}]^n\,\Delta t$$

Therefore, since $\Delta[\mathrm{P}]=[\mathrm{P}]_t-[\mathrm{P}]_0=[\mathrm{P}]_t$,

$$\frac{[\mathrm{P}]}{[\mathrm{A}]}=k[\mathrm{A}]^{m-1}[\mathrm{B}]^n\,\Delta t$$

(a) $\frac{[\text{Chloropropane}]}{[\text{Propene}]}$ independent of [Propene] implies that $m=1$.

(b) $\frac{[\text{Chloropropane}]}{[\text{HCl}]}=\begin{cases} p(\text{HCl}) & 10 \quad 7.5 \quad 5.0 \\ & 0.06 \quad 0.035 \quad 0.015 \end{cases}$

These results suggest that the ratio is proportional to about p^2, and therefore that $m=3$ when A is identified with HCl. The rate law is therefore

$$\frac{d[\text{Chloropropane}]}{dt} = k[\text{Propane}][\text{HCl}]^3$$

and the reaction is first-order in propene and third-order in HCl.

26.6 $2HCl \rightleftharpoons (HCl)_2,\ K_1;\ [(HCl)_2] = K_1[HCl]^2$

$HCl + CH_3CH{=}CH_2 \rightleftharpoons \text{Complex},\ K_2$

$$[\text{Complex}] = K_2[HCl][CH_3CH{=}CH_2]$$

$(HCl)_2 + \text{Complex} \rightarrow CH_3CHClCH_3 + 2HCl,\ k$

$$\begin{aligned}\text{rate} &= k[(HCl)_2][\text{Complex}]\\ &= kK_2[(HCl)_2][HCl][CH_3CH{=}CH_2]\\ &= \underline{kK_2K_1[HCl]^3[CH_3CH{=}CH_2]}\end{aligned}$$

Use infrared spectroscopy to search for $(HCl)_2$.

26.7 $$E_a = \frac{R\ln(k'_{\text{eff}}/k_{\text{eff}})}{\left(\frac{1}{T} - \frac{1}{T'}\right)} \quad \text{[Exercise 26.14 from eqn 13a]}$$

$$= \frac{R\ln 3}{\frac{1}{343\text{ K}} - \frac{1}{292\text{ K}}} = \underline{-20\text{ kJ mol}^{-1}}$$

But $k_{\text{eff}} = kK_1K_2$ [Problem 26.6]

$\ln k_{\text{eff}} = \ln k + \ln K_1 + \ln K_2$

$$E_a = -R\left(\frac{\partial \ln k_{\text{eff}}}{\partial(1/T)}\right)_V = E'_a + \Delta U_1 + \Delta U_2$$

since $$\left(\frac{\partial \ln K}{\partial(1/T)}\right)_V = \frac{-\Delta U}{R} \quad \text{[van't Hoff equation, Chapter 9]}$$

Therefore, setting $\Delta U \approx \Delta H$

$$\begin{aligned}E'_a &= E_a - \Delta U_1 - \Delta U_2\\ &= -20 + 14 + 14\text{ kJ mol}^{-1} = \underline{+8\text{ kJ mol}^{-1}}\end{aligned}$$

26.8 $E_a = \dfrac{R\ln(k'/k)}{\dfrac{1}{T}-\dfrac{1}{T'}}$ [Exercise 26.14 from eqn 13a]

We then draw up the following table:

T/K	300.3	300.3	341.2
T'/K	341.2	392.2	392.2
$10^{-7}\,k/(\mathrm{M}^{-1}\,\mathrm{s}^{-1})$	1.44	1.44	3.03
$10^{-7}\,k'/(\mathrm{M}^{-1}\,\mathrm{s}^{-1})$	3.03	6.9	6.9
$E_a/(\mathrm{kJ\,mol^{-1}})$	15.5	16.7	18.0

The mean is 16.7 kJ mol^{-1}. For A, use

$$A = k\,e^{E_a/RT}$$

and draw up the following table:

T/K	300.3	341.2	392.2
$10^{-7}\,k/(\mathrm{M}^{-1}\,\mathrm{s}^{-1})$	1.44	3.03	6.9
E_a/RT	6.69	5.89	5.12
$10^{-10}\,A/(\mathrm{M}^{-1}\,\mathrm{s}^{-1})$	1.16	1.10	1.16

The mean is $1.14\times10^{10}\,\mathrm{M}^{-1}\,\mathrm{s}^{-1}$.

26.9 $-\ln k/(\mathrm{M}^{-1}\,\mathrm{s}^{-1}) = -\ln(A/\mathrm{M}^{-1}\,\mathrm{s}^{-1}) + \dfrac{E_a}{RT}$ [13a]

Draw up the following table:

$\theta/°\mathrm{C}$	0	10	15	25	34.5
T/K	273	283	288	298	308
$10^3\,\mathrm{K}/T$	3.66	3.53	3.47	3.36	3.25
$-\ln k/(\mathrm{M}^{-1}\,\mathrm{s}^{-1})$	10.65	9.60	9.19	8.24	7.44

These points are plotted in Fig. 26.5. The slope is 7900, implying that $E_a = 7.9\times10^3\,R = 66\ \mathrm{kJ\,mol^{-1}}$. The intercept lies at -18.3, implying that

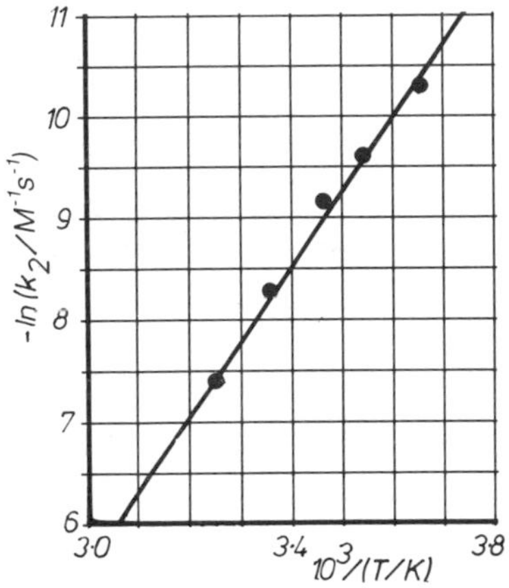

Fig 26.5

$$A/(\text{M}^{-1}\,\text{s}^{-1}) = e^{18.3} = 8.9 \times 10^7$$

Therefore, $A = \underline{8.9 \times 10^7\,\text{M}^{-1}\,\text{s}^{-1}}$.

26.10 $NH_2OH^- \rightarrow NH_2O^- + H_2O$

$NH_2O^- + O_2 \rightarrow P$

$$-\frac{d[NH_2OH]}{dt} = k_{obs}[(NH_2OH)][O_2]$$

$$-\frac{d[(NH_2OH)]}{dt} = k[NH_2O^-][O_2]$$

$k_{obs}[(NH_2OH)][O_2] = k[NH_2O^-][O_2]$

and $[(NH_2OH)] = [NH_2OH] + [NH_2O^-]$

Therefore, $k_{obs}[NH_2OH] = (k - k_{obs})[NH_2O^-]$

$$\frac{1}{k_{obs}} = \frac{1}{k} + \frac{[NH_2OH]}{k[NH_2O^-]} = \underline{\frac{1}{k} + \frac{[H^+]}{kK_a}}$$

$$\text{since } K_a = \frac{[NH_2O^-][H^+]}{[NH_2OH]}$$

Therefore, plotting $1/k_{obs}$ against $[H^+]$ should give a straight line with slope $1/kK_a$ and intercept $1/k$.

In the data, we are given $[OH^-]$, so use $K_w = [H^+][OH^-]$:

$$\frac{1}{k_{obs}}=\frac{1}{k}+\frac{K_w}{kK_a[OH^-]}$$

We therefore draw up the following table:

$[OH^-]/M$	0.50	1.00	1.6	2.4
$1/([OH^-]/M)$	2.00	1.00	0.63	0.42
$10^{-3}/(k_{obs}/s^{-1})$	4.64	3.53	3.01	2.83

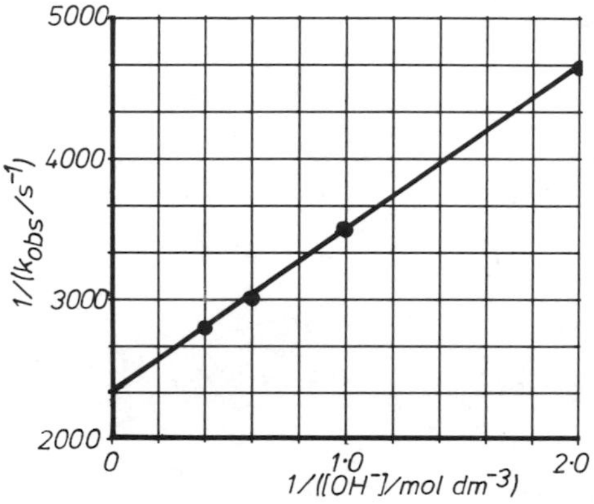

Fig 26.6

The points are plotted in Fig. 26.6. The intercept is at 2.35×10^3, which implies that

$$k=(2.35\times10^3)^{-1}\,s^{-1}=4.3\times10^{-4}\,s^{-1}$$

The slope is 1.15×10^3, implying that

$$\frac{K_w}{kK_a}=\frac{1.15\times10^3}{s^{-1}}=1.15\times10^3\,s$$

Therefore,

$$K_a=\frac{1.0\times10^{-14}}{4.3\times10^{-4}\,s^{-1}\times1.15\times10^3\,s}=2.0\times10^{-14}$$

and hence $\underline{pK_a=13.7}$.

26.11 $\dfrac{1}{k}=\dfrac{1}{k_a[A]}+\dfrac{k_a'}{k_ak_b}$ [28]

or, in terms of pressure of A:

$$\frac{1}{k}=\frac{1}{k_{a}p}+\frac{k_{a}'}{k_{a}k_{b}}$$

and we expect a straight line when $1/k$ is plotted against $1/p$. We draw up the following table:

p/Torr	84.1	11.0	2.89	0.569	0.120	0.067
$1/(p/\text{Torr})$	0.012	0.091	0.346	1.76	8.33	14.9
$10^{-4}/(k/\text{s}^{-1})$	0.336	0.448	0.649	1.17	2.55	3.30

These points are plotted in Fig. 26.7. There are marked deviations at low pressures, indicating that the Lindemann theory is deficient in that region.

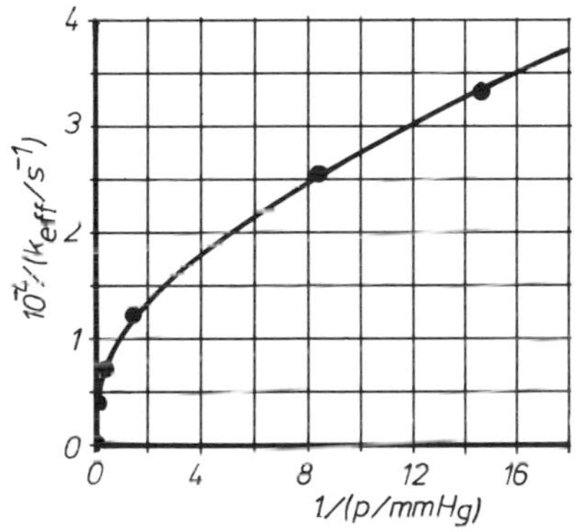

Fig 26.7

26.12 $$\frac{d[P]}{dt}=\frac{k_{b}[E]_{0}[S]}{K_{M}+[S]} \quad [24a]$$

Write $v=d[P]/dt$, then

$$\frac{1}{v}=\frac{1}{k_{b}[E]_{0}}+\frac{K_{M}}{k_{b}[E]_{0}}\times\frac{1}{[S]}$$

We therefore draw up the following table:

$10^3[S]/M$	50	17	10	5	2
$1/([S]/M)$	20.0	58.8	100	200	500
$v/(mm^3\ min^{-1})$	16.6	12.4	10.1	6.6	3.3
$1/(v/mm^3\ min^{-1})$	0.0602	0.0806	0.0990	0.152	0.303

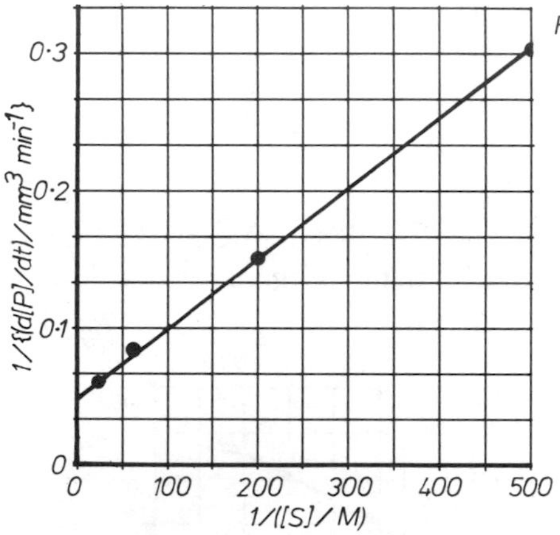

Fig 26.8

The points are plotted in Fig. 26.8. The intercept lies at 0.050, which implies that $1/k_b[E]_0 = 0.050\ mm^{-3}\ min$. The slope is 5.06×10^{-4}, which implies that

$$\frac{K_M}{k_b[E]_0} = 5.06\times10^{-4}\ mm^{-3}\ min\ M$$

and therefore that

$$K_M = \frac{5.06\times10^{-4}\ mm^{-3}\ min\ M}{0.050\ mm^{-3}\ min} = \underline{0.010\ M}$$

26.13 $2A \rightarrow B \quad \frac{d[A]}{dt} = -k[A]^2$

$$[A] = \frac{[A]_0}{1+kt[A]_0} \quad [6c]$$

$$[B] = [B]_0 + \tfrac{1}{2}([A]_0 - [A]) = \tfrac{1}{2}([A]_0 - [A])$$

In terms of the pressure,

$$p_A = \frac{p_0}{1 + ktp_0}, \; p_B = \tfrac{1}{2}(p_0 - p_A)$$

The total pressure is $p = p_A + p_B = \tfrac{1}{2}(p_0 + p_A)$; therefore,

$$p = \tfrac{1}{2}p_0\left\{1 + \frac{1}{1 + ktp_0}\right\} = \tfrac{1}{2}p_0\left\{\frac{2 + ktp_0}{1 + ktp_0}\right\}$$

and therefore

$$\frac{p}{p_0} = \frac{1 + \tfrac{1}{2}x}{1 + x}, \text{ where } x = p_0kt$$

This function is plotted in Fig. 26.9. The final pressure is $\tfrac{1}{2}p_0$, and half way to

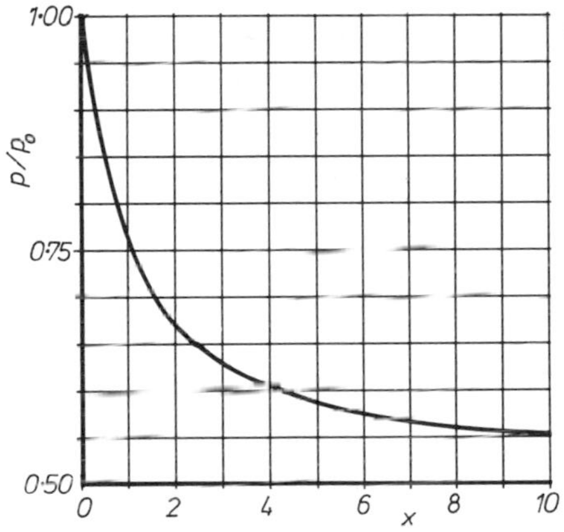

Fig 26.9

this pressure corresponds to $p = \tfrac{3}{4}p_0$. The time needed to attain this pressure is the solution of

$$\frac{1 + \tfrac{1}{2}x}{1 + x} = \tfrac{3}{4}, \text{ or } x = 1$$

Therefore, $\underline{t = 1/p_0k}$.

We test whether the data fit the expression just derived by rearranging it to

$$p_0kt = \frac{1 - (p/p_0)}{(p/p_0) - \tfrac{1}{2}} \quad [= F]$$

and draw up the following table based on $p_0 = 400$ Torr:

t/s	0	100	200	300	400
p/Torr	400	322	288	268	256
p/p_0	1	0.805	0.720	0.670	0.640
F	0	0.639	1.273	1.941	2.571

These points are plotted in Fig. 26.10. They fall on a good straight line, confirming that the reaction is second-order. The slope is 6.4×10^3, and so $p_0 k = 6.4 \times 10^{-3}\ \mathrm{s}^{-1}$. Since $p_0 = 400$ Torr, this implies that $k = 1.6 \times 10^{-5}\ \mathrm{Torr}^{-1}\ \mathrm{s}^{-1}$.

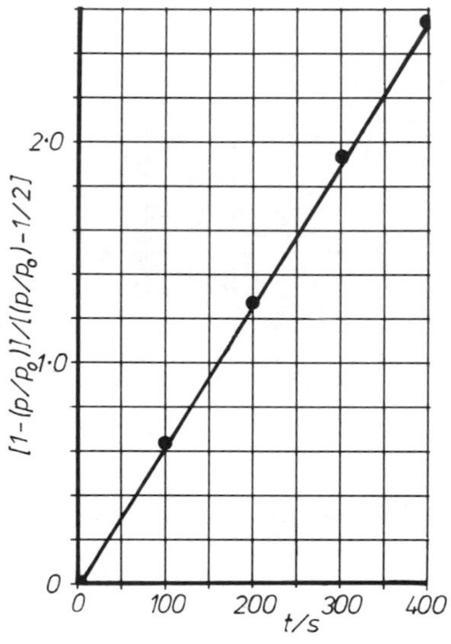

Fig 26.10

26.14 $A \rightleftharpoons B$

$$\frac{d[A]}{dt} = -k[A] + k'[B], \quad \frac{d[B]}{dt} = -k'[B] + k[A]$$

$[A] + [B] = [A]_0 + [B]_0$ at all times.

Therefore, $[B] = [A]_0 + [B]_0 - [A]$.

$$\frac{d[A]}{dt} = -k[A] + k'\{[A]_0 + [B]_0 - [A]\}$$

$$= -(k + k')[A] + k'([A]_0 + [B]_0)$$

The solution is

$$[A]=\frac{k'([A]_0+[B]_0)+(k[A]_0-k'[B]_0)\,e^{-(k+k')t}}{k+k'}$$

The final composition is found by setting $t=\infty$:

$$[A]_\infty=\left(\frac{k'}{k+k'}\right)([A]_0+[B]_0)$$

$$[B]_\infty=[A]_0+[B]_0-[A]_\infty=\left(\frac{k}{k+k'}\right)([A]_0+[B]_0)$$

Note that $[B]_\infty/[A]_\infty=k/k'$.

26.15 $\dfrac{d[P]}{dt}=k[A][B]$

Let the initial concentrations be A_0, B_0, and $[P]_0=0$. Then, when an amount x of P is formed, the amount of A changes to A_0-2x and that of B changes to B_0-3x. Therefore,

$$\frac{d[P]}{dt}=\frac{dx}{dt}=k(A_0-2x)(B_0-3x) \text{ with } x=0 \text{ at } t=0.$$

$$\int_0^t k\,dt=\int_0^x\frac{dx}{(A_0-2x)(B_0-3x)}$$

$$=\int_0^x\left(\frac{1}{2B_0-3A_0}\right)\left\{\frac{1}{3(A_0-2x)}-\frac{1}{2(B_0-3x)}\right\}dx$$

$$=\frac{-1}{6(2B_0-3A_0)}\left\{\int_0^x\frac{dx}{x-\frac{1}{2}A_0}-\int_0^x\frac{dx}{x-\frac{1}{3}B_0}\right\}$$

$$kt=\frac{-1}{6(2B_0-3A_0)}\left\{\ln\left(\frac{x-\frac{1}{2}A_0}{-\frac{1}{2}A_0}\right)-\ln\left(\frac{x-\frac{1}{3}B_0}{-\frac{1}{3}B_0}\right)\right\}$$

$$=\frac{-1}{6(2B_0-3A_0)}\ln\left\{\frac{(2x-A_0)B_0}{A_0(3x-B_0)}\right\}$$

$$=\frac{1}{6(3A_0-2B_0)}\ln\left\{\frac{(2x-A_0)B_0}{A_0(3x-B_0)}\right\}$$

26.16 $\dfrac{d[A]}{dt}=-2k[A]^2[B]$, $2A+B\rightarrow P$

(a) Let $[P]=x$ at t, then $[A]=A_0-2x$ and $[B]=B_0-x$.

Therefore,

$$\frac{d[A]}{dt}=-2\frac{dx}{dt}=-2k(A_0-2x)^2(B_0-x)$$

$$\frac{dx}{dt}=k(A_0-2x)^2(\tfrac{1}{2}A_0-x)=\tfrac{1}{2}k(A_0-2x)^3$$

$$\tfrac{1}{2}kt=\int_0^x \frac{dx}{(A_0-2x)^3}=\frac{1}{4}\left\{\left(\frac{1}{A_0-2x}\right)^2-\left(\frac{1}{A_0}\right)^2\right\}$$

Therefore,

$$\underline{kt=\frac{2x(A_0-x)}{A_0^2(A_0-2x)^2}}$$

(b) $$\frac{dx}{dt}=k(A_0-2x)^2(B_0-x)$$

$$=k(A_0-2x)^2(A_0-x) \quad [B_0=2\times\tfrac{1}{2}A_0=A_0]$$

$$kt=\int_0^x \frac{dx}{(A_0-2x)^2(A_0-x)}$$

We proceed by the method of partial fractions (which is employed in the general case too), and look for the coefficients α, β, and γ in

$$\frac{1}{(A_0-2x)^2(A_0-x)}=\frac{\alpha}{(A_0-2x)^2}+\frac{\beta}{A_0-2x}+\frac{\gamma}{A_0-x}$$

which requires that

$$\alpha(A_0-x)+\beta(A_0-2x)(A_0-x)+\gamma(A_0-2x)^2=1$$

$$(A_0\alpha+A_0^2\beta+A_0^2\gamma)-(\alpha_0+3\beta A_0+4\gamma A_0)x+(2\beta+4\gamma)x^2=1$$

This must be true for all x; therefore

$$A_0\alpha+A_0^2\beta+A_0^2\gamma=1$$

$$\alpha+3A_0\beta+4A_0\gamma=0$$

$$2\beta+4\gamma=0$$

These solve to give

$\alpha = 2/A_0$, $\beta = -2/A_0^2$, and $\gamma = 1/A_0^2$. Therefore,

$$kt = \int_0^x \left\{ \frac{(2/A_0)}{(A_0-2x)^2} - \frac{(2/A_0^2)}{A_0-2x} + \frac{(1/A_0)}{A_0-x} \right\} \mathrm{d}x$$

$$= \left\{ \frac{(1/A_0)}{A_0-2x} + \frac{1}{A_0^2}\ln(A_0-2x) - \frac{1}{A_0^2}\ln(A_0-x) \right\} \Bigg|_0^x$$

$$= \frac{2x}{A_0^2(A_0-2x)} + \frac{1}{A_0^2}\ln\left\{\frac{A_0-2x}{A_0-x}\right\}$$

26.17 $kt = \dfrac{2x(A_0-x)}{A_0^2(A_0-2x)^2}$ [Problem 26.16a]

with $[A] = A_0 - 2x$, $[B] = B_0 - x$, $B_0 = \frac{1}{2}A_0$.

(a) $[A] = \frac{1}{2}A_0$ when $x = \frac{1}{4}A_0$; then

$$kt_{1/2} = \frac{\frac{1}{2}A_0 \times \frac{3}{4}A_0}{A_0^2 \times (\frac{1}{2}A_0)^2} = \frac{3}{2A_0^2}, \text{ so } t_{1/2} = \frac{3}{2kA_0^2}$$

(b) $[B] = \frac{1}{2}B_0$ when $x = \frac{1}{2}B_0 = \frac{1}{4}A_0$; so the half-life is the same as in (a), and

$$t_{1/2} = \frac{3}{2kA_0^2}$$

(c) The reaction is

$0 = -2A - B + P$; $\nu_A = -2$, $\nu_B = -1$

Define ξ so that $\xi = 0$ initially and 1 finally, and write

$[B] = B_0(1-\xi)$, then $[P] = B_0\xi$, $[A] = A_0 - 2B_0\xi$

$$\frac{\mathrm{d}A}{\mathrm{d}t} = -2k[A]^2[B]$$

$$= -2k(A_0 - 2B_0\xi)^2 B_0(1-\xi)$$

but $B_0 = \frac{1}{2}A_0$, so $A_0\dot{\xi} = kA_0^3(1-\xi)^3$, and therefore

$$\int_0^{\xi} \frac{\mathrm{d}\xi}{(1-\xi)^3} = \int_0^t kA_0^2\,\mathrm{d}t$$

Hence,

$$kA_0^2 t = \frac{1}{2}\left\{\left(\frac{1}{1-\xi}\right)^2 - 1\right\} = \frac{\xi(2-\xi)}{2(1-\xi)^2}$$

For $\xi = \frac{1}{2}$, $kA_0^2 t_{1/2} = \dfrac{\frac{1}{2} \times \frac{3}{2}}{2 \times \frac{1}{4}} = \frac{3}{2}$

and therefore $\underline{t_{1/2} = \dfrac{3}{2kA_0^2}}$

26.18 $kt = \left(\dfrac{1}{n-1}\right)\left\{\dfrac{1}{[A]^{n-1}} - \dfrac{1}{[A]_0^{n-1}}\right\}$ [Exercise 26.18, $n \neq 1$]

At $t = t_{1/2}$, $x = \frac{1}{2}A_0$, so

$$kt_{1/2} = \left(\frac{1}{n-1}\right)\left\{\left(\frac{2}{A_0}\right)^{n-1} - \left(\frac{1}{A_0}\right)^{n-1}\right\}$$

At $t = t_{3/4}$, $x = \frac{1}{4}A_0$; $[A] = \frac{3}{4}[A]_0$

$$kt_{3/4} = \left(\frac{1}{n-1}\right)\left\{\left(\frac{4}{3A_0}\right)^{n-1} - \left(\frac{1}{A_0}\right)^{n-1}\right\}$$

Hence,

$$\underline{\frac{t_{1/2}}{t_{3/4}} = \frac{2^{n-1} - 1}{(\frac{4}{3})^{n-1} - 1}}$$

27. The kinetics of complex reactions

Exercises

27.1 Step 1: initiation; Step 2: termination; Step 3: propagation; Step 4: propagation; Step 5: propagation; Step 6: propagation; Step 7: propagation; Step 8: termination.

27.2 $$\frac{d[Cr(CO)_5]}{dt} = I - k_2[Cr(CO)_5][CO] - k_3[Cr(CO)_5][M]$$

$$+ k_4[Cr(CO)_5M] = 0 \quad \text{[steady state]}$$

Hence, $$[Cr(CO)_5] = \frac{I + k_4[Cr(CO)_5M]}{k_2[CO] + k_3[M]}$$

$$\frac{d[Cr(CO)_5M]}{dt} = k_3[Cr(CO)_5][M] - k_4[Cr(CO)_5M]$$

$$= \frac{k_3I[M] - k_2k_4[Cr(CO)_5M][CO]}{k_2[CO] + k_3[M]}$$

$$= -f[Cr(CO)_5M]$$

if $$f = \frac{k_2k_4[CO]}{k_2[CO] + k_3[M]}$$

and we have taken $k_3I[M] \ll k_2k_4[Cr(CO)_5M][CO]$. Therefore,

$$\frac{1}{f} = \frac{1}{k_4} + \frac{k_3[M]}{k_2k_4[CO]}$$

and a graph of $1/f$ against [M] should be a straight line.

27.3 $$\frac{d[R]}{dt} = 2k_1[R_2] - k_2[R][R_2] + k_3[R'] - 2k_4[R]^2$$

$$\frac{d[R']}{dt} = k_2[R][R_2] - k_3[R']$$

Apply the steady-state approximation to both equations:

$$2k_1[\mathrm{R}_2] - k_2[\mathrm{R}][\mathrm{R}_2] + k_3[\mathrm{R}'] - 2k_4[\mathrm{R}]^2 = 0$$

$$k_2[\mathrm{R}][\mathrm{R}_2] - k_3[\mathrm{R}'] = 0$$

The second solves to

$$[\mathrm{R}'] = \frac{k_2}{k_3}[\mathrm{R}][\mathrm{R}_2]$$

and then the first solves to

$$[\mathrm{R}] = \left(\frac{k_1}{k_4}[\mathrm{R}_2]\right)^{1/2}$$

Therefore,

$$\frac{\mathrm{d}[\mathrm{R}_2]}{\mathrm{d}t} = -k_1[\mathrm{R}_2] - k_2[\mathrm{R}_2][\mathrm{R}] = \underline{-k_1[\mathrm{R}_2] - k_2\left(\frac{k_1}{k_4}\right)^{1/2}[\mathrm{R}_2]^{3/2}}$$

27.4 At 700 K, the branching explosion does not occur. At 800 K, it occurs between 0.16 kPa and 4.0 kPa. At 900 K, branching occurs for pressures in excess of 0.11 kPa.

27.5 Number of photons absorbed $= \Phi^{-1} \times$ Number of molecules that react [Section 27.3]. Therefore,

$$\text{Number absorbed} = \frac{1.4 \times 10^{-3}\,\mathrm{mol} \times 6.022 \times 10^{23}\,\mathrm{einstein}^{-1}}{2.1 \times 10^2\,\mathrm{mol\,einstein}^{-1}}$$

$$= \underline{3.3 \times 10^{18}}$$

27.6 For a source of power P and wavelength λ, the amount of photons (n_γ) generated in a time t is

$$n_\gamma = \frac{Pt}{h\nu N_\mathrm{A}} = \frac{P\lambda t}{hcN_\mathrm{A}}$$

$$= \frac{100\,\mathrm{W} \times 45 \times 60\,\mathrm{s} \times 490 \times 10^{-9}\,\mathrm{m}}{6.626 \times 10^{-34}\,\mathrm{J\,s} \times 2.998 \times 10^8\,\mathrm{m\,s}^{-1} \times 6.022 \times 10^{23}\,\mathrm{mol}^{-1}}$$

$$= 1.11\,\mathrm{mol}$$

The amount of photons absorbed is 60 per cent of this incident flux, or 0.660 mol. Therefore,

$$\Phi = \frac{0.344\ \text{mol}}{0.660\ \text{mol}} = \underline{0.521}$$

Alternatively, expressing the amount of photons in einsteins [1 mol photons = 1 einstein], $\Phi = 0.521$ mol einstein^{-1}

27.7 $$\frac{d[A^-]}{dt} = k_1[AH][B] - k_2[A^-][BH^+] - k_3[A^-][A] = 0$$

Therefore,

$$[A^-] = \frac{k_1[AH][B]}{k_2[BH^+] + k_3[A]}$$

and the rate of formation of product is

$$\frac{d[P]}{dt} = k_3[A][A^-] = \frac{k_1k_3[A][AH][B]}{k_2[BH^+] + k_3[A]}$$

27.8 $$\frac{d[AH]}{dt} = k_3[HAH^+][B] \quad \text{[rate-determining]}$$

$$K = \frac{[HAH^+]}{[HA][H^+]} \qquad \text{[pre-equilibrium]}$$

and hence

$$\frac{d[AH]}{dt} = k_3K[HA][H^+][B]$$

The acidity constant of the conjugate acid of B is

$$BH^+ + H_2O \rightleftharpoons B + H_3O^+, \quad K_a = \frac{[B][H^+]}{[BH^+]}$$

Therefore,

$$\frac{d[AH]}{dt} = \underline{k_3KK_a[HA][BH^+]}$$

27.9 Step 1: initiation [radicals formed]; Steps 2 and 3: propagation [new radicals formed]; Step 4: termination [non-radical product formed].

$$\frac{\mathrm{d}[\mathrm{AH}]}{\mathrm{d}t} = -k_{\mathrm{a}}[\mathrm{AH}] - k_{\mathrm{c}}[\mathrm{AH}][\mathrm{B}]$$

$$\text{(i)}\quad \frac{\mathrm{d}[\mathrm{A}]}{\mathrm{d}t} = k_{\mathrm{a}}[\mathrm{AH}] - k_{\mathrm{b}}[\mathrm{A}] + k_{\mathrm{c}}[\mathrm{AH}][\mathrm{B}] - k_{\mathrm{d}}[\mathrm{A}][\mathrm{B}] \approx 0$$

$$\text{(ii)}\quad \frac{\mathrm{d}[\mathrm{B}]}{\mathrm{d}t} = k_{\mathrm{b}}[\mathrm{A}] - k_{\mathrm{c}}[\mathrm{AH}][\mathrm{B}] - k_{\mathrm{d}}[\mathrm{A}][\mathrm{B}] \approx 0$$

$$\left.\begin{aligned} &\text{(i+ii)}\quad [\mathrm{A}][\mathrm{B}] = \left(\frac{k_{\mathrm{d}}}{2k_{\mathrm{d}}}\right)[\mathrm{AH}] \\ &\text{(i}-\text{ii)}\quad [\mathrm{A}] = \left(\frac{k_{\mathrm{a}} + 2k_{\mathrm{c}}[\mathrm{B}]}{2k_{\mathrm{b}}}\right)[\mathrm{AH}] \end{aligned}\right\}$$

Then, solving for [A]:

$$[\mathrm{A}] = k[\mathrm{AH}],\ k = \left(\frac{k_{\mathrm{a}}}{4k_{\mathrm{b}}}\right)\left\{1 + \left[1 + \frac{4k_{\mathrm{b}}k_{\mathrm{c}}}{k_{\mathrm{a}}k_{\mathrm{d}}}\right]^{1/2}\right\}$$

from which it follows that

$$[\mathrm{B}] = \frac{k_{\mathrm{a}}[\mathrm{AH}]}{2k_{\mathrm{d}}[\mathrm{A}]} = \frac{k_{\mathrm{a}}}{2kk_{\mathrm{d}}}$$

and hence that

$$\frac{\mathrm{d}[\mathrm{AH}]}{\mathrm{d}t} = -k_{\mathrm{a}}[\mathrm{AH}] - \left(\frac{k_{\mathrm{a}}k_{\mathrm{c}}}{2kk_{\mathrm{d}}}\right)[\mathrm{AH}] = \underline{k_{\mathrm{eff}}[\mathrm{AH}]}$$

with $\underline{k_{\mathrm{eff}} = k_{\mathrm{a}} + \dfrac{k_{\mathrm{a}}k_{\mathrm{c}}}{2kk_{\mathrm{d}}}}$

27.10 $\dfrac{\mathrm{d}[\mathrm{P}]}{\mathrm{d}t} = k[\mathrm{A}]^2[\mathrm{P}]$

$[\mathrm{A}] = A_0 - x$, $[\mathrm{P}] = P_0 + x$, $\mathrm{d}[\mathrm{P}]/\mathrm{d}t = \mathrm{d}x/\mathrm{d}t$

$$\frac{\mathrm{d}x}{\mathrm{d}t} = k(A_0 - x)^2(P_0 + x)$$

$$\int_0^x \frac{dx}{(A_0-x)^2(P_0+x)} = kt$$

Solve the integral by partial fractions:

$$\frac{1}{(A_0-x)^2(P_0+x)} = \frac{\alpha}{(A_0-x)^2} + \frac{\beta}{A_0-x} + \frac{\gamma}{P_0+x}$$

$$= \frac{\alpha(P_0+x)+\beta(A_0-x)(P_0+x)+\gamma(A_0-x)^2}{(A_0-x)^2(P_0+x)}$$

$$\left.\begin{aligned} P_0\alpha + A_0P_0\beta + A_0^2\gamma &= 1 \\ \alpha + (A_0-P_0)\beta - 2A_0\gamma &= 0 \\ -\beta+\gamma &= 0 \end{aligned}\right\}$$

This set of simultaneous equations solves to

$$\alpha = \frac{1}{A_0+P_0}, \ \beta=\gamma=\frac{\alpha}{A_0+P_0}$$

Therefore,

$$kt = \left(\frac{1}{A_0+P_0}\right)\int_0^x \left\{\left(\frac{1}{A_0-x}\right)^2 + \left(\frac{1}{A_0+P_0}\right)\left(\frac{1}{A_0-x}+\frac{1}{P_0+x}\right)\right\} dx$$

$$= \left(\frac{1}{A_0+P_0}\right)\left\{\frac{1}{A_0-x} - \frac{1}{A_0} + \left(\frac{1}{A_0+P_0}\right)\left[\ln\left(\frac{A_0}{A_0-x}\right) + \ln\left(\frac{P_0+x}{P_0}\right)\right]\right\}$$

$$= \left(\frac{1}{A_0+P_0}\right)\left\{\frac{x}{A_0(A_0-x)} + \left(\frac{1}{A_0+P_0}\right)\ln\left(\frac{A_0(P_0+x)}{(A_0-x)P_0}\right)\right\}$$

Therefore, with $y=x/A_0$ and $p=P_0/A_0$,

$$A_0(A_0+P_0)kt = \frac{y}{1-y} + \frac{1}{1+p}\ln\left\{\frac{p+y}{p(1-y)}\right\}$$

The maximum rate occurs at

$$\frac{dv_P}{dt}=0, \ v_P = k[A]^2[P]$$

and hence at the solution of

$$2k\left(\frac{d[A]}{dt}\right)[A][P] + k[A]^2\frac{d[P]}{dt} = 0$$

$$-2k[\mathrm{A}][\mathrm{P}]v_{\mathrm{P}}+k[\mathrm{A}]^2v_{\mathrm{P}}=0 \quad [\text{as } v_{\mathrm{A}}=-v_{\mathrm{P}}]$$

$$k[\mathrm{A}]([\mathrm{A}]-2[\mathrm{P}])v_{\mathrm{P}}=0$$

That is, the rate is a maximum when $[\mathrm{A}]=2[\mathrm{P}]$; which occurs at $A_0-x=2P_0+2x$, or

$$x=\tfrac{1}{3}(A_0-2P_0),\ y=\tfrac{1}{3}(1-2p)$$

Substituting this condition into the integrated rate law gives

$$A_0(A_0+P_0)kt_{\max}=\left(\frac{1}{1+p}\right)\left\{\tfrac{1}{2}(1-2p)+\ln\frac{1}{2p}\right\}$$

or

$$\underline{(A_0+P_0)^2kt_{\max}=\tfrac{1}{2}-p-\ln 2p}$$

27.11 $\dfrac{\mathrm{d}[\mathrm{P}]}{\mathrm{d}t}=k[\mathrm{A}][\mathrm{P}]^2$

$$\frac{\mathrm{d}x}{\mathrm{d}t}=k(A_0-x)(P_0+x)^2 \quad [x=P-P_0]$$

$$kt=\int_0^x\frac{\mathrm{d}x}{(A_0-x)(P_0+x)^2}$$

Integrate by partial fractions [as in Exercise 27.10]:

$$kt=\left(\frac{1}{A_0+P_0}\right)\int_0^x\left\{\left(\frac{1}{P_0+x}\right)^2+\left(\frac{1}{A_0+P_0}\right)\left[\frac{1}{P_0+x}+\frac{1}{A_0-x}\right]\right\}\mathrm{d}x$$

$$=\left(\frac{1}{A_0+P_0}\right)\left\{\left(\frac{1}{P_0}-\frac{1}{P_0+x}\right)+\left(\frac{1}{A_0+P_0}\right)\left[\ln\left(\frac{P_0+x}{P_0}\right)+\ln\left(\frac{A_0}{A_0-x}\right)\right]\right\}$$

$$=\left(\frac{1}{A_0+P_0}\right)\left\{\frac{x}{P_0(P_0+x)}+\left(\frac{1}{A_0+P_0}\right)\ln\left[\frac{(P_0+x)A_0}{P_0(A_0-x)}\right]\right\}$$

Therefore, with $y=x/[\mathrm{A}]_0$ and $p=P_0/A_0$,

$$\underline{A_0(A_0+P_0)kt=\frac{y}{p(p+y)}+\left(\frac{1}{1+p}\right)\ln\left\{\frac{p+y}{p(1-y)}\right\}}$$

As in Exercise 27.10, the rate is a maximum when

$$\frac{\mathrm{d}v_{\mathrm{P}}}{\mathrm{d}t}=2k[\mathrm{A}][\mathrm{P}]\left(\frac{\mathrm{d}[\mathrm{P}]}{\mathrm{d}t}\right)+k\left(\frac{\mathrm{d}[\mathrm{A}]}{\mathrm{d}t}\right)[\mathrm{P}]^2$$

$$=2k[\mathrm{A}][\mathrm{P}]v_{\mathrm{P}}-k[\mathrm{P}]^2v_{\mathrm{P}}$$

$$=k[\mathrm{P}](2[\mathrm{A}]-[\mathrm{P}])v_{\mathrm{P}}=0$$

That is, at $[A]=\frac{1}{2}[P]$

On substitution of this condition into the integrated rate law, we find

$$A_0(A_0+P_0)kt_{max}=\frac{2-p}{2p(1+p)}+\left(\frac{1}{1+p}\right)\ln\frac{2}{p}$$

or

$$(A_0+P_0)^2kt_{max}=\frac{2-p}{2p}+\ln\frac{2}{p}$$

Problems

27.1 $UO_2^{2+}+h\nu\rightarrow(UO_2^{2+})^*$

$(UO_2^{2+})^*+(COOH)_2\rightarrow UO_2^{2+}+H_2O+CO_2+CO$

$2MnO_4^-+5(COOH)_2+6H^+\rightarrow 10CO_2+8H_2O+2Mn^{2+}$

17.0 cm^3 of 0.212 M $KMnO_4$ is equivalent to

$\frac{5}{2}\times 17.0\ cm^3\times 0.212\ M=9.01\times 10^{-3}$ mol $(COOH)_2$

The initial sample contained 5.232 g $(COOH)_2$, corresponding to 5.232 g/(90.04 g mol^{-1}) $=5.81\times 10^{-2}$ mol $(COOH)_2$. Therefore, 5.81×10^{-2} mol -9.01×10^{-3} mol $=4.91\times 10^{-2}$ mol of the acid has been consumed. A quantum efficiency of 0.53 implies that the amount of photons absorbed must have been $(4.91\times 10^{-2}$ mol$)/0.53=9.3\times 10^{-2}$ mol. Since the exposure was for 300 s, the rate of incidence of photons was $(9.3\times 10^{-2}$ mol$)/300$ s $=3.1\times 10^{-4}$ mol s^{-1}. Since 1 mol photons = 1 einstein, the incident rate is 3.1×10^{-4} einstein s^{-1} or $1.9\times 10^{20}\ s^{-1}$.

27.2 $M+h\nu_i\rightarrow M^*,\ I_a$

$M^*+Q\rightarrow M+Q,\ k_q$

$M^*\rightarrow M+h\nu_f,\ k_f$

$$\frac{d[M^*]}{dt}=I_a-k_f[M^*]-k_q[Q][M^*]\approx 0\quad \text{[steady state]}$$

and hence $[M^*]=\dfrac{I_a}{k_f+k_q[Q]}$

Then $I_f=k_f[M^*]=\dfrac{k_fI_a}{k_f+k_q[Q]}$

and so

$$\frac{1}{I_f}=\frac{1}{I_a}+\frac{k_q[Q]}{k_f I_a}$$

If the exciting light is extinguished, [M*], and hence I_f, decays as $e^{-k_f t}$ in the absence of a quencher. Therefore we can measure $k_q/k_f I_a$ from the slope of $1/I_f$ plotted against [Q], and then use k_f to determine k_q. We draw up the following table:

$10^3[Q]/M$	1	5	10
$1/I_f$	2.4	4.0	6.3

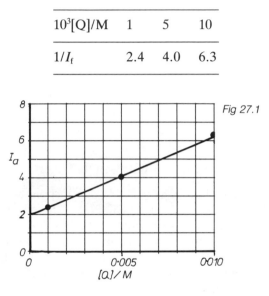

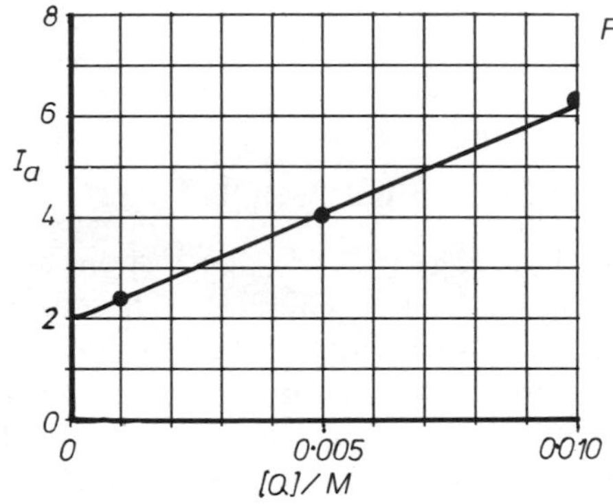

Fig 27.1

The points are plotted in Fig. 27.1. The intercept lies at 2.0, and so $I_a = 1/2.0 = 0.50$. The slope is 430, and so

$$\frac{k_q}{k_f I_a}=430\ \text{M}^{-1}$$

Then, since $I_a = 0.50$ and $k_f = (\ln 2)/t_{1/2}$,

$$k_q = 0.50 \times 430\ \text{M}^{-1} \times \frac{\ln 2}{29 \times 10^{-6}\ \text{s}} = \underline{5.1 \times 10^8\ \text{M}^{-1}\ \text{s}^{-1}}$$

27.3 $H + NO_2 \rightarrow OH + NO$, $k = 2.9 \times 10^{10}\ \text{M}^{-1}\ \text{s}^{-1}$

$OH + OH \rightarrow H_2O + O$, $k' = 1.55 \times 10^9\ \text{M}^{-1}\ \text{s}^{-1}$

$O + OH \rightarrow O_2 + H$, $k'' = 1.1 \times 10^{10}\ \text{M}^{-1}\ \text{s}^{-1}$

$[H]_0 = 4.5 \times 10^{-10}$ mol cm^{-3}, $[NO_2]_0 = 5.6 \times 10^{-10}$ mol cm^{-3}.

$$\frac{d[O]}{dt} = k'[OH]^2 + k''[O][OH]$$

$$\frac{d[O_2]}{dt} = k''[O][OH]$$

$$\frac{d[OH]}{dt} = k[H][NO_2] - 2k'[OH]^2 - k''[O][OH]$$

$$\frac{d[NO_2]}{dt} = -k[H][NO_2]$$

$$\frac{d[H]}{dt} = k''[O][OH] - k[H][NO_2]$$

These equations serve to show how even a simple sequence of reactions leads to a complicated set of non-linear differential equations. Since we are interested in the time behavior of the composition we may not invoke the steady-state assumption. The only thing left is to use a computer, and to integrate the equations numerically. The outcome of this is the set of curves shown in Fig. 27.2 (they have been sketched from the original reference). The

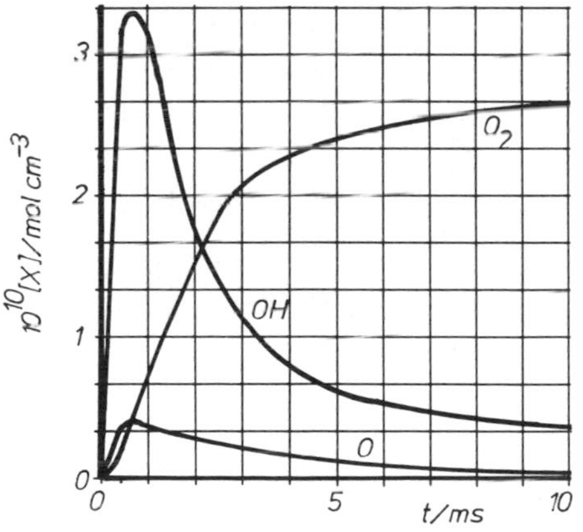

Fig 27.2

similarity to an A→B→C scheme should be noticed (and expected), and the general features can be analyzed quite simply in terms of the underlying reactions.

27.4 $O + Cl_2 \rightarrow ClO + Cl$ $\quad p(Cl_2) \approx \text{constant}$ $\quad$ [Cl_2 at high pressure]

Therefore, the reaction in probably pseudo-first order, and

$$[O] \approx [O]_0\, e^{-k't}$$

That being so,

$$\ln \frac{[O]_0}{[O]} = k't = k[Cl_2]t = k[Cl_2] \times \frac{d}{v}$$

where $k' = [Cl_2]k$, v is the flow rate, and d is the distance along the tube. We draw up the following table:

d/cm	0	2	4	6	8	10	12	14	16	18
$\ln \frac{[O]_0}{[O]}$	0.27	0.31	0.34	0.38	0.45	0.46	0.50	0.55	0.56	0.60

The points are plotted in Fig. 27.3. The slope is 0.0189, and so $k[Cl_2]/v = 0.0189\ \text{cm}^{-1}$.

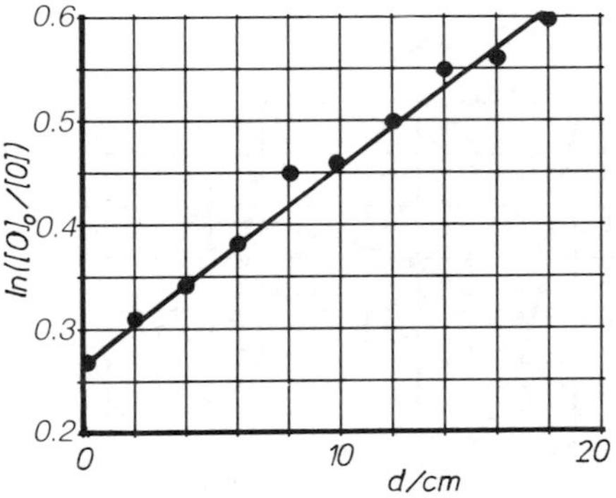

Fig 27.3

Therefore,

$$k = \frac{0.0189\ \text{cm}^{-1} \times v}{[Cl_2]} = \frac{0.0189\ \text{cm}^{-1} \times 6.66 \times 10^2\ \text{cm s}^{-1}}{2.54 \times 10^{-7}\ \text{M}}$$

$$= 5.0 \times 10^7\ \text{M}^{-1}\,\text{s}^{-1}$$

[There is a very fast $O + ClO \rightarrow Cl + O_2$ reaction, and so the answer given here is actually twice the true value.]

27.5 $CH_3CH_3 \rightarrow 2CH_3,\ k_a$

$CH_3 + CH_3CH_3 \rightarrow CH_4 + CH_3CH_2,\ k_b$

$CH_3CH_2 \rightarrow CH_2{=}CH_2 + H,\ k_c$

$H + CH_3CH_3 \rightarrow H_2 + CH_3CH_2,\ k_d$

$H + CH_3CH_2 \rightarrow CH_3CH_3,\ k_e$

$$\frac{d[CH_3CH_3]}{dt} = -k_a[CH_3CH_3] - k_b[CH_3][CH_3CH_3] - k_d[CH_3CH_3][H] + k_e[CH_3CH_2][H]$$

$$\frac{d[CH_3]}{dt} = 2k_a[CH_3CH_3] - k_b[CH_3CH_3][CH_3] = 0$$

which implies that $[CH_3] = 2k_a/k_b$.

$$\frac{d[CH_3CH_2]}{dt} = k_b[CH_3][CH_3CH_3] - k_c[CH_3CH_2] + k_d[CH_3CH_3][H] - k_e[CH_3CH_2][H] = 0$$

$$\frac{d[H]}{dt} = k_c[CH_3CH_2] - k_d[CH_3CH_3][H] - k_e[CH_3CH_2][H] = 0$$

These three equations give

$$[H] = \frac{k_c}{k_e + k_d\dfrac{[CH_3CH_3]}{[CH_3CH_2]}}$$

$$[CH_3CH_2]^2 - \left(\frac{k_a}{k_c}\right)[CH_3CH_3][CH_3CH_2] - \left(\frac{k_a k_d}{k_c k_e}\right)[CH_3CH_3]^2 = 0$$

$$\text{or } [CH_3CH_2] = \left\{\frac{k_a}{2k_c} + \left[\left(\frac{k_a}{2k_c}\right)^2 + \left(\frac{k_a k_d}{k_c k_e}\right)\right]^{1/2}\right\}[CH_3CH_3]$$

which implies that

$$[H] = \frac{k_c}{k_e + k_d/\kappa},\quad \kappa = \frac{k_a}{2k_c} + \left[\left(\frac{k_a}{2k_c}\right)^2 + \left(\frac{k_a k_d}{k_c k_e}\right)\right]^{1/2}$$

If k_a is small in the sense that only the lowest order need be retained,

$$[CH_3CH_2] \approx \left(\frac{k_a k_d}{k_c k_e}\right)^{1/2} [CH_3CH_3]$$

$$[H] \approx \frac{k_c}{k_e + k_d\left(\dfrac{k_c k_e}{k_a k_d}\right)^{1/2}} \approx \left(\frac{k_a k_c}{k_d k_e}\right)^{1/2}$$

The rate of production of ethene is therefore

$$\frac{d[CH_2CH_2]}{dt} = k_c[CH_3CH_2] = \left(\frac{k_a k_c k_d}{k_e}\right)^{1/2} [CH_3CH_3]$$

The rate of production of ethene is equal to the rate of consumption of ethane [the intermediates all have low concentrations], so

$$\frac{d[CH_3CH_3]}{dt} = -k[CH_3CH_3], \quad k = \left(\frac{k_a k_c k_d}{k_e}\right)^{1/2}$$

Different orders may arise if the reaction is sensitized so that k_a is increased.

27.6 $CH_3CHO \rightarrow CH_3 + CHO, \; k_a$

$CH_3 + CH_3\dot{C}HO \rightarrow CH_4 + CH_2CHO, \; k_b$

$CH_2CHO \rightarrow CO + CH_3, \; k_c$

$CH_3 + CH_3 \rightarrow CH_3CH_3, \; k_d$

$$\frac{d[CH_4]}{dt} = k_b[CH_3][CH_3CHO]$$

$$\frac{d[CH_3CHO]}{dt} = -k_a[CH_3CHO] - k_b[CH_3CHO][CH_3]$$

$$\frac{d[CH_3]}{dt} = k_a[CH_3CHO] - k_b[CH_3CHO][CH_3] + k_c[CH_2CHO] - 2k_d[CH_3]^2 = 0$$

$$\frac{d[CH_2CHO]}{dt} = k_b[CH_3][CH_3CHO] - k_c[CH_2CHO] = 0$$

Adding the last two equations gives

$$k_a[CH_3CHO] - 2k_d[CH_3]^2 = 0, \text{ or } [CH_3] = \left(\frac{k_a}{2k_d}\right)^{1/2} [CH_3CHO]^{1/2}$$

Therefore,

$$\frac{d[CH_4]}{dt} = k_b\left(\frac{k_a}{2k_d}\right)^{1/2}[CH_3CHO]^{3/2}$$

$$\frac{d[CH_3CHO]}{dt} = -k_a[CH_3CHO] - k_b\left(\frac{k_a}{2k_d}\right)^{1/2}[CH_3CHO]^{3/2}$$

Note that to lowest-order in k_a,

$$\frac{d[CH_3CHO]}{dt} \approx -k_b\left(\frac{k_a}{2k_d}\right)^{1/2}[CH_3CHO]^{3/2}$$

and the reaction is three-halves order in CH_3CHO.

27.7 (i) $\frac{d[COCl_2]}{dt} = k_c[COCl][Cl_2]$

(ii) $\frac{d[COCl]}{dt} = k_b[Cl][CO] - k_b'[COCl] - k_c[COCl][Cl_2] = 0$

(iii) $\frac{d[Cl]}{dt} = 2k_a[Cl_2] - 2k_a'[Cl]^2 - k_b[Cl][CO] + k_b'[COCl]$

$$+ k_c[COCl][Cl_2] = 0$$

From (ii): $[COCl] = \frac{k_b[Cl][CO]}{k_b' + k_c[Cl_2]}$ (iv)

Then (iii) becomes

$$k_a[Cl_2] - k_a'[Cl]^2 = 0, \text{ so } [Cl] = K^{1/2}[Cl_2]^{1/2}; \ K = \frac{k_a}{k_a'}$$

Substitution in (iv), and that into (i), gives the rate law

$$\frac{d[COCl_2]}{dt} = \frac{k_cK'K^{1/2}[CO][Cl_2]^{3/2}}{1 + (k_c/k_b')[Cl_2]} \text{ with } K' = k_b/k_b'$$

For the numerical solution, write $a = [COCl_2]$, $b = [Cl_2]$, $c = [CO]$, $x = [COCl]$, and $y = [Cl]$, and replace the differential equations by

(i) $a(t_{i+1}) = a(t_i) + k_cx(t_i)b(t_i)\,\Delta t$

(ii) $x(t_{i+1}) = x(t_i) + \{k_by(t_i)c(t_i) - k_b'x(t_i) - k_cx(t_i)b(t_i)\}\,\Delta t$

(ii) $y(t_{i+1}) = y(t_i) + \{2k_ab(t_i) - 2k_a'y(t_i)^2$

$- k_by(t_i)c(t_i) + k_b'x(t_i) + k_cx(t_i)b(t_i)\}\,\Delta t$

and iterate the solutions.

27.8 $\frac{\mathrm{d}[\mathrm{M}]}{\mathrm{d}t}=k_{\mathrm{i}}[\mathrm{M}][\mathrm{I}]$ [initiation]

$$\frac{\mathrm{d}[\mathrm{R}]}{\mathrm{d}t}=-2k_{\mathrm{t}}^{\circ}(1+a[\mathrm{M}])[\mathrm{R}]^2 \quad \text{[termination]}$$

$$\frac{\mathrm{d}[\mathrm{M}]}{\mathrm{d}t}=-k_{\mathrm{p}}^{\circ}(1+b[\mathrm{M}])[\mathrm{R}][\mathrm{M}] \quad \text{[propagation]}$$

In the steady state

$$\frac{\mathrm{d}[\mathrm{R}]}{\mathrm{d}t}=k_{\mathrm{i}}[\mathrm{M}][\mathrm{I}]-2k_{\mathrm{t}}^{\circ}(1+a[\mathrm{M}])[\mathrm{R}]^2=0$$

which solves to

$$[\mathrm{R}]=\left\{\frac{k_{\mathrm{i}}[\mathrm{M}][\mathrm{I}]}{2k_{\mathrm{t}}^{\circ}(1+a[\mathrm{M}])}\right\}^{1/2}$$

$$\frac{\mathrm{d}[\mathrm{M}]}{\mathrm{d}t}=-k_{\mathrm{p}}^{\circ}(1+b[\mathrm{M}])[\mathrm{M}]\left\{\frac{k_{\mathrm{i}}[\mathrm{M}][\mathrm{I}]}{2k_{\mathrm{t}}^{\circ}(1+a[\mathrm{M}])}\right\}^{1/2}$$

$$=\underline{-k_{\mathrm{p}}^{\circ}\left(\frac{k_{\mathrm{i}}}{2k_{\mathrm{t}}^{\circ}}\right)^{1/2}\left\{\frac{1+b[\mathrm{M}]}{(1+a[\mathrm{M}])^{1/2}}\right\}[\mathrm{I}]^{1/2}[\mathrm{M}]^{3/2}}$$

27.9 $\langle M\rangle_N=\frac{M}{1-p}$ [12]

$$\langle M^2\rangle_N=M^2\sum_n n^2P_n=M^2(1-p)\sum_n n^2p^{n-1} \quad [11]$$

$$=M^2(1-p)\frac{\mathrm{d}}{\mathrm{d}p}p\frac{\mathrm{d}}{\mathrm{d}p}\sum_n p^n=M^2(1-p)\frac{\mathrm{d}}{\mathrm{d}p}p\frac{\mathrm{d}}{\mathrm{d}p}(1-p)^{-1}$$

$$=\frac{M^2(1+p)}{(1-p)^2}$$

$$\langle M^2\rangle_N-\langle M\rangle_N^2=M^2\left\{\frac{1+p}{(1-p)^2}-\frac{1}{(1-p)^2}\right\}=\frac{pM^2}{(1-p)^2}$$

Hence, $\underline{\delta M = \dfrac{p^{1/2}M}{1-p}}$

27.10 $\langle M^3\rangle_N = M^3 \sum_n n^3 P_n = M^3(1-p)\sum_n n^3 p^{n-1}$ [11]

$$= M^3(1-p)\frac{\mathrm{d}}{\mathrm{d}p}\sum_n n^2 p^n$$

$$= M^3(1-p)\frac{\mathrm{d}}{\mathrm{d}p}p\frac{\mathrm{d}}{\mathrm{d}p}p\frac{\mathrm{d}}{\mathrm{d}p}\sum_n p^n$$

$$= M^3(1-p)\frac{\mathrm{d}}{\mathrm{d}p}p\frac{\mathrm{d}}{\mathrm{d}p}p\frac{\mathrm{d}}{\mathrm{d}p}(1-p)^{-1}$$

$$= \frac{M^3(1+4p+p^2)}{(1-p)^3}$$

$\langle M^2\rangle_N = \dfrac{M^2(1+p)}{(1-p)^2}$ [Problem 27.9]

Therefore, $\dfrac{\langle M^3\rangle_N}{\langle M^2\rangle_N} = \underline{\dfrac{M(1+4p+p^2)}{1-p^2}}$

27.11 (i) $\dfrac{\mathrm{d}[\mathrm{H}]}{\mathrm{d}t} = k_b[\mathrm{H_2}][\mathrm{OH}] - k_c[\mathrm{O_2}][\mathrm{H}] + k_d[\mathrm{H_2}][\mathrm{O}] - k_e[\mathrm{H}] = 0$

(ii) $\dfrac{\mathrm{d}[\mathrm{O}]}{\mathrm{d}t} = k_c[\mathrm{O_2}][\mathrm{H}] - k_d[\mathrm{H_2}][\mathrm{O}] = 0$

(iii) $\dfrac{\mathrm{d}[\mathrm{OH}]}{\mathrm{d}t} = v_a - k_b[\mathrm{H_2}][\mathrm{OH}] + k_c[\mathrm{O_2}][\mathrm{H}] + k_d[\mathrm{H_2}][\mathrm{O}] = 0$

From (ii), $[\mathrm{O}] = \left(\dfrac{k_c}{k_d}\right)\dfrac{[\mathrm{O_2}][\mathrm{H}]}{[\mathrm{H_2}]}$

From (i + iii), $v_a + 2k_d[\mathrm{H_2}][\mathrm{O}] - k_e[\mathrm{H}] = 0$

Hence $v_a + \dfrac{2k_c[\mathrm{H_2}][\mathrm{O_2}]}{[\mathrm{H_2}]} - k_e[\mathrm{H}] = 0$

and so $[\mathrm{H}]=\dfrac{v_{\mathrm{a}}}{k_{\mathrm{e}}-2k_{\mathrm{c}}[\mathrm{O_2}]}$

Thus, $[\mathrm{H}]\rightarrow\infty$ if $2k_{\mathrm{c}}[\mathrm{O_2}]\rightarrow k_{\mathrm{e}}$.

27.12 $\mathrm{A}\rightarrow 2\mathrm{R},\ I_{\mathrm{a}}$

$\mathrm{A}+\mathrm{R}\rightarrow\mathrm{R}+\mathrm{B},\ k_{\mathrm{p}}$

$\mathrm{R}+\mathrm{R}\rightarrow\mathrm{R_2},\ k_{\mathrm{t}}$

$$\frac{\mathrm{d[A]}}{\mathrm{d}t}=-I_{\mathrm{a}}-k_{\mathrm{p}}[\mathrm{A}][\mathrm{R}],\quad \frac{\mathrm{d[R]}}{\mathrm{d}t}=2I_{\mathrm{a}}-2k_{\mathrm{t}}[\mathrm{R}]^2=0$$

The latter implies that $[\mathrm{R}]=(I_{\mathrm{a}}/k_{\mathrm{t}})^{1/2}$, and so

$$\frac{\mathrm{d[A]}}{\mathrm{d}t}=-I_{\mathrm{a}}-k_{\mathrm{p}}\left(\frac{I_{\mathrm{a}}}{k_{\mathrm{t}}}\right)^{1/2}$$

$$\frac{\mathrm{d[B]}}{\mathrm{d}t}=k_{\mathrm{p}}[\mathrm{A}][\mathrm{R}]=k_{\mathrm{p}}\left(\frac{I_{\mathrm{a}}}{k_{\mathrm{t}}}\right)^{1/2}[\mathrm{A}]$$

Therefore, only the combination $k_{\mathrm{p}}/k_{\mathrm{t}}^{1/2}$ may be determined if the reaction attains a steady state.

27.13 $\mathrm{Cl_2}+h\nu\rightarrow 2\mathrm{Cl},\ I_{\mathrm{a}}$

$\mathrm{Cl}+\mathrm{CHCl_3}\rightarrow\mathrm{CCl_3}+\mathrm{HCl},\ k_{\mathrm{a}}$

$\mathrm{CCl_3}+\mathrm{Cl_2}\rightarrow\mathrm{CCl_4}+\mathrm{Cl},\ k_{\mathrm{b}}$

$2\mathrm{CCl_3}+\mathrm{Cl_2}\rightarrow 2\mathrm{CCl_4},\ k_{\mathrm{c}}$

(i) $$\frac{\mathrm{d[CCl_4]}}{\mathrm{d}t}=2k_{\mathrm{c}}[\mathrm{CCl_3}]^2[\mathrm{Cl_2}]+k_{\mathrm{b}}[\mathrm{CCl_3}][\mathrm{Cl_2}]$$

(ii) $$\frac{\mathrm{d[CCl_3]}}{\mathrm{d}t}=k_{\mathrm{a}}[\mathrm{Cl}][\mathrm{CHCl_3}]-k_{\mathrm{b}}[\mathrm{CCl_3}][\mathrm{Cl_2}]-2k_{\mathrm{c}}[\mathrm{CCl_3}]^2[\mathrm{Cl_2}]=0$$

(iii) $$\frac{\mathrm{d[Cl]}}{\mathrm{d}t}=2I_{\mathrm{a}}-k_{\mathrm{a}}[\mathrm{Cl}][\mathrm{CHCl_3}]+k_{\mathrm{b}}[\mathrm{CCl_3}][\mathrm{Cl_2}]=0$$

(iv) $$\frac{\mathrm{d[Cl_2]}}{\mathrm{d}t}=-I_{\mathrm{a}}-k_{\mathrm{b}}[\mathrm{CCl_3}][\mathrm{Cl_2}]-k_{\mathrm{c}}[\mathrm{CCl_3}]^2[\mathrm{Cl_2}]$$

Therefore,

$$I_a = k_c[CCl_3]^2[Cl_2] \quad [(ii + iii)]$$

which implies that

$$[CCl_3] = \left(\frac{1}{k_c}\right)^{1/2}\left(\frac{I_a}{[Cl_2]}\right)^{1/2}$$

Then, with (i),

$$\frac{d[CCl_4]}{dt} = 2I_a + \frac{k_b I_a^{1/2}[Cl_2]^{1/2}}{k_c^{1/2}}$$

When the pressure of chlorine is high, and the inhibition rate is slow (in the sense that the lowest powers of I_a dominate), the second term dominates the first, giving

$$\frac{d[CCl_4]}{dt} = \frac{k_b I_a^{1/2}}{k_c^{1/2}}[Cl_2]^{1/2} = \underline{k I_a^{1/2}[Cl_2]^{1/2}}$$

with $k = k_b/k_c^{1/2}$. It seems necessary to suppose that Cl + Cl recombination (which needs a third body) is unimportant.

27.14 $A \rightarrow B, \quad \frac{d[B]}{dt} = I_a,$

$B \rightarrow A, \quad \frac{d[B]}{dt} = -k[B]^2$

In the photostationary state $I_a - k[B]^2 = 0$

Hence,

$$[B] = \left(\frac{I_a}{k}\right)^{1/2} \propto [A]^{1/2} \quad [\text{because } I \propto [A]]$$

The illumination may increase the rate of the forward reaction without affecting the reverse reaction. Hence the position of equilibrium may be shifted toward products.

27.15 $A + h\nu \rightarrow A^*, \; I_a$

$A^* + A \rightarrow A_2, \; k$

$A^* \rightarrow A + h\nu_f, \; k_f; \; I_f = k_f[A^*]$

$$\Phi = \frac{-d[A]}{dt} \times \frac{1}{I_a}$$

$$\frac{d[A]}{dt} = -I_a - k[A^*][A] + k_f[A^*]$$

$$\frac{d[A^*]}{dt} = I_a - k[A^*][A] - k_f[A^*] \approx 0$$

which solves to

$$[A^*] \approx \frac{I_a}{k_f + k[A]}$$

Therefore,

$$\frac{d[A]}{dt} = -I_a + \frac{(k_f - k[A])I_a}{k_f + k[A]} = \frac{-2kI_a[A]}{k_f + k[A]}$$

Consequently,

$$\Phi = \frac{2k[A]}{k_f + k[A]}$$

If $k[A] \ll k_f$, $\Phi \approx 2(k/k_f)[A]$, and the efficiency is determined by the availability of A molecules in the vicinity of A*. If $k[A] \gg k_f$, $\Phi \approx 2$, and the rate is determined by the excitation step, because there is now plenty of A to react to form A_2.

27.16 Write the differential equations for [X] and [Y]:

(i) $$\frac{d[X]}{dt} = k_a[A][X] - k_b[X][Y]$$

(ii) $$\frac{d[Y]}{dt} = k_b[X][Y] - k_c[Y]$$

and express them as finite-difference equations:

(i) $X(t_{i+1}) = X(t_i) + k_a[A]X(t_i)\,\Delta t - k_b X(t_i) Y(t_i)\,\Delta t$

(ii) $Y(t_{i+1}) = Y(t_i) - k_c Y(t_i)\,\Delta t + k_b X(t_i)\,\Delta t$

and iterate for different values of [A], X(0), and Y(0).

For the steady state,

(i) $$\frac{d[X]}{dt} = k_a[A][X] - k_b[X][Y] = 0$$

(ii) $\dfrac{d[Y]}{dt}=k_b[X][Y]-k_c[Y]=0$

which solve to

(i) $k_b[X]=k_c$, (ii) $k_a[A]=k_b[Y]$

Hence,

$$[X]=\frac{k_c}{k_b},\ [Y]=\frac{k_a[A]}{k_b}$$

27.17 (i) $\dfrac{d[X]}{dt}=k_a[A]+k_b[X]^2[Y]-k_c[B][X]-k_d[X]$

(ii) $\dfrac{d[Y]}{dt}=-k_b[X]^2[Y]+k_c[B][X]$

Express these equations as finite-difference equations:

(i) $X(t_{i+1})=X(t_i)+\{k_a[A]+k_bX^2(t_i)Y(t_i)-k_c[B]X(t_i)-k_d[X]\}\,\Delta t$

(ii) $Y(t_{i+1})=Y(t_i)+\{k_c[B]X(t_i)-k_bX^2(t_i)Y(t_i)\}\,\Delta t$

and iterate. See Figs. 27.7 to 27.9 of the text.

27.18 (i) $\dfrac{d[X]}{dt}=k_a[A][Y]-k_b[X][Y]+k_c[B][X]-2k_d[X]^2$

(ii) $\dfrac{d[Y]}{dt}=-k_a[A][Y]-k_b[X][Y]+k_e[Z]$

Express these differential equations as finite-difference equations:

(i) $X(t_{i+1})=X(t_i)+\{k_a[A]Y(t_i)-k_bX(t_i)Y(t_i)+k_c[B]X(t_i)-2k_dX^2(t_i)\}\,\Delta t$

(ii) $Y(t_{i+1})=Y(t_i)+\{k_e[Z]-k_a[A]Y(t_i)-k_bX(t_i)Y(t_i)\}\,\Delta t$

Solve these equations by iteration. More sophisticated procedures are available programmed in the *Library of Physical Chemistry Software* that is available to accompany the text.

28. Molecular reaction dynamics

Exercises

28.1 $z=\dfrac{2^{1/2}\sigma\bar{c}p}{kT}$ [eqn 9 of Chapter 24]

and $\bar{c}=\left(\dfrac{8kT}{\pi m}\right)^{1/2}$ [eqn 7b of Chapter 24]

Therefore, $z=\dfrac{4\sigma p}{(\pi mkT)^{1/2}}$ with $\sigma\approx\pi d^2\approx 4\pi R^2$

Similarly, $Z_{AA}=\sigma\left(\dfrac{4kT}{\pi m}\right)^{1/2}\left(\dfrac{N}{V}\right)^2$ [eqn 10b of Chapter 24]

$$=\sigma\left(\frac{4kT}{\pi m}\right)^{1/2}\left(\frac{p}{kT}\right)^2 \quad [N/V=p/kT]$$

We express these equations in the form

$$z=\frac{16\pi R^2\times 1.0133\times 10^5\text{ Pa}}{\{\pi\times(M/\text{g mol}^{-1})\times 1.6605\times 10^{-27}\text{ kg}\times 1.381\times 10^{-23}\text{ J K}^{-1}\times 298.15\text{ K}\}^{1/2}}$$

$$=\frac{1.10\times 10^{30}\text{ m}^{-2}\text{ s}^{-1}\times R^2}{(M/\text{g mol}^{-1})^{1/2}}=\frac{1.10\times 10^6\times(R/\text{pm})^2\text{ s}^{-1}}{(M/\text{g mol}^{-1})^{1/2}}$$

$$Z_{AA}=4\pi R^2\left(\frac{4\times 1.381\times 10^{-23}\text{ J K}^{-1}\times 298.15\text{ K}}{\pi\times(M/\text{g mol}^{-1})\times 1.6605\times 10^{-27}\text{ kg}}\right)^{1/2}$$

$$\times\left(\frac{1.0133\times 10^5\text{ Pa}}{1.381\times 10^{-23}\text{ J K}^{-1}\times 298.15\text{ K}}\right)^2$$

$$=\frac{1.35\times 10^{55}\text{ m}^{-3}\text{ s}^{-1}\times R^2}{(M/\text{g mol}^{-1})^{1/2}}=\frac{1.35\times 10^{31}(R/\text{pm})^2}{(M/\text{g mol}^{-1})^{1/2}}\text{ m}^{-3}\text{ s}^{-1}$$

(a) NH_3; $R=190$ pm, $M=17$ g mol^{-1}

$$z=\frac{1.10\times 10^6\times 190^2\text{ s}^{-1}}{17^{1/2}}=\underline{9.6\times 10^9\text{ s}^{-1}}$$

$$Z_{AA}=\frac{1.35\times 10^{31}\times 190^2\text{ m}^{-3}\text{ s}^{-1}}{17^{1/2}}=\underline{1.2\times 10^{35}\text{ m}^{-3}\text{ s}^{-1}}$$

(b) CO; $R=180$ pm, $M=28$ g mol^{-1}

$$z=\frac{1.10\times10^{6}\times180^{2}}{28^{1/2}}\,\mathrm{s^{-1}}=\underline{6.7\times10^{9}\,\mathrm{s^{-1}}}$$

$$Z_{\mathrm{AA}}=\frac{1.35\times10^{31}\times180^{2}}{28^{1/2}}\,\mathrm{m^{-3}\,s^{-1}}=\underline{8.3\times10^{34}\,\mathrm{m^{-3}\,s^{-1}}}$$

For the percentage increase at constant volume, use

$$\frac{1}{z}\frac{\mathrm{d}z}{\mathrm{d}T}=\frac{1}{\bar{c}}\frac{\mathrm{d}\bar{c}}{\mathrm{d}T}=\frac{1}{2T},\ \frac{1}{Z}\frac{\mathrm{d}Z}{\mathrm{d}T}=\frac{1}{2T}$$

Therefore,

$$\frac{\delta z}{z}\approx\frac{\delta T}{2T}\ \text{and}\ \frac{\delta Z}{Z}\approx\frac{\delta T}{2T}$$

and since $\delta T/T=10\,\mathrm{K}/298\,\mathrm{K}=0.034$, both z and Z increase by about <u>1.7 per cent</u>.

28.2 In each case use $f=\mathrm{e}^{-E_{\mathrm{a}}/RT}$ [Section 28.1]:

(a) $$\frac{E_{\mathrm{a}}}{RT}=\frac{10\times10^{3}\,\mathrm{J\,mol^{-1}}}{8.314\,\mathrm{J\,K^{-1}\,mol^{-1}}\times300\,\mathrm{K}}=4.01,\ f=\mathrm{e}^{-4.01}=\underline{0.018}$$

$$\frac{E_{\mathrm{a}}}{RT}=\frac{10\times10^{3}\,\mathrm{J\,mol^{-1}}}{8.314\,\mathrm{J\,K^{-1}\,mol^{-1}}\times1000\,\mathrm{K}}=1.20,\ f=\mathrm{e}^{-1.20}=\underline{0.30}$$

(b) $$\frac{E_{\mathrm{a}}}{RT}=\frac{100\times10^{3}\,\mathrm{J\,mol^{-1}}}{8.314\,\mathrm{J\,K^{-1}\,mol^{-1}}\times300\,\mathrm{K}}=40.1,\ f=\mathrm{e}^{-40.1}=\underline{3.9\times10^{-18}}$$

$$\frac{E_{\mathrm{a}}}{RT}=\frac{100\times10^{3}\,\mathrm{J\,mol^{-1}}}{8.314\,\mathrm{J\,K^{-1}\,mol^{-1}}\times1000\,\mathrm{K}}=12.0,\ f=\mathrm{e}^{-12.0}=\underline{6.0\times10^{-6}}$$

28.3 The percentage increase is

$$100\times\frac{\delta f}{f}\approx100\times\frac{1}{f}\left(\frac{\mathrm{d}f}{\mathrm{d}T}\right)\times\delta T\approx\frac{100E_{\mathrm{a}}}{\mathrm{RT}^{2}}\,\delta T$$

(a) $E_{\mathrm{a}}=10\,\mathrm{kJ\,mol^{-1}}$, $\delta T=10\,\mathrm{K}$

$$100\frac{\delta f}{f}=\frac{100\times10\times10^{3}\,\mathrm{J\,mol^{-1}}\times10\,\mathrm{K}}{8.314\,\mathrm{J\,K^{-1}\,mol^{-1}}\times T^{2}}$$

$$=\frac{1.20\times10^{6}}{(T/\mathrm{K})^{2}}=\begin{cases}\underline{13\ \text{per cent}}\ \text{at 300 K}\\ \underline{1.2\ \text{per cent}}\ \text{at 1000 K}\end{cases}$$

(b) $E_a = 100\ \mathrm{kJ\ mol^{-1}}$, $\delta T = 10\ \mathrm{K}$

$$100\frac{\delta f}{f} = \frac{1.20\times 10^7}{(T/\mathrm{K})^2} = \begin{cases}\underline{130\ \text{per cent}}\ \text{at 300 K}\\ \underline{12\ \text{per cent at}}\ \text{1000 K}\end{cases}$$

28.4 $$k_d = \frac{8RT}{3\eta}\quad[7] = \frac{8\times 8.314\ \mathrm{J\ K^{-1}\ mol^{-1}}\times 298\ \mathrm{K}}{3\eta}$$

$$= \frac{6.61\times 10^3\ \mathrm{J\ mol^{-1}}}{\eta}$$

$$= \frac{6.61\times 10^3\ \mathrm{kg\ m^2\ s^{-2}\ mol^{-1}}}{(\eta/\mathrm{kg\ m^{-1}\ s^{-1}})\times \mathrm{kg\ m^{-1}\ s^{-1}}} = \frac{6.61\times 10^3\ \mathrm{m^3\ mol^{-1}\ s^{-1}}}{(\eta/\mathrm{kg\ m^{-1}\ s^{-1}})}$$

$$= \frac{6.61\times 10^6\ \mathrm{M^{-1}\ s^{-1}}}{(\eta/\mathrm{kg\ m^{-1}\ s^{-1}})} = \frac{6.61\times 10^9\ \mathrm{M^{-1}\ s^{-1}}}{(\eta/\mathrm{cP})}$$

(a) Water, $\eta = 1.00\ \mathrm{cP}$, $k_d = \underline{6.61\times 10^9\ \mathrm{M^{-1}\ s^{-1}}}$

(b) Pentane, $\eta = 0.22\ \mathrm{cP}$, $k_d = \dfrac{6.61\times 10^9}{0.22}\ \mathrm{M^{-1}\ s^{-1}} = \underline{3.0\times 10^{10}\ \mathrm{M^{-1}\ s^{-1}}}$

(c) Decylbenzene, $\eta = 3.36\ \mathrm{cP}$, $k_d = \dfrac{6.61\times 10^9}{3.36}\ \mathrm{M^{-1}\ s^{-1}} = \underline{2.0\times 10^9\ \mathrm{M^{-1}\ s^{-1}}}$

28.5 $$k_2 = \sigma\left(\frac{8kT}{\pi\mu}\right)^{1/2} N_A\, \mathrm{e}^{-E_a/RT}\quad[1]$$

$$= (3.72\times 10^{12}\ \mathrm{M^{-1}\ min^{-1}})\times \mathrm{e}^{-E_a/RT}$$

$$= \frac{3.72\times 10^{12}}{60}\times 10^{-3}\ \mathrm{m^3\ mol^{-1}\ s^{-1}}\times \mathrm{e}^{-E_a/RT}$$

Therefore, we must evaluate

$$\sigma = \frac{3.72\times 10^9}{60}\ \mathrm{m^3\ mol^{-1}\ s^{-1}}\times\left(\frac{\pi\mu}{8kT}\right)^{1/2}\frac{1}{N_A}$$

with $\mu = \dfrac{16\times 100}{16+100}\ \mathrm{u} = 13.79\ \mathrm{u}$

$$\sigma = \frac{3.72\times 10^9\ \mathrm{m^3\ mol^{-1}\ s^{-1}}}{60\times 6.022\times 10^{23}\ \mathrm{mol^{-1}}}\times\left(\frac{\pi\times 13.79\times 1.6605\times 10^{-27}\ \mathrm{kg}}{8\times 1.381\times 10^{-23}\ \mathrm{J\ K^{-1}}\times 298\ \mathrm{K}}\right)^{1/2}$$

$= 1.52\times 10^{-19}\ \mathrm{m^2}$, or $\underline{0.152\ \mathrm{nm^2}}$

28.6 $P=\dfrac{\sigma^*}{\sigma}$

For the mean collision cross section, write $\sigma_A=\pi d_A^2$, $\sigma_B=\pi d_B^2$, and $\sigma=\pi d^2$, with $d=\frac{1}{2}(d_A+d_B)$:

$$\sigma=\tfrac{1}{4}\pi(d_A+d_B)^2=\tfrac{1}{4}\pi(d_A^2+d_B^2+2d_Ad_B)$$
$$=\tfrac{1}{4}(\sigma_A+\sigma_B+2\sigma_A^{1/2}\sigma_B^{1/2})$$
$$=\tfrac{1}{4}\{0.95+0.65+2\times(0.95\times0.65)^{1/2}\}\ \text{nm}^2=1.03\ \text{nm}^2$$

Therefore,

$$P\approx\frac{9.2\times10^{-22}\ \text{m}^2}{1.03\times10^{-18}\ \text{m}^2}=\underline{8.9\times10^{-4}}$$

28.7 $\dfrac{\text{d[P]}}{\text{d}t}=k_2[\text{A}][\text{B}]$

$$k_2=4\pi R^*DN_A\quad[6]=4\pi R^*(D_A+D_B)N_A$$
$$=\frac{2kTN_A}{3\eta}(R_A+R_B)\times\left(\frac{1}{R_A}+\frac{1}{R_B}\right)$$
$$=\frac{3RT}{3\eta}(R_A+R_B)\times\left(\frac{1}{R_A}+\frac{1}{R_B}\right)$$
$$=\frac{2\times8.314\ \text{J K}^{-1}\ \text{mol}^{-1}\times313\ \text{K}}{3\times2.37\times10^{-3}\ \text{kg m}^{-1}\ \text{s}^{-1}}\times(299+825)\times\left(\frac{1}{299}+\frac{1}{825}\right)$$
$$=3.7\times10^6\ \text{mol}^{-1}\ \text{m}^3\ \text{s}^{-1}=3.7\times10^9\ \text{M}^{-1}\ \text{s}^{-1}$$

Therefore, the initial rate is

$$\frac{\text{d[P]}}{\text{d}t}=3.7\times10^9\ \text{M}^{-1}\ \text{s}^{-1}\times0.150\ \text{M}\times0.330\ \text{M}$$
$$=\underline{1.8\times10^8\ \text{M s}^{-1}}$$

28.8 $\Delta H^{\ddagger}=E_a-RT\quad[20b]$

$$k_2=B\,\text{e}^{\Delta S^{\ddagger}/R}\,\text{e}^{-\Delta H^{\ddagger}/RT},\ B=\frac{kT}{h}\times\frac{RT}{p^{\ominus}}\quad[19]$$
$$=B\,\text{e}^{\Delta S^{\ddagger}/R}\,\text{e}^{-E_a/RT}\,\text{e}=A\,\text{e}^{-E_a/RT}$$

Therefore,

$$A = \mathrm{e}\, B\, \mathrm{e}^{\Delta S^{\ddagger}/R}\text{, implying that } \Delta S^{\ddagger} = R\left(\ln\frac{A}{B} - 1\right)$$

Therefore, since $\Delta H^{\ddagger} = 8681\ \mathrm{K} \times R$,

$$E_a = \Delta H^{\ddagger} + RT = (8681\ \mathrm{K} + 303\ \mathrm{K})R$$

$$= 8984\ \mathrm{K} \times 8.314\ \mathrm{J\ K^{-1}\ mol^{-1}} = \underline{74.7\ \mathrm{kJ\ mol^{-1}}}$$

$$B = \frac{1.381 \times 10^{-23}\ \mathrm{J\ K^{-1}} \times 303\ \mathrm{K}}{6.626 \times 10^{-34}\ \mathrm{J\ s}} \times \frac{8.314\ \mathrm{J\ K^{-1}\ mol^{-1}} \times 303\ \mathrm{K}}{10^{5}\ \mathrm{Pa}}$$

$$= 1.59 \times 10^{11}\ \mathrm{m^3\ mol^{-1}\ s^{-1}} = 1.59 \times 10^{14}\ \mathrm{M^{-1}\ s^{-1}}$$

and hence

$$\Delta S^{\ddagger} = R\left\{\ln\left(\frac{2.05 \times 10^{13}\ \mathrm{M^{-1}\ s^{-1}}}{1.59 \times 10^{14}\ \mathrm{M^{-1}\ s^{-1}}}\right) - 1\right\}$$

$$= 8.314\ \mathrm{J\ K^{-1}\ mol^{-1}} \times (-3.05) = \underline{-25\ \mathrm{J\ K^{-1}\ mol^{-1}}}$$

28.9 $\Delta H^{\ddagger} = E_a - RT$ [20b], $\Delta H^{\ddagger} = 9134\ \mathrm{K} \times R = \underline{75.9\ \mathrm{kJ\ mol^{-1}}}$

$$\Delta S^{\ddagger} = R\left(\ln\frac{A}{B} - 1\right) \quad \text{[Exercise 28.9]}$$

with $B = \frac{kT}{h} \times \frac{RT}{p^{\ominus}}$ [19] $= 1.59 \times 10^{14}\ \mathrm{M^{-1}\ s^{-1}}$ at 30 °C

Therefore,

$$\Delta S^{\ddagger} = 8.314\ \mathrm{J\ K^{-1}\ mol^{-1}} \times \left\{\ln\left(\frac{7.78 \times 10^{14}}{1.59 \times 10^{14}}\right) - 1\right\}$$

$$= \underline{+4.9\ \mathrm{J\ K^{-1}\ mol^{-1}}}$$

Hence,

$$\Delta G^{\ddagger} = \Delta H^{\ddagger} - T\Delta S^{\ddagger} = 75.9 - 303 \times 4.9 \times 10^{-3}\ \mathrm{kJ\ mol^{-1}}$$

$$= \underline{74.4\ \mathrm{kJ\ mol^{-1}}}$$

28.10 $\Delta H^{\ddagger} = E_a - 2RT$ [20a]

$$= 56.8 - 2 \times 8.314 \times 10^{-3} \times 338\ \mathrm{kJ\ mol^{-1}} = 51.2\ \mathrm{kJ\ mol^{-1}}$$

$k_2 = A\,e^{-E_a/RT}$ implies that

$$A = k_2\,e^{E_a/RT}$$
$$= 7.84 \times 10^{-3}\,\text{kPa}^{-1}\,\text{s}^{-1} \times e^{56.8\times 10^3/8.314\times 338}$$
$$= 4.70\bar{5} \times 10^{6}\,\text{kPa}^{-1}\,\text{s}^{-1} = 4.70\bar{5} \times 10^{3}\,\text{Pa}^{-1}\,\text{s}^{-1}$$

In terms of molar concentrations

$$V = k_2 p_A p_B = k_2 (RT)^2 [\text{A}][\text{B}]$$

and instead of

$$\frac{dp_A}{dt} = -k_2 p_A p_B$$

we have $\dfrac{d[\text{A}]}{dt} = -k_2 RT[\text{A}][\text{B}]$

and hence use

$$A = 4.70\bar{5} \times 10^{3}\,\text{Pa}^{-1}\,\text{s}^{-1} \times 8.314\,\text{J K}^{-1}\,\text{mol}^{-1} \times 338\,\text{K}$$
$$= 1.32\bar{2} \times 10^{7}\,\text{m}^3\,\text{mol}^{-1}\,\text{s}^{-1}$$

Then

$$B = \frac{kT}{h} \times \frac{RT}{p^{\ominus}}$$
$$= \frac{1.381 \times 10^{-23} \times 338\,\text{K}}{6.626 \times 10^{-34}\,\text{J s}} \times \frac{8.314\,\text{J K}^{-1}\,\text{mol}^{-1} \times 338\,\text{K}}{10^5\,\text{Pa}}$$
$$= 1.98 \times 10^{11}\,\text{m}^3\,\text{s}^{-1}\,\text{mol}^{-1}$$

and

$$\Delta S^{\ddagger} = R\left\{\ln\left(\frac{A}{B}\right) - 2\right\} \quad [22]$$
$$= 8.314\,\text{J K}^{-1}\,\text{mol}^{-1} \times \left\{\ln\frac{1.32\bar{2} \times 10^{7}}{1.98 \times 10^{11}} - 2\right\} = \underline{-96.6\,\text{J K}^{-1}\,\text{mol}^{-1}}$$

and hence

$$\Delta G^{\ddagger} = \Delta H^{\ddagger} - T\Delta S^{\ddagger} = 51.2 - 338 \times (-96.6 \times 10^{-3})\,\text{kJ mol}^{-1}$$
$$= \underline{+83.9\,\text{kJ mol}^{-1}}$$

28.11 $k_2 = N_A \sigma^* \left(\dfrac{8kT}{\pi\mu}\right)^{1/2} e^{-\Delta E_0/RT}$, which implies that

$$A = N_A\sigma^*\left(\frac{8kT}{\pi\mu}\right)^{1/2}$$

Therefore,

$$\frac{A}{B} = \frac{N_A\sigma^* hp^\ominus}{kT \times RT}\left(\frac{8kT}{\pi\mu}\right)^{1/2} = \frac{8^{1/2}\sigma^* hp^\ominus}{(\pi\mu k^3T^3)^{1/2}}$$

For identical particles, $\mu = \frac{1}{2}m$, so

$$\frac{A}{B} = \frac{4\sigma^* hp^\ominus}{(\pi m k^3 T^3)^{1/2}}$$

$$= \frac{4 \times 0.4 \times 10^{-18}\,\text{m}^2 \times 6.626 \times 10^{-34}\,\text{J s} \times 10^5\,\text{Pa}}{\{\pi \times 50 \times 1.6605 \times 10^{-27}\,\text{kg} \times (1.381 \times 10^{-23}\,\text{J K}^{-1} \times 300\,\text{K})^3\}^{1/2}}$$

$$= 7.78 \times 10^{-4}$$

and hence

$$\Delta S^\ddagger = R\left\{\ln\left(\frac{A}{B}\right) - 2\right\} = 8.314\,\text{J K}^{-1}\,\text{mol}^{-1}\{\ln 7.78 \times 10^{-4} - 2\}$$

$$= \underline{-76\,\text{J K}^{-1}\,\text{mol}^{-1}}$$

28.12 $B = \frac{kT}{h} \times \frac{RT}{p^\ominus}$

$$= \frac{1.381 \times 10^{-23}\,\text{J K}^{-1} \times 298.15\,\text{K}}{6.626 \times 10^{-34}\,\text{J s}} \times \frac{8.314\,\text{J K}^{-1}\,\text{mol}^{-1} \times 298.15\,\text{K}}{10^5\,\text{Pa}}$$

$$= 1.540 \times 10^{11}\,\text{m}^3\,\text{mol}^{-1}\,\text{s}^{-1}$$

$$= 1.540 \times 10^{14}\,\text{M}^{-1}\,\text{s}^{-1}$$

Therefore,

(a) $\Delta S^\ddagger = R\left\{\ln\left(\frac{4.6 \times 10^{12}}{1.540 \times 10^{14}}\right) - 2\right\} = \underline{-45.8\,\text{J K}^{-1}\,\text{mol}^{-1}}$

(b) $\Delta H^\ddagger = E_a - 2RT = 10.0 - 2 \times 2.48\,\text{kJ mol}^{-1}$

$$= \underline{+5.0\,\text{kJ mol}^{-1}}$$

(c) $\Delta G^\ddagger = \Delta H^\ddagger - T\Delta S^\ddagger = 5.0 - 298.15\,\text{K} \times (-45.8 \times 10^{-3})\,\text{kJ mol}^{-1}$

$$= \underline{+18.7\,\text{kJ mol}^{-1}}$$

28.13 If cleavage of a C—D or C—H bond is involved in the rate-determining step, use

$$\frac{k_2(\mathrm{D})}{k_2(\mathrm{H})}=\mathrm{e}^{\lambda},\ \lambda=\left(\frac{\hbar k_\mathrm{f}^{1/2}}{2kT}\right)\left\{\frac{1}{\mu_\mathrm{CD}^{1/2}}-\frac{1}{\mu_\mathrm{CH}^{1/2}}\right\}\quad[16]$$

$$\mu(\mathrm{CD})\approx\frac{2\times 12}{2+12}\,\mathrm{u}=1.71\,\mathrm{u}$$

$$\mu(\mathrm{CH})\approx\frac{1\times 12}{1+12}\,\mathrm{u}=0.92\,\mathrm{u}$$

$$\lambda\approx\frac{1.054\times10^{-34}\,\mathrm{J\,s}\times(450\,\mathrm{N\,m^{-1}})^{1/2}}{2\times1.381\times10^{-23}\,\mathrm{J\,K^{-1}}\times298\,\mathrm{K}}\times\left\{\frac{1}{1.71^{1/2}}-\frac{1}{0.92^{1/2}}\right\}\times\frac{1}{(1.6605\times10^{-27}\,\mathrm{kg})^{1/2}}$$

$$\approx -1.85$$

Hence, $\dfrac{k_2(\mathrm{D})}{k_2(\mathrm{H})}=\mathrm{e}^{-1.85}=0.156$

That is, $k_2(\mathrm{H})\approx 6.4\times k_2(\mathrm{D})$, in reasonable accord with the data.

28.14 (a) $\dfrac{k_2(\mathrm{T})}{k_2(\mathrm{H})}=\mathrm{e}^{\lambda},\ \lambda=\left(\dfrac{\hbar k_\mathrm{f}^{1/2}}{2kT}\right)\left\{\dfrac{1}{\mu_\mathrm{CT}^{1/2}}-\dfrac{1}{\mu_\mathrm{CH}^{1/2}}\right\}$

$$\mu_\mathrm{CT}=\frac{12\times3}{12+3}\,\mathrm{u}=2.40\,\mathrm{u},\ \mu_\mathrm{CH}=0.92\,\mathrm{u}$$

$$\lambda=\frac{1.054\times10^{-34}\,\mathrm{J\,s}\times k_\mathrm{f}^{1/2}}{2\times1.381\times10^{-23}\,\mathrm{J\,K^{-1}}\times T}$$

$$\times\left\{\frac{1}{(\mu_\mathrm{CT}/\mathrm{u})^{1/2}}-\frac{1}{(\mu_\mathrm{CH}/\mathrm{u})^{1/2}}\right\}\times\frac{1}{(1.6605\times10^{-27}\,\mathrm{kg})^{1/2}}$$

$$=\frac{93.65\times(k_\mathrm{f}/\mathrm{N\,m^{-1}})^{1/2}}{(T/\mathrm{K})}\times\left\{\frac{1}{(\mu_\mathrm{CT}/\mathrm{u})^{1/2}}-\frac{1}{(\mu_\mathrm{CH}/\mathrm{u})^{1/2}}\right\}$$

$$=\frac{93.65\times450^{1/2}}{298}\times\left\{\frac{1}{2.40^{1/2}}-\frac{1}{0.92^{1/2}}\right\}=-2.65$$

Therefore, $\dfrac{k_2(\mathrm{T})}{k_2(\mathrm{H})}=\mathrm{e}^{-2.65}=0.071$, so $\underline{k_2(\mathrm{H})\approx 14k_2(\mathrm{T})}$

$$\text{(b)}\ \lambda = \frac{93.65 \times 1750^{1/2}}{298} \times \left\{ \frac{1}{7.20^{1/2}} - \frac{1}{6.86^{1/2}} \right\} = -0.12$$

$$\text{since}\ \mu(^{12}\text{C}^{16}\text{O}) = \frac{12 \times 16}{12+16}\,\text{u} = 6.8\overline{6}\,\text{u}$$

$$= \mu(^{12}\text{C}^{18}\text{O}) = \frac{12 \times 18}{12+18}\,\text{u} = 7.2\overline{0}\,\text{u}$$

$$\text{Therefore,}\ \frac{k(^{12}\text{C}^{18}\text{O})}{k(^{12}\text{C}^{16}\text{O})} = \text{e}^{-0.12} = 0.89$$

and $k(^{12}\text{C}^{16}\text{O}) \approx \underline{1.1 \times k(^{12}\text{C}^{18}\text{O})}$

Increasing the temperature reduces the magnitude of λ, so the isotope effect is likewise reduced.

28.15 $\lg k_2 = \lg k_2^\circ + 2Az_Az_BI^{1/2}$ [24]

Hence, $\lg k_2^\circ = \lg k_2 - 2Az_Az_BI^{1/2}$

$$= \lg 12.2 - 2 \times 0.509 \times 1 \times (-1) \times 0.0525^{1/2} = 1.32$$

and $k_2^\circ = \underline{20.9\ \text{M}^{-2}\ \text{min}^{-1}}$

28.16 Fig. 28.1 shows that $\lg k_r$ is proportional to the ionic strength for neutral

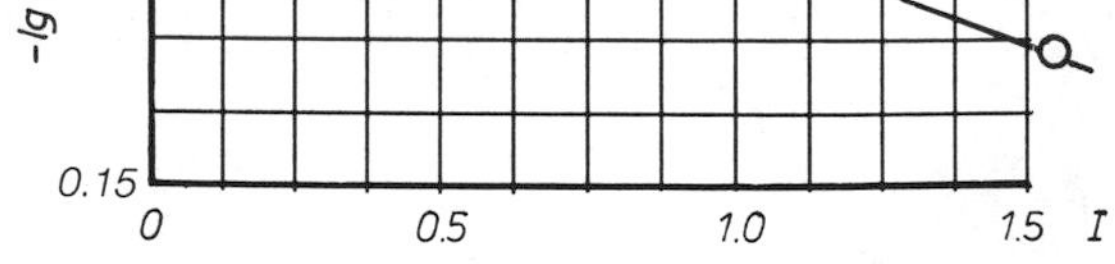

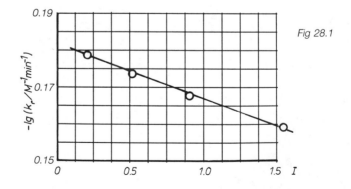

Fig 28.1

molecules. From the graph, the intercept at $I = 0$ is -0.18, so $\underline{k_r^\circ = 0.66\ \text{M}^{-1}\ \text{min}^{-1}}$.

28.17 $K_a = \dfrac{[H^+][A^-]}{[HA]\gamma_{HA}}\gamma_\pm^2 \approx \dfrac{[H^+][A^-]\gamma_\pm^2}{[HA]}$

Therefore, $[H^+] = \dfrac{[HA]K_a}{[A^-]\gamma_\pm^2}$

and $\lg[H^+] = \lg K_a + \lg\dfrac{[HA]}{[A^-]} - 2\lg\gamma_\pm$

$$= \lg K_a + \lg\frac{[HA]}{[A^-]} - 2AI^{1/2}$$

Write $v = k_2[H^+][B]$,

then $\lg v = \lg(k_2[B]) + \lg[H^+]$

$$= \lg(k_2[B]) + \lg\frac{[HA]}{[A^-]} + 2AI^{1/2}$$

$$= \lg v^\circ + 2AI^{1/2},\quad v^\circ = k_2\frac{[B][HA]}{[A^-]}$$

That is, the logarithm of the rate should be proportional to the square root of the ionic strength, $\underline{\lg v \propto I^{1/2}}$.

Problems

28.1 $A = N_A\sigma^*\left(\dfrac{8kT}{\pi\mu}\right)^{1/2}$ [Exercise 28.11; $\mu = \frac{1}{2}m(CH_3)$]

$$= \sigma^* \times 6.022\times10^{23}\ \text{mol}^{-1}\times\left(\frac{8\times1.381\times10^{-23}\ \text{J K}^{-1}\times298\ \text{K}}{\pi\times\frac{1}{2}\times15.03\times1.6605\times10^{-27}\ \text{kg}}\right)^{1/2}$$

$$= 5.52\times10^{26}\times\sigma^*\ \text{mol}^{-1}\ \text{m s}^{-1}$$

(a) $\sigma^* = \dfrac{2.4\times10^{10}\ \text{mol}^{-1}\ \text{dm}^3\ \text{s}^{-1}}{5.52\times10^{26}\ \text{mol}^{-1}\ \text{m s}^{-1}} = \dfrac{2.4\times10^{7}\ \text{mol}^{-1}\ \text{m}^3\ \text{s}^{-1}}{5.52\times10^{26}\ \text{mol}^{-1}\ \text{m s}^{-1}}$

$$= \underline{4.4\times10^{-20}\ \text{m}^2}$$

(b) Take $\sigma \approx \pi d^2 = \pi\times(154\times2\times10^{-12}\ \text{m})^2 = 3.0\times10^{-19}\ \text{m}^2$

Hence $P = \dfrac{\sigma^*}{\sigma} = \dfrac{4.4\times10^{-20}}{3.0\times10^{-19}} = \underline{0.15}$

28.2 Draw up the following table as the basis of an Arrhenius plot:

T/K	600	700	800	1000
10^3 K/T	1.67	1.43	1.25	1.00
$k/(\text{cm}^3\,\text{mol}^{-1}\,\text{s}^{-1})$	4.6×10^2	9.7×10^3	1.3×10^5	3.1×10^6
$\ln(k/\text{cm}^3\,\text{mol}^{-1}\,\text{s}^{-1})$	6.13	9.18	11.8	15.0

The points are plotted in Fig. 28.2. The least-squares intercept is at 28.3,

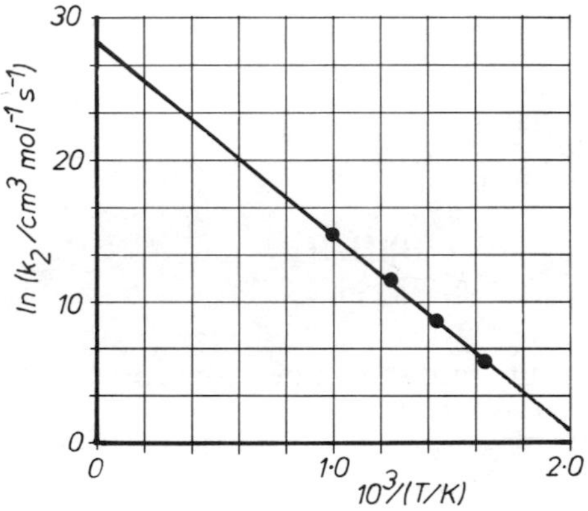

Fig 28.2

which implies that

$$A/(\text{cm}^3\,\text{mol}^{-1}\,\text{s}^{-1}) = e^{28.3} = 2.0\times10^{12}$$

As in Problem 28.1,

$$\sigma^* = \frac{A_{\text{exptl}}}{N_A(8kT/\pi\mu)^{1/2}} \text{ with } \mu = \tfrac{1}{2}m(\text{NO}_2)$$

$$= \frac{A_{\text{exptl}}}{4N_A}\left(\frac{\pi m}{kT}\right)^{1/2} = \frac{2.0\times10^6\,\text{m}^3\,\text{mol}^{-1}\,\text{s}^{-1}}{4\times6.022\times10^{23}\text{mol}^{-1}}\times\left(\frac{\pi\times46\times1.6605\times10^{-27}\,\text{kg}}{1.381\times10^{-23}\text{J K}^{-1}\times750\,\text{K}}\right)^{1/2}$$

$$= 4.0\times10^{-21}\,\text{m}^2, \text{ or } \underline{4.0\times10^{-3}\,\text{nm}^2}$$

$$P = \frac{\sigma^*}{\sigma} = \frac{4.0\times10^{-3}\,\text{nm}^2}{0.60\,\text{nm}^2} = \underline{0.007}$$

28.3 For radical recombination, $E_a = 0$. The maximum rate of recombination is obtained when $P = 1$ (or more), and then

$$k_2 = A = \sigma^* N_A \left(\frac{8kT}{\pi\mu}\right)^{1/2} = 4\sigma^* N_A \left(\frac{kT}{\pi m}\right)^{1/2} \quad [\mu = \tfrac{1}{2}m]$$

$$\sigma^* \approx \pi d^2 = \pi \times (308 \times 10^{-12}\,\text{m})^2 = 3.0 \times 10^{-19}\,\text{m}^2$$

Hence,

$$k_2 = 4 \times 3.0 \times 10^{-19}\,\text{m}^2 \times 6.022 \times 10^{23}\,\text{mol}^{-1} \times \left(\frac{1.381 \times 10^{-23}\,\text{J K}^{-1} \times 298\,\text{K}}{\pi \times 15.03 \times 1.6605 \times 10^{-27}\,\text{kg}}\right)^{1/2}$$

$$= 1.7 \times 10^8\,\text{m}^3\,\text{mol}^{-1}\,\text{s}^{-1} = \underline{1.7 \times 10^{11}\,\text{M}^{-1}\,\text{s}^{-1}}$$

This rate constant is for the rate law

$$v = k_2[CH_3]^2$$

Therefore, $\dfrac{d[CH_3]}{dt} = -2k_2[CH_3]^2$

and its solution is

$$\frac{1}{[CH_3]} - \frac{1}{[CH_3]_0} = 2k_2 t$$

For 90 per cent recombination, $[CH_3] = 0.10 \times [CH_3]_0$, which occurs when

$$2k_2 t = \frac{9}{[CH_3]_0}, \text{ or } t = \frac{9}{2k_2[CH_3]_0}$$

The concentration of CH_3 radicals in a mixture in which the mole fraction is $2 \times 0.10/(1 + 0.10) = 0.18$ and the total pressure is p is $0.20p$, expressed as a molar concentration. That is

$$[CH_3]_0 = \frac{0.20p}{RT}$$

Therefore,

$$t = \frac{9RT}{k_2 \times 0.40p} = \frac{9 \times 8.314\,\text{J K}^{-1}\,\text{mol}^{-1} \times 298\,\text{K}}{1.7 \times 10^8\,\text{m}^3\,\text{mol}^{-1}\,\text{s}^{-1} \times 0.36 \times 1.013 \times 10^5\,\text{Pa}}$$

$$= \underline{3.6\,\text{ns}}$$

28.4 Draw up the following table for an Arrhenius plot:

$\theta/°C$	−24.82	−20.73	−17.02	−13.00	−8.95
T/K	248.33	252.42	256.13	260.15	264.20
$10^3/(T/K)$	4.027	3.962	3.904	3.844	3.785
$\ln(k/s^{-1})$	−9.01	−8.37	−7.73	−7.07	−6.55

The points are plotted in Fig. 28.3. The intercept at $1/T=0$ is +34.8 and the

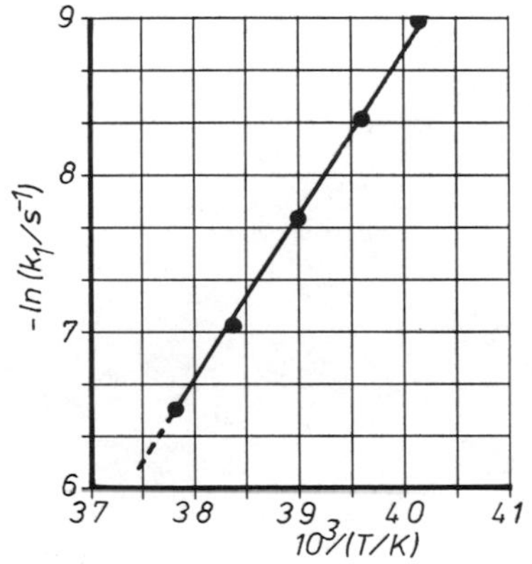

Fig 28.3

slope is -10.91×10^3. The former implies that $\ln(A/s^{-1})=34.8$, and hence that $A=1.3\times10^{15}\,s^{-1}$. The slope implies that $E_a/R=10.91\times10^3$ K, and hence that $\underline{E_a=90.7\text{ kJ mol}^{-1}}$.

In solution $\Delta H^\ddagger=E_a-RT$, so at −20 °C,

$$\Delta H^\ddagger=90.7\text{ kJ mol}^{-1}-8.314\text{ J K}^{-1}\times253\text{ K}=\underline{+88.6\text{ kJ mol}^{-1}}$$

For a first-order reaction we write

$$k_1=A\,e^{-E_a/RT}=\frac{kT}{h}\,e^{-\Delta G^\ddagger/RT}=\frac{kT}{h}\,e^{\Delta S^\ddagger/R}\,e^{-\Delta H^\ddagger/RT}$$

and hence identify $\Delta S^\ddagger$ by writing

$$k_1=\frac{kT}{h}\,e^{\Delta S^\ddagger/R}\,e^{-E_a/RT}\,e=A\,e^{-E_a/RT}$$

and hence obtaining

$$\Delta S^{\ddagger} = R\left\{\ln\left(\frac{hA}{kT}\right) - 1\right\}$$

$$= 8.314\,\mathrm{J\,K^{-1}\,mol^{-1}} \times \left\{\ln\left(\frac{6.626\times10^{-34}\,\mathrm{J\,s}\times1.3\times10^{15}\,\mathrm{s^{-1}}}{1.381\times10^{-23}\,\mathrm{J\,K^{-1}}\times253\,\mathrm{K}}\right) - 1\right\}$$

$$= \underline{+37.5\,\mathrm{J\,K^{-1}\,mol^{-1}}}$$

Therefore,

$$\Delta G^{\ddagger} = \Delta H^{\ddagger} - T\,\Delta S^{\ddagger} = 88.6\,\mathrm{kJ\,mol^{-1}} - 253\,\mathrm{K}\times37.5\,\mathrm{J\,K^{-1}\,mol^{-1}}$$

$$= \underline{+79.1\,\mathrm{kJ\,mol^{-1}}}$$

28.5 $\lg k = \lg k^{\circ} + 2Az_{\mathrm{A}}z_{\mathrm{B}}I^{1/2}$ with $A = 0.509\,\mathrm{M}^{-1/2}$.

This expression suggests that we should plot $\lg k$ against $I^{1/2}$ and determine z_{B} from the slope, since we know that $|z_{\mathrm{A}}| = 1$. We draw up the following table:

I/M	0.0025	0.0037	0.0045	0.0065	0.0085
$(I/\mathrm{M})^{1/2}$	0.050	0.061	0.0067	0.081	0.092
$\lg(k/\mathrm{M^{-1}\,s^{-1}})$	0.021	0.049	0.064	0.072	0.100

These points are plotted in Fig. 28.4. The slope of the limiting line is 2.4.

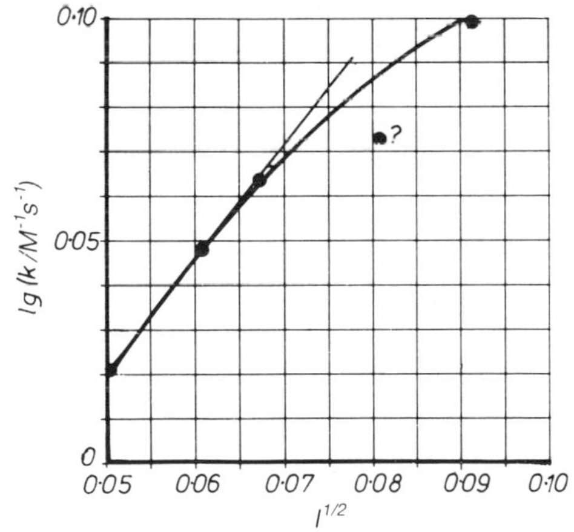

Fig 28.4

Since this slope is equal to $2Az_{\mathrm{A}}z_{\mathrm{B}} \times \mathrm{M}^{1/2} = 1.018z_{\mathrm{A}}z_{\mathrm{B}}$, we have $z_{\mathrm{A}}z_{\mathrm{B}} = 2.4$. But $|z_{\mathrm{A}}| = 1$, and so $|z_{\mathrm{B}}| = 2$. Furthermore, z_{A} and z_{B} have the same sign because $z_{\mathrm{A}}z_{\mathrm{B}} > 0$. (The data refer to I^- and $\mathrm{S_2O_8^{2-}}$.)

28.6 The work w needed to bring two ions from infinity to a separation $R^\ddagger$ in a medium of relative permittivity ε_r is

$$w = \frac{z'z''e^2}{4\pi\varepsilon_0\varepsilon_r R^\ddagger} \quad \text{[Coulomb potential} \times \text{charge]}$$

The electrical work is a contribution to the Gibbs function, so

$$\Delta\bar{G}^\ddagger = \Delta G^\ddagger + \frac{z'z''N_A e^2}{4\pi\varepsilon_0\varepsilon_r R^\ddagger}$$

Since $k_{\text{eff}} \propto e^{-\Delta G^\ddagger/RT}$, the effect of ionic charge is to change k_{eff} to $\bar{k}_{\text{eff}}$, where

$$\bar{k}_{\text{eff}} = k_{\text{eff}} \exp\left(\frac{-z'z''N_A e^2}{4\pi\varepsilon_0\varepsilon_r R^\ddagger RT}\right) = k_{\text{eff}} \exp\left(\frac{-z'z''e^2}{4\pi\varepsilon_0\varepsilon_r R^\ddagger kT}\right)$$

$$\ln \bar{k}_{\text{eff}} = \ln k_{\text{eff}} - \frac{z'z''e^2}{4\pi\varepsilon_0\varepsilon_r R^\ddagger kT}$$

If z' and z'' have the same sign, $\bar{k}_{\text{eff}} < k_{\text{eff}}$; if they have opposite signs, $\bar{k}_{\text{eff}} > k_{\text{eff}}$ because the formation of the complex is favored. Note that the higher the value of ε_r, the smaller the effect of ionic charge. We shall write the expression above as

$$\ln \bar{k}_{\text{eff}} = \ln k_{\text{eff}} - \frac{z'z''B}{\varepsilon_r}, \quad B = \frac{e^2}{4\pi\varepsilon_o R^\ddagger kT}$$

and plot $\ln \bar{k}_{\text{eff}}$ (or $\lg \bar{k}_{\text{eff}}$) against $1/\varepsilon_r$, expecting to get a straight line with slope proportional to $z'z''$. We draw up the following tables:

(a) Bromophenol blue; $z'z'' = (-1) \times (-2) = 2$

ε_r	60	65	70	75	79
$10^3/\varepsilon_r$	16.7	15.4	14.3	13.3	12.7
$\lg \bar{k}_{\text{eff}}$	−0.987	0.201	0.751	1.172	1.401

(b) Azodicarbonate; $z'z'' = (-2) \times (+1) = -2$

ε_r	27	35	45	55	65	79
$10^3/\varepsilon_r$	37.0	28.6	22.2	18.2	15.4	12.7
$\lg \bar{k}_{\text{eff}}$	12.95	12.22	11.58	11.14	10.73	10.34

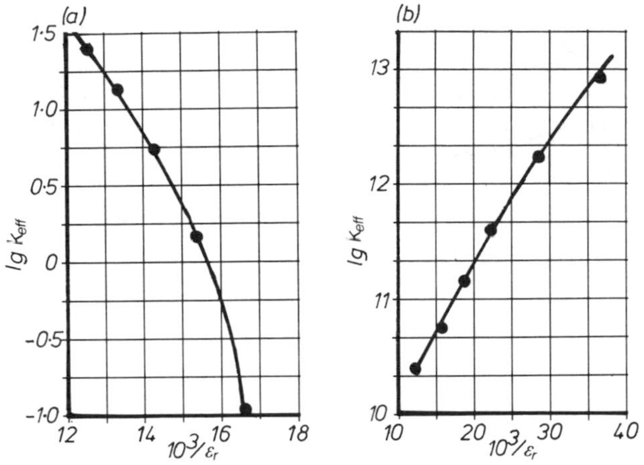

Fig 28.5

The points are plotted in Fig. 28.5. The lines are reasonably straight and have slopes with signs appropriate to the activated complex.

28.7 $\dfrac{\sigma^*}{\sigma} \approx \left\{\dfrac{e^2}{4\pi\varepsilon_0 d(I - E_{ea})}\right\}^2$ [Example 28.2]

Taking $\sigma = \pi d^2$ gives

$$\sigma^* \approx \pi\left\{\frac{e^2}{4\pi\varepsilon_0[I(\mathrm{M}) - E_{ea}(\mathrm{X}_2)]}\right\}^2 \approx \left\{\frac{6.5\ \mathrm{nm}^2}{(I - E_{ea})/\mathrm{eV}}\right\}^2$$

Thus, σ^* is predicted to increase as $I - E_{ea}$ decreases. The data let us construct the following table:

σ^*/nm^2	Cl_2	Br_2	I_2
Na	0.45	0.42	0.56
K	0.72	0.68	0.97
Rb	0.77	0.72	1.05
Cs	0.97	0.90	1.34

All values of σ^* in the table are smaller than the experimental ones, but they do show the correct trends down the columns. The variation with E_{ea} across the table is not so good, possibly because the electron affinities used here are poor estimates. Can you find better values to use?

28.8 $[\mathrm{J}]^* = k\int_0^t [\mathrm{J}]\,\mathrm{e}^{-kt}\,\mathrm{d}t + [\mathrm{J}]\,\mathrm{e}^{-kt}$ [10]

$$\frac{\partial[\mathrm{J}]^*}{\partial t} = k[\mathrm{J}]\,\mathrm{e}^{-kt} + \frac{\partial[\mathrm{J}]}{\partial t}\,\mathrm{e}^{-kt} - k[\mathrm{J}]\,\mathrm{e}^{-kt}$$

$$= \left(\frac{\partial[\mathrm{J}]}{\partial t}\right)\mathrm{e}^{-kt}$$

$$\frac{\partial^2[\mathrm{J}]^*}{\partial x^2} = k\int_0^t \left(\frac{\partial^2[\mathrm{J}]}{\partial x^2}\right)\mathrm{e}^{-kt}\,\mathrm{d}t + \left(\frac{\partial^2[\mathrm{J}]}{\partial x^2}\right)\mathrm{e}^{-kt}$$

Then, since

$$D\frac{\partial^2[\mathrm{J}]}{\partial x^2} = \frac{\partial[\mathrm{J}]}{\partial t} \quad [9,\ k=0]$$

we find that

$$D\frac{\partial^2[\mathrm{J}]^*}{\partial x^2} = k\int_0^t \left(\frac{\partial[\mathrm{J}]}{\partial t}\right)\mathrm{e}^{-kt}\,\mathrm{d}t + \left(\frac{\partial[\mathrm{J}]}{\partial t}\right)\mathrm{e}^{-kt}$$

$$= k\int_0^t \left(\frac{\partial[\mathrm{J}]^*}{\partial t}\right)\mathrm{d}t + \frac{\partial[\mathrm{J}]^*}{\partial t}$$

$$= k[\mathrm{J}]^* + \frac{\partial[\mathrm{J}]^*}{\partial t}$$

which rearranges to eqn 9. When $t=0$, $[\mathrm{J}]^* = [\mathrm{J}]$, and so the same initial conditions are satisfied. (The same boundary conditions are also satisfied.)

28.9 Use an integration routine or, failing that, Simpson's rule specified in Example 22.6. Write $z^2 = kx^2/4D$, $\tau = kt$, $j = (A/n_0)(\pi D/k)^{1/2}[\mathrm{J}]^*$, and evaluate

$$j = \int_0^\tau \left(\frac{1}{\tau}\right)^{1/2}\mathrm{e}^{-z^2/\tau}\,\mathrm{e}^{-\tau}\,\mathrm{d}\tau + \left(\frac{1}{\tau}\right)^{1/2}\mathrm{e}^{-z^2/\tau}\,\mathrm{e}^{-\tau}$$

28.10 $q^{\ominus\mathrm{T}}/N_\mathrm{A} = 2.561\times10^{-2}(T/\mathrm{K})^{5/2}(M/\mathrm{g\,mol^{-1}})^{3/2}$ [Box 20.2]

For $T\approx300$ K, $M\approx50\ \mathrm{g\,mol^{-1}}$, $q^{\ominus\mathrm{T}}/N_\mathrm{A}\approx \underline{1.4\times10^{7}}$

$$q^\mathrm{R}(\text{Non-linear}) = \frac{1.027}{\sigma}\times\frac{(T/\mathrm{K})^{3/2}}{(ABC/\mathrm{cm^{-3}})^{1/2}} \quad [\text{Box } 20.2]$$

For $T \approx 300$ K, $A \approx B \approx C = 2$ cm^{-1}, $\sigma \approx 2$, $q^{\rm R}(\text{NL}) \approx \underline{900}$

$$q^{\rm R}(\text{Linear}) = \frac{0.6950}{\sigma} \times \frac{(T/\text{K})}{(B/\text{cm}^{-1})} \quad [\text{Box 20.2}]$$

For $T \approx 300$ K, $B \approx 1$ cm^{-1}, $\sigma \approx 1$, $q^{\rm R}(\text{L}) \approx \underline{200}$,

$q^{\rm V} \approx \underline{1}$ and $q^{\rm E} \approx \underline{1}$ [Box 20.2]

$$k_2 = \frac{\kappa kT}{h} \bar{K} \quad [15]$$

$$= \frac{\kappa kT}{h} \times \frac{RT}{p} \times \frac{N_{\rm A}\bar{q}_{\rm C}^{\ominus}}{q_{\rm A}^{\ominus}q_{\rm B}^{\ominus}} \text{e}^{-\Delta E_0/RT} \quad [14\text{c}] \approx A\,\text{e}^{-E_{\rm a}/RT}$$

We then use

$q_{\rm A}^{\ominus}/N_{\rm A} = q_{\rm A}^{\ominus T}/N_{\rm A} \approx 1.4 \times 10^7$ [above]

$q_{\rm B}^{\ominus}/N_{\rm A} = q_{\rm B}^{\ominus T}/N_{\rm B} \approx 1.4 \times 10^7$ [above]

$\bar{q}_{\rm C}^{\ominus}/N_{\rm A} = q_{\rm C}^{\ominus T}q^{\rm R}(\text{L})/N_{\rm A} \approx 2^{3/2} \times 1.4 \times 10^7 \times 200 = 7.9 \times 10^9$

[The factor of $2^{3/2}$ comes from $m_{\rm C} = m_{\rm A} + m_{\rm B} \approx 2m_{\rm A}$ and $q^{\rm T} \propto m^{3/2}$]

$$\frac{RT}{p^{\ominus}} \approx \frac{8.314\ \text{J K}^{-1}\,\text{mol}^{-1} \times 300\ \text{K}}{10^5\ \text{Pa}} = 2.5 \times 10^{-2}\ \text{m}^3\,\text{mol}^{-1}$$

$$\frac{\kappa kT}{h} \approx \frac{kT}{h} = \frac{1.381 \times 10^{-23}\ \text{J K}^{-1} \times 300\ \text{K}}{6.626 \times 10^{-34}\ \text{J s}} = 6.25 \times 10^{12}\ \text{s}^{-1}$$

Therefore,

$$A \approx \frac{6.25 \times 10^{12}\ \text{s}^{-1} \times 2.5 \times 10^{-2}\ \text{m}^3\,\text{mol}^{-1} \times 7.9 \times 10^9}{(1.4 \times 10^7)^2}$$

$\approx 6.3 \times 10^6\ \text{m}^3\,\text{mol}^{-1}\,\text{s}^{-1}$, or $\underline{6.3 \times 10^9\ \text{M}^{-1}\,\text{s}^{-1}}$

If all three species are non-linear,

$q_{\rm A}^{\ominus}/N_{\rm A} \approx 1.4 \times 10^7 \times 900 = 1.3 \times 10^{10} \approx q_{\rm B}^{\ominus}/N_{\rm A}$

$\bar{q}_{\rm C}^{\ominus}/N_{\rm A} \approx 2^{3/2} \times 1.4 \times 10^7 \times 900 = 3.6 \times 10^{10}$

$$A \approx \frac{6.25 \times 10^{12}\ \text{s}^{-1} \times 2.5 \times 10^{-2}\ \text{m}^3\,\text{mol}^{-1} \times 3.6 \times 10^{10}}{(1.3 \times 10^{10})^2}$$

$\approx 33\ \text{m}^3\,\text{mol}^{-1}\,\text{s}^{-1}$, or $3.3 \times 10^4\ \text{M}^{-1}\,\text{s}^{-1}$

Therefore,

$$P=\frac{A(\text{NL})}{A(\text{L})}=\frac{3.3\times10^{4}}{6.3\times10^{9}}=\underline{5.2\times10^{-6}}$$

28.11 The structure of the activated complex is shown in Fig. 28.6a. The three moments of inertia are:

$$I_{\text{A}}=2m_{\text{D}}\times(44\text{ pm})^2=1.3\times10^{-47}\text{ kg m}^2$$

$$I_{\text{B}}=m_{\text{H}}\times(68\text{ pm})^2+2m_{\text{D}}\times(17\text{ pm})^2=9.6\times10^{-48}\text{ kg m}^2$$

$$I_{\text{C}}=m_{\text{H}}\times(68\text{ pm})^2+2m_{\text{D}}\times(48\text{ pm})^2=2.3\times10^{-47}\text{ kg m}^2$$

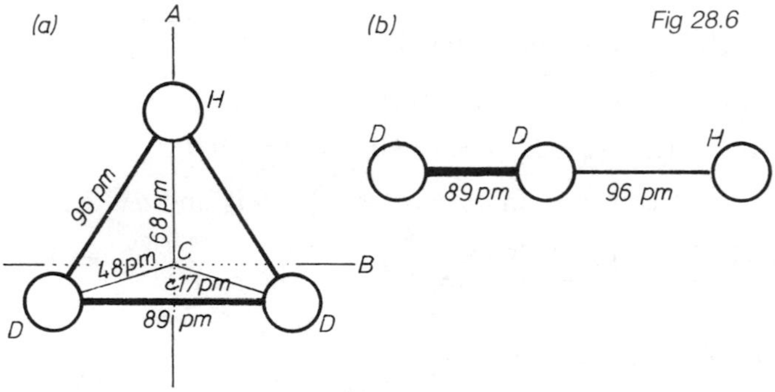

Fig 28.6

The rotational constants are therefore

$$A=\frac{\hbar}{4\pi cI_{\text{A}}}=\frac{1.054\times10^{-34}\text{ J s}}{4\pi\times2.998\times10^{10}\text{ cm s}^{-1}\times I_{\text{A}}}$$

$$=\frac{2.8\times10^{-46}\text{ cm}^{-1}}{(I_{\text{A}}/\text{kg m}^2)}=22\text{ cm}^{-1}$$

$$B=\frac{2.8\times10^{-46}\text{ cm}^{-1}}{9.6\times10^{-48}}=29\text{ cm}^{-1}$$

$$C=\frac{2.8\times10^{-46}\text{ cm}^{-1}}{2.3\times10^{-47}}=12\text{ cm}^{-1}$$

Since $I(\text{D}_2)=2m_{\text{D}}\times(37\text{ pm})^2=21\times10^{-48}\text{ kg m}^2$, we also have $B(\text{D}_2)=31\text{ cm}^{-1}$. Then from Box 20.2,

$$q^{\ddagger R} = 1.027 \times \tfrac{1}{2} \times \frac{400^{3/2}}{(22 \times 29 \times 12)^{1/2}} = 47$$

$$q^{R}(D_2) = 0.695 \times \tfrac{1}{2} \times \frac{400}{31} = 4.5$$

The vibrational partition functions are

$$q^{V} = \frac{1}{1 - e^{-hc\tilde{\nu}/kT}} \text{ for each mode}$$

$$\approx \frac{1}{1 - e^{-\tilde{\nu}/280\,\text{cm}^{-1}}} \approx 1.03 \quad [\text{for } \tilde{\nu} = 1000\,\text{cm}^{-1}]$$

The complex has $2N - 6 = 3$ modes, but one is the reaction coordinate and is discarded. Hence, $q^{\ddagger V} \approx (1.03)^2 = 1.06$. For D_2 itself, $q^{V} \approx 1$. The translational partition functions are

H: $q^{\ominus T}/N_A = 2.561 \times 10^{-2} \times 400^{5/2} \times 1.01^{3/2} = 8.3 \times 10^4$

D: $q^{\ominus T}/N_A = 2.3 \times 10^5$

Complex: $q^{\ominus T}/N_A = 4.3 \times 10^5$

The electronic partition functions are

$q^{E}(H) = 2$ [doublet ground state], $q^{E}(D_2) = 1$

$q^{\ddagger E}(\text{Complex}) = 2$ [odd number of electrons, presumably a doublet]

Therefore, bringing all these fragments together with

$$\frac{kT}{h} = \frac{1.381 \times 10^{-23}\,\text{J K}^{-1} \times 400\,\text{K}}{6.626 \times 10^{-34}\,\text{J s}} = 8.34 \times 10^{12}\,\text{s}^{-1}$$

$$\frac{RT}{p^{\ominus}} = 3.28 \times 10^{-2}\,\text{m}^3\,\text{mol}^{-1}$$

gives

$$A = \frac{8.34 \times 10^{12}\,\text{s}^{-1} \times 3.28 \times 10^{-2}\,\text{m}^3\,\text{mol}^{-1} \times 4.3 \times 10^5 \times 47 \times 1.06 \times 2}{8.3 \times 10^4 \times 2.3 \times 10^5 \times 4.5 \times 1.03 \times 2}$$

$$= 6.6 \times 10^{10}\,\text{M}^{-1}\,\text{s}^{-1}$$

$$k \approx A\,e^{-E_a/RT} = 6.6 \times 10^{10}\,\text{M}^{-1}\,\text{s}^{-1} \times e^{-10.5\overline{2}}$$

$$\approx \underline{1.8 \times 10^6\,\text{M}^{-1}\,\text{s}^{-1}}$$

(The experimental value is about $4\times10^5\,\mathrm{M}^{-1}\,\mathrm{s}^{-1}$.)

28.12 The structure of the activated complex is shown in Fig. 28.6b. The (one) moment of inertia is [Table 16.1]

$$I=\left(\frac{m_\mathrm{H}m_\mathrm{D}}{m}\right)(96\ \mathrm{pm}+89\ \mathrm{pm})^2+\left(\frac{m_\mathrm{D}}{m}\right)\{m_\mathrm{H}\times(96\ \mathrm{pm})^2+m_\mathrm{D}\times(89\ \mathrm{pm})^2\}$$

$$=3.9\times10^{-47}\ \mathrm{kg\,m^2}$$

$$B=\frac{2.8\times10^{-46}\ \mathrm{cm}^{-1}}{3.9\times10^{-47}}\quad[\text{Problem 28.11}]=7.1\ \mathrm{cm}^{-1}$$

$$q^\mathrm{R}=0.6952\times\frac{400}{7.1}\quad[\sigma=1]=39$$

Since $3N-5=4$, there are four vibrational modes of the complex, and counting one as a reaction coordinate gives $q^\mathrm{V}\approx(1.03)^3=1.09$. All other contributions are as in Problem 28.11, which gave $6.6\times10^{10}\,\mathrm{M}^{-1}\,\mathrm{s}^{-1}$. Therefore

$$A\approx6.6\times10^{10}\,\mathrm{M}^{-1}\,\mathrm{s}^{-1}\times\frac{39}{47}\times\frac{1.09}{1.06}=5.6\times10^{10}\,\mathrm{M}^{-1}\,\mathrm{s}^{-1}$$

and hence k should be modified by the same factor (0.85), to give $k=\underline{1.5\times10^6\,\mathrm{M}^{-1}\,\mathrm{s}^{-1}}$.

28.13 Consider (for example) the following models (in order of complexity). (1) Collinear attack, varying R(HD) and R(DD) independently. (2) Broadside attack, varying $R(\mathrm{H{-}D_2})$ and R(DD) independently. (3) Attack at same angle θ to the D—D axis, once again varying bond lengths independently. At this level of simplicity, you have to modify only the rotational partition functions in order to go between the various models.

28.14 $q^\ddagger=q_z^{\ddagger\mathrm{V}}q_x^{\ddagger\mathrm{V}}$ [y is the direction of diffusion]

$q=q_x^\mathrm{V}q_y^\mathrm{V}q_z^\mathrm{V}$ [for an atom at the bottom of a well]

For classical vibration, $q^\mathrm{V}\approx kT/h\nu$. The rate of diffusion is essentially the rate of change of concentration at a particular region of the surface, $-\mathrm{d}[x]/\mathrm{d}t$. This is also equal to $[x]^\ddagger\nu$, and as $K^\ddagger=[x]^\ddagger/[x]$ we arrive at

$$-\frac{\mathrm{d}[x]}{\mathrm{d}t}=\nu[x]K^\ddagger=k_1[x]$$

Therefore,

$$k_1 = \nu K^{\ddagger} = \nu\left(\frac{kT}{h\nu}\right)\left(\frac{q^{\ddagger}}{q}\right) e^{-\beta\Delta E}$$

where $q^{\ddagger}$ and q are the (vibrational) partition functions at the top and foot of the well respectively. Therefore,

$$k_1 = \frac{kT}{h}\left\{\frac{(kT/h\nu^{\ddagger})^2}{(kT/h\nu)^3}\right\} e^{-\beta\Delta E} = \underline{\frac{\nu^3}{\nu^{\ddagger 3}} e^{-\beta\Delta E}}$$

(a) $\nu^{\ddagger} = \nu;\ k_1 = \nu\, e^{-\beta\Delta E}$

$k_1 \approx 10^{11}\ \text{Hz}\ e^{-60\times 10^3/8.314\times 500} = 5.4\times 10^4\ \text{s}^{-1}$

But $D = \lambda^2/2\tau \approx \frac{1}{2}d^2k_1$ [Chapter 25, eqn 28]

$= \frac{1}{2}\times(316\ \text{pm})^2\times 5.4\times 10^4\ \text{s}^{-1} = \underline{2.7\times 10^{-15}\ \text{m}^2\ \text{s}^{-1}}$

(b) $\nu^{\ddagger} = \frac{1}{2}\nu;\ k_1 = 4\nu\, e^{-\beta\Delta E} = 2.2\times 10^5\ \text{s}^{-1}$

$D = 4\times 2.7\times 10^{-15}\ \text{m}^2\ \text{s}^{-1} = \underline{1.1\times 10^{-14}\ \text{m}^2\ \text{s}^{-1}}$

28.15 $k_1 = \dfrac{kT}{h}\times\dfrac{q^{\ddagger}}{q} e^{-\beta\Delta E}$ [Problem 28.14]

$$q^{\ddagger} = q_z^{\ddagger V} q_y^{\ddagger V} q^{R} \approx \left(\frac{kT}{h\nu}\right)^2 q^{R}$$

$$q^{R} \approx \frac{1.027}{\sigma}\times\frac{(T/\text{K})^{3/2}}{(B/\text{cm}^{-1})^{3/2}}\quad [\text{Box 20.2, A} = \text{B} = \text{C}]\quad \approx 80$$

$$q = q_z^{V} q_y^{V} q_x^{V} \approx \left(\frac{kT}{h\nu}\right)^3$$

Therefore,

$$k_1 \approx 80\times\frac{\nu^3}{\nu^{\ddagger 2}} e^{-\beta\Delta E} \approx 80\times 5.4\times 10^4\ \text{s}^{-1}\quad [\text{Problem 28.14}]$$

$$= 4\times 10^6\ \text{s}^{-1}$$

Consequently,

$D \approx 80\times 2.7\times 10^{-15}\ \text{m}^2\ \text{s}^{-1} = \underline{2\times 10^{-12}\ \text{m}^2\ \text{s}^{-1}}$ if $\nu^{\ddagger} = \nu$

and $\underline{8\times 10^{-12}\ \text{m}^2\ \text{s}^{-1}}$ if $\nu^{\ddagger} = \frac{1}{2}\nu$.

28.16 The change in intensity of the beam, dI, is proportional to the number of scatterers per unit volume, $\mathcal{N}_s$, the intensity of the beam, I, and the path length dl. The constant of proportionality is defined as the collision cross section, σ. Therefore,

$$dI = -\sigma \mathcal{N}_s I \, dl, \text{ or } d \ln I = -\sigma \mathcal{N}_s \, dl$$

If the incident intensity (at $l=0$) is I_0 and the emergent intensity is I, we can write

$$\ln \frac{I}{I_0} = -\sigma \mathcal{N}_s l, \text{ or } \underline{I = I_0 \, e^{-\sigma \mathcal{N}_s l}}$$

28.17 It follows that, since $\mathcal{N}_s$ and l are the same for the two experiments,

$$\frac{\sigma(CH_2F_2)}{\sigma(Ar)} = \frac{\ln 0.6}{\ln 0.9} \quad \text{[Problem 28.16]} \quad = \underline{5}$$

CH_2F_2 is a polar molecule; Ar is not. CsCl is a polar ion pair and is scattered more strongly by the polar CH_2F_2.

29. Processes at solid surfaces

Exercises

29.1 $$Z_W/(\text{cm}^{-2}\,\text{s}^{-1}) = \frac{3.51\times10^{22}\times(p/\text{Torr})}{\{(T/\text{K})\times(M/\text{g mol}^{-1})\}^{1/2}} \quad [1]$$

$$= \frac{2.03\times10^{21}\times(p/\text{Torr})}{(M/\text{g mol}^{-1})^{1/2}} \quad [T=298\ \text{K}]$$

Hence, we can draw up the following table:

	H_2	C_3H_8	
$M/(\text{g mol}^{-1})$	2.02	44.09	
$Z_W/(\text{cm}^{-2}\,\text{s}^{-1})$			
(i) 100 Pa	1.1×10^{21}	2.3×10^{20}	[100 Pa = 0.750 Torr]
(ii) 10^{-7} Torr	1.4×10^{14}	3.1×10^{13}	

29.2 $$p/\text{Torr} = \frac{\{Z_W/(\text{cm}^{-2}\,\text{s}^{-1})\}\times\{(T/\text{K})\times(M/\text{g mol}^{-1})\}^{1/2}}{3.51\times10^{22}}$$

$$= \frac{\{Z_W/(\text{cm}^{-2}\,\text{s}^{-1})\}\times(425\times39.95)^{1/2}}{3.51\times10^{22}}$$

$$= 3.71\times10^{-21}\times Z_W/(\text{cm}^{-2}\,\text{s}^{-1})$$

The collision rate required is

$$Z_W = \frac{4.5\times10^{20}\,\text{s}^{-1}}{\pi\times(0.075\ \text{cm})^2} = 2.5\bar{5}\times10^{22}\ \text{cm}^{-2}\,\text{s}^{-1}$$

Hence $p = 3.71\times10^{-21}\times2.5\bar{5}\times10^{22}\ \text{Torr} = \underline{94\ \text{Torr}}$

29.3 $$Z_W = \frac{3.51\times10^{22}\times\left(\dfrac{35\times760}{1.0133\times10^5}\right)}{(80\times4.00)^{1/2}}\ \text{cm}^{-2}\,\text{s}^{-1} \quad [1,\ p\ \text{converted to Torr}]$$

$$= 5.2\times10^{20}\ \text{cm}^{-2}\,\text{s}^{-1} = 5.2\times10^{24}\ \text{m}^{-2}\,\text{s}^{-1}$$

The area occupied by a Cu atom is $\frac{1}{2}\times(3.61\times10^{-10}\,\text{m})^2=6.52\times10^{-20}\,\text{m}^2$ [in an fcc unit cell, there is the equivalent of two Cu atoms per face]. Therefore,

$$\text{rate per Cu atom}=5.2\times10^{24}\,\text{m}^{-2}\,\text{s}^{-1}\times6.52\times10^{-20}\,\text{m}^2=\underline{3.4\times10^5\,\text{s}^{-1}}$$

29.4 The entropy of adsorption is typical of chemisorption [Table 29.2]. The residence lifetime is

$$t_{1/2}=\tau_0\,\mathrm{e}^{E_a/RT}\quad[10]$$
$$\approx1\times10^{-14}\,\text{s}\times\mathrm{e}^{120\times10^3/8.314\times400}\quad[E_a\approx-\Delta H_{ad}]$$
$$\approx\underline{50\,\text{s}}$$

29.5 $t_{1/2}=\tau_0\,\mathrm{e}^{E_a/RT}$ [10]

$$E_a=\frac{R\ln(t'_{1/2}/t_{1/2})}{\left(\frac{1}{T'}-\frac{1}{T}\right)}=\frac{8.314\,\text{J K}^{-1}\,\text{mol}^{-1}\times\ln\left(\frac{0.36}{3.49}\right)}{\frac{1}{2548\,\text{K}}-\frac{1}{2362\,\text{K}}}$$
$$=\underline{610\,\text{kJ mol}^{-1}}$$

$$\tau_0=t_{1/2}\,\mathrm{e}^{-E_a/RT}=3.49\,\text{s}\times\mathrm{e}^{-610\times10^3/8.314\times2362}=\underline{0.11\,\text{ps}}$$

29.6 $E_a=\dfrac{R\ln(t'_{1/2}/t_{1/2})}{\left(\frac{1}{T'}-\frac{1}{T}\right)}$ [Exercise 29.5]

with $t'_{1/2}/t_{1/2}\approx1.35$

$$E_a=\frac{8.314\,\text{J K}^{-1}\,\text{mol}^{-1}\times\ln1.35}{\left(\frac{1}{600\,\text{K}}-\frac{1}{1000\,\text{K}}\right)}=\underline{3.7\,\text{kJ mol}^{-1}}$$

29.7 $\theta=\dfrac{Kp}{1+Kp}$ [2], which implies that $p=\left(\dfrac{\theta}{1-\theta}\right)\dfrac{1}{K}$

(a) $p=\dfrac{0.15}{0.85}\times\dfrac{1}{0.85\,\text{kPa}^{-1}}=\underline{0.21\,\text{kPa}}$

(b) $p=\dfrac{0.95}{0.05}\times\dfrac{1}{0.85\,\text{kPa}^{-1}}=\underline{22\,\text{kPa}}$

29.8 $\dfrac{m_1}{m_2}=\dfrac{\theta_1}{\theta_2}=\dfrac{p_1}{p_2}\times\dfrac{1+Kp_2}{1+Kp_1}$

which solves to

$$K=\frac{(m_1p_2/m_2p_1)-1}{p_2-(m_1p_2/m_2)}=\frac{\left(\dfrac{m_1}{m_2}\right)\left(\dfrac{p_2}{p_1}\right)-1}{1-\left(\dfrac{m_1}{m_2}\right)}\times\frac{1}{p_2}$$

$$=\frac{\dfrac{0.44}{0.19}\times\dfrac{3.0}{26.0}-1}{1-\dfrac{0.44}{0.19}}\times\frac{1}{3.0\,\text{kPa}}=0.19\,\text{kPa}^{-1}$$

Therefore,

$$\theta_1=\frac{0.19\,\text{kPa}\times 26.0\,\text{kPa}}{1+0.19\,\text{kPa}^{-1}\times 26.0\,\text{kPa}}=\underline{0.83}$$

$$\theta_2=\frac{0.19\times 3.0}{1+0.19\times 3.0}=0.36$$

29.9 $t_{1/2}\approx\tau_0\,e^{E_a/RT}$ [10] $=10^{-13}\,\text{s}\times e^{E_a/(2.48\,\text{kJ mol}^{-1})}$ [at 298 K]

(a) $E_a=15\,\text{kJ mol}^{-1}$, $t_{1/2}=10^{-13}\,\text{s}\times e^{6.05}=\underline{4\times10^{-11}\,\text{s}}$

(b) $E_a=150\,\text{kJ mol}^{-1}$, $t_{1/2}=10^{-13}\,\text{s}\times e^{60.5}=\underline{2\times10^{13}\,\text{s}}$

The latter corresponds to about 600 000 y. At 1000 K, $t_{1/2}=10^{-13}\,\text{s}\times e^{E_a/8.314\,\text{kJ mol}^{-1}}$

(a) $t_{1/2}=\underline{6\times10^{-13}\,\text{s}}$, (b) $t_{1/2}=\underline{7\times10^{-6}\,\text{s}}$

29.10 $\theta=\dfrac{Kp}{1+Kp}$ [2], which implies that $K=\dfrac{\theta}{1-\theta}\times\dfrac{1}{p}$

But $\ln\dfrac{K'}{K}=\dfrac{\Delta H}{R}\left(\dfrac{1}{T}-\dfrac{1}{T'}\right)$ [van't Hoff equation]

Since θ at the new temperature is the same, $K \propto \frac{1}{p}$ and

$$\ln\frac{p}{p'}=\frac{\Delta H}{R}\left(\frac{1}{T}-\frac{1}{T'}\right)$$

$$=\frac{-10.2\ \text{kJ mol}^{-1}}{8.314\ \text{J K}^{-1}\ \text{mol}^{-1}}\times\left(\frac{1}{298\ \text{K}}-\frac{1}{313\ \text{K}}\right)$$

$$=-0.197$$

which implies that $p'=12\ \text{kPa}\times e^{0.197}=\underline{14\ \text{kPa}}$

29.11 (a) On gold, $\theta \approx 1$, and $v=k\theta \approx$ constant, a zeroth-order reaction. (b) On platinum, $\theta \approx Kp$ (as $Kp \ll 1$), so $v=kKp$, and the reaction is first-order.

29.12 (a) For adsorption without dissociation,

$$\theta=\frac{Kp}{1+Kp}, \text{ which implies that } \frac{1}{\theta}=1-\frac{1}{Kp}$$

and a plot of θ against $1/p$ should give a straight line.

(b) For adsorption with partial dissociation,

$$\theta=\frac{(Kp)^{1/2}}{1+(Kp)^{1/2}}\quad [3], \text{ which implies that } \frac{1}{\theta}=1+\frac{1}{(Kp)^{1/2}}$$

and a plot of θ against $1/p^{1/2}$ should give a straight line.

(c) For adsorption with complete dissociation,

$$\theta=\frac{(Kp)^{1/3}}{1+(Kp)^{1/3}}\quad \text{[by the same argument that led to eqn 3]}$$

which implies that

$$\frac{1}{\theta}=1+\frac{1}{(Kp)^{1/3}}$$

and so a plot of $1/\theta$ against $1/p^{1/3}$ should give a straight line. In each case we could rearrange the expressions into

$$\frac{p^n}{\theta}=p^n+\frac{1}{K^n}\quad [n=1, \tfrac{1}{2}, \tfrac{1}{3}]$$

$$\text{or } \frac{p^n}{V} = \frac{p^n}{V^\circ} + \frac{1}{V^\circ K^n}$$

and plot p^n/V against p^n, to expect a straight line.

29.13 Rate of adsorption of $A = k_{aA} p_A N(1 - \theta_A - \theta_B)$

Rate of desorption of $A = k_{dA} N \theta_A$

At equilibrium, the rates are equal, and so

$$k_{aA} p_A N(1 - \theta_A - \theta_B) = k_{dA} N \theta_A$$

Similarly for B:

$$k_{aB} p_B N(1 - \theta_A - \theta_B) = k_{dB} N \theta_B$$

Solve this pair of simultaneous equations, writing

$$K_A = \frac{k_{aA}}{k_{dA}}, \quad K_B = \frac{k_{aB}}{k_{dB}}$$

which gives

$$\theta_A = \frac{K_A p_A}{1 + K_A p_A + K_B p_B}, \quad \theta_B = \frac{K_B p_B}{1 + K_A p_A + K_B p_B}$$

is required.

29.14 $\theta = \dfrac{Kp}{1 + Kp}$ and $\theta' = \dfrac{K'p'}{1 + K'p'}$

but $\theta = \theta'$, so

$$\frac{Kp}{1 + Kp} = \frac{K'p'}{1 + K'p'}$$

which requires $Kp = K'p'$. We also know that

$$\Delta H^\ominus_{ad} = RT^2 \left(\frac{\partial \ln K}{\partial T}\right)_\theta \quad [4]$$

and can therefore write

$$\Delta H^\ominus_{ad} \approx RT^2 \left(\frac{\ln K' - \ln K}{T' - T}\right) = \frac{RT^2 \ln(K'/K)}{T' - T}$$

$$\approx \frac{RT^2 \ln(p/p')}{T' - T} \approx \frac{8.314\ \text{J K}^{-1}\ \text{mol}^{-1} \times (220\ \text{K})^2 \times \ln\left(\dfrac{4.8}{32}\right)}{60\ \text{K}}$$

$$= \underline{-13\ \text{kJ mol}^{-1}}$$

29.15 The desorption time for a given volume is proportional to the half-life of the adsorbed species, and as

$$t_{1/2}=\tau_0\,e^{E_a/RT} \quad [10]$$

we can write

$$E_a=\frac{R\ln(t_{1/2}/t'_{1/2})}{\left(\frac{1}{T}-\frac{1}{T'}\right)}=\frac{R\ln(t/t')}{\frac{1}{T}-\frac{1}{T'}}$$

where t and t' are the two desorption times. We evaluate E_a from the data for the two ranges of temperature:

$$E_a=\frac{8.314\ \mathrm{J\ K^{-1}\ mol^{-1}}}{\left(\frac{1}{1856\ \mathrm{K}}-\frac{1}{1978\ \mathrm{K}}\right)}\times\ln\frac{27}{2}=650\ \mathrm{kJ\ mol^{-1}}$$

$$E_a=\frac{8.314\ \mathrm{J\ K^{-1}\ mol^{-1}}}{\left(\frac{1}{1978\ \mathrm{K}}-\frac{1}{2070\ \mathrm{K}}\right)}\times\ln\frac{2}{0.3}=700\ \mathrm{kJ\ mol^{-1}}$$

To one significant figure, these values correspond to <u>700 kJ mol^{-1}</u>

We write

$$t=t_0\,e^{700\times10^3/8.314\times1856}=t_0\times5.03\times10^{19}$$

Therefore, since $t=27$ min, $t_0=5.4\times10^{-19}$ min. Consequently,

(a) At 298 K,

$$t=5.4\times10^{-19}\ \mathrm{min}\times e^{700\times10^3/8.314\times298}=\underline{2\times10^{104}\ \mathrm{min}}$$

which is just about for ever.

(b) At 3000 K,

$$t=5.4\times10^{-19}\ \mathrm{min}\times e^{700\times10^3/8.314\times298}=8\times10^{-7}\ \mathrm{min},$$

which corresponds to <u>50 μs</u>.

29.16 The rate of the reaction appears to be independent of the pressure of ammonia, so the reaction is <u>zeroth order</u>. Check this by writing

$$\frac{dp(NH_3)}{dt}=-k,\ \text{so}\ p(NH_3)=p_0(NH_3)-kt$$

and verifying that $\Delta p/t$ is a constant, where $\Delta p = p_0 - p$.

(i) $\Delta p/t = \dfrac{8\ \text{kPa}}{500\ \text{s}} = 16\ \text{Pa s}^{-1}$

(ii) $\Delta p/t = \dfrac{15\ \text{kPa}}{1000\ \text{s}} = 15\ \text{Pa s}^{-1}$

The two values are essentially the same, and $k = \underline{16\ \text{Pa s}^{-1}}$. A zeroth-order reaction occurs when the gas pressure is so high that the same amount of adsorbed species is always present whatever the pressure (that is, θ is constant even though p varies).

Problems

29.1 Refer to Fig. 29.1. The (100) and (110) faces each expose two atoms,

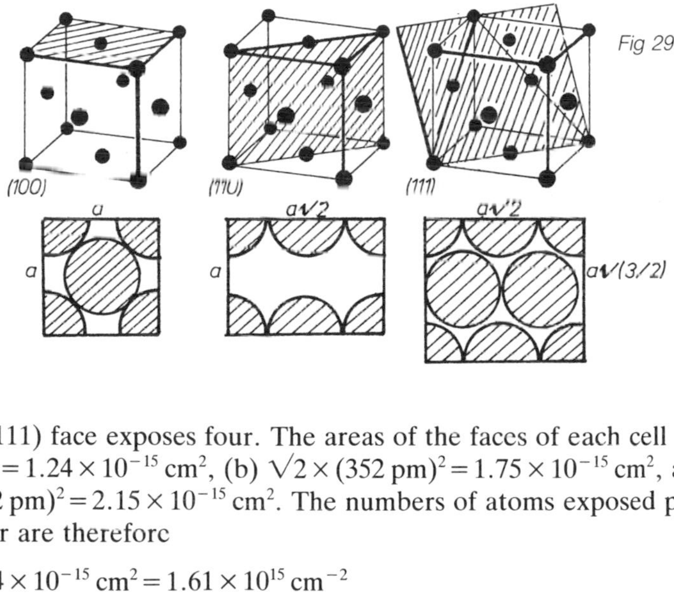

Fig 29.1

and the (111) face exposes four. The areas of the faces of each cell are (a) $(352\ \text{pm})^2 = 1.24 \times 10^{-15}\ \text{cm}^2$, (b) $\sqrt{2} \times (352\ \text{pm})^2 = 1.75 \times 10^{-15}\ \text{cm}^2$, and (c) $\sqrt{3} \times (352\ \text{pm})^2 = 2.15 \times 10^{-15}\ \text{cm}^2$. The numbers of atoms exposed per square centimeter are therefore

(a) $2/1.24 \times 10^{-15}\ \text{cm}^2 = 1.61 \times 10^{15}\ \text{cm}^{-2}$

(b) $2/1.75 \times 10^{-15}\ \text{cm}^2 = 1.14 \times 10^{15}\ \text{cm}^{-2}$

(c) $4/2.15 \times 10^{-15}\ \text{cm}^2 = 1.86 \times 10^{15}\ \text{cm}^{-2}$

For the collision frequencies calculated in Exercise 29.1, the frequency of collision per atom is calculated by dividing the values given there by the number densities just calculated. We can therefore draw up the following table:

	Hydrogen		Propane	
$Z/(\text{atom}^{-1}\,\text{s}^{-1})$	100 Pa	10^{-7} Torr	100 Pa	10^{-7} Torr
(100)	6.8×10^5	8.7×10^{-2}	1.4×10^5	1.9×10^{-2}
(110)	9.6×10^5	1.2×10^{-1}	2.0×10^5	2.7×10^{-2}
(111)	5.9×10^5	7.5×10^{-2}	1.2×10^5	1.7×10^{-2}

29.2 Refer to Fig. 29.2. The (100) face exposes one atom per unit cell, and

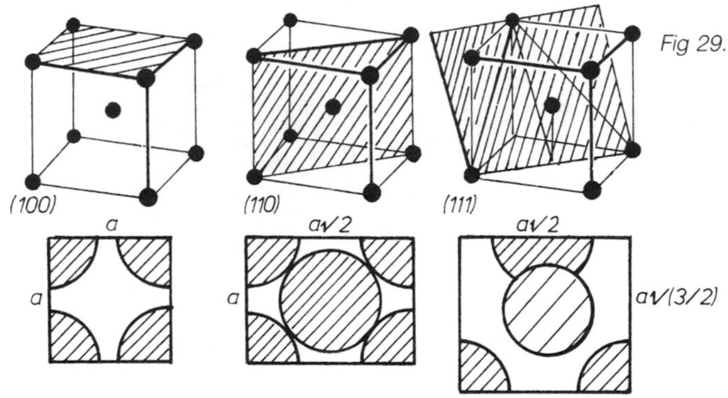

Fig 29.2

the (110) and (111) faces expose about two. The areas of the three types of face are (a) $(316\,\text{pm})^2=9.99\times10^{-16}\,\text{cm}^2$, (b) $\sqrt{2}\times(316\,\text{pm})^2=1.41\times10^{-15}\,\text{cm}^2$, and (c) $\sqrt{3}\times(316\,\text{pm})^2=1.73\times10^{-15}\,\text{cm}^2$. The number densities of exposed atoms are therefore

(a) $1/9.99\times10^{-16}\,\text{cm}^2=1.00\times10^{15}\,\text{cm}^{-2}$

(b) $2/1.41\times10^{-15}\,\text{cm}^2=1.41\times10^{15}\,\text{cm}^{-2}$

(c) $2/1.73\times10^{-15}\,\text{cm}^2=1.16\times10^{15}\,\text{cm}^{-2}$

and the average number exposed is $\frac{1}{2}\,(1.00+1.41)\times10^{15}\,\text{cm}^{-2}=1.20\times10^{15}\,\text{cm}^{-2}$. By the same procedure as in Problem 29.1, we draw up the following table:

	Hydrogen		Propane	
$Z/(\text{atom}^{-1}\,\text{s}^{-1})$	100 Pa	10^{-7} Torr	100 Pa	10^{-7} Torr
(100)	1.0×10^{6}	1.4×10^{-1}	2.3×10^{5}	3.1×10^{-2}
(110)	7.8×10^{5}	1.0×10^{-1}	1.6×10^{5}	2.2×10^{-2}
(111)	9.5×10^{5}	1.2×10^{-1}	2.0×10^{5}	2.7×10^{-2}

29.3 We draw up the following table:

p/Torr	0.19	0.97	1.90	4.05	7.50	11.95
$(p/V_a)/(\text{Torr cm}^{-3})$	4.52	5.95	8.60	12.6	18.3	25.4

p/V_A is plotted against p in Fig. 29.3. The low-pressure points fall on a

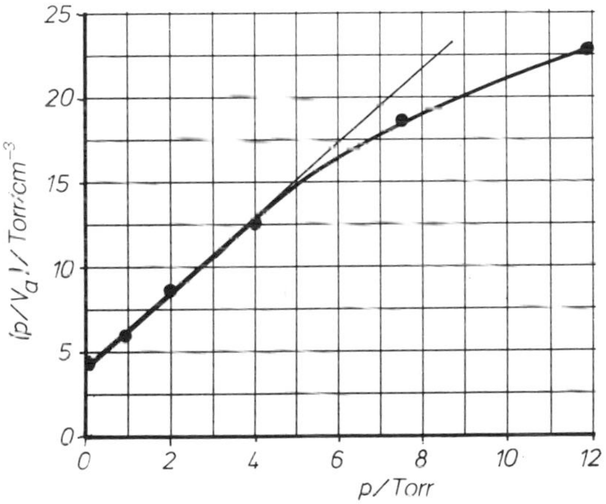

Fig 29.3

straight line with intercept 4.0 and slope 2.1. It follows that $1/V_a^\circ=$ $2.1\ \text{Torr cm}^{-3}/\text{Torr}=2.1\ \text{cm}^{-3}$, or $V_a^\circ=\underline{0.48\ \text{cm}^3}$ and $1/KV_a^\circ=4.0\ \text{Torr cm}^{-3}$. Therefore,

$$K=\frac{1}{4.0\ \text{Torr cm}^{-3}\times0.48\ \text{cm}^3}=\underline{0.52\ \text{Torr}^{-1}}$$

29.4 $$\frac{z}{(1-z)V}=\frac{1}{cV_{\text{mon}}}+\frac{(c-1)z}{cV_{\text{mon}}}\quad[6],\ z=\frac{p}{p^*}$$

We therefore draw up the following tables:

(a) 0 °C, $p^* = 3222$ Torr

p/Torr	105	282	492	594	620	755	798
$10^3 z$	32.6	87.5	152.7	184.4	192.4	234.3	247.7
$\dfrac{10^3 z}{(1-z)(V/\text{cm}^3)}$	3.04	7.10	12.1	14.1	15.4	17.7	20.0

(b) 18 °C, $p^* = 6148$ Torr

p/Torr	39.5	62.7	108	219	466	555	601	765
$10^3 z$	6.4	10.2	17.6	35.6	75.8	90.3	97.8	124.4
$\dfrac{10^3 z}{(1-z)(V/\text{cm}^3)}$	0.70	1.05	1.74	3.27	6.36	7.58	8.09	10.08

The points are plotted in Fig. 29.4, but we analyze the data by a least-squares

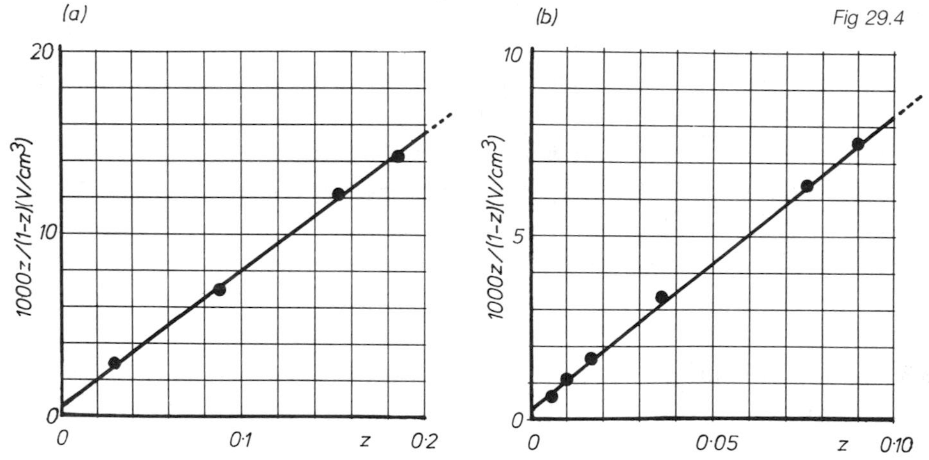

procedure. The intercepts are at (a) 0.466 and (b) 0.303. Hence,

$$\frac{1}{cV_{\text{mon}}} = \text{(a) } 0.466 \times 10^{-3}\ \text{cm}^{-3},\ \text{(b) } 0.303 \times 10^{-3}\ \text{cm}^{-3}$$

The slopes of the lines are (a) 76.10 and (b) 79.54. Hence,

$$\frac{c-1}{cV_{\text{mon}}} = \text{(a) } 76.10\times10^{-3}\,\text{cm}^3,\ \text{(b) } 79.54\times10^{-3}\,\text{cm}^{-3}$$

Solving the equations gives

$$c-1 = \text{(a) } 163.\overline{3},\ \text{(b) } 262.\overline{5}$$

and hence

$$c = \text{(a) } \underline{164.\overline{3}},\ \text{(b) } \underline{263.\overline{5}}$$

$$V_{\text{mon}} = \text{(a) } \underline{13.1\,\text{cm}^3},\ \text{(b) } \underline{12.5\,\text{cm}^3}$$

29.5 For $V_a = c_1 p^{1/c_2}$ [9], $\ln V_a = \ln c_1 + \dfrac{1}{c_2}\ln p$. To test the Freundlich isotherm, we plot $\ln V_a$ against $\ln p$, and to test the Langmuir isotherm, we plot p/V_a against p. Draw up the following table:

p/Torr	100	200	300	400
$\ln(p/\text{Torr})$	4.61	5.30	5.70	5.99
$\ln(V_a/\text{cm}^3)$	4.58	4.97	5.20	5.37
$(p/V_a)/(\text{Torr cm}^{-3})$	1.03	1.39	1.65	1.87

The points are plotted in Fig. 29.5. The Freundlich isotherm (a) gives a

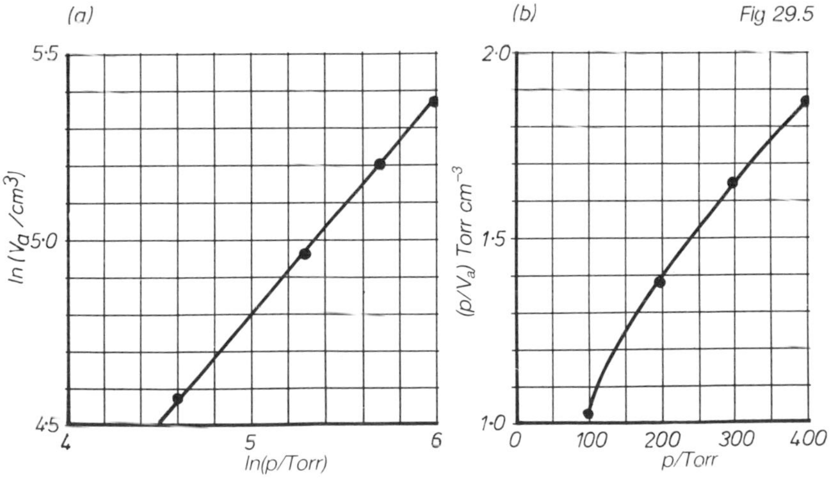

significantly better straight line, and so gives the better representation of the data.

29.6 We repeat the analysis specified in Problem 29.5, and begin by drawing up the following table:

p/Torr	100	200	300	400	500	600
$\ln(p/\text{Torr})$	4.61	5.30	5.70	5.99	6.21	6.40
$\ln(V_a/\text{cm}^3)$	−2.04	−1.90	−1.80	−1.82	−1.74	−1.71
$(p/V_a)/(\text{Torr cm}^{-3})$	769	1330	1850	2410	2860	3330

The points are plotted in Fig. 29.6. The Langmuir isotherm (b) gives a better

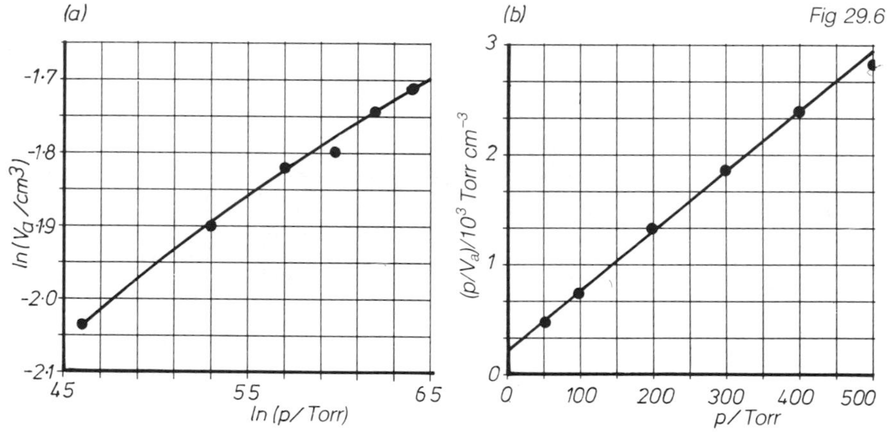

straight line and so is a better representation of the data. From that plot we find an intercept at 297 and a slope of 5.1. It follows that $1/V_a^\circ = 5.1\ \text{cm}^{-3}$ and hence that $V_a^\circ = \underline{0.20\ \text{cm}^3}$. Since $1/KV_a^\circ = 297\ \text{Torr cm}^{-3}$,

$$K = \frac{1}{297\ \text{Torr cm}^{-3} \times 0.19\bar{6}\ \text{cm}^3} = \underline{0.017\bar{2}\ \text{Torr}^{-1}}$$

Since $V_a^\circ = 0.20\ \text{cm}^3$ (at STP), the number of molecules adsorbed is

$$N = \frac{pV_a^\circ}{kT} = \frac{1.0133 \times 10^5\ \text{Pa} \times 0.20 \times 10^{-6}\ \text{m}^3}{1.381 \times 10^{-23}\ \text{J K}^{-1} \times 298\ \text{K}} = 4.8 \times 10^{18}$$

The total area of the sample is $6.2 \times 10^3\ \text{cm}^2 = 6.2 \times 10^{17}\ \text{nm}^2$, so the area occupied by each molecule is

$$\sigma = \frac{6.2 \times 10^{17}\ \text{nm}^2}{4.8 \times 10^{18}} = \underline{0.13\ \text{nm}^2}$$

When the pressure is 1 atm, corresponding to 760 Torr,

$$V_a = \theta V_a^\circ = \frac{KpV_a^\circ}{1+Kp}$$

$$= \frac{0.017\bar{2}\ \text{Torr}^{-1} \times 760\ \text{Torr} \times 0.20\ \text{cm}^3}{1 + 0.017\bar{2}\ \text{Torr}^{-1} \times 760\ \text{Torr}} = \underline{0.19\ \text{cm}^3}$$

29.7 For the Langmuir and BET isotherm tests we draw up the following table (using $p^* = 200$ kPa $= 1500$ Torr):

p/Torr	100	200	300	400	500	600
$(p/V_a)/(\text{Torr cm}^{-3})$	5.59	6.06	6.38	6.58	6.64	6.57
$10^3 z$	67	133	200	267	333	400
$\dfrac{10^3 z}{(1-z)(V/\text{cm}^3)}$	4.01	4.66	5.32	5.98	6.64	7.30

p/V_a is plotted against p in Fig. 29.7a, and $10^3 z/(1-z)V$ is plotted against z in

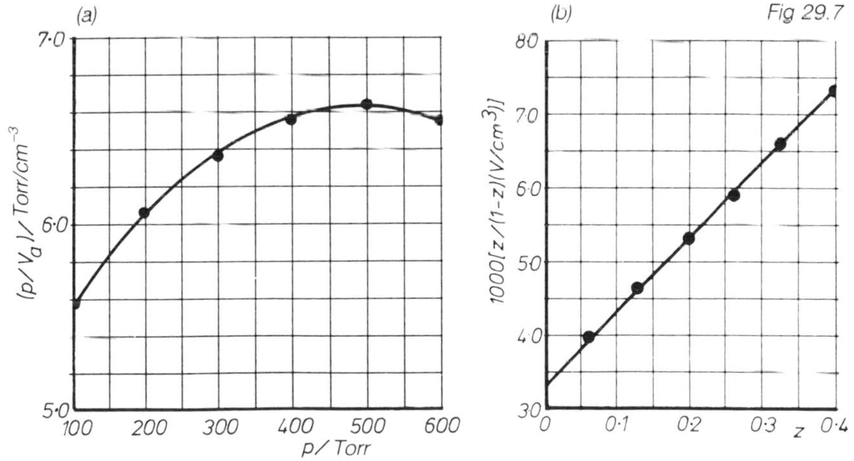

Fig 29.7

Fig. 29.7b. We see that the BET isotherm is a much better representation of the data than the Langmuir isotherm. The intercept in Fig. 29.7b is at

3.33×10^{-3}, and so $1/cV_{mon}=3.33\times10^{-3}\,cm^{-3}$. The slope of the graph is 9.93, and so

$$\frac{c-1}{cV_{mon}}=9.93\times10^{-3}\,cm^{-3}$$

Therefore, $c-1=2.98$, and hence $\underline{c=3.98}$, $\underline{V_{mon}=75.4\,cm^3}$.

29.8 $\theta=c_1p^{1/c_2}$ [9].

We adapt this isotherm to a liquid by noting that $w_a\propto\theta$ and replacing p by [A], the concentration of the acid. Then $w_a=c_1[A]^{1/c_2}$ (with c_1, c_2 modified constants), and hence

$$\lg w_a=\lg c_1+\frac{1}{c_2}\times\lg[A]$$

We draw up the following table:

[A]/M	0.05	0.10	0.50	1.0	1.5
lg([A]/M)	−1.30	−1.00	−0.30	−0.00	0.18
lg(w_a/g)	−1.40	−1.22	−0.92	−0.80	−0.72

These points are plotted in Fig. 29.8a. They fall on a reasonably straight line

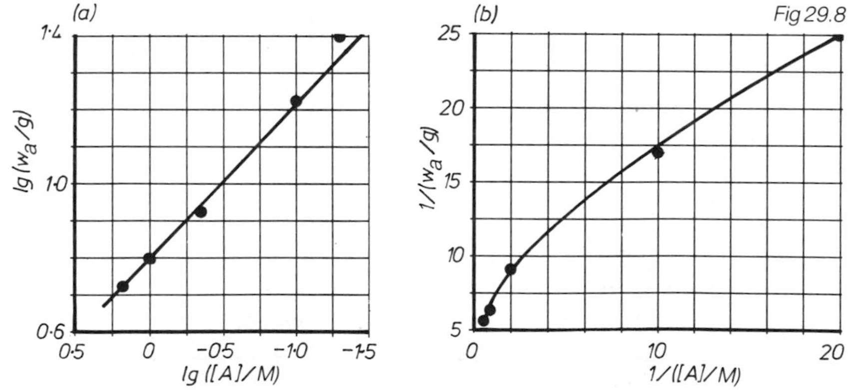

with slope 0.42 and intercept −0.80. Therefore, $c_2=1/0.42=\underline{2.4}$ and $c_1=\underline{0.16}$. (The units of c_1 are bizarre: $c_1=0.16\,g\,mol^{-0.42}\,dm^{1.36}$.)

The test of the Langmuir isotherm begins by adapting the gas-phase adsorption isotherm to

$$w_a = \frac{K[A]}{1+K[A]}$$

and arranging it into the form

$$\frac{1}{w_a} = 1 + \frac{1}{K[A]}$$

We draw up the following table:

$[A]/M$	0.05	0.10	0.50	1.0	1.5
$1/([A]/M)$	20	10	2.0	1.0	0.67
$1/(w_a/g)$	25	17	8.3	6.3	5.3

The points are plotted in Fig. 29.8b. The points do not fall on such a good straight line, so we conclude that the Freundlich isotherm is a better representation of the data than the Langmuir isotherm.

29.9 $\theta = \dfrac{Kp}{1+Kp}$ and $1-\theta = \dfrac{1}{1+Kp}$

For a strongly adsorbed species, $Kp \gg 1$ and $1-\theta = 1/Kp$. Since the reaction rate is proportional to the pressure of ammonia and the fraction of sites left uncovered by the strongly adsorbed hydrogen product, we can write

$$\frac{dp(NH_3)}{dt} = -k_c p(NH_3)(1-\theta) \approx -\underline{\frac{k_c p(NH_3)}{Kp(H_2)}}$$

To solve the rate law, we write

$$p(H_2) = \tfrac{3}{2}\{p_0(NH_3) - p(NH_3)\} \quad [NH_3 \rightarrow \tfrac{1}{2}N_2 + \tfrac{3}{2}H_2]$$

from which it follows that, with $p = p(NH_3)$,

$$\frac{-dp}{dt} = \frac{kp}{p_0 - p}, \quad k = \frac{2k_c}{3K}$$

This equation integrates as follows:

$$\int_{p_0}^{p} \left(1 - \frac{p_0}{p}\right) dp = k \int_0^t dt$$

or

$$\frac{p-p_0}{t}=k+\frac{p_0}{t}\ln\frac{p}{p_0}$$

We write

$$F=\frac{p_0}{t}\ln\frac{p}{p_0},\quad G=\frac{p-p_0}{t}$$

and obtain

$$G=k+F$$

Hence, a plot of G against F should give a straight line with intercept k at $F=0$. Alternatively, the difference $G-F$ should be a constant, k. We draw up the following table:

t/s	0	30	60	100	160	200	250
p/Torr	100	88	84	80	77	74	72
$G/(\mathrm{Torr\ s^{-1}})$		−0.40	−0.27	−0.20	−0.14	−0.13	−0.11
$F/(\mathrm{Torr\ s^{-1}})$		−0.43	−0.29	−0.22	−0.16	−0.15	−0.13
$(G-F)/(\mathrm{Torr\ s^{-1}})$		0.03	0.02	0.02	0.02	0.02	0.02

Thus, the data fit the rate law, and we find $\underline{k=0.02\ \mathrm{Torr\ s^{-1}}}$.

29.10 $\dfrac{-\mathrm{d}p}{\mathrm{d}t}=k_c p(1-\theta)=\dfrac{kp}{1+Kp'}$ [Problem 29.9]

where $p=p(\mathrm{NH_3})$ and $p'=p(\mathrm{H_2})$. For the reaction $\mathrm{A}\rightarrow\mathrm{B}+\mathrm{C}$, p denotes $p(\mathrm{A})$ and p' denotes $p(\mathrm{B})$, but $p'=p_0-p$ [from the stoichiometry]. Therefore,

$$-\frac{\mathrm{d}p}{\mathrm{d}t}=\frac{kp}{1+Kp_0-Kp}$$

and

$$\int_{p_0}^{p}\left\{K-\left(\frac{1+Kp_0}{p}\right)\right\}\mathrm{d}p=\int_0^t k\,\mathrm{d}t=kt$$

The integration leads to

$$(p-p_0)K-(1+Kp_0)\ln\left(\frac{p}{p_0}\right)=kt$$

and we write

$$F=\left(\frac{p_0}{t}\right)\ln\left(\frac{p}{p_0}\right),\quad G=\frac{p-p_0}{t}$$

and hence obtain

$$KG-\left(\frac{1+Kp_0}{p_0}\right)F=k$$

and hence

$$G=\frac{k}{K}+\left(\frac{1+Kp_0}{Kp_0}\right)F$$

Therefore, by plotting G against F, we should get a straight line with intercept k/K at $F=0$ and slope $1+1/Kp_0$. We draw up the following table:

t/s	0	315	750	1400	2250	3450	3150
p/Torr	95	85	75	65	55	45	35
F/(Torr s^{-1})		−0.034	−0.030	−0.026	−0.023	−0.021	−0.018
G/(Torr s^{-1})		−0.032	−0.027	−0.021	−0.018	−0.014	−0.012

These points are plotted in Fig. 29.9. The extrapolated intercept lies at 0.013,

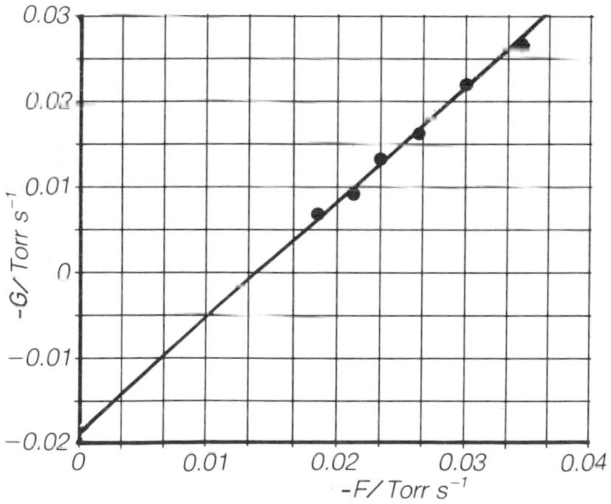

Fig 29.9

and so $k/K=0.013$ Torr s^{-1}. The slope is 1.32, and so

$$\frac{1+Kp_0}{Kp_0}=1.32$$

Therefore, $Kp_0=3.13$. As $p_0=95$ Torr, $K=0.033\ \text{Torr}^{-1}$. Combining this result with the value of k/K obtained from the intercept gives $\underline{k=4.3\times 10^{-4}\ \text{s}^{-1}}$.

29.11 Refer in Fig. 29.10. Evaluate the sum of $\pm 1/r_i$, where r_i is the distance

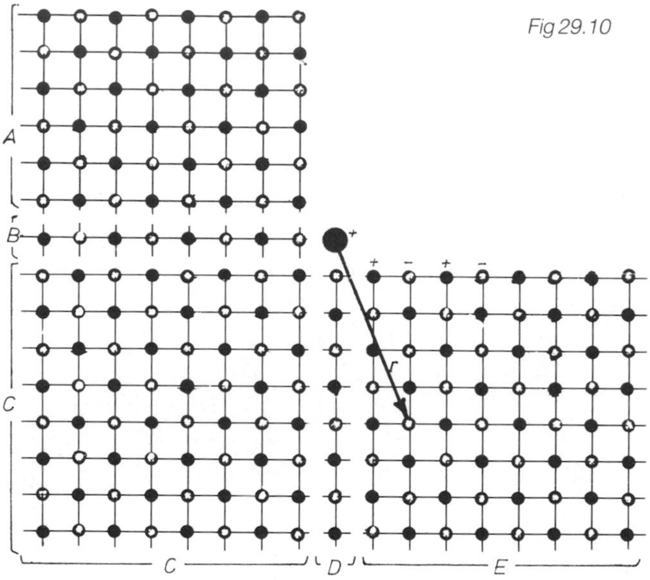

Fig 29.10

from the ion i to the ion of interest, taking $+1/r$ for ions of like charge and $-1/r$ for ions of opposite charge. The array has been divided into five zones. Zones B and D can be summed analytically to give $-\ln 2=-0.69$. The summation over the other zones, each of which gives the same result, is tedious because of the very slow convergence of the sum. Unless you make a very clever choice of the sequence of ions (grouping them so that their contributions almost cancel), you will find the following values for arrays of different sizes:

10×10	20×20	50×50	100×100	200×200
0.259	0.273	0.283	0.286	0.289

The final figure is in good agreement with the analytical value, 0.2892597 . . .

(a) For a cation above a flat surface, the energy (relative to the energy at infinity, and in units of $e^2/4\pi\varepsilon$) is

$$\text{Zone C}+\text{D}+\text{E}=0.29-0.69+0.29=\underline{-0.11}$$

which implies an attractive state.

(b) For a cation at the foot of a high cliff, the energy is

$$\text{Zone A}+\text{B}+\text{C}+\text{D}+\text{E}=3\times 0.29+2\times(-0.69)=\underline{-0.51}$$

which is significantly more attractive. Hence, the latter is the more likely settling point (if potential energy considerations such as these are dominant).

29.12 $v=\dfrac{kK_{A}p_{A}K_{B}p_{B}}{(1+K_{A}p_{A}+K_{B}p_{B})^2}$ [14]

and we interpret v as $-\mathrm{d}p_{A}/\mathrm{d}t$. We make the substitutions

$$p_{A}=p-x,\ p_{B}=p-x\quad [p_{A}(0)=p_{B}(0)=p,\ \mathrm{A}+\mathrm{B}\rightarrow\mathrm{P}]$$

and write

$A=kK_{A}K_{B}$, $B=1+Kp$, $K=K_{A}+K_{B}$, then the equation to solve is

$$\frac{\mathrm{d}x}{\mathrm{d}t}=\frac{A(p-x)^2}{(B-kx)^2}$$

and hence

$$\int_0^t A\,\mathrm{d}t=\int_0^x\frac{(B-Kx)^2}{(p-x)^2}\,\mathrm{d}x$$

$$=\int_0^x\frac{B^2\,\mathrm{d}x}{(p-x)^2}-2BK\int_0^x\frac{x\,\mathrm{d}x}{(p-x)^2}+K^2\int_0^x\frac{x^2\,\mathrm{d}x}{(p-x)^2}$$

We use

$$\int\frac{\mathrm{d}x}{(p-x)^2}=\frac{1}{p-x}+C$$

$$\int\frac{x\,\mathrm{d}x}{(p-x)^2}=\frac{p}{p-x}+\ln(p-x)+C$$

$$\int\frac{x^2\,\mathrm{d}x}{(p-x)^2}=\frac{x(x-2p)}{x-p}+2p\ln(p-x)+C$$

Hence

$$At = B^2\left\{\frac{1}{p-x} - \frac{1}{p}\right\} - 2BK\left\{\frac{p}{p-x} - 1 + \ln\left(\frac{x-p}{-p}\right)\right\}$$

$$+ K^2\left\{\frac{x(x-2p)}{x-p} + 2p\ln\left(\frac{x-p}{-p}\right)\right\}$$

$$= \frac{xB^2}{p(p-x)} - 2BK\left\{\frac{x}{p-x} + \ln\left(\frac{p-x}{p}\right)\right\}$$

$$+ K^2\left\{\frac{x(x-2p)}{x-p} + 2p\ln\left(\frac{p-x}{p}\right)\right\}$$

$$= \left(\frac{x}{p(p-x)}\right)\{B^2 - 2BKp + K^2p(2p-x)\}$$

$$+ 2(pK^2 - BK)\ln\left(\frac{p-x}{p}\right)$$

Now substitute $B = 1 + Kp$ and obtain

$$\underline{At = \frac{1}{p}\left(\frac{x}{p-x}\right) + K^2x + 2K\ln\left(\frac{p}{p-x}\right)}$$

For $p = 1$, $K_A \approx K_B \approx 1$, $A \approx k$ we find

$$kt = \frac{x}{1-x} + 4x - 4\ln(1-x)$$

which is plotted in Fig. 29.11.

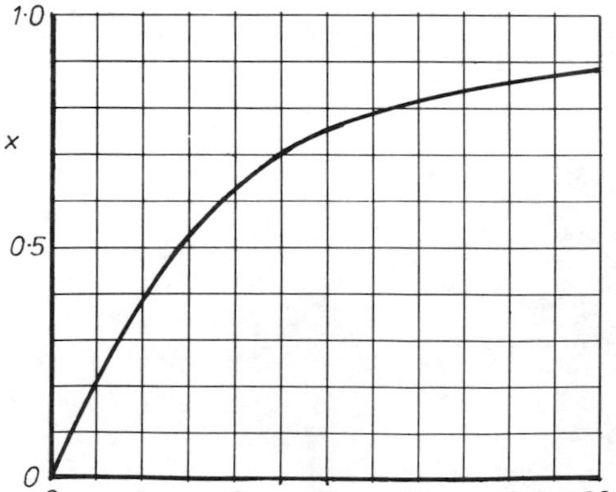

Fig 29.11

29.13 $\theta(\mathrm{F})=\dfrac{(Kp_{\mathrm{F}})^{1/2}}{1+(Kp_{\mathrm{F}})^{1/2}}$ [3], $\theta(\mathrm{B})=c_1 p_{\mathrm{B}}^{1/2}$ [9]

and the reaction rate is

$$v=k'\theta(\mathrm{F})\theta(\mathrm{B})=\frac{k'c_1K^{1/2}p_{\mathrm{F}}^{1/2}p_{\mathrm{B}}^{1/2}}{1+(Kp_{\mathrm{F}})^{1/2}}$$

We write $k=k'c_1K^{1/2}$, and the reaction rate is then

$$v=\frac{kp_{\mathrm{F}}^{1/2}p_{\mathrm{B}}^{1/2}}{1+K^{1/2}p_{\mathrm{F}}^{1/2}}$$

When $(Kp_{\mathrm{F}})^{1/2}\gg 1$, $v\approx\left(\dfrac{k}{K}\right)^{1/2}p_{\mathrm{B}}^{1/2}$

and the rate is independent of p_{F}.

29.14 Refer to Fig. 2.12. Let the number density of atoms in the solid be $\mathcal{N}$.

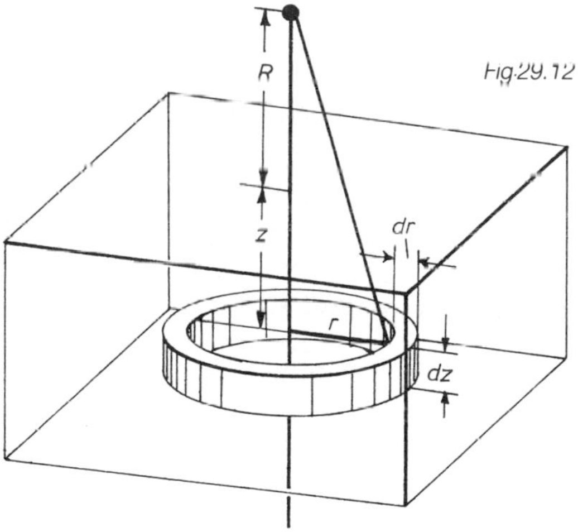

Fig.29.12

Then the number in the annulus between r and $r+\mathrm{d}r$ and thickness $\mathrm{d}z$ at a depth z below the surface is $2\pi\mathcal{N}r\,\mathrm{d}r\,\mathrm{d}z$. The interaction energy of these atoms and the single adsorbate atom at a height R above the surface is

$$\mathrm{d}U=\frac{-2\pi\mathcal{N}r\,\mathrm{d}z\,C_6}{\{(R+z)^2+r^2\}^3}$$

if the individual atoms interact as $-C_6/d^6$, with $d^2=(R+z)^2+r^2$. The total interaction energy of the atom with the semi-infinite slab of uniform density is therefore

$$U=-2\pi\mathcal{N}C_6\int_0^\infty \mathrm{d}r\int_0^\infty \mathrm{d}z\,\frac{r}{\{(R+z)^2+r^2\}^3}$$

We then use

$$\int_0^\infty \frac{r\,\mathrm{d}r}{(a^2+r^2)^3}=\tfrac{1}{2}\int_0^\infty \frac{\mathrm{d}r^2}{(a^2+r^2)^3}=\tfrac{1}{2}\int_0^\infty \frac{\mathrm{d}x}{(a^2+x)^3}=\frac{1}{4a^4}$$

and obtain

$$U=-\tfrac{1}{2}\pi\mathcal{N}C_6\int_0^\infty \frac{\mathrm{d}z}{(R+z)^4}=\frac{-\pi\mathcal{N}C_6}{6R^3}$$

This result confirms that $U\propto 1/R^3$. [A shorter procedure is to use a dimensional argument, but we need the explicit expression in the following.] When

$$V=4\varepsilon\left\{\left(\frac{\sigma}{R}\right)^{12}-\left(\frac{\sigma}{R}\right)^{6}\right\}=\frac{C_{12}}{R^{12}}-\frac{C_6}{R^6}$$

we also need the contribution from C_{12}:

$$U'=2\pi\mathcal{N}C_{12}\int_0^\infty \mathrm{d}r\int_0^\infty \mathrm{d}z\,\frac{r}{\{(R+z)^2+r^2\}^6}$$

$$=2\pi\mathcal{N}C_{12}\times\frac{1}{10}\int_0^\infty \frac{\mathrm{d}z}{(R+z)^{10}}=\frac{2\pi\mathcal{N}C_{12}}{90R^9}$$

and therefore the total interaction energy is

$$U=\frac{2\pi\mathcal{N}C_{12}}{90R^9}-\frac{\pi\mathcal{N}C_6}{6R^3}$$

We can express this result in terms of ε and σ by noting that

$C_{12}=4\varepsilon\sigma^{12}$ and $C_6=4\varepsilon\sigma^6$, for then

$$U=8\pi\varepsilon\sigma^3\mathcal{N}\left\{\frac{1}{90}\left(\frac{\sigma}{R}\right)^9-\frac{1}{12}\left(\frac{\sigma}{R}\right)^3\right\}$$

For the position of equilibrium, we look for the value of R for which $\mathrm{d}U/\mathrm{d}R=0$:

$$\frac{dU}{dR}=8\pi\varepsilon\sigma^3\mathcal{N}\left\{-\frac{1}{10}\left(\frac{\sigma^9}{R^{10}}\right)+\frac{1}{4}\left(\frac{\sigma^3}{R^4}\right)\right\}=0$$

Therefore, $\dfrac{\sigma^9}{10R^{10}}=\dfrac{\sigma^3}{4R^4}$

which implies that $R=(\frac{2}{5})^{1/6}\sigma=\underline{0.858\sigma}$. For $\sigma=342$ pm, $R\approx294$ pm.

29.15 A general change in the Gibbs function of a one-component system with a surface is

$$dG=-S\,dT+V\,dp+\gamma\,d\sigma+\mu\,dn$$

Let $G=G(g)+G(\sigma)$ and $n=n(g)+n(\sigma)$; then

$$dG(g)=-S(g)\,dT+V(g)\,dp+\mu(g)\,dn(g)$$

$$dG(\sigma)=-S(\sigma)\,dT+\gamma\,d\sigma+\mu(\sigma)\,dn(\sigma)$$

At equilibrium, $\mu(\sigma)=\mu(g)=\mu$. At constant temperature, $dG(\sigma)=\gamma\,d\sigma+\mu\,dn(\sigma)$. Since dG in an exact differential, this expression integrates to

$$G(\sigma)=\gamma\sigma+\mu n(\sigma)$$

Therefore,

$$dG(\sigma)=\sigma\,d\gamma+\gamma\,d\sigma+\mu\,dn(\sigma)+n(\sigma)\,d\mu$$

But since

$$dG(\sigma)=\gamma\,d\sigma+\mu\,dn(\sigma)$$

we conclude that

$$\sigma\,d\gamma+n(\sigma)\,d\mu==0$$

Since $d\mu=RT\,d\ln p$, this relation is equivalent to

$$n(\sigma)=-\frac{\sigma\,d\gamma}{d\mu}=-\frac{\sigma}{RT}\left(\frac{d\gamma}{d\ln p}\right)$$

Now express $n(\sigma)$ as an adsorbed volume using

$$n(\sigma)=\frac{p^{\ominus}V_a}{RT^{\ominus}}$$

and express $d\gamma$ as a kind of chemical potential through

$$d\mu'=\frac{RT^{\ominus}}{p^{\ominus}}\,d\gamma$$

evaluated at a standard temperature and pressure ($T^{\ominus}$ and $p^{\ominus}$), then

$$\underline{-\frac{\sigma}{RT}\left(\frac{d\mu'}{d\ln p}\right)=V_a}$$

29.16 $\mathrm{d}\mu' = -c_2\left(\frac{RT}{\sigma}\right)\mathrm{d}V_\mathrm{a}$

which implies that

$$\frac{\mathrm{d}\mu'}{\mathrm{d}\ln p} = \frac{-c_2RT}{\sigma}\left(\frac{\mathrm{d}V_\mathrm{a}}{\mathrm{d}\ln p}\right)$$

However, we established in Problem 29.15 that

$$\frac{\mathrm{d}\mu'}{\mathrm{d}\ln p} = \frac{-RTV_\mathrm{a}}{\sigma}$$

Therefore,

$$-c_2\left(\frac{RT}{\sigma}\right)\left(\frac{\mathrm{d}V_\mathrm{a}}{\mathrm{d}\ln p}\right) = \frac{-RTV_\mathrm{a}}{\sigma}, \text{ or } c_2\,\mathrm{d}\ln V_\mathrm{a} = \mathrm{d}\ln p$$

Hence

$$\mathrm{d}\ln V_\mathrm{a}^{c_2} = \mathrm{d}\ln p, \text{ and therefore } \underline{V_\mathrm{a} = c_1p^{1/c_2}}$$

29.17 $\theta = \frac{Kp}{1+Kp}, \ \theta = \frac{V_\mathrm{a}}{V_\mathrm{a}^\circ}$

$$p = \frac{\theta}{K(1-\theta)} = \frac{V_\mathrm{a}}{K(V_\mathrm{a}^\circ - V_\mathrm{a})}$$

$$\frac{\mathrm{d}p}{\mathrm{d}V_\mathrm{a}} = \frac{1}{K(V_\mathrm{a}^\circ - V_\mathrm{a})} + \frac{V_\mathrm{a}}{K(V_\mathrm{a}^\circ - V_\mathrm{a})^2} = \frac{V_\mathrm{a}^\circ}{K(V_\mathrm{a}^\circ - V_\mathrm{a})^2}$$

$$\mathrm{d}\mu' = -\left(\frac{RT}{\sigma}\right)V_\mathrm{a}\,\mathrm{d}\ln p = \frac{-RT}{p\sigma}V_\mathrm{a}\,\mathrm{d}p$$

$$= -\left(\frac{RT}{\sigma}\right)\left\{\frac{K(V_\mathrm{a}^\circ - V_\mathrm{a})}{V_\mathrm{a}}\right\}V_\mathrm{a}\left\{\frac{V_\mathrm{a}^\circ}{K(V_\mathrm{a}^\circ - V_\mathrm{a})^2}\right\}\mathrm{d}V_\mathrm{a}$$

$$= -\left(\frac{RT}{\sigma}\right)\frac{V_\mathrm{a}^\circ\,\mathrm{d}V_\mathrm{a}}{(V_\mathrm{a}^\circ - V_\mathrm{a})}$$

Therefore, we can adopt any of several forms,

$$\mathrm{d}\mu' = -\left\{\frac{(RT/\sigma)V_\mathrm{a}^\circ}{V_\mathrm{a}^\circ - V_\mathrm{a}}\right\}\mathrm{d}V_\mathrm{a} = -\left\{\frac{(RT/\sigma)}{1-\theta}\right\}\mathrm{d}V_\mathrm{a}$$

$$= -\left\{\frac{(RTV_\mathrm{a}^\circ/\sigma)}{1-\theta}\right\}\mathrm{d}\theta = \frac{RTV_\mathrm{a}^\circ}{\sigma}\mathrm{d}\ln(1-\theta)$$

30. Dynamic electrochemistry

Exercises

30.1 $\ln j = \ln j_0 + (1-\alpha)f\eta$ [14a, $f = F/RT$]

$\ln\dfrac{j'}{j} = (1-\alpha)f(\eta' - \eta)$, which implies that for a current density j' we require an overpotential

$$\eta' = \eta + \frac{\ln(j'/j)}{(1-\alpha)f}$$

$$= 125\text{ mV} + \frac{\ln\left(\dfrac{75}{55}\right)}{(1-0.39)\times(25.69\text{ mV})^{-1}} = \underline{138\text{ mV}}$$

30.2 $j_0 = j\,e^{-(1-\alpha)\eta f}$ [14a]

$$= 55.0\text{ mA cm}^{-2} \times e^{-0.61\times125\text{ mV}/25.69\text{ mV}}$$

$$= \underline{2.8\text{ mA cm}^{-2}}$$

30.3 $j_L = \dfrac{zFDc}{\delta}$ [19] $= \dfrac{cRT\lambda}{zF\delta}$ [Example 30.4]

$$= \frac{2.5\times10^{-3}\,\text{M}\times25.69\times10^{-3}\text{ V}\times61.9\text{ S cm}^2\text{ mol}^{-1}}{0.40\times10^{-3}\text{ m}}$$

$$= 9.9\text{ M V S cm}^2\text{ mol}^{-1}\text{ m}^{-1}$$

$$= 9.9\text{ mol m}^{-3}\times10^3\times\text{V }\Omega^{-1}\times10^{-4}\text{ m}^2\text{ mol}^{-1}\text{ m}^{-1}$$

$$= \underline{0.99\text{ A m}^{-2}} \quad [1\text{ V }\Omega^{-1} = 1\text{ A}]$$

30.4 $\dfrac{j}{j_0} = e^{(1-\alpha)f\eta} - e^{-\alpha f\eta}$ [11]

$$= e^{\frac{1}{2}f\eta} - e^{-\frac{1}{2}f\eta} \quad [\alpha = 0.5]$$

$$= 2\sinh(\tfrac{1}{2}f\eta) \quad \left[\sinh x = \frac{e^x - e^{-x}}{2}\right]$$

and we use $\frac{1}{2}f\eta = \frac{1}{2} \times \dfrac{\eta}{25.69\ \text{mV}} = 0.01946(\eta/\text{mV})$

The resulting graph is shown in Fig. 30.1.

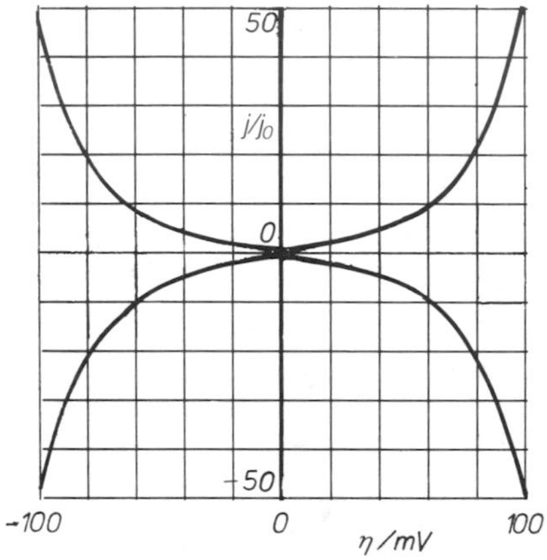

Fig 30.1

30.5 $j = 2j_0 \sinh(\frac{1}{2}f\eta)$ [Exercise 30.4]

$= 1.58\ \text{mA cm}^{-2} \times \sinh(0.01946\eta/\text{mV})$

(a) $\eta = 10\ \text{mV}$

$j = 1.58\ \text{mA cm}^{-2} \times \sinh 0.1946 = \underline{0.31\ \text{mA cm}^{-2}}$

(b) $\eta = 100\ \text{mV}$

$j = 1.58\ \text{mA cm}^{-2} \times \sinh 1.946 = \underline{5.41\ \text{mA cm}^{-2}}$

(c) $\eta = -0.5\ \text{V}$

$j = 1.58\ \text{mA cm}^{-2} \times \sinh(-9.73) \approx \underline{8300\ \text{mA cm}^{-2}}$

30.6 $I = jS = 2j_0S \sinh(0.01946\eta/\text{mV})$ [Exercise 30.4]

$$= 2 \times 2.5\ \text{mA cm}^{-2} \times 1.0\ \text{cm}^2 \times \sinh\left\{\frac{0.01946(E - E^\ominus)}{\text{mV}}\right\}$$

$$= 5.0\ \text{mA} \times \sinh\{0.01946(E - E^\ominus)/\text{mV}\}$$

[The zero-current cell potential is $E^\ominus$ when the ions are at unit activity.] We can then draw up the following table:

E/mV	500	600	700	771	800	900	1000
$\lvert I\rvert$/mA	487	69.5	9.32	0	2.97	30.6	215

30.7 $E=E^{\ominus}+\frac{RT}{F}\ln\frac{a(\mathrm{Fe}^{3+})}{a(\mathrm{Fe}^{2+})}$ [Nernst equation]

$$E/\mathrm{mV}=771+25.7\ln\frac{a(\mathrm{Fe}^{3+})}{a(\mathrm{Fe}^{2+})}$$

$$\eta/\mathrm{mV}=1000-E/\mathrm{mV}=229-25.7\ln\frac{a\mathrm{Fe}^{3+})}{a(\mathrm{Fe}^{2+})}$$

and hence

$$I-2j_0S\sinh(0.01946\eta/\mathrm{mV})$$

$$=5.0\ \mathrm{mA}\times\sinh\left\{4.46-0.50\ln\frac{a(\mathrm{Fe}^{3+})}{a(\mathrm{Fe}^{2+})}\right\}$$

We can therefore draw up the following table:

$a(\mathrm{Fe}^{3+})/a(\mathrm{Fe}^{2+})$	0.1	0.3	0.6	1.0	3.0	6.0	10.0
$\lvert I\rvert$/mA	684	395	278	215	124	88	68.0

The current falls to zero when

$$4.46=0.50\ln\frac{a(\mathrm{Fe}^{3+})}{a(\mathrm{Fe}^{2+})}$$

which occurs when $a(\mathrm{Fe}^{3+})=7480\times a(\mathrm{Fe}^{2+})$.

30.8 $I=2j_0S\sinh(0.01946\eta/\mathrm{mV})$ [Exercise 30.4]

$$\eta=51.39\ \mathrm{mV}\times\sinh^{-1}\left(\frac{I}{2j_0S}\right)$$

$$=51.39\ \mathrm{mV}\times\sinh^{-1}\left(\frac{20\ \mathrm{mA}}{2\times2.5\ \mathrm{mA\ cm^{-2}}\times1.0\ \mathrm{cm^2}}\right)$$

$$=51.39\ \mathrm{mV}\times\sinh^{-1}4.0=\underline{108\ \mathrm{mV}}.$$

30.9 The current-density of electrons is j_0/e because each one carries a charge of magnitude e. Therefore,

(a) $\mathrm{Pt|H_2|H^+}$; $j_0 = 0.79\ \mathrm{mA\ cm^{-2}}$ [Table 30.1]

$$J = \frac{0.79\ \mathrm{mA\ cm^{-2}}}{1.602\times10^{-19}\ \mathrm{C}} = \underline{4.9\times10^{15}\ \mathrm{cm^{-2}\ s^{-1}}}$$

(b) $\mathrm{Pt|Fe^{3+}, Fe^{2+}}$; $j_0 = 2.5\ \mathrm{mA\ cm^{-2}}$

$$J = \frac{2.5\ \mathrm{mA\ cm^{-2}}}{1.602\times10^{-19}\ \mathrm{C}} = \underline{1.6\times10^{16}\ \mathrm{cm^{-2}\ s^{-1}}}$$

(c) $\mathrm{Pb|H_2|H^+}$; $j_0 = 5.0\times10^{-12}\ \mathrm{A\ cm^{-2}}$

$$J = \frac{5.0\times10^{-12}\ \mathrm{A\ cm^{-2}}}{1.602\times10^{-19}\ \mathrm{C}} = \underline{3.1\times10^{7}\ \mathrm{cm^{-2}\ s^{-1}}}$$

There are approximately $1.0\ \mathrm{cm^2}/(280\ \mathrm{pm})^2 = 1.3\times10^{15}$ atoms in each square centimeter of surface. The numbers of electrons per atom are therefore $\underline{3.8\ \mathrm{s^{-1}}}$, $\underline{12\ \mathrm{s^{-1}}}$, and $\underline{2.4\times10^{-8}\ \mathrm{s^{-1}}}$ respectively. The last corresponds to less than one event per year.

30.10 $\eta = \dfrac{RTj}{Fj_0}$ [13]

which implies that

$$I = Sj = \left(\frac{Sj_0F}{RT}\right)\eta$$

An ohmic conductor of resistance r obeys $\eta = Ir$, and so we can identify the resistance as

$$r = \frac{RT}{Sj_0F} = \frac{25.69\times10^{-3}\ \mathrm{V}}{1.0\ \mathrm{cm^2}\times j_0}$$

$$= \frac{25.69\times10^{-3}\ \Omega}{(j_0/\mathrm{A\ cm^{-2}})} \quad [1\ \mathrm{V} = 1\ \mathrm{A}\ \Omega]$$

(a) $\mathrm{Pt|H_2|H^+}$; $j_0 = 7.9\times10^{-4}\ \mathrm{A\ cm^{-2}}$

$$r = \frac{25.69\times10^{-3}\ \Omega}{7.9\times10^{-4}} = \underline{33\ \Omega}$$

(b) $\mathrm{Hg|H_2|H^+}$; $j_0 = 0.79\times10^{-12}\ \mathrm{A\ cm^{-2}}$

$$r = \frac{25.69\times10^{-3}\ \Omega}{0.79\times10^{-12}} = 3.3\times10^{10}\ \Omega, \text{ or } \underline{33\ \mathrm{G}\Omega}$$

30.11 For deposition of cations, a significant net current towards the electrodes is necessary. For copper and zinc, we have $E^{\ominus} \approx 0.45$ V and -0.76 V respectively. Therefore, deposition of copper occurs when the potential falls below 0.34 V and continues until the copper ions are exhausted to the point that the limiting current density is reached. Then a further reduction in potential to below -0.76 V brings about the deposition of zinc.

30.12 Take $\gamma = 1$. The deposition of copper and zinc will occur when E is less than 0.34 V and -0.76 V respectively. When the concentrations are 0.010 M, the electrode potentials that must be overcome are reduced by $(RT/2F) \ln 0.010 = -0.06$ V, and the deposition potentials for copper and zinc are respectively $\underline{28.0\text{ V}}$ and $\underline{-0.82\text{ V}}$.

30.13 Hydrogen evolution occurs significantly (in the sense of having a current density of 1 mA cm^{-2}, which is 6.2×10^{15} electrons cm^{-2} s^{-1}, or 1.0×10^{-8} mol cm^{-2} s^{-1}, corresponding to about 1 cm^3 of gas per hour) when the overpotential is -1 V. Since $E = E^{\ominus} + (RT/F) \ln a(\text{H}^+) = -59 \text{ mV} \times \text{pH}$, this rate of evolution occurs when the potential at the electrode is about $-1.06 \text{ V} \approx -1$ V (when pH ≈ 1). But both Ag^+ ($E^{\ominus} = 0.80$ V) and Cd^{2+} ($E^{\ominus} = -0.44$ V) have more positive deposition potentials and so deposit first.

30.14 Zinc will deposit from a solution of unit activity when the potential is below -0.76 V. The hydrogen ion current toward the zinc electrode is then

$$j(\text{H}^+) = 5 \times 10^{-11} \text{ A cm}^{-2} \times e^{760/51.4}$$

$$= 1.3 \times 10^{-4} \text{ A cm}^{-2}, \text{ or } \underline{0.14 \text{ mA cm}^{-2}}$$

This corresponds to a negligible rate of evolution of hydrogen [Exercise 31.13], and so zinc may be deposited from the solution.

30.15 Use the same argument as in Exercise 30.14. The hydrogen-ion current toward the platinum electrode when zinc starts to deposit is

$$j(\text{H}^+) = 0.79 \text{ mA cm}^{-2} \times e^{760/51.4}$$

$$= \underline{2.1 \times 10^3 \text{ A cm}^{-2}}$$

and so there will be a considerable evolution of hydrogen before the zinc deposition potential is attained.

30.16 Since $E^{\ominus}(\text{Mg}, \text{Mg}^{2+}) = -2.37$ V, magnesium deposition will occur when the potential is reduced to below this value. The hydrogen ion current density is then

$$j(\text{H}^+) = 5 \times 10^{-11} \text{ A cm}^{-2} \times e^{2370/51.4} = \underline{5.3 \times 10^9 \text{ A cm}^{-2}}$$

which is a lot of hydrogen (10^6 L cm^{-2} s^{-1}), and so magnesium will not be plated out.

30.17 $j_L = \dfrac{FDc}{\delta}$ [19], and so $\delta = \dfrac{FDc}{j_L}$

Therefore,

$$\delta = \frac{9.65 \times 10^4 \text{ C mol}^{-1} \times 1.14 \times 10^{-9} \text{ m}^2 \text{ s}^{-1} \times 0.66 \text{ mol m}^{-3}}{28.9 \times 10^{-2} \text{ A m}^{-2}}$$

$$= 2.5 \times 10^{-4} \text{ m, or } \underline{0.25 \text{ mm}}$$

30.18 The values of $E^{\ominus}(\text{M, M}^+)$ are all far apart, and so simultaneous deposition of the simple ions is unexpected. However, if the activities of the ions are modified by complexation with CN^- ions, the deposition potentials may be brought into coincidence. The CN^- has a different stability constant for complex formation with each ion, and so modifies the deposition potentials to different extents.

30.19 The cell half-reactions are

$$Cd(OH)_2 + 2e^- \rightarrow Cd + 2OH^-, \; E^{\ominus} = -0.81 \text{ V}$$

$$NiO(OH) + e^- \rightarrow Ni(OH)_2 + OH^-, \; E^{\ominus} = +0.49 \text{ V}$$

Therefore, the standard cell potential is $\underline{-1.30 \text{ V}}$. If the cell is working reversibly yet producing 100 mA, the power it produces is

$$P = IE = 100 \times 10^{-3} \text{ A} \times 1.3 \text{ V} = \underline{0.13 \text{ W}}$$

30.20 $E^{\ominus} = -\Delta G^{\ominus}/\nu F$

(a) $H_2 + \frac{1}{2}O_2 \rightarrow H_2O$; $\Delta G^{\ominus} = -237$ kJ mol^{-1}

Since $\nu = 2$,

$$E^{\ominus} = \frac{-(-237 \text{ kJ mol}^{-1})}{2 \times 96.48 \text{ kC mol}^{-1}} = \underline{+1.23 \text{ V}}$$

(b) $CH_4 + 2O_2 \rightarrow CO_2 + 2H_2O$

$$\Delta G^{\ominus} = 2\Delta G_f^{\ominus}(H_2O) + \Delta G_f^{\ominus}(CO_2) - \Delta G_f^{\ominus}(CH_4)$$

$$= 2 \times (-237.1) + (-394.4) - (-50.7) \text{ kJ mol}^{-1}$$

$$= -817.9 \text{ kJ mol}^{-1}$$

As written, the reaction corresponds to the transfer of eight electrons. It follows that, for the species in their standard states,

$$E^{\ominus} = \frac{-(-817.9\ \text{kJ mol}^{-1})}{8 \times 96.48\ \text{kC mol}^{-1}} = \underline{+1.06\ \text{V}}$$

30.21 (a) $E(\mathrm{H_2, H^+}) = -0.059\ \text{V pH} = -7 \times 0.059\ \text{V} = -0.41\ \text{V}$

(b) $E(\mathrm{O_2, H^+}) = 1.23\ \text{V} - 0.059\ \text{V pH} = +0.82\ \text{V}$

$$E(\mathrm{M, M^+}) = E^{\ominus}(\mathrm{M, M^+}) + \left(\frac{0.059\ \text{V}}{z_+}\right) \lg 10^{-6}$$

$$= E^{\ominus}(\mathrm{M, M^+}) - \frac{0.35\ \text{V}}{z_+}$$

Corrosion will occur if $E(\mathrm{a})$ or $E(\mathrm{b}) > E(\mathrm{M, M^+})$.

(i) $E^{\ominus}(\mathrm{Fe, Fe^{2+}}) = -0.44\ \text{V},\ z_+ = 2$

$E(\mathrm{Fe, Fe^{2+}}) = -0.44 - 0.18\ \text{V} = -0.62\ \text{V} < E(\text{a and b})$

(ii) $E(\mathrm{Cu, Cu^+}) = 0.52 - 0.35\ \text{V} = 0.17\ \text{V} \begin{cases} > E(\mathrm{a}) \\ < E(\mathrm{b}) \end{cases}$

$E(\mathrm{Cu, Cu^{2+}}) = 0.40 - 0.18\ \text{V} = 0.16\ \text{V} \begin{cases} > E(\mathrm{a}) \\ < E(\mathrm{b}) \end{cases}$

(iii) $E(\mathrm{Pb, Pb^{2+}}) = -0.13 - 0.18\ \text{V} = -0.31\ \text{V} \begin{cases} > E(\mathrm{a}) \\ < E(\mathrm{b}) \end{cases}$

(iv) $E(\mathrm{Al, Al^{3+}}) = -1.66 - 0.12\ \text{V} = -1.78\ \text{V} < E(\text{a and b})$

(v) $E(\mathrm{Ag, Ag^+}) = 0.80 - 0.35\ \text{V} = 0.45\ \text{V} \begin{cases} > E(\mathrm{a}) \\ < E(\mathrm{b}) \end{cases}$

(vi) $E(\mathrm{Cr, Cr^{3+}}) = -0.74 - 0.12\ \text{V} = -0.86\ \text{V} < E(\text{a and b})$

(vii) $E(\mathrm{Co, Co^{2+}}) = -0.28 - 0.15\ \text{V} = -0.43\ \text{V} < E(\text{a and b})$

Therefore, the metals with a thermodynamic tendency to corrode in moist conditions at pH = 7 are Fe, Al, Co, Cr if oxygen is absent, but if oxygen is present, all seven elements have a tendency to corrode.

Problems

30.1 $\ln j = \ln j_0 + (1-\alpha) f\eta$ [14a]

Draw up the following table:

η/mV	50	100	150	200	250
$\ln(j/\text{mA cm}^{-2})$	0.98	2.19	3.40	4.61	5.81

The points are plotted in Fig. 30.2. The intercept is at −0.25, and so

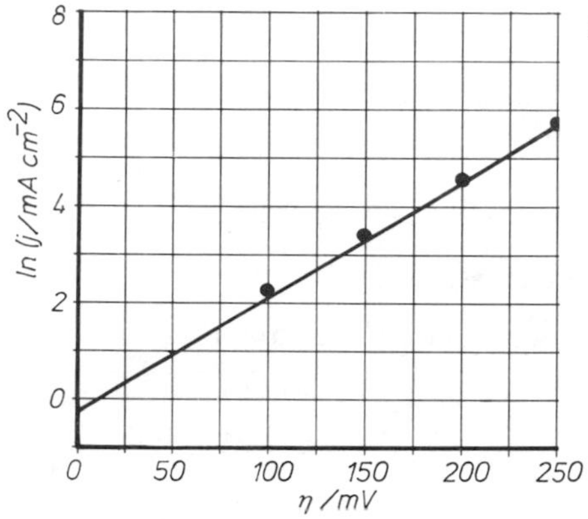

Fig 30.2

$j_0/(\text{mA cm}^{-2}) = e^{-0.25} = \underline{0.78}$. The slope is 0.0243, and so $(1-\alpha)F/RT = 0.0243\ \text{mV}^{-1}$. It follows that $1-\alpha = 0.62$, and so $\underline{\alpha = 0.38}$. If η were large but negative,

$$|j| \approx j_0 e^{-\alpha f \eta} = 0.78\ \text{mA cm}^{-2} \times e^{-0.38\eta/25.7\ \text{mV}}$$

$$= 0.78\ \text{mA cm}^{-2} \times e^{-0.015(\eta/\text{mV})}$$

and we can draw up the following table:

η/mV	−50	−100	−150	−200	−250
$j/(\text{mA cm}^{-2})$	1.65	3.50	7.40	15.7	33.2

30.2 $j_L = \dfrac{cRT\lambda}{zF\delta}$ [Example 30.4]

Draw up the following table using $j_L = I/S$ with $S = 40\ \text{cm}^2$:

c/M	0.250	0.125	0.063	0.031
$j_L/(\mathrm{mA\ cm^{-2}})$	5.38	2.68	1.23	0.58

The points are plotted in Fig. 30.3. They fall on a good straight line with slope 22.3. It follows that

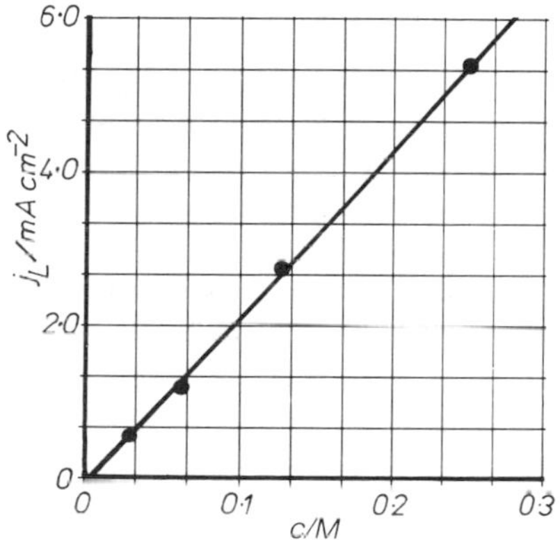

Fig 30.3

$$\frac{RT}{zF}\times\frac{\lambda}{\delta}=22.3\ \mathrm{mA\ cm^{-2}/M}=0.223\ \mathrm{A\ m\ mol^{-1}}$$

and therefore, since

$$\frac{RT\lambda}{zF}=\tfrac{1}{2}\times 0.0257\ \mathrm{V}\times 40\ \mathrm{S\ cm^2\ mol^{-1}}$$

$$=0.514\ \mathrm{V\ S\ cm^2\ mol^{-1}}=0.514\times 10^{-4}\ \mathrm{A\ m^2\ mol^{-1}}$$

$$\delta=\frac{0.514\times 10^{-4}\ \mathrm{A\ m^2\ mol^{-1}}}{0.223\ \mathrm{A\ m\ mol^{-1}}}=\underline{0.23\ \mathrm{mm}}$$

30.3 $E=E^{\ominus}+\dfrac{RT}{zF}\ln a(\mathrm{M^+})$

Deposition may occur when the potential falls to below E and so simultaneous deposition will occur if

$$E^{\ominus}(\text{Sn, Sn}^{2+}) + \frac{RT}{2F}\ln a(\text{Sn}^{2+}) = E^{\ominus}(\text{Pb, Pb}^{2+}) + \frac{RT}{2F}\ln a(\text{Pb}^{2+})$$

or

$$\ln\frac{a(\text{Sn}^{2+})}{a(\text{Pb}^{2+})} = \left(\frac{2F}{RT}\right)\{E^{\ominus}(\text{Pb, Pb}^{2+}) - E^{\ominus}(\text{Sn, Sn}^{2+})\}$$

$$= \frac{2\times(-0.126+0.136)\text{ V}}{0.0257\text{ V}} = 0.78$$

That is, we require $\underline{a(\text{Sn}^{2+}) \approx 2.2a(\text{Pb}^{2+})}$

30.4 $E = E_e - IR_s + \frac{2RT}{zF}\ln g$ [23a]

$$g = \frac{(I/Aj_0)^{2z}}{\left(1-\frac{I}{Aj_L}\right)^{1/2}\left(1-\frac{I}{Aj'_L}\right)^{1/2}}$$

with $j_L = \frac{RT\lambda}{zcF\delta}$ [Example 30.4]

$$R_s = \frac{l}{\kappa A} = \frac{l}{cA\Lambda_m} \text{ with } \Lambda_m = \lambda_+ + \lambda_-$$

Therefore,

$$E = E_e - \frac{Il}{cA\Lambda_m} - \frac{2RT}{zF}\ln g$$

with $g = \frac{(I^2/A^2 j_0 j'_0)}{\left\{1-\left(\frac{I}{Aa\lambda_+}\right)\right\}^{1/2}\left\{1-\left(\frac{I}{Aa'\lambda'_+}\right)\right\}^{1/2}}$

with $a = \frac{RT\lambda_+ c}{zF}$ and $a' = \frac{RT\lambda'_+ c'}{z'F}$

For the cell Zn|$ZnSO_4$(*aq*)||$CuSO_4$(*aq*)|Cu, $l = 5$ cm, $A = 5\text{ cm}^2$, $c(\text{M}^+) = c(\text{M}'^+) = 1$ M, $z = z' = 2$, $\lambda_+ = 107\text{ S cm}^2\text{ mol}^{-1}$, $\lambda'_+ = 106\text{ S cm}^2\text{ mol}^{-1}$ [so we can use $\lambda'_+ \approx \lambda_+$]. $\Lambda_m \approx 107 + 160\text{ S cm}^2\text{ mol}^{-1} = 267\text{ S cm}^2\text{ mol}^{-1}$ for both electrolyte solutions. $\delta \approx 0.25$ mm [Problem 30.2], $j_0 \approx 1\text{ mA cm}^{-2} \approx j'_0$. We can also take

$$E^{\ominus}(a\approx 1) = E^{\ominus}(\text{Cu, Cu}^{2+}) - E^{\ominus}(\text{Zn, Zn}^{2+})$$
$$= 0.34 - (-0.76)\text{ V} = 1.10\text{ V}$$

$$R_s = \frac{5\ \text{cm}}{1\ \text{M} \times 267\ \text{S cm}^2\ \text{mol}^{-1} \times 5\ \text{cm}^2} = 4\ \Omega$$

$$j_L \approx j_L^+ = \tfrac{1}{2} \times \frac{0.0257\ \text{V} \times 107\ \text{S cm}^2\ \text{mol}^{-1} \times 1\ \text{M}}{0.25 \times 10^{-3}\ \text{m}}$$

$$\approx 5.5 \times 10^{-2}\ \text{S V cm}^{-2} = 5.5 \times 10^{-2}\ \text{A cm}^{-2}$$

It follows that

$$E/\text{V} = 1.10 - 3.8(I/\text{A}) - 0.0257 \ln\left\{\frac{(I/5 \times 10^{-3}\ \text{A})^2}{1 - 3.6(I/\text{A})}\right\}$$

$$= 1.10 - 3.8(I/\text{A}) - 0.0257 \ln\left\{\frac{4 \times 10^4(I/\text{A})^2}{1 - 3.6(I/\text{A})}\right\}$$

This function is plotted in Fig. 30.4. The power is

$$P = IE$$

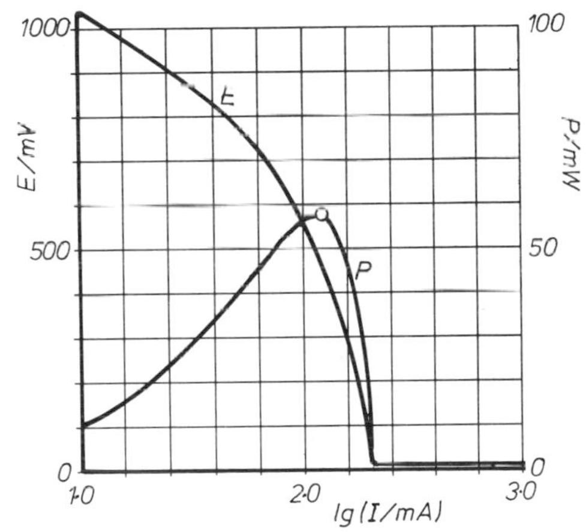

Fig 30.4

and so

$$P/\text{W} = 1.10(I/\text{A}) - 3.8(I/\text{A})^2 - 0.0257(I/\text{A}) \ln\left\{\frac{4 \times 10^4(I/\text{A})^2}{1 - 3.6(I/\text{A})}\right\}$$

This function is also plotted in Fig. 30.4. Maximum power is delivered at about 120 mA and 0.6 V, and is about 60 mW.

30.5 $E = E_e - \left(\dfrac{4RT}{zF}\right) \ln\left\{\dfrac{I}{A(j_0 j_0')^{1/2}}\right\} - IR_s$ [21]

$$P = IE = IE_e - aI \ln\left(\frac{I}{I_0}\right) - I^2 R_s$$

where $a = 4RT/zF$ and $I_0 = A(j_0 j_0')^{1/2}$. For maximum power,

$$\frac{dP}{dI} = E_e - a \ln\left(\frac{I}{I_0}\right) - a - 2IR_s = 0$$

which requires

$$\ln\left(\frac{I}{I_0}\right) = \left(\frac{E_a}{a} - 1\right) - \frac{2IR_s}{a}$$

This expression may be written

$$\ln\left(\frac{I}{I_0}\right) = c_1 - c_2 I; \; c_1 = \frac{E_e}{a} - 1, \; c_2 = \frac{2R_s}{a} = \frac{zFR_s}{2RT}$$

For the present calculation, use the data in Problem 30.4. Then

$$I_0 = A(j_0 j_0')^{1/2} = 5\ \text{cm}^2 \times (1\ \text{mA cm}^{-2}) = 5\ \text{mA}$$

$$c_1 = \frac{2 \times 1.10\ \text{V}}{4 \times 0.0257\ \text{V}} - 1 = 20.4$$

$$c_2 = \frac{2 \times 3.8\ \Omega}{2 \times 0.0257\ \text{V}} = 14\overline{8}\ \Omega\ \text{V}^{-1} = 14\overline{8}\ \text{A}^{-1}$$

That is,

$$\ln(0.20I/\text{mA}) = 20.4 - 0.148(I/\text{mA})$$

We then draw up the following table:

I/mA	115	116	117	118	119
$\ln(0.20I/\text{mA})$	3.14	3.14	3.15	3.16	3.18
$20.4 - 0.148(I/\text{mA})$	3.38	3.23	3.08	2.94	2.64

The two sets of points are plotted in Fig. 30.5. The lines intersect at $I =$ 116.5 mA, which therefore corresponds to the current at which maximum power is delivered. The power at this current is

$$P = 116.5\ \text{mA} \times 1.10\ \text{V} - 0.0154\ \text{V} \times 116.5\ \text{mA} \times \ln\left(\frac{116.5}{5}\right) - (116.5\ \text{mA})^2 \times 3.8\ \Omega = \underline{58\ \text{mW}}.$$

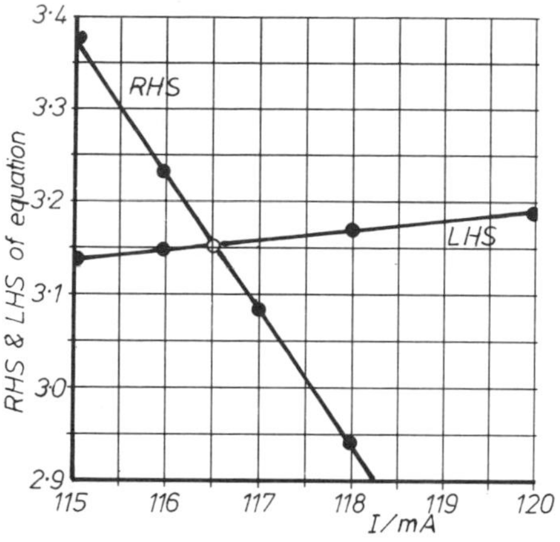

Fig 30.5

30.6 $I_{\text{corr}}=\overline{Aj_0}\,e^{fE/4}$ [26]

with $E=-0.62-(-0.94)\text{ V}=0.32\text{ V}$ [as in Exercise 30.21].

$I_{\text{corr}}\approx 0.25\times10^{-6}\text{ A}\times e^{0.32/4\times0.0257}\approx \underline{6\,\mu\text{A}}$

30.7 $j=j_0\{e^{(1-\alpha)f\eta}-e^{-\alpha f\eta}\}$

$$=j_0\{1+(1-\alpha)\eta f+\tfrac{1}{2}(1-\alpha)^2\eta^2f^2+\cdots$$
$$-1+\alpha f\eta-\tfrac{1}{2}\alpha^2\eta^2f^2+\cdots\}$$
$$=j_0\{\eta f+\tfrac{1}{2}(\eta f)^2(1-2\alpha)+\cdots\}$$

$\langle j\rangle=j_0\{\langle\eta\rangle f+\tfrac{1}{2}(1-2\alpha)f^2\langle\eta^2\rangle+\cdots\}$

$\langle\eta\rangle=0$ because $\dfrac{\omega}{2\pi}\displaystyle\int_0^{2\pi/\omega}\cos\omega t\,dt=0$ [$2\pi/\omega$ is the period]

$\langle\eta^2\rangle=\tfrac{1}{2}\eta_0^2$ because $\dfrac{\omega}{2\pi}\displaystyle\int_0^{2\pi/\omega}\cos^2\omega t\,dt=\tfrac{1}{2}$

Therefore,

$$\underline{\langle j\rangle=\tfrac{1}{4}(1-2\alpha)f^2j_0\eta_0^2}$$

and $\langle j\rangle=0$ when $\alpha=\tfrac{1}{2}$. For the mean current,

$$\langle I\rangle=\tfrac{1}{4}(1-2\alpha)f^2j_0S\eta_0^2$$

$$=\tfrac{1}{4}\times(1-0.76)\times\frac{7.90\times10^{-4}\text{ A cm}^{-2}\times1.0\text{ cm}^2}{(0.0257\text{ V})^2}\times(10\text{ mV})^2$$

$$=\underline{7.2\,\mu\text{A}}$$

30.8 Let η oscillate between η_+ and η_- around a mean value η_0. Then if η_- is large and positive (and $\eta_+ > \eta_-$),

$j \approx j_0\,e^{(1-\alpha)\eta f} = j_0\,e^{1/2\eta f}$ $[\alpha = 0.5]$

and η varies as depicted in Fig. 30.6a. Therefore, j is a chain of increasing and

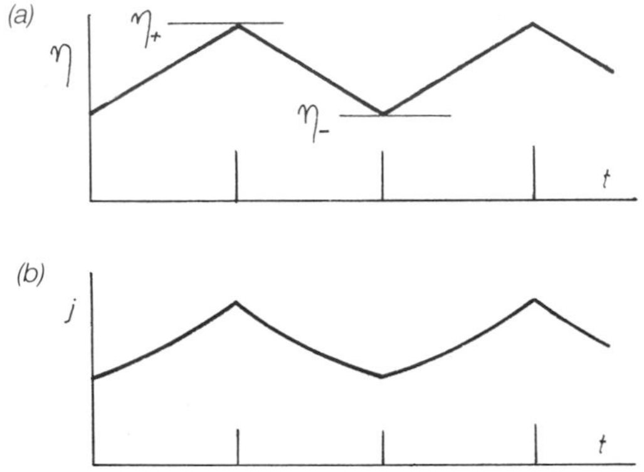

Fig 30.6

decreasing exponential functions,

$j = j_0\,e^{(\eta_- + \gamma t)f/2} \propto e^{t/\tau}$, during the increasing phase of η, where $\tau = 2RT/\gamma F$, γ a constant, and

$j = j_0\,e^{(\eta_+ - \gamma t)f/2} \propto e^{-t/\tau}$, during the decreasing phase.

This is depicted in Fig. 30.6b.

30.9 $j = \left(\dfrac{cFD}{\delta}\right)\{1 - e^{f\eta^c}\}$ [19b; $z = 1$]

$= j_L(1 - e^{F\eta^c/RT})$

The form of this expression is illustrated in Fig. 30.7. For an anion current,

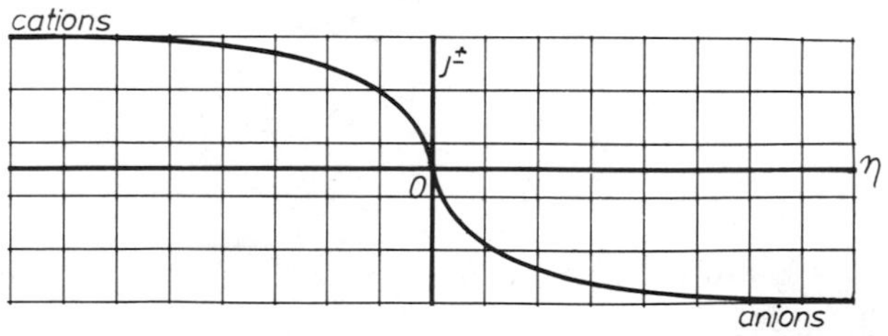

Fig 30.7

the sign of η^c is changed, and the current of anions approaches its limiting value as η^c becomes more positive (Fig. 30.7).

APPENDIX:

Linear regression

We seek the constants a and b in the expression $y = a + bx$ that give closest agreement with the experimental points. The technique is called linear regression by the method of least squares. The recipe is as follows.

(1) Let (x_i, y_i) be the pairs of data points, i running from 1 to N.

(2) Form $\langle x\rangle = (1/N)\sum_i x_i$, $\langle y\rangle = (1/N)\sum_i y_i$

$$\langle xy\rangle = (1/N)\sum_i x_i y_i$$

$$\langle x^2\rangle = (1/N)\sum_i x_i^2,\quad \langle y^2\rangle = (1/N)\sum_i y_i^2$$

(3) Then $a = \langle y\rangle - b\langle x\rangle$

$$b = \left\{\frac{\langle xy\rangle - \langle x\rangle\langle y\rangle}{\langle x^2\rangle - \langle x\rangle^2}\right\}$$

(4) The quality of the fit is assessed by the coefficient of determination, r^2, where

$$r^2 = \frac{[\langle xy\rangle - \langle x\rangle\langle y\rangle]^2}{[\langle x^2\rangle - \langle x\rangle^2][\langle y^2\rangle - \langle y\rangle^2]}$$

The closer r^2 is to 1, the better the fit.